STUDENT
SOLUTIONS MANUAL

MARK McCOMBS

UNIVERSITY OF NORTH CAROLINA, CHAPEL HILL

COLLEGE ALGEBRA

ENHANCED WITH GRAPHING UTILITIES

THIRD EDITION

MICHAEL SULLIVAN • MICHAEL SULLIVAN, III

Prentice
Hall

Upper Saddle River, NJ 07458

Editor in Chief: Sally Yagan
Acquisitions Editor: Eric Frank
Associate Editor: Dawn Murrin
Supplement Editor: Aja Shevelew
Assistant Managing Editor: John Matthews
Production Editor: Donna Crilly
Supplement Cover Manager: Paul Gourhan
Supplement Cover Designer: Joanne Alexandris
Manufacturing Buyer: Ilene Kahn

© 2003 by Pearson Education, Inc.
Pearson Education, Inc.
Upper Saddle River, NJ 07458

Printed in the United States of America

10 9 8 7 6 5 4 3 2 1

ISBN 0-13-009243-6

Pearson Education Ltd., *London*
Pearson Education Australia Pty. Ltd., *Sydney*
Pearson Education Singapore, Pte. Ltd.
Pearson Education North Asia Ltd., *Hong Kong*
Pearson Education Canada, Inc., *Toronto*
Pearson Educacíon de Mexico, S.A. de C.V.
Pearson Education—Japan, *Tokyo*
Pearson Education Malaysia, Pte. Ltd.
Pearson Education, *Upper Saddle River, New Jersey*

Contents

Chapter 4   Polynomial and Rational Functions

Chapter 5   The Zeros of a Polynomial Function

Chapter 6   Exponential and Logarithmic Functions

Chapter 7   Systems of Equations and Inequalities

Chapter 8   Sequences; Induction; The Binomial Theorem

Chapter 9   Counting and Probability

Chapter 10   The Conics

Preface

The <u>Student</u> <u>Solutions</u> <u>Manual</u> to accompany <u>College Algebra Enhanced with Graphing</u> <u>Utilities</u>, <u>3rd</u> <u>Edition</u> by Michael Sullivan and Michael Sullivan, III contains detailed solutions to all of the odd-numbered problems in the textbook. TI-83 graphing calculator screens have been included to demonstrate the use of the graphics calculator in solving and in checking solutions to the problems where requested. Every attempt has been made to make this manual as error free as possible. If you have suggestions, error corrections, or comments please feel free to write to me about them.

A number of people need to be recognized for their contributions in the preparation of this manual. Thanks go to Sally Yagan, Dawn Murrin and Audra Walsh at Prentice Hall. Thanks also to Warren Wegner for his meticulous error-checking of the solutions.

I especially wish to thank my mother, Sarah, and my brothers, Kirk and Doug, for their unwavering support and encouragement.

Finally, I am also greatly indebted to the Leroy Carr and Skip James for helping me endure the long hours of editing the manuscript.

Mark A. McCombs
Department of Mathematics
Campus Box 3250
University of North Carolina at Chapel Hill
Chapel Hill, NC 27599
mccombs@math.unc.edu

Review

R.1 Real Numbers

1. (a) $\{2, 5\}$
   (b) $\{-6, 2, 5\}$
   (c) $\left\{-6, \dfrac{1}{2}, -1.333\ldots, 2, 5\right\}$
   (d) $\{\pi\}$
   (e) $\left\{-6, \dfrac{1}{2}, -1.333\ldots, \pi, 2, 5\right\}$

3. (a) $\{1\}$
   (b) $\{0, 1\}$
   (c) $\left\{0, 1, \dfrac{1}{2}, \dfrac{1}{3}, \dfrac{1}{4}\right\}$
   (d) None
   (e) $\left\{0, 1, \dfrac{1}{2}, \dfrac{1}{3}, \dfrac{1}{4}\right\}$

5. (a) None
   (b) None
   (c) None
   (d) $\left\{\sqrt{2}, \pi, \sqrt{2}+1, \pi+\dfrac{1}{2}\right\}$
   (e) $\left\{\sqrt{2}, \pi, \sqrt{2}+1, \pi+\dfrac{1}{2}\right\}$

7. (a) 18.953
   (b) 18.952

9. (a) 28.653
   (b) 28.653

11. (a) 0.063
    (b) 0.062

13. (a) 9.999
    (b) 9.998

15. (a) 0.429
    (b) 0.428

17. (a) 34.733
    (b) 34.733

19. $3 + 2 = 5$

21. $x + 2 = 3 \cdot 4$

23. $3y = 1 + 2$

25. $x - 2 = 6$

27. $\dfrac{x}{2} = 6$

29. $9 - 4 + 2 = 5 + 2 = 7$

31. $-6 + 4 \cdot 3 = -6 + 12 = 6$

33. $4 + 5 - 8 = 9 - 8 = 1$

35. $4 + \dfrac{1}{3} = \dfrac{12+1}{3} = \dfrac{13}{3}$

37. $6 - [3 \cdot 5 + 2 \cdot (3 - 2)]$
    $= 6 - [15 + 2 \cdot (1)]$
    $= 6 - 17 = -11$

39. $2 \cdot (3 - 5) + 8 \cdot 2 - 1$
    $= 2 \cdot (-2) + 16 - 1$
    $= -4 + 16 - 1$
    $= 12 - 1 = 11$

41. $10 - [6 - 2 \cdot 2 + (8 - 3)] \cdot 2$
    $= 10 - [6 - 4 + 5] \cdot 2$
    $= 10 - [2 + 5] \cdot 2$
    $= 10 - [7] \cdot 2 = 10 - 14 = -4$

43. $(5 - 3)\dfrac{1}{2} = (2)\dfrac{1}{2} = 1$

45. $\dfrac{4+8}{5-3} = \dfrac{12}{2} = 6$

47. $\dfrac{3}{5} \cdot \dfrac{10}{21} = \dfrac{2}{7}$

49. $\dfrac{6}{25}\cdot\dfrac{10}{27}=\dfrac{4}{45}$

51. $\dfrac{3}{4}+\dfrac{2}{5}=\dfrac{15+8}{20}=\dfrac{23}{20}$

53. $\dfrac{5}{6}+\dfrac{9}{5}=\dfrac{25+54}{30}=\dfrac{79}{30}$

55. $\dfrac{5}{18}+\dfrac{1}{12}=\dfrac{10+3}{36}=\dfrac{13}{36}$

57. $\dfrac{1}{30}-\dfrac{7}{18}=\dfrac{3-35}{90}$
    $=-\dfrac{32}{90}=-\dfrac{16}{45}$

59. $\dfrac{3}{20}-\dfrac{2}{15}=\dfrac{9-8}{60}$
    $=\dfrac{1}{60}$

61. $\dfrac{\left(\dfrac{5}{18}\right)}{\left(\dfrac{11}{27}\right)}=\dfrac{5}{18}\cdot\dfrac{27}{11}=\dfrac{15}{22}$

63. $6(x+4)=6x+24$

65. $x(x-4)=x^2-4x$

67. $(x+2)(x+4)$
    $=x^2+4x+2x+8$
    $=x^2+6x+8$

69. $(x-2)(x+1)$
    $=x^2+x-2x-2$
    $=x^2-x-2$

71. $(x-8)(x-2)$
    $=x^2-2x-8x+16$
    $=x^2-10x+16$

73. $(x+2)(x-2)$
    $=x^2-2x+2x-4$
    $=x^2-4$

75. $2x+3x$
    $=x(2+3)$
    $=x(5)=5x$

77. $2(3\cdot 4)=2(12)=24$
    $(2\cdot 3)\cdot(2\cdot 4)=(6)(8)=48$

79. Subtraction is not commutative; for example: $2-3\neq 3-2$.

81. Division is not commutative; for example: $\dfrac{2}{3}\neq\dfrac{3}{2}$.

83. The Symmetric Property of Equality implies that if $2=x$, then $x=2$.

85. There are no real numbers that are both rational and irrational, since an irrational number, by definition, is a number that cannot be expressed as the ratio of two integers.
   Every real number is either a rational number or an irrational number, since the decimal form of a real number either involves an infinitely repeating pattern of digits or an infinite, non-repeating string of digits.

87. $x=0.\overline{9}\Rightarrow 10x=9.\overline{9}$
   Now compute $10x=9.\overline{9}$

$$\underline{-\ x=0.\overline{9}}$$

$$9x=9\Rightarrow x=\dfrac{9}{9}=1$$

   So $0.99999\ldots\ldots$ equals 1.

Review

R.2 Algebra Review

1.

3. $\dfrac{1}{2} > 0$ 5. $-1 > -2$ 7. $\pi > 3.14$ 9. $\dfrac{1}{2} = 0.5$

11. $\dfrac{2}{3} < 0.67$ 13. $x > 0$ 15. $x < 2$ 17. $x \le 1$

19. Graph on the number line: $x \ge -2$ 21. Graph on the number line: $x > -1$

23. $d(C,D) = d(0,1) = |1-0| = |1| = 1$ 25. $d(D,E) = d(1,3) = |3-1| = |2| = 2$

27. $d(A,E) = d(-3,3) = |3-(-3)| = |6| = 6$

29. $x + 2y = -2 + 2 \cdot 3 = -2 + 6 = 4$ 31. $5xy + 2 = 5(-2)(3) + 2 = -30 + 2 = -28$

33. $\dfrac{2x}{x-y} = \dfrac{2(-2)}{-2-3} = \dfrac{-4}{-5} = \dfrac{4}{5}$ 35. $\dfrac{3x+2y}{2+y} = \dfrac{3(-2)+2(3)}{2+3} = \dfrac{-6+6}{5} = \dfrac{0}{5} = 0$

37. $|x+y| = |3+(-2)| = |1| = 1$ 39. $|x| + |y| = |3| + |-2| = 3 + 2 = 5$

41. $\dfrac{|x|}{x} = \dfrac{|3|}{3} = \dfrac{3}{3} = 1$

43. $|4x - 5y| = |4(3) - 5(-2)| = |12 + 10| = |22| = 22$

45. $||4x| - |5y|| = ||4(3)| - |5(-2)|| = ||12| - |-10|| = |12 - 10| = |2| = 2$

47. $\dfrac{x^2 - 1}{x}$ Part (c) must be excluded.

The value $x = 0$ must be excluded from the domain because it causes division by 0.

49. $\dfrac{x}{x^2-9}=\dfrac{x}{(x-3)(x+3)}$ Part (a) must be excluded.

The values $x = -3$ and $x = 3$ must be excluded from the domain because they cause division by 0.

51. $\dfrac{x^2}{x^2+1}$ None of the given values are excluded. The domain is all real numbers.

53. $\dfrac{x^2+5x-10}{x^3-x}=\dfrac{x^2+5x-10}{x(x-1)(x+1)}$ Parts (b), (c), and (d) must be excluded.

The values $x = 0$, $x = 1$, and $x = -1$ must be excluded from the domain because they cause division by 0.

55. $\dfrac{4}{x-5}$ Domain $=\{x | x \neq 5\}$ 57. $\dfrac{x}{x+4}$ Domain $=\{x | x \neq -4\}$

59. $C=\dfrac{5}{9}(F-32)=\dfrac{5}{9}(32-32)=\dfrac{5}{9}(0)=0$

61. $C=\dfrac{5}{9}(F-32)=\dfrac{5}{9}(77-32)=\dfrac{5}{9}(45)=25$

63. $A = l \cdot w$ 65. $C = \pi \cdot d$ 67. $A = \dfrac{\sqrt{3}}{4}\cdot x^2$

69. $V = \dfrac{4}{3}\pi \cdot r^3$ 71. $V = x^3$

73. (a)   If $x = 1000$, $C = 4000 + 2x = 4000 + 2(1000) = 4000 + 2000 = \$6000$
     (b)   If $x = 2000$, $C = 4000 + 2x = 4000 + 2(2000) = 4000 + 4000 = \$8000$

75. $|x-115|\leq 5$
     (a) $|x-115|=|113-115|=|-2|=2\leq 5$ 113 volts is acceptable.
     (b) $|x-115|=|109-115|=|-6|=6 \nleq 5$ 109 volts is _not_ acceptable.

77. $|x-3|\leq 0.01$
     (a) $|x-3|=|2.999-3|=|-0.001|=0.001\leq 0.01$ A radius of 2.999 centimeters is acceptable.
     (b) $|x-3|=|2.89-3|=|-0.11|=0.11 \nleq 0.01$ A radius of 2.89 centimeters is _not_ acceptable.

79. $\dfrac{1}{3}=0.333333...>0.333 \implies \dfrac{1}{3}$ is larger by approximately $0.0003333...$

81. No.

83.   Answers will vary.

Review

R.3 Geometry Review

1. $a = 5,\ b = 12,\ c^2 = a^2 + b^2 = 5^2 + 12^2 = 25 + 144 = 169 \implies c = 13$

3. $a = 10,\ b = 24,\ c^2 = a^2 + b^2 = 10^2 + 24^2 = 100 + 576 = 676 \implies c = 26$

5. $a = 7,\ b = 24,\ c^2 = a^2 + b^2 = 7^2 + 24^2 = 49 + 576 = 625 \implies c = 25$

7. $5^2 = 3^2 + 4^2 \implies 25 = 9 + 16 \implies 25 = 25$
    The given triangle is a right triangle. The hypotenuse is 5.

9. $6^2 = 4^2 + 5^2 \implies 36 = 16 + 25 \implies 36 \neq 41$
    The given triangle is not a right triangle.

11. $25^2 = 7^2 + 24^2 \implies 625 = 49 + 576 \implies 625 = 625$
    The given triangle is a right triangle. The hypotenuse is 25.

13. $6^2 = 3^2 + 4^2 \implies 36 = 9 + 16 \implies 36 \neq 25$
    The given triangle is not a right triangle.

15. $A = l \cdot w = 4 \cdot 2 = 8 \text{ in}^2$
                            17. $A = \dfrac{1}{2} b \cdot h = \dfrac{1}{2}(2)(4) = 4 \text{ in}^2$

19. $A = \pi r^2 = \pi (5)^2 = 25\pi \text{ m}^2$ $C = 2\pi r = 2\pi (5) = 10\pi \text{ m}$

21. $V = lwh = 8 \cdot 4 \cdot 7 = 224 \text{ ft}^2$

23. $V = \dfrac{4}{3}\pi r^3 = \dfrac{4}{3}\pi \cdot 4^3 = \dfrac{256}{3}\pi \text{ cm}^3$ $S = 4\pi r^2 = 4\pi \cdot 4^2 = 64\pi \text{ cm}^2$

25. $V = \pi r^2 h = \pi (9)^2 (8) = 648\pi \text{ in}^3$

27. The diameter of the circle is 2, so its radius is 1. $A = \pi r^2 = \pi (1)^2 = \pi$ square units

29. The diameter of the circle is the length of the diagonal of the square.
    $$d^2 = 2^2 + 2^2 = 4 + 4 = 8 \implies d = \sqrt{8} = 2\sqrt{2} \qquad r = \sqrt{2}$$
    The area of the circle is: $A = \pi r^2 = \pi \left(\sqrt{2}\right)^2 = 2\pi$ square units

31. The total distance traveled is 4 times the circumference of the wheel.

Total distance $= 4C = 4(\pi d) = 4\pi \cdot 16 = 64\pi \approx 201.1$ inches ≈ 16.8 feet

33. Area of the border = area of EFGH – area of ABCD $= 10^2 - 6^2 = 100 - 36 = 64$ ft^2

35. Area of the window = area of the rectangle + area of the semicircle.

$$A = (6)(4) + \frac{1}{2} \cdot \pi \cdot 2^2 = 24 + 2\pi \approx 30.28 \text{ ft}^2$$

Perimeter of the window = 2 heights + width + one-half the circumference.

$$P = 2(6) + 4 + \frac{1}{2} \cdot \pi(4) = 12 + 4 + 2\pi = 16 + 2\pi \approx 22.28 \text{ feet}$$

37. Convert 20 feet to miles, and solve the Pythagorean theorem to find the distance:

$20 \text{ feet} = 20 \text{ feet} \cdot \dfrac{1 \text{ mile}}{5280 \text{ feet}} = 0.003788 \text{ miles}$

$d^2 = (3960 + 0.003788)^2 - 3960^2 = 30$

$d \approx 5.477 \text{ miles}$

39. Convert 100 feet to miles, and solve the Pythagorean theorem to find the distance:

$$100 \text{ feet} = 100 \text{ feet} \cdot \frac{1 \text{ mile}}{5280 \text{ feet}} = 0.018939 \text{ miles}$$

$$d^2 = (3960 + 0.018939)^2 - 3960^2 = 150 \Rightarrow d \approx 12.247 \text{ miles}$$

Convert 150 feet to miles, and solve the Pythagorean theorem to find the distance:

$$150 \text{ feet} = 150 \text{ feet} \cdot \frac{1 \text{ mile}}{5280 \text{ feet}} = 0.028409 \text{ miles}$$

$$d^2 = (3960 + 0.028409)^2 - 3960^2 = 225 \Rightarrow d \approx 15 \text{ miles}$$

41. Given a rectangle with perimeter = 1000 feet, the largest area will be enclosed by a square with dimensions 250 by 250 feet. That is, the area $= 250^2 = 62500$ square feet.

A circular pool with circumference = 1000 feet yields the equation : $2\pi r = 1000 \Rightarrow r = \dfrac{500}{\pi}$

The area enclosed by the circular pool is:

$$A = \pi r^2 = \pi \left(\frac{500}{\pi}\right)^2 = \frac{500^2}{\pi} \approx 79577.47 \text{ square feet}$$

Therefore, a circular pool will enclose the most area.

Review

R.4   Integer Exponents

1. $4^2 = 16$

3. $4^{-2} = \dfrac{1}{4^2} = \dfrac{1}{16}$

5. $-4^{-2} = -\dfrac{1}{4^2} = -\dfrac{1}{16}$

7. $4^0 \cdot 2^{-3} = 1 \cdot \dfrac{1}{2^3} = 1 \cdot \dfrac{1}{8} = \dfrac{1}{8}$

9. $2^{-3} + \left(\dfrac{1}{2}\right)^3 = \dfrac{1}{2^3} + \dfrac{1^3}{2^3} = \dfrac{1}{8} + \dfrac{1}{8} = \dfrac{1}{4}$

11. $3^{-6} \cdot 3^4 = 3^{-6+4} = 3^{-2} = \dfrac{1}{3^2} = \dfrac{1}{9}$

13. $\dfrac{\left(3^2\right)^2}{\left(2^3\right)^2} = \dfrac{3^4}{2^6} = \dfrac{81}{64}$

15. $\left(\dfrac{2}{3}\right)^{-3} = \dfrac{1}{\left(\dfrac{2}{3}\right)^3} = \dfrac{1}{\left(\dfrac{2^3}{3^3}\right)} = \dfrac{3^3}{2^3} = \dfrac{27}{8}$

17. $\dfrac{2^3 \cdot 3^2}{2^4 \cdot 3^{-2}} = \dfrac{2^3}{2^4} \cdot \dfrac{3^2}{3^{-2}} = 2^{3-4} \cdot 3^{2-(-2)} = 2^{-1} \cdot 3^4 = \dfrac{1}{2} \cdot 81 = \dfrac{81}{2}$

19. $\left(\dfrac{9}{2}\right)^{-2} = \dfrac{1}{\left(\dfrac{9}{2}\right)^2} = \dfrac{1}{\left(\dfrac{9^2}{2^2}\right)} = \dfrac{2^2}{9^2} = \dfrac{4}{81}$

21. $\dfrac{2^{-2}}{3} = \dfrac{\left(\dfrac{1}{2^2}\right)}{3} = \dfrac{\left(\dfrac{1}{4}\right)}{3} = \dfrac{1}{4} \cdot \dfrac{1}{3} = \dfrac{1}{12}$

23. $\dfrac{-3^{-1}}{2^{-1}} = \dfrac{\left(-\dfrac{1}{3}\right)}{\left(\dfrac{1}{2}\right)} = -\dfrac{1}{3} \cdot \dfrac{2}{1} = -\dfrac{2}{3}$

24. $\dfrac{-2^{-3}}{-1} = \dfrac{\left(-\dfrac{1}{2^3}\right)}{-1} = -\dfrac{1}{8} \cdot \dfrac{1}{-1} = \dfrac{1}{8}$

25. $x^0 y^2 = 1 \cdot y^2 = y^2$

27. $x\,y^{-2} = x \cdot \dfrac{1}{y^2} = \dfrac{x}{y^2}$

29. $\left(8x^3\right)^{-2} = \dfrac{1}{\left(8x^3\right)^2} = \dfrac{1}{8^2 \cdot x^6} = \dfrac{1}{64x^6}$

31. $-4x^{-1} = -4 \cdot \dfrac{1}{x} = -\dfrac{4}{x}$

33. $3x^0 = 3 \cdot 1 = 3$

35. $\dfrac{x^{-2} y^3}{x\,y^4} = \dfrac{x^{-2}}{x} \cdot \dfrac{y^3}{y^4} = x^{-2-1} y^{3-4} = x^{-3} y^{-1} = \dfrac{1}{x^3} \cdot \dfrac{1}{y} = \dfrac{1}{x^3 y}$

37. $x^{-1}y^{-1} = \dfrac{1}{x} \cdot \dfrac{1}{y} = \dfrac{1}{xy}$

39. $\dfrac{x^{-1}}{y^{-1}} = \dfrac{\left(\dfrac{1}{x}\right)}{\left(\dfrac{1}{y}\right)} = \dfrac{1}{x} \cdot \dfrac{y}{1} = \dfrac{y}{x}$

41. $\left(\dfrac{4y}{5x}\right)^{-2} = \dfrac{1}{\left(\dfrac{4y}{5x}\right)^{2}} = \dfrac{1}{\left(\dfrac{(4y)^2}{(5x)^2}\right)} = \dfrac{(5x)^2}{(4y)^2} = \dfrac{5^2 \cdot x^2}{4^2 \cdot y^2} = \dfrac{25x^2}{16y^2}$

43. $x^{-2}y^{-2} = \dfrac{1}{x^2} \cdot \dfrac{1}{y^2} = \dfrac{1}{x^2 y^2}$

45. $\dfrac{x^{-1}y^{-2}z^3}{x^2 y z^3} = \dfrac{x^{-1}}{x^2} \cdot \dfrac{y^{-2}}{y} \cdot \dfrac{z^3}{z^3} = x^{-1-2}y^{-2-1}z^{3-3} = x^{-3}y^{-3}z^0 = \dfrac{1}{x^3} \cdot \dfrac{1}{y^3} \cdot 1 = \dfrac{1}{x^3 y^3}$

47. $\dfrac{(-2)^3 x^4 (yz)^2}{3^2 x y^3 z^4} = \dfrac{-8x^4 y^2 z^2}{9 x y^3 z^4} = \dfrac{-8}{9} x^{4-1}y^{2-3}z^{2-4} = \dfrac{-8}{9}x^3 y^{-1}z^{-2} = \dfrac{-8}{9}x^3 \cdot \dfrac{1}{y} \cdot \dfrac{1}{z^2} = -\dfrac{8x^3}{9yz^2}$

49. $\dfrac{\left(\dfrac{x}{y}\right)^{-2} \cdot \left(\dfrac{y}{x}\right)^4}{x^2 y^3} = \dfrac{\left(\dfrac{y^2}{x^2} \cdot \dfrac{y^4}{x^4}\right)}{x^2 y^3} = \dfrac{y^6}{x^6} \cdot \dfrac{1}{x^2 y^3} = \dfrac{y^3}{x^8}$

51. $\left(\dfrac{3x^{-1}}{4y^{-1}}\right)^{-2} = \dfrac{1}{\left(\dfrac{3x^{-1}}{4y^{-1}}\right)^2} = \dfrac{1}{\dfrac{(3x^{-1})^2}{(4y^{-1})^2}} = \dfrac{(4y^{-1})^2}{(3x^{-1})^2} = \dfrac{4^2 y^{-2}}{3^2 x^{-2}} = \dfrac{\left(16 \cdot \dfrac{1}{y^2}\right)}{\left(9 \cdot \dfrac{1}{x^2}\right)} = \dfrac{16}{9} \cdot \dfrac{x^2}{y^2} = \dfrac{16x^2}{9y^2}$

53. $\dfrac{(xy^{-1})^{-2}}{xy^3} = \dfrac{x^{-2}y^2}{xy^3} = \dfrac{x^{-2}}{x} \cdot \dfrac{y^2}{y^3} = x^{-2-1}y^{2-3} = x^{-3}y^{-1} = \dfrac{1}{x^3 y}$

55. $\left(\dfrac{x}{y^2}\right)^{-2} \cdot (y^2)^{-1} = \dfrac{x^{-2}}{(y^2)^{-2}} \cdot \dfrac{1}{y^2} = \dfrac{x^{-2}}{y^{-4}y^2} = \dfrac{x^{-2}}{y^{-2}} = \dfrac{\left(\dfrac{1}{x^2}\right)}{\left(\dfrac{1}{y^2}\right)} = \dfrac{y^2}{x^2}$

57. If $x = 2$, $\quad 2x^3 - 3x^2 + 5x - 4 = 2 \cdot 2^3 - 3 \cdot 2^2 + 5 \cdot 2 - 4 = 16 - 12 + 10 - 4 = 10$
    If $x = 1$, $\quad 2x^3 - 3x^2 + 5x - 4 = 2 \cdot 1^3 - 3 \cdot 1^2 + 5 \cdot 1 - 4 = 2 - 3 + 5 - 4 = 0$

59. $\dfrac{(666)^4}{(222)^4} = \left(\dfrac{666}{222}\right)^4 = 3^4 = 81$

61. $(8.2)^6 \approx 304{,}006.671$

63. $(6.1)^{-3} \approx 0.004$

65. $(-2.8)^6 \approx 481.890$

67. $(-8.11)^{-4} \approx 0.000$

69. $454.2 = 4.542 \times 10^2$

71. $0.013 = 1.3 \times 10^{-2}$

73. $32,155 = 3.2155 \times 10^4$

75. $0.000423 = 4.23 \times 10^{-4}$

77. $6.15 \times 10^4 = 61,500$

79. $1.214 \times 10^{-3} = 0.001214$

81. $1.1 \times 10^8 = 110,000,000$

83. $8.1 \times 10^{-2} = 0.081$

85. $4 \times 10^8 = 400,000,000$ meters

87. $5 \times 10^{-7} = 0.0000005$ meters

89. $0.0005 = 5 \times 10^{-4}$ inches

91. $64,000,000 \cdot 30 = \left(6.4 \times 10^7\right)\left(3 \times 10^1\right) = 19.2 \times 10^8 = 1.92 \times 10^9$

93. $186,000 \cdot 60 \cdot 60 \cdot 24 \cdot 365 = \left(1.86 \times 10^5\right)\left(6 \times 10^1\right)\left(6 \times 10^1\right)\left(2.4 \times 10^1\right)\left(3.65 \times 10^2\right)$
$$= 586.5696 \times 10^{10} = 5.865696 \times 10^{12}$$

95. Answers will vary.

Review

R.5 Polynomials

1. $2x^3$ Monomial; Variable: x; Coefficient: 2; Degree: 3

3. $\dfrac{8}{x}$ Not a monomial.

5. $-2xy^2$ Monomial; Variable: x, y; Coefficient: -2; Degree: 3

7. $\dfrac{8x}{y}$ Not a monomial

9. $x^2 + y^2$ Not a monomial.

11. $3x^2 - 5$ Polynomial; Degree: 2

13. 5   Polynomial; Degree: 0

15. $3x^2 - \dfrac{5}{x}$ Not a polynomial.

17. $2y^3 - \sqrt{2}$ Polynomial; Degree: 3

19. $\dfrac{x^2 + 5}{x^3 - 1}$ Not a polynomial.

21. $(x^2 + 4x + 5) + (3x - 3) = x^2 + (4x + 3x) + (5 - 3) = x^2 + 7x + 2$

23. $(x^3 - 2x^2 + 5x + 10) - (2x^2 - 4x + 3) = x^3 - 2x^2 + 5x + 10 - 2x^2 + 4x - 3$
$$= x^3 + (-2x^2 - 2x^2) + (5x + 4x) + (10 - 3)$$
$$= x^3 - 4x^2 + 9x + 7$$

25. $\left(6x^5 + x^3 + x\right) + \left(5x^4 - x^3 + 3x^2\right) = 6x^5 + 5x^4 + 3x^2 + x$

27. $(x^2 - 3x + 1) + 2(3x^2 + x - 4) = x^2 - 3x + 1 + 6x^2 + 2x - 8 = 7x^2 - x - 7$

29. $6(x^3 + x^2 - 3) - 4(2x^3 - 3x^2) = 6x^3 + 6x^2 - 18 - 8x^3 + 12x^2 = -2x^3 + 18x^2 - 18$

31. $\left(x^2 - x + 2\right) + \left(2x^2 - 3x + 5\right) - \left(x^2 + 1\right) = x^2 - x + 2 + 2x^2 - 3x + 5 - x^2 - 1$
$$= 2x^2 - 4x + 6$$

33. $9\left(y^2 - 3y + 4\right) - 6\left(1 - y^2\right) = 9y^2 - 27y + 36 - 6 + 6y^2 = 15y^2 - 27y + 30$

35. $x(x^2 + x - 4) = x^3 + x^2 - 4x$

37. $-2x^2(4x^3 + 5) = -8x^5 - 10x^2$

39. $(x+1)(x^2+2x-4) = x(x^2+2x-4)+1(x^2+2x-4)$
$$= x^3+2x^2-4x+x^2+2x-4 = x^3+3x^2-2x-4$$

41. $(x+2)(x+4) = x^2+4x+2x+8 = x^2+6x+8$

43. $(2x+5)(x+2) = 2x^2+4x+5x+10 = 2x^2+9x+10$

45. $(x-4)(x+2) = x^2+2x-4x-8 = x^2-2x-8$

47. $(x-3)(x-2) = x^2-2x-3x+6 = x^2-5x+6$

49. $(2x+3)(x-2) = 2x^2-4x+3x-6 = 2x^2-x-6$

51. $(-2x+3)(x-4) = -2x^2+8x+3x-12 = -2x^2+11x-12$

53. $(-x-2)(-2x-4) = 2x^2+4x+4x+8 = 2x^2+8x+8$

55. $(x-2y)(x+y) = x^2+xy-2xy-2y^2 = x^2-xy-2y^2$

57. $(-2x-3y)(3x+2y) = -6x^2-4xy-9xy-6y^2 = -6x^2-13xy-6y^2$

59. $(x-7)(x+7) = x^2-7^2 = x^2-49$

61. $(2x+3)(2x-3) = (2x)^2-3^2 = 4x^2-9$

63. $(x+4)^2 = x^2+2\cdot x\cdot 4+4^2 = x^2+8x+16$

65. $(x-4)^2 = x^2-2\cdot x\cdot 4+4^2 = x^2-8x+16$

67. $(3x+4)(3x-4) = (3x)^2-4^2 = 9x^2-16$

69. $(2x-3)^2 = (2x)^2-2(2x)(3)+3^2 = 4x^2-12x+9$

71. $(x+y)(x-y) = (x)^2-(y)^2 = x^2-y^2$

73. $(3x+y)(3x-y) = (3x)^2-(y)^2 = 9x^2-y^2$

75. $(x+y)^2 = x^2+2xy+y^2$

77. $(x-2y)^2 = x^2+2(x\cdot(-2y))+(2y)^2 = x^2-4xy+4y^2$

79. $(x-2)^3 = x^3-3\cdot x^2\cdot 2+3\cdot x\cdot 2^2-2^3 = x^3-6x^2+12x-8$

81. $(2x+1)^3 = (2x)^3+3(2x)^2(1)+3(2x)\cdot 1^2+1^3 = 8x^3+12x^2+6x+1$

83. Divide:

$$\begin{array}{r} 4x^2 - 3x + 1 \\ x\overline{\smash{)}4x^3 - 3x^2 + x + 1} \\ \underline{4x^3} \\ -3x^2 + x + 1 \\ \underline{-3x^2} \\ x + 1 \\ \underline{x} \\ 1 \end{array}$$

Check:

$$(x)(4x^2 - 3x + 1) + (1) = 4x^3 - 3x^2 + x + 1$$

The quotient is $4x^2 - 3x + 1$; the remainder is 1.

85. Divide:

$$\begin{array}{r} 4x^2 - 11x + 23 \\ x + 2\overline{\smash{)}4x^3 - 3x^2 + x + 1} \\ \underline{4x^3 + 8x^2} \\ -11x^2 + x \\ \underline{-11x^2 - 22x} \\ 23x + 1 \\ \underline{23x + 46} \\ -45 \end{array}$$

Check:

$$(x + 2)(4x^2 - 11x + 23) + (-45)$$
$$= 4x^3 - 11x^2 + 23x + 8x^2 - 22x + 46 - 45$$
$$= 4x^3 - 3x^2 + x + 1$$

The quotient is $4x^2 - 11x + 23$; the remainder is –45.

87. Divide:

$$\begin{array}{r} 4x - 3 \\ x^2\overline{\smash{)}4x^3 - 3x^2 + x + 1} \\ \underline{4x^3} \\ -3x^2 + x + 1 \\ \underline{-3x^2} \\ x + 1 \end{array}$$

Check:

$$(x^2)(4x - 3) + (x + 1) = 4x^3 - 3x^2 + x + 1$$

The quotient is $4x - 3$; the remainder is $x + 1$.

89. Divide:

$$\begin{array}{r} 4x - 3 \\ x^2 + 2\overline{\smash{)}4x^3 - 3x^2 + x + 1} \\ \underline{4x^3 + 8x} \\ -3x^2 - 7x \\ \underline{-3x^2 - 6} \\ -7x + 7 \end{array}$$

Check:

$$(x^2 + 2)(4x - 3) + (-7x + 7)$$
$$= 4x^3 - 3x^2 + 8x - 6 - 7x + 7 = 4x^3 - 3x^2 + x + 1$$

The quotient is $4x - 3$; the remainder is $-7x + 7$.

91. Divide:

$$2x^3 - 1 \overline{)\begin{array}{r} 2 \\ 4x^3 - 3x^2 + x + 1 \\ \underline{4x^3 \qquad\qquad - 2} \\ -3x^2 + x + 3 \end{array}}$$

Check :

$(2x^3 - 1)(2) + (-3x^2 + x + 3)$

$= 4x^3 - 2 - 3x^2 + x + 3 = 4x^3 - 3x^2 + x + 1$

The quotient is 2; the remainder is $-3x^2 + x + 3$.

93. Divide:

$$2x^2 + x + 1 \overline{)\begin{array}{r} 2x - \dfrac{5}{2} \\ 4x^3 - 3x^2 + \ x + \ 1 \\ \underline{4x^3 + 2x^2 + 2x} \\ -5x^2 - \ x \\ \underline{-5x^2 - \dfrac{5}{3}x - \dfrac{5}{2}} \\ \dfrac{3}{2}x + \dfrac{7}{2} \end{array}}$$

Check :

$\left(2x^2 + x + 12\right)\left(x - \dfrac{5}{2}\right) + \left(\dfrac{3}{2}x + \dfrac{7}{2}\right)$

$= 4x^3 - 5x^2 + 2x^2 - \dfrac{5}{2}x + 2x - \dfrac{5}{2} + \dfrac{3}{2}x + \dfrac{7}{2} = 4x^3 - 3x^2 + x + 1$

The quotient is $2x - \dfrac{5}{2}$; the remainder is $\dfrac{3}{2}x + \dfrac{7}{2}$.

95. Divide:

$$x - 1 \overline{)\begin{array}{r} -4x^2 - 3x - 3 \\ -4x^3 + \ x^2 + 0x - 4 \\ \underline{-4x^3 + 4x^2} \\ -3x^2 \\ \underline{-3x^2 + 3x} \\ -3x - 4 \\ \underline{-3x + 3} \\ -7 \end{array}}$$

Check :

$(x - 1)(-4x^2 - 3x - 3) + (-7)$

$= -4x^3 - 3x^2 - 3x + 4x^2 + 3x + 3 - 7 = -4x^3 + x^2 - 4$

The quotient is $-4x^2 - 3x - 3$; the remainder is –7.

97. Divide:

$$x^2 + x + 1 \overline{)\begin{array}{r} x^2 - x - 1 \\ x^4 + 0x^3 - \ x^2 + 0x + 1 \\ \underline{x^4 + \ x^3 + \ x^2} \\ -x^3 - 2x^2 \\ \underline{-x^3 - \ x^2 - x} \\ -x^2 + x + 1 \\ \underline{-x^2 - x - 1} \\ 2x + 2 \end{array}}$$

Check:

$(x^2 + x + 1)(x^2 - x - 1) + 2x + 2$

$= x^4 + x^3 + x^2 - x^3 - x^2 - x - x^2 - x - 1 + 2x + 2$

$= x^4 - x^2 + 1$

The quotient is $x^2 - x - 1$; the remainder is $2x + 2$.

99. Divide:

$$x - a \overline{) x^3 + 0x^2 + 0x - a^3}$$
quotient: $x^2 + ax + a^2$

$$\underline{x^3 - ax^2}$$
$$ax^2$$
$$\underline{ax^2 - a^2x}$$
$$a^2x - a^3$$
$$\underline{a^2x - a^3}$$
$$0$$

Check:

$$(x - a)(x^2 + ax + a^2) + 0$$
$$= x^3 + ax^2 + a^2x - ax^2 - a^2x - a^3 = x^3 - a^3$$

The quotient is $x^2 + ax + a^2$; the remainder is 0.

101. $\dfrac{x^3 - 2x^2 + 3x + 5}{x + 2} = ax^2 + bx + c + \dfrac{d}{x + 2}$

In order to find $a + b + c + d$, we do the long division and then look at the coefficients of the quotient and remainder.

Divide:

$$x + 2 \overline{) x^3 - 2x^2 + 3x + 5}$$
quotient: $x^2 - 4x + 11$

$$\underline{x^3 + 2x^2}$$
$$-4x^2 + 3x + 5$$
$$\underline{-4x^2 - 8x}$$
$$11x + 5$$
$$\underline{11x + 22}$$
$$-17$$

therefore,

$$\dfrac{x^3 - 2x^2 + 3x + 5}{x + 2} = x^2 - 4x + 11 + \dfrac{-17}{x + 2}$$
$$a + b + c + d = 1 - 4 + 11 - 17 = -9$$

103. When we add two polynomials $p_1(x)$ and $p_2(x)$, where the degree of $p_1(x) \neq$ the degree of $p_2(x)$, each term of $p_1(x)$ will be added to each term of $p_2(x)$. Since only the terms with equal degrees will combine via addition, the degree of the sum polynomial will be the degree of the highest powered term overall, that is, the degree of the polynomial that had the higher degree.

105. Answers will vary.

Review

R.6 Factoring Polynomials

1. $3x + 6 = 3(x + 2)$

3. $ax^2 + a = a(x^2 + 1)$

5. $x^3 + x^2 + x = x(x^2 + x + 1)$

7. $2x^2 - 2x = 2x(x - 1)$

9. $3x^2 y - 6xy^2 + 12xy = 3xy(x - 2y + 4)$

11. $x^2 - 1 = x^2 - 1^2 = (x - 1)(x + 1)$

13. $4x^2 - 1 = (2x)^2 - 1^2 = (2x - 1)(2x + 1)$

15. $x^2 - 16 = x^2 - 4^2 = (x - 4)(x + 4)$

17. $25x^2 - 4 = (5x - 2)(5x + 2)$

19. $x^2 + 2x + 1 = (x + 1)^2$

21. $x^2 + 4x + 4 = (x + 2)^2$

23. $x^2 - 10x + 25 = (x - 5)^2$

25. $4x^2 + 4x + 1 = (2x + 1)^2$

27. $16x^2 + 8x + 1 = (4x + 1)^2$

29. $x^3 - 27 = x^3 - 3^3 = (x - 3)(x^2 + 3x + 9)$

31. $x^3 + 27 = x^3 + 3^3 = (x + 3)(x^2 - 3x + 9)$

33. $8x^3 + 27 = (2x)^3 + 3^3 = (2x + 3)(4x^2 - 6x + 9)$

35. $x^2 + 5x + 6 = (x + 2)(x + 3)$

37. $x^2 + 7x + 6 = (x + 6)(x + 1)$

39. $x^2 + 7x + 10 = (x + 2)(x + 5)$

41. $x^2 - 10x + 16 = (x - 2)(x - 8)$

43. $x^2 - 7x - 8 = (x + 1)(x - 8)$

45. $x^2 + 7x - 8 = (x + 8)(x - 1)$

47. $2x^2 + 4x + 3x + 6 = 2x(x + 2) + 3(x + 2) = (x + 2)(2x + 3)$

49. $2x^2 - 4x + x - 2 = 2x(x - 2) + 1(x - 2) = (x - 2)(2x + 1)$

51. $6x^2 + 9x + 4x + 6 = 3x(2x + 3) + 2(2x + 3) = (2x + 3)(3x + 2)$

53. $3x^2 + 4x + 1 = (3x + 1)(x + 1)$

55. $2z^2 + 5z + 3 = (2z + 3)(z + 1)$

57. $3x^2 + 2x - 8 = (3x - 4)(x + 2)$

59. $3x^2 - 2x - 8 = (3x + 4)(x - 2)$

61. $3x^2 + 14x + 8 = (3x + 2)(x + 4)$

63. $3x^2 + 10x - 8 = (3x - 2)(x + 4)$

65. $x^2 - 36 = (x-6)(x+6)$

67. $2 - 8x^2 = 2(1 - 4x^2) = 2(1-2x)(1+2x)$

69. $x^2 + 7x + 10 = (x+2)(x+5)$

71. $x^2 - 10x + 21 = (x-7)(x-3)$

73. $4x^2 - 8x + 32 = 4(x^2 - 2x + 8)$

75. $x^2 + 4x + 16$ is prime because there are no factors of 16 whose sum is 4.

77. $15 + 2x - x^2 = -(x^2 - 2x - 15) = -(x-5)(x+3)$

79. $3x^2 - 12x - 36 = 3(x^2 - 4x - 12) = 3(x-6)(x+2)$

81. $y^4 + 11y^3 + 30y^2 = y^2(y^2 + 11y + 30) = y^2(y+5)(y+6)$

83. $4x^2 + 12x + 9 = (2x+3)^2$

85. $6x^2 + 8x + 2 = 2(3x^2 + 4x + 1) = 2(3x+1)(x+1)$

87. $x^4 - 81 = (x^2 - 9)(x^2 + 9) = (x-3)(x+3)(x^2 + 9)$

89. $x^6 - 2x^3 + 1 = (x^3 - 1)^2 = \left[(x-1)(x^2 + x + 1)\right]^2 = (x-1)^2(x^2 + x + 1)^2$

91. $x^7 - x^5 = x^5(x^2 - 1) = x^5(x-1)(x+1)$

93. $16x^2 + 24x + 9 = (4x+3)^2$

95. $5 + 16x - 16x^2 = -(16x^2 - 16x - 5) = -(4x-5)(4x+1)$

97. $4y^2 - 16y + 15 = (2y-5)(2y-3)$

99. $1 - 8x^2 - 9x^4 = -(9x^4 + 8x^2 - 1) = -(9x^2 - 1)(x^2 + 1) = -(3x-1)(3x+1)(x^2 + 1)$

101. $x(x+3) - 6(x+3) = (x+3)(x-6)$

103. $(x+2)^2 - 5(x+2) = (x+2)[(x+2) - 5] = (x+2)(x-3)$

105. $(3x-2)^3 - 27 = [(3x-2) - 3][(3x-2)^2 + 3(3x-2) + 9]$
$= (3x-5)(9x^2 - 12x + 4 + 9x - 6 + 9) = (3x-5)(9x^2 - 3x + 7)$

107. $3(x^2 + 10x + 25) - 4(x+5) = 3(x+5)^2 - 4(x+5)$
$= (x+5)[3(x+5) - 4] = (x+5)(3x + 15 - 4) = (x+5)(3x+11)$

109. $x^3 + 2x^2 - x - 2 = x^2(x+2) - (x+2) = (x+2)(x^2 - 1) = (x+2)(x-1)(x+1)$

111. $x^4 - x^3 + x - 1 = x^3(x-1) + (x-1) = (x-1)(x^3+1) = (x-1)(x+1)(x^2-x+1)$

113. Factors of 4   1, 4   2, 2   −1, −4   −2, −2
     Sum   5   4   −5   −4
     None of the sums of the factors is 0, so $x^2 + 4$ is prime.

115. Answers will vary.

Review

R.7 Rational Expressions

1. $\dfrac{3x+9}{x^2-9} = \dfrac{3(x+3)}{(x-3)(x+3)} = \dfrac{3}{x-3}$

3. $\dfrac{x^2-2x}{3x-6} = \dfrac{x(x-2)}{3(x-2)} = \dfrac{x}{3}$

5. $\dfrac{24x^2}{12x^2-6x} = \dfrac{24x^2}{6x(2x-1)} = \dfrac{4x}{2x-1}$

7. $\dfrac{y^2-25}{2y^2-8y-10} = \dfrac{(y+5)(y-5)}{2(y^2-4y-5)} = \dfrac{(y+5)(y-5)}{2(y-5)(y+1)} = \dfrac{y+5}{2(y+1)}$

9. $\dfrac{x^2+4x-5}{x^2-2x+1} = \dfrac{(x+5)(x-1)}{(x-1)(x-1)} = \dfrac{x+5}{x-1}$

11. $\dfrac{x^2+5x-14}{2-x} = \dfrac{(x+7)(x-2)}{2-x} = \dfrac{(x+7)(x-2)}{(-1)(-2+x)} = \dfrac{(x+7)(x-2)}{(-1)(x-2)} = -(x+7)$

13. $\dfrac{3x+6}{5x^2} \cdot \dfrac{x}{x^2-4} = \dfrac{3(x+2)}{5x^2} \cdot \dfrac{x}{(x-2)(x+2)} = \dfrac{3}{5x(x-2)}$

15. $\dfrac{4x^2}{x^2-16} \cdot \dfrac{x-4}{2x} = \dfrac{4x^2}{(x-4)(x+4)} \cdot \dfrac{x-4}{2x} = \dfrac{2x}{x+4}$

17. $\dfrac{4x-8}{-3x} \cdot \dfrac{12}{12-6x} = \dfrac{4(x-2)}{-3x} \cdot \dfrac{12}{6(2-x)} = \dfrac{4(x-2)}{-3x} \cdot \dfrac{2}{(-1)(x-2)} = \dfrac{8}{3x}$

19. $\dfrac{x^2-3x-10}{x^2+2x-35} \cdot \dfrac{x^2+4x-21}{x^2+9x+14} = \dfrac{(x-5)(x+2)}{(x+7)(x-5)} \cdot \dfrac{(x+7)(x-3)}{(x+7)(x+2)} = \dfrac{x-3}{x+7}$

21. $\dfrac{\left(\dfrac{6x}{x^2-4}\right)}{\left(\dfrac{3x-9}{2x+4}\right)} = \dfrac{6x}{x^2-4} \cdot \dfrac{2x+4}{3x-9} = \dfrac{6x}{(x-2)(x+2)} \cdot \dfrac{2(x+2)}{3(x-3)} = \dfrac{4x}{(x-2)(x-3)}$

23. $\dfrac{\left(\dfrac{8x}{x^2-1}\right)}{\left(\dfrac{10}{x+1}\right)} = \dfrac{8x}{x^2-1} \cdot \dfrac{x+1}{10} = \dfrac{8x}{(x-1)(x+1)} \cdot \dfrac{x+1}{10} = \dfrac{4x}{5(x-1)}$

25. $\dfrac{\left(\dfrac{4-x}{4+x}\right)}{\left(\dfrac{4x}{x^2-16}\right)} = \dfrac{4-x}{4+x} \cdot \dfrac{x^2-16}{4x} = \dfrac{4-x}{4+x} \cdot \dfrac{(x+4)(x-4)}{4x} = \dfrac{(4-x)(x-4)}{4x} = -\dfrac{(x-4)^2}{4x}$

27. $\dfrac{\left(\dfrac{x^2+7x+12}{x^2-7x+12}\right)}{\left(\dfrac{x^2+x-12}{x^2-x-12}\right)} = \dfrac{x^2+7x+12}{x^2-7x+12} \cdot \dfrac{x^2-x-12}{x^2+x-12} = \dfrac{(x+3)(x+4)}{(x-3)(x-4)} \cdot \dfrac{(x-4)(x+3)}{(x+4)(x-3)} = \dfrac{(x+3)^2}{(x-3)^2}$

29. $\dfrac{\left(\dfrac{2x^2-x-28}{3x^2-x-2}\right)}{\left(\dfrac{4x^2+16x+7}{3x^2+11x+6}\right)} = \dfrac{2x^2-x-28}{3x^2-x-2} \cdot \dfrac{3x^2+11x+6}{4x^2+16x+7} = \dfrac{(2x+7)(x-4)}{(3x+2)(x-1)} \cdot \dfrac{(3x+2)(x+3)}{(2x+7)(2x+1)}$

$= \dfrac{(x-4)(x+3)}{(x-1)(2x+1)}$

31. $\dfrac{x}{2} + \dfrac{5}{2} = \dfrac{x+5}{2}$

33. $\dfrac{x^2}{2x-3} - \dfrac{4}{2x-3} = \dfrac{x^2-4}{2x-3} = \dfrac{(x+2)(x-2)}{2x-3}$

35. $\dfrac{x+1}{x-3} + \dfrac{2x-3}{x-3} = \dfrac{x+1+2x-3}{x-3} = \dfrac{3x-2}{x-3}$

37. $\dfrac{3x+5}{2x-1} - \dfrac{2x-4}{2x-1} = \dfrac{(3x+5)-(2x-4)}{2x-1} = \dfrac{3x+5-2x+4}{2x-1} = \dfrac{x+9}{2x-1}$

39. $\dfrac{4}{x-2} + \dfrac{x}{2-x} = \dfrac{4}{x-2} - \dfrac{x}{x-2} = \dfrac{4-x}{x-2}$

41. $\dfrac{4}{x-1} - \dfrac{2}{x+2} = \dfrac{4(x+2)}{(x-1)(x+2)} - \dfrac{2(x-1)}{(x+2)(x-1)} = \dfrac{4x+8-2x+2}{(x+2)(x-1)} = \dfrac{2x+10}{(x+2)(x-1)}$

$= \dfrac{2(x+5)}{(x+2)(x-1)}$

43. $\dfrac{x}{x+1} + \dfrac{2x-3}{x-1} = \dfrac{x(x-1)}{(x+1)(x-1)} + \dfrac{(2x-3)(x+1)}{(x-1)(x+1)} = \dfrac{x^2-x+2x^2-x-3}{(x-1)(x+1)}$

$= \dfrac{3x^2-2x-3}{(x-1)(x+1)}$

45. $\dfrac{x-3}{x+2} - \dfrac{x+4}{x-2} = \dfrac{(x-3)(x-2)}{(x+2)(x-2)} - \dfrac{(x+4)(x+2)}{(x-2)(x+2)} = \dfrac{x^2-5x+6-(x^2+6x+8)}{(x+2)(x-2)}$

$= \dfrac{x^2-5x+6-x^2-6x-8}{(x+2)(x-2)} = \dfrac{-11x-2}{(x+2)(x-2)}$

47. $\dfrac{x}{x^2-4}+\dfrac{1}{x}=\dfrac{x^2+x^2-4}{(x)(x^2-4)}=\dfrac{2x^2-4}{(x)(x^2-4)}=\dfrac{2(x^2-2)}{(x)(x-2)(x+2)}$

49. $x^2-4=(x+2)(x-2)$

$x^2-x-2=(x+1)(x-2)$

$\therefore$ LCM is $(x+2)(x-2)(x+1)$

51. $x^3-x=x(x^2-1)=x(x+1)(x-1)$

$x^2-x=x(x-1)$

$\therefore$ LCM is $x(x+1)(x-1)$

53. $4x^3-4x^2+x=x(4x^2-4x+1)=x(2x-1)(2x-1)$

$2x^3-x^2=x^2(2x-1)$

x^3

$\therefore$ LCM is $x^3(2x-1)^2$

55. $x^3-x=x(x^2-1)=x(x+1)(x-1)$

$x^3-2x^2+x=x(x^2-2x+1)=x(x-1)^2$

$x^3-1=(x-1)(x^2+x+1)$

$\therefore$ LCM is $x(x+1)(x-1)^2(x^2+x+1)$

57. $\dfrac{x}{x^2-7x+6}-\dfrac{x}{x^2-2x-24}=\dfrac{x}{(x-6)(x-1)}-\dfrac{x}{(x-6)(x+4)}$

$=\dfrac{x(x+4)}{(x-6)(x-1)(x+4)}-\dfrac{x(x-1)}{(x-6)(x+4)(x-1)}$

$=\dfrac{x^2+4x-x^2+x}{(x-6)(x+4)(x-1)}=\dfrac{5x}{(x-6)(x+4)(x-1)}$

59. $\dfrac{4x}{x^2-4}-\dfrac{2}{x^2+x-6}=\dfrac{4x}{(x-2)(x+2)}-\dfrac{2}{(x+3)(x-2)}$

$=\dfrac{4x(x+3)}{(x-2)(x+2)(x+3)}-\dfrac{2(x+2)}{(x+3)(x-2)(x+2)}$

$=\dfrac{4x^2+12x-2x-4}{(x-2)(x+2)(x+3)}=\dfrac{4x^2+10x-4}{(x-2)(x+2)(x+3)}$

$=\dfrac{2(2x^2+5x-2)}{(x-2)(x+2)(x+3)}$

61. $\dfrac{3}{(x-1)^2(x+1)}+\dfrac{2}{(x-1)(x+1)^2}=\dfrac{3(x+1)+2(x-1)}{(x-1)^2(x+1)^2}=\dfrac{3x+3+2x-2}{(x-1)^2(x+1)^2}$

$=\dfrac{5x+1}{(x-1)^2(x+1)^2}$

63. $\dfrac{x+4}{x^2-x-2} - \dfrac{2x+3}{x^2+2x-8} = \dfrac{x+4}{(x-2)(x+1)} - \dfrac{2x+3}{(x+4)(x-2)}$

$$= \dfrac{(x+4)(x+4)}{(x-2)(x+1)(x+4)} - \dfrac{(2x+3)(x+1)}{(x+4)(x-2)(x+1)}$$

$$= \dfrac{x^2+8x+16-(2x^2+5x+3)}{(x-2)(x+1)(x+4)} = \dfrac{-x^2+3x+13}{(x-2)(x+1)(x+4)}$$

65. $\dfrac{1}{x} - \dfrac{2}{x^2+x} + \dfrac{3}{x^3-x^2} = \dfrac{1}{x} - \dfrac{2}{x(x+1)} + \dfrac{3}{x^2(x-1)} = \dfrac{x(x+1)(x-1)-2x(x-1)+3(x+1)}{x^2(x+1)(x-1)}$

$$= \dfrac{x(x^2-1)-2x^2+2x+3x+3}{x^2(x+1)(x-1)} = \dfrac{x^3-x-2x^2+5x+3}{x^2(x+1)(x-1)} = \dfrac{x^3-2x^2+4x+3}{x^2(x+1)(x-1)}$$

67. $\dfrac{1}{h}\left(\dfrac{1}{x+h} - \dfrac{1}{x}\right) = \dfrac{1}{h}\left(\dfrac{1\cdot x}{(x+h)x} - \dfrac{1(x+h)}{x(x+h)}\right) = \dfrac{1}{h}\left(\dfrac{x-x-h}{x(x+h)}\right) = \dfrac{-h}{hx(x+h)} = \dfrac{-1}{x(x+h)}$

69. $\dfrac{1+\dfrac{1}{x}}{1-\dfrac{1}{x}} = \dfrac{\left(\dfrac{x}{x}+\dfrac{1}{x}\right)}{\left(\dfrac{x}{x}-\dfrac{1}{x}\right)} = \dfrac{\left(\dfrac{x+1}{x}\right)}{\left(\dfrac{x-1}{x}\right)} = \dfrac{x+1}{x}\cdot\dfrac{x}{x-1} = \dfrac{x+1}{x-1}$

71. $\dfrac{x-\dfrac{1}{x}}{x+\dfrac{1}{x}} = \dfrac{\left(\dfrac{x^2}{x}-\dfrac{1}{x}\right)}{\left(\dfrac{x^2}{x}+\dfrac{1}{x}\right)} = \dfrac{\left(\dfrac{x^2-1}{x}\right)}{\left(\dfrac{x^2+1}{x}\right)} = \dfrac{x^2-1}{x}\cdot\dfrac{x}{x^2+1} = \dfrac{(x-1)(x+1)}{x^2+1}$

73. $\dfrac{\left(\dfrac{x+4}{x-2}-\dfrac{x-3}{x+1}\right)}{x+1} = \dfrac{\left(\dfrac{(x+4)(x+1)}{(x-2)(x+1)}-\dfrac{(x-3)(x-2)}{(x+1)(x-2)}\right)}{x+1} = \dfrac{\left(\dfrac{x^2+5x+4-(x^2-5x+6)}{(x-2)(x+1)}\right)}{x+1}$

$$= \dfrac{10x-2}{(x-2)(x+1)}\cdot\dfrac{1}{x+1} = \dfrac{2(5x-1)}{(x-2)(x+1)^2}$$

75. $\dfrac{\left(\dfrac{x-2}{x+2}+\dfrac{x-1}{x+1}\right)}{\left(\dfrac{x}{x+1}-\dfrac{2x-3}{x}\right)} = \dfrac{\left(\dfrac{(x-2)(x+1)}{(x+2)(x+1)}+\dfrac{(x-1)(x+2)}{(x+1)(x+2)}\right)}{\left(\dfrac{x^2}{(x+1)(x)}-\dfrac{(2x-3)(x+1)}{x(x+1)}\right)} = \dfrac{\left(\dfrac{x^2-x-2+x^2+x-2}{(x+2)(x+1)}\right)}{\left(\dfrac{x^2-(2x^2-x-3)}{x(x+1)}\right)}$

$$= \dfrac{\left(\dfrac{2x^2-4}{(x+2)(x+1)}\right)}{\left(\dfrac{-x^2+x+3}{x(x+1)}\right)} = \dfrac{2(x^2-2)}{(x+2)(x+1)}\cdot\dfrac{x(x+1)}{-(x^2-x-3)} = \dfrac{2x(x^2-2)}{-(x+2)(x^2-x-3)} = \dfrac{-2x(x^2-2)}{(x+2)(x^2-x-3)}$$

77. $1-\dfrac{1}{\left(1-\dfrac{1}{x}\right)} = 1-\dfrac{1}{\left(\dfrac{x-1}{x}\right)} = 1-1\cdot\dfrac{x}{x-1} = \dfrac{x-1-x}{x-1} = \dfrac{-1}{x-1} = -\dfrac{1}{x-1}$

79. $\dfrac{1}{f} = (n-1)\left(\dfrac{1}{R_1}+\dfrac{1}{R_2}\right)$

$\dfrac{R_1\cdot R_2}{f} = (n-1)\left(\dfrac{1}{R_1}+\dfrac{1}{R_2}\right)R_1\cdot R_2 \rightarrow \dfrac{R_1\cdot R_2}{f} = (n-1)(R_2+R_1)$

$\dfrac{f}{R_1\cdot R_2} = \dfrac{1}{(n-1)(R_2+R_1)} \rightarrow f = \dfrac{R_1\cdot R_2}{(n-1)(R_2+R_1)}$

$f = \dfrac{0.1(0.2)}{(1.5-1)(0.2+0.1)} = \dfrac{0.02}{0.5(0.3)} = \dfrac{0.02}{0.15} = \dfrac{2}{15}$ meters

81. $1+\dfrac{1}{x} = \dfrac{x+1}{x} \Rightarrow a=1, b=1, c=0$

$1+\dfrac{1}{1+\dfrac{1}{x}} = 1+\dfrac{1}{\left(\dfrac{x+1}{x}\right)} = 1+\dfrac{x}{x+1} = \dfrac{x+1+x}{x+1} = \dfrac{2x+1}{x+1} \Rightarrow a=2, b=1, c=1$

$1+\dfrac{1}{1+\dfrac{1}{1+\dfrac{1}{x}}} = 1+\dfrac{1}{\left(\dfrac{2x+1}{x+1}\right)} = 1+\dfrac{x+1}{2x+1} = \dfrac{2x+1+x+1}{2x+1} = \dfrac{3x+2}{2x+1} \Rightarrow a=3, b=2, c=1$

$1+\dfrac{1}{1+\dfrac{1}{1+\dfrac{1}{1+\dfrac{1}{x}}}} = 1+\dfrac{1}{\left(\dfrac{3x+2}{2x+1}\right)} = 1+\dfrac{2x+1}{3x+2} = \dfrac{3x+2+2x+1}{3x+2} = \dfrac{5x+3}{3x+2} \Rightarrow a=5, b=3, c=2$

If we continue this process, the values of *a*, *b* and *c* produce the following sequences:
$a: 1,2,3,5,8,13,21,....$

$b: 1,1,2,3,5,8,13,21,.....$

$c: 0,1,1,2,3,5,8,13,21,.....$

In each case we have the *Fibonacci Sequence*, where the next value in the list is obtained from the sum of the previous 2 values in the list.

83. Answers will vary.

Review

R.8   Square Roots; Radicals

1. $\sqrt{25} = 5$ 3. $\sqrt[3]{27} = 3$ 5. $\sqrt[3]{-64} = -4$ 7. $\sqrt{\dfrac{1}{9}} = \dfrac{1}{3}$

9. $\sqrt{25x^4} = 5x^2$ 11. $\sqrt[3]{8(1+x)^3} = 2(1+x)$ 13. $\sqrt{8} = \sqrt{4 \cdot 2} = 2\sqrt{2}$

15. $\sqrt{50} = \sqrt{25 \cdot 2} = 5\sqrt{2}$ 17. $\sqrt[3]{16} = \sqrt[3]{8 \cdot 2} = 2\sqrt[3]{2}$

19. $\sqrt[3]{-16} = \sqrt[3]{-8 \cdot 2} = -2\sqrt[3]{2}$ 21. $\sqrt{\dfrac{25x^3}{9x}}, x \neq 0 \ = \sqrt{\dfrac{25x^2}{9}} = \dfrac{5}{3}|x|$

23. $\sqrt[4]{x^{12}y^8} = \sqrt[4]{\left(x^3\right)^4 \left(y^2\right)^4} = x^3 y^2$ 25. $\sqrt{36x} = 6\sqrt{x}$

27. $\sqrt{3x^2}\sqrt{12x} = \sqrt{36x^2 \cdot x} = 6x\sqrt{x}$ 29. $\dfrac{\sqrt{3xy^3}\sqrt{2x^2y}}{\sqrt{6x^3y^4}}, x > 0, y > 0$

31. $\sqrt{\dfrac{16y^4}{9x^2}}, x > 0, y \geq 0 \ = \dfrac{4y^2}{3x}$

33. $\left(\sqrt{5}\sqrt[3]{9}\right)^2 = 5\sqrt[3]{81} = 5\sqrt[3]{27 \cdot 3} = 5 \cdot 3\sqrt[3]{3} = 15\sqrt[3]{3}$

35. $\sqrt{\dfrac{2x-3}{2x^4 + 3x^3}}\sqrt{\dfrac{x}{4x^2-9}}, x > \dfrac{3}{2}$

     $= \sqrt{\dfrac{2x-3}{2x^4+3x^3} \cdot \dfrac{x}{4x^2-9}} = \sqrt{\dfrac{2x-3}{x^3(2x+3)} \cdot \dfrac{x}{(2x+3)(2x-3)}} = \sqrt{\dfrac{1}{x^2(2x+3)^2}} = \dfrac{1}{x(2x+3)}$

37. $\sqrt{\dfrac{x-1}{x+1}}\sqrt{\dfrac{x^2+2x+1}{x^2-1}}, x > 1$

     $= \sqrt{\dfrac{x-1}{x+1} \cdot \dfrac{x^2+2x+1}{x^2-1}} = \sqrt{\dfrac{x-1}{x+1} \cdot \dfrac{(x+1)^2}{(x-1)(x+1)}} = \sqrt{\dfrac{(x+1)^2}{(x+1)^2}} = \sqrt{1} = 1$

39. $3\sqrt{2} + 4\sqrt{2} = 7\sqrt{2}$

41. $-\sqrt{18} + 2\sqrt{8} = -\sqrt{9\cdot 2} + 2\sqrt{4\cdot 2} = -3\sqrt{2} + 4\sqrt{2} = \sqrt{2}$

43. $5\sqrt[3]{2} - 2\sqrt[3]{54} = 5\sqrt[3]{2} - 2\sqrt[3]{27\cdot 2} = 5\sqrt[3]{2} - 6\sqrt[3]{2} = -\sqrt[3]{2}$

45. $\sqrt{8x^3} - 3\sqrt{50x}, x \geq 0$

$\sqrt{4\cdot 2x^3} - 3\sqrt{25\cdot 2x} = 2x\sqrt{2x} - 15\sqrt{2x} = \sqrt{2x}(2x - 15)$

47. $\sqrt[3]{16x^4 y} - 3x\sqrt[3]{2xy} + 5\sqrt[3]{-2xy^4} = \sqrt[3]{8\cdot 2x^4 y} - 3x\sqrt[3]{2xy} - 5y\sqrt[3]{2xy}$

$= 2x\sqrt[3]{2xy} - 3x\sqrt[3]{2xy} - 5y\sqrt[3]{2xy} = \sqrt[3]{2xy}(2x - 3x - 5y) = \sqrt[3]{2xy}(-x - 5y)$

49. $(3\sqrt{6})(4\sqrt{3}) = 12\sqrt{18} = 12\sqrt{9\cdot 2} = 36\sqrt{2}$

51. $\sqrt{3}(\sqrt{3} - 4) = 3 - 4\sqrt{3}$ 53. $3\sqrt{7}(2\sqrt{7} + 3) = 6\cdot 7 + 9\sqrt{7} = 42 + 9\sqrt{7}$

55. $(\sqrt{2} - 1)^2 = (\sqrt{2})^2 - 2\sqrt{2} + 1 = 2 - 2\sqrt{2} + 1 = 3 - 2\sqrt{2}$

57. $(\sqrt[3]{2} - 1)^3 = (\sqrt[3]{2})^3 - 3(\sqrt[3]{2})^2 + 3(\sqrt[3]{2}) - 1 = 2 - 3(\sqrt[3]{2})^2 + 3(\sqrt[3]{2}) - 1$

$= 1 - 3(\sqrt[3]{2})(\sqrt[3]{2} - 1) = 1 - 3\sqrt[3]{4} + 3\sqrt[3]{2}$

59. $(2\sqrt{x} - 3)(2\sqrt{x} + 5), x \geq 0$ $= 4x - 6\sqrt{x} + 10\sqrt{x} - 15 = 4x + 4\sqrt{x} - 15$

61. $\sqrt{1 - x^2} - \dfrac{1}{\sqrt{1 - x^2}}, -1 < x < 1$ $= \dfrac{\sqrt{1 - x^2}\cdot\sqrt{1 - x^2} - 1}{\sqrt{1 - x^2}} = \dfrac{1 - x^2 - 1}{\sqrt{1 - x^2}} = \dfrac{-x^2}{\sqrt{1 - x^2}}\cdot\dfrac{\sqrt{1 - x^2}}{\sqrt{1 - x^2}}$

$= \dfrac{-x^2\sqrt{1 - x^2}}{(1 + x)(1 - x)} = -\dfrac{x^2\sqrt{1 - x^2}}{(1 + x)(1 - x)}$

63. $\dfrac{2}{\sqrt{5}}\cdot\dfrac{\sqrt{5}}{\sqrt{5}} = \dfrac{2\sqrt{5}}{5}$ 65. $\dfrac{8}{\sqrt{6}}\cdot\dfrac{\sqrt{6}}{\sqrt{6}} = \dfrac{8\sqrt{6}}{6} = \dfrac{4\sqrt{6}}{3}$

67. $\dfrac{1}{\sqrt{x}}, x > 0$ $\dfrac{1}{\sqrt{x}}\cdot\dfrac{\sqrt{x}}{\sqrt{x}} = \dfrac{\sqrt{x}}{x}$ 69. $\dfrac{3}{5 + \sqrt{2}}\cdot\dfrac{5 - \sqrt{2}}{5 - \sqrt{2}} = \dfrac{3(5 - \sqrt{2})}{25 - 2} = \dfrac{3(5 - \sqrt{2})}{23}$

71. $\dfrac{3}{4 + \sqrt{7}}\cdot\dfrac{4 - \sqrt{7}}{4 - \sqrt{7}} = \dfrac{3(4 - \sqrt{7})}{16 - 7} = \dfrac{3(4 - \sqrt{7})}{9} = \dfrac{4 - \sqrt{7}}{3}$

73. $\dfrac{\sqrt{5}}{2+3\sqrt{5}}\cdot\dfrac{2-3\sqrt{5}}{2-3\sqrt{5}}=\dfrac{\sqrt{5}\left(2-3\sqrt{5}\right)}{4-9\cdot5}=\dfrac{\sqrt{5}\left(2-3\sqrt{5}\right)}{4-45}=\dfrac{\sqrt{5}\left(2-3\sqrt{5}\right)}{-41}=\dfrac{2\sqrt{5}-15}{-41}$

75. $\dfrac{\sqrt{3}-\sqrt{2}}{\sqrt{3}+\sqrt{2}}\cdot\dfrac{\sqrt{3}-\sqrt{2}}{\sqrt{3}-\sqrt{2}}=\dfrac{3-2\sqrt{3}\sqrt{2}+2}{3-2}=5-2\sqrt{6}$

77. $\dfrac{1}{\sqrt{x}+2}, x\geq0$ $\dfrac{1}{\sqrt{x}+2}\cdot\dfrac{\sqrt{x}-2}{\sqrt{x}-2}=\dfrac{\sqrt{x}-2}{x-4}, x\geq0, x\neq4$

79. $\sqrt{2}\approx1.41$ 81. $\sqrt[3]{4}\approx1.59$

83. $\dfrac{2+\sqrt{3}}{3-\sqrt{5}}\approx4.89$ 85. $\dfrac{3\sqrt[3]{5}-\sqrt{2}}{\sqrt{3}}\approx2.15$

87. (a) $V=40(12)^{2}\sqrt{\dfrac{96}{12}-0.608}\approx15660.422$ gallons

(b) $V=40(1)^{2}\sqrt{\dfrac{96}{1}-0.608}\approx390.68$ gallons

89. $T=2\pi\sqrt{\dfrac{64}{32}}=2\pi\sqrt{2}\approx8.89$ seconds

91. 8 inches = 8/12 feet = 2/3 feet

$T=2\pi\sqrt{\dfrac{\left(\dfrac{2}{3}\right)}{32}}=2\pi\sqrt{\dfrac{1}{48}}=2\pi\left(\dfrac{1}{4\sqrt{3}}\right)=\dfrac{\pi}{2\sqrt{3}}=\dfrac{\pi\sqrt{3}}{6}\approx0.91$ seconds

93. if $a=-5$, then $\sqrt{a^{2}}=\sqrt{(-5)^{2}}=\sqrt{25}=5\neq a$.

Since we use the principal square root, which is always non-negative,
$$\sqrt{a^{2}}=\begin{cases}a & \text{if } a\geq0 \\ -a & \text{if } a<0\end{cases}$$
which is the definition of $|a|$, so $\sqrt{a^{2}}=|a|$.

Review

R.9   Rational Exponents

1. $8^{2/3} = \left(2^3\right)^{2/3} = 2^2 = 4$

3. $(-27)^{1/3} = \left((-3)^3\right)^{1/3} = -3$

5. $(4)^{-3/2} = \left(2^2\right)^{-3/2} = (2)^{-6/2} = (2)^{-3} = \dfrac{1}{2^3} = \dfrac{1}{8}$

7. $9^{-3/2} = \left(3^2\right)^{-3/2} = 3^{-3} = \dfrac{1}{3^3} = \dfrac{1}{27}$

9. $\left(\dfrac{9}{4}\right)^{3/2} = \left(\dfrac{3^2}{2^2}\right)^{3/2} = \dfrac{3^{6/2}}{2^{6/2}} = \dfrac{3^3}{2^3} = \dfrac{27}{8}$

11. $\left(\dfrac{4}{9}\right)^{-3/2} = \left(\dfrac{2^2}{3^2}\right)^{-3/2} = \dfrac{2^{-6/2}}{3^{-6/2}} = \dfrac{2^{-3}}{3^{-3}} = \dfrac{3^3}{2^3} = \dfrac{27}{8}$

13. $4^{1.5} = 4^{3/2} = \left(2^2\right)^{3/2} = 2^{6/2} = 2^3 = 8$

15. $\left(\dfrac{1}{4}\right)^{-1.5} = \left(\dfrac{1}{4}\right)^{-3/2} = 4^{3/2} = \left(2^2\right)^{3/2} = 2^{6/2} = 2^3 = 8$

17. $\left(\sqrt{3}\right)^6 = \left(3^{1/2}\right)^6 = 3^{6/2} = 3^3 = 27$

19. $\left(\sqrt{5}\right)^{-2} = \left(5^{1/2}\right)^{-2} = 5^{-2/2} = 5^{-1} = \dfrac{1}{5}$

21. $3^{1/2} \cdot 3^{3/2} = 3^{1/2+3/2} = 3^2 = 9$

23. $\dfrac{7^{1/3}}{7^{4/3}} = 7^{1/3-4/3} = 7^{-3/3} = 7^{-1} = \dfrac{1}{7}$

25. $2^{1/3} \cdot 4^{1/3} = (2 \cdot 4)^{1/3} = 8^{1/3} = \left(2^3\right)^{1/3} = 2^{3/3} = 2^1 = 2$

27. $\sqrt[4]{3} \cdot \sqrt[4]{27} = \sqrt[4]{3 \cdot 27} = \sqrt[4]{81} = 81^{1/4} = \left(3^4\right)^{1/4} = 3^{4/4} = 3^1 = 3$

29. $\left(\sqrt[4]{2}\right)^{-4} = \left(2^{1/4}\right)^{-4} = 2^{-4/4} = 2^{-1} = \dfrac{1}{2}$

31. $\left(\sqrt[3]{6}\right)^2 = \left(6^{1/3}\right)^2 = 6^{2/3} = \sqrt[3]{6^2} = \sqrt[3]{36}$

33. $\sqrt{2}\,\sqrt[3]{2} = 2^{1/2} \cdot 2^{1/3} = 2^{1/2+1/3} = 2^{5/6} = \sqrt[6]{32}$

35. $\sqrt[8]{x^4} = \left(x^4\right)^{1/8} = x^{4/8} = x^{1/2}$

37. $\sqrt{x^3}\,\sqrt[4]{x} = x^{3/2} \cdot x^{1/4} = x^{3/2+1/4} = x^{7/4}$

39. $x^{3/2} \cdot x^{-1/2} = x^{3/2-1/2} = x^1 = x$

41. $\left(x^3 y^6\right)^{2/3} = \left(x^3\right)^{2/3}\left(y^6\right)^{2/3} = x^2 y^4$ 43. $\left(x^2 y\right)^{1/3}\left(x y^2\right)^{2/3} = x^{2/3} y^{1/3} x^{2/3} y^{4/3} = x^{4/3} y^{5/3}$

45. $\left(16 x^2 y^{-1/3}\right)^{3/4} = \left(2^4 x^2 y^{-1/3}\right)^{3/4} = 2^3 x^{3/2} y^{-1/4} = \dfrac{8 x^{3/2}}{y^{1/4}}$

47. $\left(\dfrac{x^{2/5} y^{-1/5}}{x^{-1/3}}\right)^{15} = \left(\dfrac{x^{2/5} x^{1/3}}{y^{1/5}}\right)^{15} = \dfrac{x^{30/5} x^{15/3}}{y^{15/5}} = \dfrac{x^6 x^5}{y^3} = \dfrac{x^{6+5}}{y^3} = \dfrac{x^{11}}{y^3}$

49. $\dfrac{x}{(1+x)^{1/2}} + 2(1+x)^{1/2} = \dfrac{x + 2(1+x)^{1/2}(1+x)^{1/2}}{(1+x)^{1/2}} = \dfrac{x + 2(1+x)}{(1+x)^{1/2}} = \dfrac{x + 2 + 2x}{(1+x)^{1/2}} = \dfrac{3x + 2}{(1+x)^{1/2}}$

51. $2x\left(x^2+1\right)^{1/2} + x^2 \cdot \dfrac{1}{2}\left(x^2+1\right)^{-1/2} \cdot 2x = 2x\left(x^2+1\right)^{1/2} + \dfrac{x^3}{\left(x^2+1\right)^{1/2}}$

$$= \dfrac{2x\left(x^2+1\right)^{1/2} \cdot \left(x^2+1\right)^{1/2} + x^3}{\left(x^2+1\right)^{1/2}} = \dfrac{2x\left(x^2+1\right)^{1/2+1/2} + x^3}{\left(x^2+1\right)^{1/2}} = \dfrac{2x\left(x^2+1\right)^1 + x^3}{\left(x^2+1\right)^{1/2}}$$

$$= \dfrac{2x^3 + 2x + x^3}{\left(x^2+1\right)^{1/2}} = \dfrac{3x^3 + 2x}{\left(x^2+1\right)^{1/2}} = \dfrac{x\left(3x^2+2\right)}{\left(x^2+1\right)^{1/2}}$$

53. $\sqrt{4x+3} \cdot \dfrac{1}{2\sqrt{x-5}} + \sqrt{x-5} \cdot \dfrac{1}{5\sqrt{4x+3}}, x > 5$

$$= \dfrac{\sqrt{4x+3}}{2\sqrt{x-5}} + \dfrac{\sqrt{x-5}}{5\sqrt{4x+3}} = \dfrac{\sqrt{4x+3} \cdot 5 \cdot \sqrt{4x+3} + \sqrt{x-5} \cdot 2 \cdot \sqrt{x-5}}{10\sqrt{x-5}\sqrt{4x+3}}$$

$$= \dfrac{5(4x+3) + 2(x-5)}{10\sqrt{(x-5)(4x+3)}} = \dfrac{20x + 15 + 2x - 10}{10\sqrt{(x-5)(4x+3)}} = \dfrac{22x + 5}{10\sqrt{(x-5)(4x+3)}}$$

55. $\dfrac{\left(\sqrt{1+x} - x \cdot \dfrac{1}{2\sqrt{1+x}}\right)}{1+x} = \dfrac{\left(\sqrt{1+x} - \dfrac{x}{2\sqrt{1+x}}\right)}{1+x} = \dfrac{\left(\dfrac{2\sqrt{1+x}\sqrt{1+x} - x}{2\sqrt{1+x}}\right)}{1+x}$

$$= \dfrac{2(1+x) - x}{2(1+x)^{1/2}} \cdot \dfrac{1}{1+x} = \dfrac{2+x}{2(1+x)^{3/2}}$$

57. $\dfrac{(x+4)^{1/2}-2x(x+4)^{-1/2}}{x+4}=\dfrac{\left((x+4)^{1/2}-\dfrac{2x}{(x+4)^{1/2}}\right)}{x+4}=\dfrac{\left((x+4)^{1/2}\cdot\dfrac{(x+4)^{1/2}}{(x+4)^{1/2}}-\dfrac{2x}{(x+4)^{1/2}}\right)}{x+4}$

$=\dfrac{\left(\dfrac{x+4-2x}{(x+4)^{1/2}}\right)}{x+4}=\dfrac{-x+4}{(x+4)^{1/2}}\cdot\dfrac{1}{x+4}=\dfrac{-x+4}{(x+4)^{3/2}}=\dfrac{4-x}{(x+4)^{3/2}}$

59. $\dfrac{\left(\dfrac{x^2}{(x^2-1)^{1/2}}-(x^2-1)^{1/2}\right)}{x^2},x<-1\ \text{or}\ x>1$

$=\dfrac{\left(\dfrac{x^2-(x^2-1)^{1/2}\cdot(x^2-1)^{1/2}}{(x^2-1)^{1/2}}\right)}{x^2}=\dfrac{x^2-(x^2-1)^{1/2}\cdot(x^2-1)^{1/2}}{(x^2-1)^{1/2}}\cdot\dfrac{1}{x^2}$

$=\dfrac{x^2-(x^2-1)}{(x^2-1)^{1/2}}\cdot\dfrac{1}{x^2}=\dfrac{x^2-x^2+1}{(x^2-1)^{1/2}}\cdot\dfrac{1}{x^2}=\dfrac{1}{x^2(x^2-1)^{1/2}}$

61. $\dfrac{\dfrac{1+x^2}{2\sqrt{x}}-2x\sqrt{x}}{(1+x^2)^2},x>0$

$=\dfrac{\left(\dfrac{1+x^2-(2\sqrt{x})(2x\sqrt{x})}{2\sqrt{x}}\right)}{(1+x^2)^2}=\dfrac{1+x^2-(2\sqrt{x})(2x\sqrt{x})}{2\sqrt{x}}\cdot\dfrac{1}{(1+x^2)^2}$

$=\dfrac{1+x^2-4x^2}{2\sqrt{x}}\cdot\dfrac{1}{(1+x^2)^2}=\dfrac{1-3x^2}{2\sqrt{x}(1+x^2)^2}$

63. $(x+1)^{3/2}+x\cdot\dfrac{3}{2}(x+1)^{1/2}=(x+1)^{1/2}\left(x+1+\dfrac{3}{2}x\right)=(x+1)^{1/2}\left(\dfrac{5}{2}x+1\right)=\dfrac{1}{2}(x+1)^{1/2}(5x+2)$

65. $6x^{1/2}(x^2+x)-8x^{3/2}-8x^{1/2}=2x^{1/2}(3(x^2+x)-4x-4)=2x^{1/2}(3x^2-x-4)$

$=2x^{1/2}(3x-4)(x+1)$

67. $3(x^2+4)^{4/3}+x\cdot4(x^2+4)^{1/3}\cdot2x=(x^2+4)^{1/3}[3(x^2+4)+8x^2]$

$=(x^2+4)^{1/3}[3x^2+12+8x^2]=(x^2+4)^{1/3}(11x^2+12)$

69. $4(3x+5)^{1/3}(2x+3)^{3/2}+3(3x+5)^{4/3}(2x+3)^{1/2}, x \geq -\dfrac{3}{2}$

$= (3x+5)^{1/3}(2x+3)^{1/2}[4(2x+3)+3(3x+5)] = (3x+5)^{1/3}(2x+3)^{1/2}(8x+12+9x+15)$

$= (3x+5)^{1/3}(2x+3)^{1/2}(17x+27)$

71. $3x^{-1/2}+\dfrac{3}{2}x^{1/2}, x>0$

$= \dfrac{3}{x^{1/2}}+\dfrac{3}{2}x^{1/2} = \dfrac{3\cdot 2+3x^{1/2}\cdot x^{1/2}}{2x^{1/2}} = \dfrac{6+3x}{2x^{1/2}} = \dfrac{3(2+x)}{2x^{1/2}}$

Review

R.R Review Exercises

1.   (a)   none
      (b) $\{-10\}$
      (c) $\left\{-10, 0.65, 1.343434\ldots, \dfrac{1}{9}\right\}$
      (d) $\{\sqrt{7}\}$
      (e) $\left\{-10, 0.65, 1.343434\ldots, \sqrt{7}, \dfrac{1}{9}\right\}$

3. $-6 + 4\cdot(8-3)$
$$= -6 + 4\cdot(5) = -6 + 20 = 14$$

5. $\dfrac{\left(\dfrac{5}{18}\right)}{\left(\dfrac{11}{27}\right)} = \left(\dfrac{5}{18}\right)\left(\dfrac{27}{11}\right) = \left(\dfrac{5}{2}\right)\left(\dfrac{3}{11}\right) = \dfrac{15}{22}$

7. $4(x-3) = 4x - 12$

9.   Graph on the number line: $x > 3$

11. $d(P,Q) = d(-2,3) = |3-(-2)| = |3+2| = |5| = 5$

13. $\dfrac{4x}{x+y} = \dfrac{4(-5)}{-5+7} = \dfrac{-20}{2} = -10$

15. $\dfrac{3}{x-6}$ Domain $= \{x | x \neq 6\}$

17. $16^{1/2} = \sqrt{16} = 4$

19. $2\sqrt{4x^3} + \sqrt{16x} = 2\cdot 2x\sqrt{x} + 4\sqrt{x} = 4x\sqrt{x} + 4\sqrt{x} = 4\sqrt{x}(x+1)$

21. $\left(25x^{-4/3}y^{-2/3}\right)^{3/2} = \left(5^2 x^{-4/3}y^{-2/3}\right)^{3/2} = 5^3 x^{-2}y^{-1} = \dfrac{125}{x^2 y}$

23. $-5x^3$, the coefficient is -5 and the degree $= 3$

25. $\left(2x^4 - 8x^3 + 5x - 1\right) + \left(6x^3 + x^2 + 4\right) = 2x^4 - 2x^3 + x^2 + 5x + 3$

27. $(2x+1)(3x-5) = 6x^2 - 10x + 3x - 5 = 6x^2 - 7x - 5$

29. $(4x+1)(4x-1) = 16x^2 - 1$

31. $(x+1)(x+2)(x-3) = \left(x^2 + 2x + x + 2\right)(x-3) = \left(x^2 + 3x + 2\right)(x-3)$
$$= x^3 - 3x^2 + 3x^2 - 9x + 2x - 6 = x^3 - 7x - 6$$

33. Divide:

$$
\begin{array}{r}
3x^2 + 8x + 25 \\
x-3\overline{)3x^3 - x^2 + x + 4} \\
\underline{3x^3 - 9x^2} \\
8x^2 + x + 4 \\
\underline{8x^2 - 24x} \\
25x + 4 \\
\underline{25x - 75} \\
79
\end{array}
$$

Check :

$(x-3)(3x^2 + 8x + 25) + (79)$

$= 3x^3 + 8x^2 + 25x - 9x^2 - 24x - 75 + 79$

$= 3x^3 - x^2 + x + 4$

The quotient is $3x^2 + 8x + 25$; the remainder is 79.

35. Divide:

$$
\begin{array}{r}
-3x^2 + 4 \\
x^2+1\overline{)-3x^4 + 0 \cdot x^3 + x^2 + 0 \cdot x + 2} \\
\underline{-3x^4 \qquad - 3x^2} \\
4x^2 \qquad +2 \\
\underline{4x^2 \qquad +4} \\
-2
\end{array}
$$

Check :

$(x^2+1)(-3x^2+4)+(-2)$

$=-3x^4 + 4x^2 - 3x^2 + 4 - 2$

$=-3x^4 + x^2 + 2$

The quotient is $-3x^2 + 4$; the remainder is -2.

37. Divide:

$$
\begin{array}{r}
x^4 - x^3 + x^2 - x + 1 \\
x+1\overline{)x^5 + 0 \cdot x^4 + 0 \cdot x^3 + 0 \cdot x^2 + 0 \cdot x + 1} \\
\underline{x^5 + x^4} \\
- x^4 \qquad\qquad\qquad +1 \\
\underline{- x^4 - x^3} \\
x^3 \qquad\qquad +1 \\
\underline{x^3 + x^2} \\
- x^2 \qquad +1 \\
\underline{-x^2 - x} \qquad +1 \\
x \quad +1 \\
\underline{x \qquad +1} \\
0
\end{array}
$$

Check :

$(x+1)(x^4 - x^3 + x^2 - x + 1) + (0)$

$= x^5 - x^4 + x^3 - x^2 + x + x^4 - x^3 + x^2 - x + 1$

$= x^5 + 1$

The quotient is $x^4 - x^3 + x^2 - x + 1$; the remainder is 0.

39. $x^2 + 5x - 14 = (x+7)(x-2)$

41. $6x^2 - 5x - 6 = (3x+2)(2x-3)$

43. $3x^2 - 15x - 42 = (3x+6)(x-7) = 3(x+2)(x-7)$

45. $8x^3 + 1 = (2x+1)\left((2x)^2 - (2x)(1) + 1^2\right) = (2x+1)\left(4x^2 - 2x + 1\right)$

47. $2x^3 + 3x^2 - 2x - 3 = x^2(2x+3) - (2x+3) = (2x+3)\left(x^2 - 1\right)$
$$= (2x+3)(x-1)(x+1)$$

49. $25x^2 - 4 = (5x+2)(5x-2)$

51. $9x^2 + 1$; a sum of perfect squares is always prime over the set of real numbers

53. $x^2 + 8x + 16 = (x+4)(x+4) = (x+4)^2$

55. $\dfrac{2x^2 + 11x + 14}{x^2 - 4} = \dfrac{(2x+7)(x+2)}{(x+2)(x-2)} = \dfrac{2x+7}{x-2}$

57. $\dfrac{9x^2 - 1}{x^2 - 9} \cdot \dfrac{3x - 9}{9x^2 + 6x + 1} = \dfrac{(3x+1)(3x-1)}{(x+3)(x-3)} \cdot \dfrac{3(x-3)}{(3x+1)^2} = \dfrac{3(3x-1)}{(x+3)(3x+1)}$

59. $\dfrac{x+1}{x-1} - \dfrac{x-1}{x+1} = \dfrac{(x+1)(x+1) - (x-1)(x-1)}{(x-1)(x+1)} = \dfrac{\left(x^2 + 2x + 1\right) - \left(x^2 - 2x + 1\right)}{(x-1)(x+1)}$

$$= \dfrac{x^2 + 2x + 1 - x^2 + 2x - 1}{(x-1)(x+1)} = \dfrac{4x}{(x-1)(x+1)}$$

61. $\dfrac{3x+4}{x^2 - 4} - \dfrac{2x-3}{x^2 + 4x + 4} = \dfrac{3x+4}{(x+2)(x-2)} - \dfrac{2x-3}{(x+2)^2} = \dfrac{(3x+4)(x+2) - (2x-3)(x-2)}{(x+2)^2(x-2)}$

$$= \dfrac{3x^2 + 6x + 4x + 8 - \left(2x^2 - 4x - 3x + 6\right)}{(x+2)^2(x-2)} = \dfrac{3x^2 + 10x + 8 - \left(2x^2 - 7x + 6\right)}{(x+2)^2(x-2)}$$

$$= \dfrac{3x^2 + 10x + 8 - 2x^2 + 7x - 6}{(x+2)^2(x-2)} = \dfrac{x^2 + 17x + 2}{(x+2)^2(x-2)}$$

63. $\dfrac{\left(\dfrac{x^2 - 1}{x^2 - 5x + 6}\right)}{\left(\dfrac{x+1}{x-2}\right)} = \left(\dfrac{x^2 - 1}{x^2 - 5x + 6}\right)\left(\dfrac{x-2}{x+1}\right) = \left(\dfrac{(x+1)(x-1)}{(x-3)(x-2)}\right)\left(\dfrac{x-2}{x+1}\right) = \dfrac{x-1}{x-3}$

65. $\sqrt{\dfrac{9x^2}{25y^4}}, x \geq 0, y > 0 \quad = \dfrac{\sqrt{9x^2}}{\sqrt{25y^4}} = \dfrac{3x}{5y^2}$

67. $\sqrt[3]{27x^4 y^{12}} = \left(\sqrt[3]{27}\right)\left(\sqrt[3]{x^4}\right)\left(\sqrt[3]{y^{12}}\right) = 3x\sqrt[3]{x}\,y^4$

69. $\dfrac{4}{\sqrt{5}} \cdot \dfrac{\sqrt{5}}{\sqrt{5}} = \dfrac{4\sqrt{5}}{5}$

71. $\dfrac{2}{1-\sqrt{2}} \cdot \dfrac{1+\sqrt{2}}{1+\sqrt{2}} = \dfrac{2\left(1+\sqrt{2}\right)}{1-\left(\sqrt{2}\right)^2} = \dfrac{2\left(1+\sqrt{2}\right)}{1-2} = \dfrac{2\left(1+\sqrt{2}\right)}{-1} = -2\left(1+\sqrt{2}\right)$

73. $\dfrac{1+\sqrt{5}}{1-\sqrt{5}} \cdot \dfrac{1+\sqrt{5}}{1+\sqrt{5}} = \dfrac{1+2\sqrt{5}+\left(\sqrt{5}\right)^2}{1-\left(\sqrt{5}\right)^2} = \dfrac{1+2\sqrt{5}+5}{1-5} = \dfrac{6+2\sqrt{5}}{-4} = \dfrac{-3-\sqrt{5}}{2} = -\dfrac{3+\sqrt{5}}{2}$

75. $\left(2+x^2\right)^{1/2} + x \cdot \dfrac{1}{2}\left(2+x^2\right)^{-1/2} \cdot 2x$

$= \left(2+x^2\right)^{1/2} + \dfrac{2x^2}{2\left(2+x^2\right)^{1/2}} = \left(2+x^2\right)^{1/2} + \dfrac{x^2}{\left(2+x^2\right)^{1/2}}$

$= \dfrac{\left(2+x^2\right)^{1/2}\left(2+x^2\right)^{1/2} + x^2}{\left(2+x^2\right)^{1/2}} = \dfrac{2+x^2+x^2}{\left(2+x^2\right)^{1/2}} = \dfrac{2+2x^2}{\left(2+x^2\right)^{1/2}} = \dfrac{2\left(1+x^2\right)}{\left(2+x^2\right)^{1/2}}$

77. $\dfrac{\left(x+4\right)^{1/2} \cdot 2x - x^2 \cdot \dfrac{1}{2}\left(x+4\right)^{-1/2}}{x+4}, x > -4$

$= \dfrac{\left(x+4\right)^{1/2} \cdot 2x - \dfrac{x^2}{2\left(x+4\right)^{1/2}}}{x+4} = \dfrac{\left(\dfrac{2\left(x+4\right)^{1/2}\left(x+4\right)^{1/2} \cdot 2x - x^2}{2\left(x+4\right)^{1/2}}\right)}{x+4}$

$= \dfrac{\left(\dfrac{2\left(x+4\right) \cdot 2x - x^2}{2\left(x+4\right)^{1/2}}\right)}{x+4} = \dfrac{\left(\dfrac{4x^2 - x^2 + 16x}{2\left(x+4\right)^{1/2}}\right)}{x+4} = \left(\dfrac{3x^2 + 16x}{2\left(x+4\right)^{1/2}}\right)\left(\dfrac{1}{x+4}\right) = \dfrac{3x^2 + 16x}{2\left(x+4\right)^{3/2}} = \dfrac{x\left(3x+16\right)}{2\left(x+4\right)^{3/2}}$

79. $281,421,906 = 2.81421906 \times 10^8$

81. $12^2 + 16^2 = 144 + 256 = 400 = 20^2$, therefore we have a right triangle by the converse of the Pythagorean Theorem.

83. Total annual earnings per share
   = (1st quarter earnings) + (2nd quarter earnings) + (3rd quarter earnings) + (4th quarter earnings)
   = 1.2 - 0. 75 - 0.30 + 0.20 = \$0.35 per share.

85.

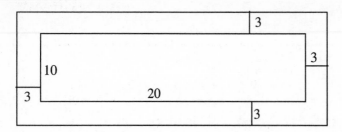

Deck Area = Total Area - Pool Area $= (20+6)(10+6) - (20)(10) = 26\cdot 16 - 200 = 216$ square feet

Deck Perimeter $= 2(26+16) = 84$ feet

87.   Recall that 1 mile = 5280 feet. Consider the diagram (not drawn to scale) showing the bridge at point B, relative to the center of Earth, using the radius of Earth as 3960 miles. Let P refer to the furthest point on the horizon from which the bridge is visible. Note also that $35{,}000$ feet $= \dfrac{35{,}000}{5280}$ miles.

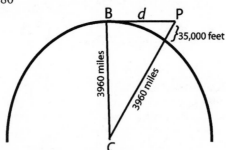

Apply the Pythagorean Theorem to the right triangle, ΔCBP,

$$(3960)^2 + (d)^2 = \left(3960 + \frac{35000}{5280}\right)^2$$

$$(d)^2 = \left(3960 + \frac{35000}{5280}\right)^2 - (3960)^2 \Rightarrow d = \sqrt{\left(3960 + \frac{35000}{5280}\right)^2 - (3960)^2} \approx 229.22 \text{ miles.}$$

Therefore, the bridge can be seen at point P on the horizon, whenever point P is less than or equal to 229.22 miles away from the bridge. So the pilot could see the bridge when the plane was 139 miles from San Francisco. Moreover, he could see a maximum distance of 2299.22 miles.

89 - 91.   Answers will vary.

Graphs

1.1 Rectangular Coordinates; Graphing Utilities

1. (a) Quadrant II
   (b) Positive x-axis
   (c) Quadrant III
   (d) Quadrant I
   (e) Negative y-axis
   (f) Quadrant IV

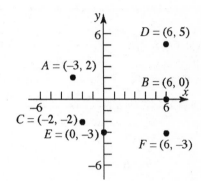

3. The points will be on a vertical line that is two units to the right of the y-axis.

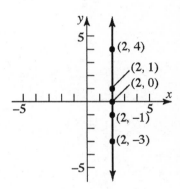

5. $(-1, 4)$; Quadrant II

7. $(3, 1)$; Quadrant I

9.	11.	13.	15.	17.	19.
$X\min = -11$	$X\min = -30$	$X\min = -10$	$X\min = -6$	$X\min = -6$	$X\min = 3$
$X\max = 5$	$X\max = 50$	$X\max = 110$	$X\max = 6$	$X\max = 6$	$X\max = 9$
$X\,\text{scl} = 1$	$X\,\text{scl} = 10$	$X\,\text{scl} = 10$	$X\,\text{scl} = 2$	$X\,\text{scl} = 2$	$X\,\text{scl} = 1$
$Y\min = -3$	$Y\min = -90$	$Y\min = -10$	$Y\min = -4$	$Y\min = -1$	$Y\min = 2$
$Y\max = 6$	$Y\max = 50$	$Y\max = 160$	$Y\max = 4$	$Y\max = 3$	$Y\max = 10$
$Y\,\text{scl} = 1$	$Y\,\text{scl} = 10$	$Y\,\text{scl} = 10$	$Y\,\text{scl} = 2$	$Y\,\text{scl} = 1$	$Y\,\text{scl} = 2$

21. $d(P_1, P_2) = \sqrt{(2-0)^2 + (1-0)^2} = \sqrt{4+1} = \sqrt{5}$

23. $d(P_1, P_2) = \sqrt{(-2-1)^2 + (2-1)^2} = \sqrt{9+1} = \sqrt{10}$

25. $d(P_1, P_2) = \sqrt{(5-3)^2 + (4-8)^2} = \sqrt{2^2 + (-4)^2} = \sqrt{4+16} = \sqrt{20} = 2\sqrt{5}$

27. $d(P_1, P_2) = \sqrt{(6-(-3))^2 + (0-2)^2} = \sqrt{9^2 + (-2)^2} = \sqrt{81+4} = \sqrt{85}$

29. $d(P_1, P_2) = \sqrt{(6-4)^2 + (4-(-3))^2} = \sqrt{2^2 + 7^2} = \sqrt{4+49} = \sqrt{53}$

31. $d(P_1, P_2) = \sqrt{(2.3-(-0.2))^2 + (1.1-0.3)^2} = \sqrt{(2.5)^2 + (0.8)^2}$
$$= \sqrt{6.25+0.64} = \sqrt{6.89} \approx 2.625$$

33. $d(P_1, P_2) = \sqrt{(0-a)^2 + (0-b)^2} = \sqrt{a^2 + b^2}$

35. $P_1 = (1,3); P_2 = (5,15)$
$$d(P_1, P_2) = \sqrt{(5-1)^2 + (15-3)^2}$$
$$= \sqrt{(4)^2 + (12)^2}$$
$$= \sqrt{16+144}$$
$$= \sqrt{160} = 4\sqrt{10}$$

37. $P_1 = (-4,6); P_2 = (4,-8)$
$$d(P_1, P_2) = \sqrt{(4-(-4))^2 + (-8-6)^2}$$
$$= \sqrt{(8)^2 + (-14)^2}$$
$$= \sqrt{64+196}$$
$$= \sqrt{260} = 2\sqrt{65}$$

39. $A = (-2,5), \quad B = (1,3), \quad C = (-1,0)$

$d(A,B) = \sqrt{(1-(-2))^2 + (3-5)^2} = \sqrt{3^2 + (-2)^2}$
$$= \sqrt{9+4} = \sqrt{13}$$
$d(B,C) = \sqrt{(-1-1)^2 + (0-3)^2} = \sqrt{(-2)^2 + (-3)^2}$
$$= \sqrt{4+9} = \sqrt{13}$$
$d(A,C) = \sqrt{(-1-(-2))^2 + (0-5)^2} = \sqrt{1^2 + (-5)^2}$
$$= \sqrt{1+25} = \sqrt{26}$$

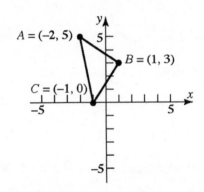

Verifying that Δ ABC is a right triangle by the Pythagorean Theorem:
$$[d(A,B)]^2 + [d(B,C)]^2 = [d(A,C)]^2$$
$$\left(\sqrt{13}\right)^2 + \left(\sqrt{13}\right)^2 = \left(\sqrt{26}\right)^2$$
$$13+13 = 26$$
$$26 = 26$$
The area of a triangle is $A = \frac{1}{2} \cdot bh$. In this problem,
$$A = \frac{1}{2} \cdot [d(A,B)] \cdot [d(B,C)] = \frac{1}{2} \cdot \sqrt{13} \cdot \sqrt{13} = \frac{1}{2} \cdot 13 = \frac{13}{2} \text{ square units}$$

41. $A = (-5, 3)$, $B = (6, 0)$, $C = (5, 5)$

$$d(A, B) = \sqrt{(6 - (-5))^2 + (0 - 3)^2} = \sqrt{11^2 + (-3)^2}$$
$$= \sqrt{121 + 9} = \sqrt{130}$$
$$d(B, C) = \sqrt{(5 - 6)^2 + (5 - 0)^2} = \sqrt{(-1)^2 + 5^2}$$
$$= \sqrt{1 + 25} = \sqrt{26}$$
$$d(A, C) = \sqrt{(5 - (-5))^2 + (5 - 3)^2} = \sqrt{10^2 + 2^2}$$
$$= \sqrt{100 + 4} = \sqrt{104}$$

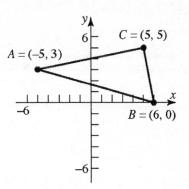

Verifying that Δ ABC is a right triangle by the Pythagorean Theorem:
$$[d(A, C)]^2 + [d(B, C)]^2 = [d(A, B)]^2$$
$$\left(\sqrt{104}\right)^2 + \left(\sqrt{26}\right)^2 = \left(\sqrt{130}\right)^2$$
$$104 + 26 = 130$$
$$130 = 130$$

The area of a triangle is $A = \dfrac{1}{2} \cdot bh$. In this problem,

$$A = \frac{1}{2} \cdot [d(A, C)] \cdot [d(B, C)] = \frac{1}{2} \cdot \sqrt{104} \cdot \sqrt{26} = \frac{1}{2} \cdot \sqrt{2704} = \frac{1}{2} \cdot 52 = 26 \text{ square units}$$

43. $A = (4, -3)$, $B = (0, -3)$, $C = (4, 2)$

$$d(A, B) = \sqrt{(0 - 4)^2 + (-3 - (-3))^2} = \sqrt{(-4)^2 + 0^2}$$
$$= \sqrt{16 + 0} = \sqrt{16} = 4$$
$$d(B, C) = \sqrt{(4 - 0)^2 + (2 - (-3))^2} = \sqrt{4^2 + 5^2}$$
$$= \sqrt{16 + 25} = \sqrt{41}$$
$$d(A, C) = \sqrt{(4 - 4)^2 + (2 - (-3))^2} = \sqrt{0^2 + 5^2}$$
$$= \sqrt{0 + 25} = \sqrt{25} = 5$$

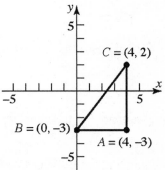

Verifying that Δ ABC is a right triangle by the Pythagorean Theorem:
$$[d(A, B)]^2 + [d(A, C)]^2 = [d(B, C)]^2$$
$$4^2 + 5^2 = \left(\sqrt{41}\right)^2 \rightarrow 16 + 25 = 41 \rightarrow 41 = 41$$

The area of a triangle is $A = \dfrac{1}{2} \cdot bh$. In this problem,

$$A = \frac{1}{2} \cdot [d(A, B)] \cdot [d(A, C)] = \frac{1}{2} \cdot 4 \cdot 5 = 10 \text{ square units}$$

45. All points having an x-coordinate of 2 are of the form (2, y). Those which are 5 units from (−2, −1) are:

$$\sqrt{(2-(-2))^2 + (y-(-1))^2} = 5 \rightarrow \sqrt{4^2 + (y+1)^2} = 5$$

$$\text{Squaring both sides:} \quad 4^2 + (y+1)^2 = 25$$

$$16 + y^2 + 2y + 1 = 25$$

$$y^2 + 2y - 8 = 0 \Rightarrow (y+4)(y-2) = 0$$

$$\Rightarrow y = -4 \text{ or } y = 2$$

Therefore, the points are (2, −4) or (2, 2).

47. All points on the x-axis are of the form (x, 0). Those which are 5 units from (4, −3) are:

$$\sqrt{(x-4)^2 + (0-(-3))^2} = 5 \rightarrow \sqrt{(x-4)^2 + 3^2} = 5$$

$$\text{Squaring both sides:} \quad (x-4)^2 + 9 = 25$$

$$x^2 - 8x + 16 + 9 = 25 \Rightarrow x^2 - 8x = 0$$

$$x(x-8) = 0 \Rightarrow x = 0 \text{ or } x = 8$$

Therefore, the points are (0, 0) or (8, 0).

49. The coordinates of the midpoint are:

$$(x,y) = \left(\frac{x_1 + x_2}{2}, \frac{y_1 + y_2}{2}\right) = \left(\frac{5+3}{2}, \frac{4+2}{2}\right) = \left(\frac{8}{2}, \frac{6}{2}\right) = (4,3)$$

51. The coordinates of the midpoint are:

$$(x,y) = \left(\frac{x_1 + x_2}{2}, \frac{y_1 + y_2}{2}\right) = \left(\frac{-3+6}{2}, \frac{2+0}{2}\right) = \left(\frac{3}{2}, \frac{2}{2}\right) = \left(\frac{3}{2}, 1\right)$$

53. The coordinates of the midpoint are:

$$(x,y) = \left(\frac{x_1 + x_2}{2}, \frac{y_1 + y_2}{2}\right) = \left(\frac{4+6}{2}, \frac{-3+1}{2}\right) = \left(\frac{10}{2}, \frac{-2}{2}\right) = (5,-1)$$

55. The coordinates of the midpoint are:

$$(x,y) = \left(\frac{x_1 + x_2}{2}, \frac{y_1 + y_2}{2}\right) = \left(\frac{-0.2+2.3}{2}, \frac{0.3+1.1}{2}\right) = \left(\frac{2.1}{2}, \frac{1.4}{2}\right) = (1.05, 0.7)$$

57. The coordinates of the midpoint are:

$$(x,y) = \left(\frac{x_1 + x_2}{2}, \frac{y_1 + y_2}{2}\right) = \left(\frac{a+0}{2}, \frac{b+0}{2}\right) = \left(\frac{a}{2}, \frac{b}{2}\right)$$

59. The midpoint of AB is: $D = \left(\frac{0+6}{2}, \frac{0+0}{2}\right) = (3,0)$

The midpoint of AC is: $E = \left(\frac{0+4}{2}, \frac{0+4}{2}\right) = (2, 2)$

The midpoint of BC is: $F = \left(\frac{6+4}{2}, \frac{0+4}{2}\right) = (5,2)$

$$d(C,D) = \sqrt{(0-4)^2 + (3-4)^2} = \sqrt{(-4)^2 + (-1)^2} = \sqrt{16+1} = \sqrt{17}$$

$$d(B,E) = \sqrt{(2-6)^2 + (2-0)^2} = \sqrt{(-4)^2 + 2^2} = \sqrt{16+4} = \sqrt{20} = 2\sqrt{5}$$

$$d(A,F) = \sqrt{(2-0)^2 + (5-0)^2} = \sqrt{2^2 + 5^2} = \sqrt{4+25} = \sqrt{29}$$

61. $d(P_1,P_2) = \sqrt{(-4-2)^2 + (1-1)^2} = \sqrt{(-6)^2 + 0^2} = \sqrt{36} = 6$

$d(P_2,P_3) = \sqrt{(-4-(-4))^2 + (-3-1)^2} = \sqrt{0^2 + (-4)^2} = \sqrt{16} = 4$

$d(P_1,P_3) = \sqrt{(-4-2)^2 + (-3-1)^2} = \sqrt{(-6)^2 + (-4)^2} = \sqrt{36+16} = \sqrt{52} = 2\sqrt{13}$

Since $\left[d(P_1,P_2)\right]^2 + \left[d(P_2,P_3)\right]^2 = \left[d(P_1,P_3)\right]^2$, the triangle is a right triangle.

63. $d(P_1,P_2) = \sqrt{(0-(-2))^2 + (7-(-1))^2} = \sqrt{2^2 + 8^2} = \sqrt{4+64} = \sqrt{68} = 2\sqrt{17}$

$d(P_2,P_3) = \sqrt{(3-0)^2 + (2-7)^2} = \sqrt{3^2 + (-5)^2} = \sqrt{9+25} = \sqrt{34}$

$d(P_1,P_3) = \sqrt{(3-(-2))^2 + (2-(-1))^2} = \sqrt{5^2 + 3^2} = \sqrt{25+9} = \sqrt{34}$

Since $d(P_2,P_3) = d(P_1,P_3)$, the triangle is isosceles.

Since $\left[d(P_1,P_3)\right]^2 + \left[d(P_2,P_3)\right]^2 = \left[d(P_1,P_2)\right]^2$, the triangle is also a right triangle.

Therefore, the triangle is an isosceles right triangle.

65.   Using the Pythagorean Theorem:

$$90^2 + 90^2 = d^2$$
$$8100 + 8100 = d^2$$
$$16200 = d^2$$
$$d = \sqrt{16200} = 90\sqrt{2} \approx 127.28 \text{ feet}$$

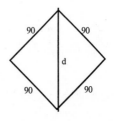

67.   (a)   First: (90, 0), Second: (90, 90)
Third: (0, 90)

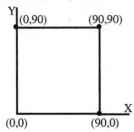

(b)   Using the distance formula:

$$d = \sqrt{(310-90)^2 + (15-90)^2}$$
$$= \sqrt{220^2 + (-75)^2}$$
$$= \sqrt{54025} \approx 232.4 \text{ feet}$$

(c)   Using the distance formula:

$$d = \sqrt{(300-0)^2 + (300-90)^2}$$
$$= \sqrt{300^2 + 210^2}$$
$$= \sqrt{134100} \approx 366.2 \text{ feet}$$

69. The Intrepid heading east moves a distance $30t$ after t
     hours. The truck heading south moves a distance $40t$
     after t hours. Their distance apart after t hours is:

$$d = \sqrt{(30t)^2 + (40t)^2}$$
$$= \sqrt{900t^2 + 1600t^2}$$
$$= \sqrt{2500t^2}$$
$$= 50t$$

Graphs

1.2 Introduction to Graphing Equations

1. $y = x^4 - \sqrt{x}$

   $0 = 0^4 - \sqrt{0}$ $1 = 1^4 - \sqrt{1}$ $0 = (-1)^4 - \sqrt{-1}$

   $0 = 0$ $1 \neq 0$ $0 \neq 1 - \sqrt{-1}$

   $(0, 0)$ is on the graph of the equation.

3. $y^2 = x^2 + 9$

   $3^2 = 0^2 + 9$ $0^2 = 3^2 + 9$ $0^2 = (-3)^2 + 9$

   $9 = 9$ $0 \neq 18$ $0 \neq 18$

   $(0, 3)$ is on the graph of the equation.

5. $x^2 + y^2 = 4$

   $0^2 + 2^2 = 4$ $(-2)^2 + 2^2 = 4$ $\sqrt{2}^2 + \sqrt{2}^2 = 4$

   $4 = 4$ $8 \neq 4$ $4 = 4$

   $(0, 2)$ and $\left(\sqrt{2},\ \sqrt{2} \right)$ are on the graph of the equation.

7. $(-1, 0), (1, 0)$

9. $\left(-\dfrac{\pi}{2}, 0 \right), \left(\dfrac{\pi}{2}, 0 \right), (0, 1)$

11. $(0, 0)$

13. $(-4, 0), (-1, 0), (4, 0), (0, -3)$

15. $(-1.5, 0), (1.5, 0), (0, -2)$

17. none

19. $y = 5x + 4$

   $2 = 5a + 4 \Rightarrow -2 = 5a \Rightarrow a = -\dfrac{2}{5}$

21. $2x + 3y = 6$

   $2a + 3b = 6$

23. $y = x + 2$

   y - intercept : Let $x = 0$, then $y = 2$ $(0, 2)$

   x - intercept : Let $y = 0$, then $x = -2$ $(-2, 0)$

25. $y = 2x + 8$

y - intercept : Let $x = 0$, then $y = 8$ $(0,8)$

x - intercept : Let $y = 0$, then $x = -4$ $(-4,0)$

27. $y = x^2 - 1$

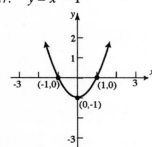

y - intercept : Let $x = 0$, then $y = -1$ $(0,-1)$

x - intercept : Let $y = 0$, then $x = \pm1$ $(-1,0);(1,0)$

29. $y = -x^2 + 4$

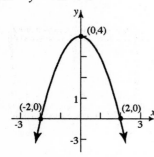

y - intercept : Let $x = 0$, then $y = 4$ $(0,4)$

x - intercept : Let $y = 0$, then $x = \pm2$ $(-2,0);(2,0)$

31. $2x + 3y = 6$

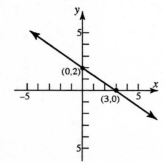

y - intercept : Let $x = 0$, then $y = 2$ $(0,2)$

x - intercept : Let $y = 0$, then $x = 3$ $(3,0)$

33. $9x^2 + 4y = 36$

y-intercept : Let $x = 0$, then $y = 9$ $(0,9)$

x-intercept : Let $y = 0$, then $x = \pm 2$ $(-2,0); (2,0)$

35. $y = 2x - 13$

Use VALUE and ZERO (or ROOT) on the graph of $y_1 = 2x - 13$.

y-intercept: $(0,-13)$ x-intercept: $(6.5,0)$

37. $y = 2x^2 - 15$

Use VALUE and ZERO (or ROOT) on the graph of $y_1 = 2x^2 - 15$.

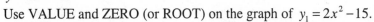

y-intercept: $(0,-15)$ x-intercepts: $(-2.74,0),\ (2.74,0)$

39. $3x - 2y = 43$

Use VALUE and ZERO (or ROOT) on the graph of $y_1 = 1.5x - 43/2$.

y-intercept: $(0,-21.5)$ x-intercept: $(14.33,0)$

41. $5x^2 + 3y = 37$

Use VALUE and ZERO (or ROOT) on the graph of $y_1 = (-5/3)x^2 + 37/3$.

y-intercept: $(0, 12.33)$ x-intercepts: $(-2.72, 0),\ (2.72, 0)$

43.   (a)

(b)   Since $\sqrt{x^2} = |x|$, then for all x, the graphs of $y = \sqrt{x^2}$ and $y = |x|$ are the same.

(c)   For $y = (\sqrt{x})^2$, the domain of the variable x is $x \geq 0$; for $y = x$, the domain of the variable x is all real numbers. Thus, $(\sqrt{x})^2 = x$ only for $x \geq 0$.

(d)   For $y = \sqrt{x^2}$, the range of the variable y is $y \geq 0$; for $y = x$, the range of the variable y is all real numbers. Also, $\sqrt{x^2} = x$ only if $x \geq 0$.

45.   Answers will vary

Chapter 1

Graphs

1.3 Solving Equations Using a Graphing Utility; Linear and Quadratic Equations

1. $x^3 - 4x + 2 = 0$; Use ZERO (or ROOT) on the graph of $y_1 = x^3 - 4x + 2$.

The solution set is $\{-2.21, 0.54, 1.68\}$.

3. $-2x^4 + 5 = 3x - 2$; Use ZERO (or ROOT) on the graph of $y_1 = -2x^4 - 3x + 7$.

The solution set is $\{-1.55, 1.15\}$.

5. $x^4 - 2x^3 + 3x - 1 = 0$; Use ZERO (or ROOT) on the graph of $y_1 = x^4 - 2x^3 + 3x - 1$.

The solution set is $\{-1.12, 0.36\}$.

7. $-x^3 - \dfrac{5}{3}x^2 + \dfrac{7}{2}x + 2 = 0$;

Use ZERO (or ROOT) on the graph of $y_1 = -x^3 - (5/3)x^2 + (7/2)x + 2$.

The solution set is $\{-2.69, -0.49, 1.51\}$.

9. $-\dfrac{2}{3}x^4 - 2x^3 + \dfrac{5}{2}x = -\dfrac{2}{3}x^2 + \dfrac{1}{2}$

Use ZERO (or ROOT) on the graph of $y_1 = -(2/3)x^4 - 2x^3 + (2/3)x^2 + (5/2)x - 1/2$.

The solution set is $\{-2.86, -1.34, 0.20, 1.00\}$.

11. $x^4 - 5x^2 + 2x + 11 = 0$

Use ZERO (or ROOT) on the graph of $y_1 = x^4 - 5x^2 + 2x + 11$.

There are no real solutions.

13.
$$3x + 2 = 6$$
$$3x + 2 - 2 = 6 - 2$$
$$3x = 4$$
$$\frac{3x}{3} = \frac{4}{3} \Rightarrow x = \frac{4}{3}$$
The solution set is $\left\{ \dfrac{4}{3} \right\}$.

15.
$$2t - 6 = 3 - t$$
$$2t - 6 + 6 = 3 - t + 6$$
$$2t = 9 - t$$
$$2t + t = 9 - t + t$$
$$3t = 9 \Rightarrow \frac{3t}{3} = \frac{9}{3} \Rightarrow t = 3$$
The solution set is $\{3\}$.

17.
$$6 - x = 2x + 12$$
$$6 - x - 6 = 2x + 12 - 6$$
$$-x = 2x + 6$$
$$-x - 2x = 2x + 6 - 2x$$
$$-3x = 6$$
$$\frac{-3x}{-3} = \frac{6}{-3} \Rightarrow x = -2$$
The solution set is $\{-2\}$.

19.
$$3 + 2n = 5n + 7$$
$$3 + 2n - 3 = 5n + 7 - 3$$
$$2n = 5n + 4$$
$$2n - 5n = 5n + 4 - 5n$$
$$-3n = 4$$
$$\frac{-3n}{-3} = \frac{4}{-3} \Rightarrow n = -\frac{4}{3}$$
The solution set is $\left\{ -\dfrac{4}{3} \right\}$.

21.
$$2(3 + 2x) = 3(x - 4)$$
$$6 + 4x = 3x - 12$$
$$6 + 4x - 6 = 3x - 12 - 6$$
$$4x = 3x - 18$$
$$4x - 3x = 3x - 18 - 3x$$
$$x = -18$$
The solution set is $\{-18\}$.

23.
$$8x - (2x + 1) = 3x - 13$$
$$8x - 2x - 1 = 3x - 13$$
$$6x - 1 = 3x - 13$$
$$6x - 1 + 1 = 3x - 13 + 1$$
$$6x = 3x - 12$$
$$6x - 3x = 3x - 12 - 3x$$
$$3x = -12$$
$$\frac{3x}{3} = \frac{-12}{3} \Rightarrow x = -4$$
The solution set is $\{-4\}$.

25.
$$\frac{2}{3}p = \frac{1}{2}p + \frac{1}{3}$$
$$6\left(\frac{2}{3}p\right) = 6\left(\frac{1}{2}p + \frac{1}{3}\right)$$
$$4p = 3p + 2$$
$$4p - 3p = 3p + 2 - 3p$$
$$p = 2$$
The solution set is $\{2\}$.

27.
$$0.9t = 0.4 + 0.1t$$
$$0.9t - 0.1t = 0.4 + 0.1t - 0.1t$$
$$0.8t = 0.4$$
$$\frac{0.8t}{0.8} = \frac{0.4}{0.8}$$
$$t = 0.5$$
The solution set is $\{0.5\}$.

29.
$$\frac{x+1}{3}+\frac{x+2}{7}=5$$

$$(21)\left(\frac{x+1}{3}+\frac{x+2}{7}\right)=(5)(21)$$

$$(21)\left(\frac{x+1}{3}\right)+(21)\left(\frac{x+2}{7}\right)=105$$

$$7(x+1)+(3)(x+2)=105$$

$$7x+7+3x+6=105$$

$$10x+13=105$$

$$10x+13-13=105-13$$

$$10x=92$$

$$\frac{10x}{10}=\frac{92}{10}\Rightarrow x=9.2$$

The solution set is $\{9.2\}$.

31.
$$\frac{5}{y}+\frac{4}{y}=3$$

$$y\left(\frac{5}{y}+\frac{4}{y}\right)=y(3)$$

$$5+4=3y$$

$$9=3y$$

$$\frac{9}{3}=\frac{3y}{3}$$

$$y=3$$

and since y = 3 does not cause a denominator to equal zero, the solution set is $\{3\}$.

33.
$$(x+7)(x-1)=(x+1)^2$$

$$x^2-x+7x-7=x^2+2x+1$$

$$x^2+6x-7=x^2+2x+1$$

$$x^2+6x-7-x^2=x^2+2x+1-x^2$$

$$6x-7=2x+1$$

$$6x-7-2x=2x+1-2x$$

$$4x-7=1$$

$$4x-7+7=1+7$$

$$4x=8\Rightarrow\frac{4x}{4}=\frac{8}{4}\Rightarrow x=2$$

The solution set is $\{2\}$.

35.
$$x(2x-3)=(2x+1)(x-4)$$

$$2x^2-3x=2x^2-7x-4$$

$$2x^2-3x-2x^2=2x^2-7x-4-2x^2$$

$$-3x=-7x-4$$

$$-3x+7x=-7x-4+7x$$

$$4x=-4$$

$$\frac{4x}{4}=\frac{-4}{4}\Rightarrow x=-1$$

The solution set is $\{-1\}$.

37. $x^2-9x=0$

$x(x-9)=0\Rightarrow x=0$ or $x-9=0\Rightarrow x=9$

The solution set is $\{0, 9\}$.

39.
$$x^2-25=0$$

$$(x+5)(x-5)=0$$

$$x+5=0\Rightarrow x=-5$$

or $x-5=0\Rightarrow x=5$

The solution set is $\{-5, 5\}$.

41.
$$z^2+z-6=0$$

$$(z+3)(z-2)=0$$

$$z+3=0\Rightarrow z=-3$$

or $z-2=0\Rightarrow z=2$

The solution set is $\{-3, 2\}$.

43.
$$2x^2-5x-3=0$$

$$(2x+1)(x-3)=0$$

$$2x+1=0\Rightarrow x=-\frac{1}{2}$$

or $x-3=0\Rightarrow x=3$

The solution set is $\left\{-\frac{1}{2},3\right\}$

45.
$$3t^2 - 48 = 0$$
$$3(t^2 - 16) = 0$$
$$3(t + 4)(t - 4) = 0$$
$$t + 4 = 0 \Rightarrow t = -4$$
or $t - 4 = 0 \Rightarrow t = 4$
The solution set is $\{-4, 4\}$.

47.
$$x(x + 8) + 12 = 0$$
$$x^2 + 8x + 12 = 0$$
$$(x + 6)(x + 2) = 0 \Rightarrow x = -6, x = -2$$
The solution set is $\{-6, -2\}$.

49.
$$4x^2 + 9 = 12x$$
$$4x^2 - 12x + 9 = 0$$
$$(2x - 3)^2 = 0 \Rightarrow x = \frac{3}{2}$$
The solution set is $\left\{\frac{3}{2}\right\}$.

51.
$$2x^2 - x = 15$$
$$2x^2 - x - 15 = 0$$
$$(2x + 5)(x - 3) = 0$$
$$2x + 5 = 0 \Rightarrow x = -\frac{5}{2}$$
or $x - 3 = 0 \Rightarrow x = 3$
The solution set is $\left\{-\frac{5}{2}, 3\right\}$.

53.
$$\frac{4(x - 2)}{x - 3} + \frac{3}{x} = \frac{-3}{x(x - 3)}$$
$$x(x - 3)\left(\frac{4(x - 2)}{x - 3} + \frac{3}{x}\right) = \left(\frac{-3}{x(x - 3)}\right)x(x - 3)$$
$$x(x - 3)\left(\frac{4(x - 2)}{x - 3}\right) + x(x - 3)\left(\frac{3}{x}\right) = -3$$
$$x(4(x - 2)) + (x - 3)(3) = -3$$
$$4x^2 - 8x + 3x - 9 = -3$$
$$4x^2 - 5x - 6 = 0$$
$$(4x + 3)(x - 2) = 0$$
$$4x + 3 = 0 \Rightarrow x = -\frac{3}{4}$$
or $x - 2 \Rightarrow x = 2$
Since neither of these values causes a
denominator to equal zero, the solution set
is $\left\{-\frac{3}{4}, 2\right\}$.

55.
$$x^3 + x^2 - 20x = 0$$
$$x(x^2 + x - 20) = 0$$
$$x(x - 4)(x + 5) = 0$$
$$x = 0$$
or $x - 4 = 0 \Rightarrow x = 4$
or $x + 5 = 0 \Rightarrow x = -5$
The solution set is $\{-5, 0, 4\}$.

57.
$$x^3 + x^2 - x - 1 = 0$$
$$x^2(x + 1) - (x + 1) = 0$$
$$(x + 1)(x^2 - 1) = 0$$
$$(x + 1)(x + 1)(x - 1) = 0$$
$$(x + 1)^2(x - 1) = 0$$
$$(x + 1)^2 = 0 \Rightarrow x = -1$$
or $x - 1 = 0 \Rightarrow x = 1$
The solution set is $\{-1, 1\}$.

59. $x^3 - 3x^2 - 4x + 12 = 0$
$x^2(x-3) - 4(x-3) = 0$
$(x-3)(x^2 - 4) = 0$
$(x-3)(x+2)(x-2) = 0$
$(x-3)^2 = 0 \Rightarrow x = 3$
or $x + 2 = 0 \Rightarrow x = -2$
or $x - 2 = 0 \Rightarrow x = 2$
The solution set is $\{-2, 2, 3\}$.

61. $x^2 = 25 \Rightarrow x = \pm\sqrt{25} \Rightarrow x = \pm 5$
The solution set is $\{-5, 5\}$.

63. $(x-1)^2 = 4$
$x - 1 = \pm\sqrt{4}$
$x - 1 = \pm 2$
$x - 1 = 2$ or $x - 1 = -2$
$\Rightarrow x = 3$ or $x = -1$
The solution set is $\{-1, 3\}$.

65. $(2x+3)^2 = 9$
$2x + 3 = \pm\sqrt{9}$
$2x + 3 = \pm 3$
$2x + 3 = 3$ or $2x + 3 = -3$
$\Rightarrow x = 0$ or $x = -3$
The solution set is $\{-3, 0\}$.

67. $\left(\dfrac{8}{2}\right)^2 = 4^2 = 16$

69. $\left(\dfrac{\left(-\dfrac{1}{2}\right)}{2}\right)^2 = \left(-\dfrac{1}{4}\right)^2 = \dfrac{1}{16}$

71. $x^2 + 4x = 21$
$x^2 + 4x + 4 = 21 + 4$
$(x+2)^2 = 25$
$x + 2 = \pm\sqrt{25} \Rightarrow x + 2 = \pm 5$
$x = -2 \pm 5 \Rightarrow x = 3$ or $x = -7$
The solution set is $\{-7, 3\}$.

73. $x^2 - \dfrac{1}{2}x - \dfrac{3}{16} = 0$
$x^2 - \dfrac{1}{2}x = \dfrac{3}{16}$
$x^2 - \dfrac{1}{2}x + \dfrac{1}{16} = \dfrac{3}{16} + \dfrac{1}{16}$
$\left(x - \dfrac{1}{4}\right)^2 = \dfrac{1}{4}$
$x - \dfrac{1}{4} = \pm\sqrt{\dfrac{1}{4}} = \pm\dfrac{1}{2}$
$x = \dfrac{1}{4} \pm \dfrac{1}{2} \Rightarrow x = \dfrac{3}{4}$
or $x = -\dfrac{1}{4}$
The solution set is $\left\{-\dfrac{1}{4}, \dfrac{3}{4}\right\}$.

75. $3x^2 + x - \dfrac{1}{2} = 0$

$$x^2 + \dfrac{1}{3}x - \dfrac{1}{6} = 0$$

$$x^2 + \dfrac{1}{3}x = \dfrac{1}{6}$$

$$x^2 + \dfrac{1}{3}x + \dfrac{1}{36} = \dfrac{1}{6} + \dfrac{1}{36}$$

$$\left(x + \dfrac{1}{6}\right)^2 = \dfrac{7}{36}$$

$$x + \dfrac{1}{6} = \pm\sqrt{\dfrac{7}{36}} = \pm\dfrac{\sqrt{7}}{6}$$

$$x = -\dfrac{1}{6} \pm \dfrac{\sqrt{7}}{6}$$

The solution set is $\left\{-\dfrac{1}{6} + \dfrac{\sqrt{7}}{6}, -\dfrac{1}{6} - \dfrac{\sqrt{7}}{6}\right\}$.

77. $x^2 - 4x + 2 = 0$

$a = 1, \quad b = -4, \quad c = 2$

$$x = \dfrac{-(-4) \pm \sqrt{(-4)^2 - 4(1)(2)}}{2(1)}$$

$$= \dfrac{4 \pm \sqrt{16 - 8}}{2} = \dfrac{4 \pm \sqrt{8}}{2}$$

$$= \dfrac{4 \pm 2\sqrt{2}}{2} = 2 \pm \sqrt{2}$$

The solution set is $\left\{2 - \sqrt{2}, 2 + \sqrt{2}\right\}$.

79. $x^2 - 4x - 1 = 0$

$a = 1, \quad b = -4, \quad c = -1$

$$x = \dfrac{-(-4) \pm \sqrt{(-4)^2 - 4(1)(-1)}}{2(1)}$$

$$= \dfrac{4 \pm \sqrt{16 + 4}}{2} = \dfrac{4 \pm \sqrt{20}}{2}$$

$$= \dfrac{4 \pm 2\sqrt{5}}{2} = 2 \pm \sqrt{5}$$

The solution set is $\left\{2 - \sqrt{5}, 2 + \sqrt{5}\right\}$.

81. $2x^2 - 5x + 3 = 0$

$a = 2, \quad b = -5, \quad c = 3$

$$x = \dfrac{-(-5) \pm \sqrt{(-5)^2 - 4(2)(3)}}{2(2)}$$

$$= \dfrac{5 \pm \sqrt{25 - 24}}{4} = \dfrac{5 \pm 1}{4}$$

The solution set is $\left\{1, \dfrac{3}{2}\right\}$.

83. $4y^2 - y + 2 = 0$

$a = 4, \quad b = -1, \quad c = 2$

$$y = \dfrac{-(-1) \pm \sqrt{(-1)^2 - 4(4)(2)}}{2(4)}$$

$$= \dfrac{1 \pm \sqrt{1 - 32}}{8} = \dfrac{1 \pm \sqrt{-31}}{8}$$

No real solution.

85. $4x^2 = 1 - 2x$

$$4x^2 + 2x - 1 = 0$$

$a = 4, \quad b = 2, \quad c = -1$

$$x = \dfrac{-2 \pm \sqrt{2^2 - 4(4)(-1)}}{2(4)}$$

$$= \dfrac{-2 \pm \sqrt{4 + 16}}{8} = \dfrac{-2 \pm \sqrt{20}}{8}$$

$$= \dfrac{-2 \pm 2\sqrt{5}}{8} = \dfrac{-1 \pm \sqrt{5}}{4}$$

The solution set is $\left\{\dfrac{-1 - \sqrt{5}}{4}, \dfrac{-1 + \sqrt{5}}{4}\right\}$.

87. $4x^2 = 9x + 2$

$4x^2 - 9x - 2 = 0$

$a = 4, \quad b = -9, \quad c = -2$

$x = \dfrac{-(-9) \pm \sqrt{(-9)^2 - 4(4)(-2)}}{2(4)}$

$= \dfrac{9 \pm \sqrt{81 + 32}}{8} = \dfrac{9 \pm \sqrt{113}}{8}$

The solution set is $\left\{ \dfrac{9 - \sqrt{113}}{8}, \dfrac{9 + \sqrt{113}}{8} \right\}$.

89. $9t^2 - 6t + 1 = 0$

$a = 9, \quad b = -6, \quad c = 1$

$t = \dfrac{-(-6) \pm \sqrt{(-6)^2 - 4(9)(1)}}{2(9)}$

$= \dfrac{6 \pm \sqrt{36 - 36}}{18} = \dfrac{6 \pm 0}{18} = \dfrac{1}{3}$

The solution set is $\left\{ \dfrac{1}{3} \right\}$.

91. $\dfrac{3}{4}x^2 - \dfrac{1}{4}x - \dfrac{1}{2} = 0$

$4\left(\dfrac{3}{4}x^2 - \dfrac{1}{4}x - \dfrac{1}{2} \right) = (0)(4)$

$3x^2 - x - 2 = 0$

$a = 3, \quad b = -1, \quad c = -2$

$x = \dfrac{-(-1) \pm \sqrt{(-1)^2 - 4(3)(-2)}}{2(3)}$

$= \dfrac{1 \pm \sqrt{1 + 24}}{6} = \dfrac{1 \pm \sqrt{25}}{6} = \dfrac{1 \pm 5}{6}$

$\Rightarrow x = \dfrac{1 + 5}{6} \ \text{ or } \ x = \dfrac{1 - 5}{6}$

$x = \dfrac{6}{6} = 1 \text{ or } x = \dfrac{-4}{6} = -\dfrac{2}{3}$

The solution set is $\left\{ -\dfrac{2}{3}, 1 \right\}$.

93. $4 - \dfrac{1}{x} - \dfrac{2}{x^2} = 0$

$\left(x^2 \right)\left(4 - \dfrac{1}{x} - \dfrac{2}{x^2} \right) = (0)\left(x^2 \right)$

$4x^2 - x - 2 = 0$

$a = 4, \quad b = -1, \quad c = -2$

$x = \dfrac{-(-1) \pm \sqrt{(-1)^2 - 4(4)(-2)}}{2(4)}$

$= \dfrac{1 \pm \sqrt{1 + 32}}{8} = \dfrac{1 \pm \sqrt{33}}{8}$

Since neither of these values causes a denominator to equal zero, the solution set is

$\left\{ \dfrac{1 + \sqrt{33}}{8}, \dfrac{1 - \sqrt{33}}{8} \right\}$.

95. $x^2 - 5 = 0$

$x^2 = 5 \Rightarrow x = \pm\sqrt{5}$

The solution set is $\left\{ -\sqrt{5}, \sqrt{5} \right\}$.

97. $16x^2 - 8x + 1 = 0$

$(4x - 1)(4x - 1) = 0$

$4x - 1 = 0 \Rightarrow x = \dfrac{1}{4}$

The solution set is $\left\{ \dfrac{1}{4} \right\}$.

99.
$$10x^2 - 19x - 15 = 0$$
$$(5x + 3)(2x - 5) = 0$$
$$5x + 3 = 0 \text{ or } 2x - 5 = 0$$
$$\Rightarrow x = -\frac{3}{5} \text{ or } x = \frac{5}{2}$$
The solution set is $\left\{-\frac{3}{5}, \frac{5}{2}\right\}$.

101.
$$2 + z = 6z^2$$
$$0 = 6z^2 - z - 2$$
$$0 = (3z - 2)(2z + 1)$$
$$3z - 2 = 0 \text{ or } 2z + 1 = 0$$
$$\Rightarrow z = \frac{2}{3} \text{ or } x = -\frac{1}{2}$$
The solution set is $\left\{-\frac{1}{2}, \frac{2}{3}\right\}$.

103.
$$x^2 + \sqrt{2}x = \frac{1}{2} \Rightarrow x^2 + \sqrt{2}x - \frac{1}{2} = 0$$
$$2\left(x^2 + \sqrt{2}x - \frac{1}{2}\right) = (0)(2)$$
$$2x^2 + 2\sqrt{2}x - 1 = 0$$
$$a = 2, \quad b = 2\sqrt{2}, \quad c = -1$$
$$x = \frac{-(2\sqrt{2}) \pm \sqrt{(2\sqrt{2})^2 - 4(2)(-1)}}{2(2)}$$
$$= \frac{-2\sqrt{2} \pm \sqrt{8 + 8}}{4} = \frac{-2\sqrt{2} \pm \sqrt{16}}{4}$$
$$= \frac{-2\sqrt{2} \pm 4}{4} = \frac{-\sqrt{2} \pm 2}{2}$$
The solution set is $\left\{\dfrac{-\sqrt{2} + 2}{2}, \dfrac{-\sqrt{2} - 2}{2}\right\}$

105.
$$x^2 + x = 4$$
$$x^2 + x - 4 = 0$$
$$a = 1, \quad b = 1, \quad c = -4$$
$$x = \frac{-(1) \pm \sqrt{(1)^2 - 4(1)(-4)}}{2(1)}$$
$$= \frac{-1 \pm \sqrt{1 + 16}}{2} = \frac{-1 \pm \sqrt{17}}{2}$$
The solution set is $\left\{\dfrac{-1 + \sqrt{17}}{2}, \dfrac{-1 - \sqrt{17}}{2}\right\}$.

107.
$$2x^2 - 6x + 7 = 0$$
$$a = 2, \quad b = -6, \quad c = 7$$
$$b^2 - 4ac = (-6)^2 - 4(2)(7)$$
$$= 36 - 56 = -20$$
Since the discriminant < 0, we have no real solutions.

109.
$$9x^2 - 30x + 25 = 0$$
$$a = 9, \quad b = -30, \quad c = 25$$
$$b^2 - 4ac = (-30)^2 - 4(9)(25)$$
$$= 900 - 900 = 0$$
since the discriminant $= 0$, we have one repeated real solution.

111.
$$3x^2 + 5x - 8 = 0$$
$$a = 3, \quad b = 5, \quad c = -8$$
$$b^2 - 4ac = (5)^2 - 4(3)(-8)$$
$$= 25 + 96 = 121$$
since the discriminant > 0, we have two unequal real solutions.

113.
$$ax - b = c, \quad a \neq 0$$
$$ax - b + b = c + b$$
$$ax = c + b$$
$$\frac{ax}{a} = \frac{c + b}{a}$$
$$x = \frac{c + b}{a}$$

115. $\dfrac{x}{a} + \dfrac{x}{b} = c, \quad a \neq 0,\ b \neq 0,\ a \neq -b$

$$ab\left(\dfrac{x}{a} + \dfrac{x}{b}\right) = ab \cdot c$$

$$bx + ax = abc$$

$$x(a + b) = abc$$

$$\dfrac{x(a + b)}{a + b} = \dfrac{abc}{a + b}$$

$$x = \dfrac{abc}{a + b}$$

117. $x + 2a = 16 + ax - 6a$

when $x = 4$;

$$4 + 2a = 16 + a(4) - 6a$$

$$4 + 2a = 16 + 4a - 6a$$

$$4 + 2a = 16 - 2a$$

$$4a = 12$$

$$a = 3$$

119. Solving for R:

$$\dfrac{1}{R} = \dfrac{1}{R_1} + \dfrac{1}{R_2}$$

$$RR_1R_2\left(\dfrac{1}{R}\right) = RR_1R_2\left(\dfrac{1}{R_1} + \dfrac{1}{R_2}\right)$$

$$R_1R_2 = RR_2 + RR_1$$

$$R_1R_2 = R(R_2 + R_1)$$

$$\dfrac{R_1R_2}{R_2 + R_1} = \dfrac{R(R_2 + R_1)}{R_2 + R_1}$$

$$\dfrac{R_1R_2}{R_2 + R_1} = R$$

121. Solving for R:

$$F = \dfrac{mv^2}{R}$$

$$RF = R\left(\dfrac{mv^2}{R}\right)$$

$$RF = mv^2$$

$$\dfrac{RF}{F} = \dfrac{mv^2}{F} \Rightarrow R = \dfrac{mv^2}{F}$$

123. Step 7 is only allowed if $x \neq 2$. But step 1 states that $x = 2$, so we have a contradiction.

125. In order to solve $\dfrac{5}{x+3} + 3 = \dfrac{8+x}{x+3}$, we multiply each term by the expression

"$x + 3$"   to get $(x + 3)\left(\dfrac{5}{x+3} + 3\right) = \left(\dfrac{8+x}{x+3}\right)(x + 3)$.

Now, provided $x \neq -3$, we can cancel the denominators to get

$$5 + (x + 3)(3) = 8 + x$$

$$5 + 3x + 9 = 8 + x \Rightarrow 2x = -6 \Rightarrow x = -3$$

However, we already stated that $x \neq -3$. So we have a contradiction.

Chapter 1

Graphs

1.4 Setting Up Equations; Applications

1. Let A represent the area of the circle and r the radius.
    The area of a circle is the product of π times the square of the radius. $A = \pi r^2$

3. Let A represent the area of the square and s the length of a side.
    The area of the square is the square of the length of a side. $A = s^2$

5. Let F represent the force, m the mass, and a the acceleration.
    Force equals the product of the mass times the acceleration. $F = ma$

7. Let W represent the work, F the force, and d the distance.
    Work equals force times distance. $W = Fd$

9. C = total variable cost in dollars, x = number of dishwashers manufactured.
    $C = 150x$

11. | Amount in Bonds | Amount in CD's | Total |
    |---|---|---|
    | x | $x - 2000$ | 20,000 |

    $x + x - 2000 = 20000$

    $2x - 2000 = 20000$

    $2x = 22000 \Rightarrow x = 11000$

    $11,000 will be invested in bonds. $9,000 will be invested in CD's.

13. | David | Paige | Dan | Total |
    |---|---|---|---|
    | x | $\dfrac{3}{4}x$ | $\dfrac{1}{2}x$ | 900,000 |

    $$x + \frac{3}{4}x + \frac{1}{2}x = 900{,}000$$

    $$\frac{9}{4}x = 900{,}000$$

    $$x = \frac{4}{9}(900{,}000) \Rightarrow x = 400{,}000$$

    David receives $400,000. Paige receives $300,000. Dan receives $200,000.

15.

	Dollars per hour	Number of hours worked	Money earned
Regular wage	x	40	$40x$
Overtime wage	$1.5x$	8	$(1.5x)(8)$

$$40x + (1.5x)(8) = 442$$

Laura's regular hourly wage is $8.50.

$$40x + 12x = 442 \Rightarrow 52x = 442 \Rightarrow x = \frac{442}{52} = 8.50$$

17. Let x represent the number of touchdowns scored.
Then $x - 2$ represents the number of extra points scored.

	No. scored	Point value	Points earned
touchdown	x	6	$6x$
extra point	$x - 2$	1	$(x-2)(1)$
safety	1	2	$(1)(2)$
field goal	2	3	$(2)(3)$

We know that the total points scored $= 41$, so we have

$$6x + x - 2 + 2 + 6 = 41$$

$$7x + 6 = 41$$

$$7x = 35$$

$$x = 5$$

The Bears scored 5 touchdowns.

19. $l = $ length, $w = $ width

$$2l + 2w = 60 \qquad \text{Perimeter } = 2l + 2w$$

$$l = w + 8 \qquad \text{The length is 8 more than the width.}$$

$$2(w + 8) + 2w = 60$$

$$2w + 16 + 2w = 60$$

$$4w + 16 = 60 \Rightarrow 4w = 44 \Rightarrow w = 11 \text{ feet, } l = 19 \text{ feet}$$

21. Let x represent the score on the final exam and construct the table

	Test1	Test2	Test3	Test4	Test5	Final Exam	Final Exam
score	80	83	71	61	95	x	x
weight	1/7	1/7	1/7	1/7	1/7	1/7	1/7

Compute the final average and set equal to 80.

$$\left(\frac{1}{7}\right)(80 + 83 + 71 + 61 + 95 + x + x) = 80$$

Now solve for x:

$$\left(\frac{1}{7}\right)(390 + 2x) = 80 \Rightarrow 390 + 2x = 560 \Rightarrow 2x = 170 \Rightarrow x = 85$$

Brooke needs to score an 85 on the final exam to get an average of 80 in the course.

23. Let x represent the original price of the house.
   Then $0.15x$ represents the reduction in the price of the house.
      original price – reduction = new price
$$x - 0.15x = 125,000$$
$$0.85x = 125,000$$
$$x = 147,058.82$$
   The original price of the house was \$147,058.82.
   The amount of the savings is $0.15(\$147,058.82) = \$22,058.82$.

25. Let x represent the price the bookstore pays for the book (publisher price).
   Then $0.25x$ represents the mark up on the book.
   The selling price of the book is \$56.00.
      publisher price + mark up = selling price
$$x + 0.25x = 56.00$$
$$1.25x = 56.00$$
$$x = \frac{56.00}{1.25} = 44.80$$
   The bookstore pays \$44.80 for the book.

27. Let x represent the amount of money invested in bonds.
   Then $50,000 - x$ represents the amount of money invested in CD's.

	Principle	Rate	Time (yrs)	Interest
Bonds	x	0.15	1	$0.15x$
CD's	$50,000 - x$	0.07	1	$0.07(50,000 - x)$

   Since the total interest is to be \$6,000, we have:
$$0.15x + 0.07(50,000 - x) = 6,000$$
$$(100)(0.15x + 0.07(50,000 - x)) = (6,000)(100)$$
$$15x + 7(50,000 - x) = 600,000$$
$$15x + 350,000 - 7x = 600,000$$
$$8x + 350,000 = 600,000 \Rightarrow 8x = 250,000 \Rightarrow x = 31,250$$
   \$31,250 should be invested in bonds at 15% and \$18,750 should be invested in CD's at 7%.

29. Let x represent the amount of money loaned at 8%.
   Then $12,000 - x$ represents the amount of money loaned at 18%.

	Principle	Rate	Time (yrs)	Interest
Loan at 8%	x	0.08	1	$0.08x$
Loan at 18%	$12,000 - x$	0.18	1	$0.18(12,000 - x)$

   Since the total interest is to be \$1,000, we have:
$$0.08x + 0.18(12,000 - x) = 1,000$$
$$(100)(0.08x + 0.18(12,000 - x)) = (1,000)(100)$$
$$8x + 18(12,000 - x) = 100,000$$
$$8x + 216,000 - 18x = 100,000$$
$$-10x + 216,000 = 100,000 \Rightarrow -10x = -116,000 \Rightarrow x = 11,600$$
   \$11,600 is loaned at 8% and \$400 is loaned at 18%.

31.   Let x represent the number of pounds of Earl Gray tea.
      Then $100 - x$ represents the number of pounds of Orange Pekoe tea.

	No. of pounds	Price per pound	Total Value
Earl Gray	x	$5.00	$5x$
Orange Pekoe	$100 - x$	$3.00	$3(100 - x)$
Blend	100	$4.50	$4.50(100)$

$$5x + 3(100 - x) = 4.50(100)$$

$$5x + 300 - 3x = 450 \Rightarrow 2x + 300 = 450$$

$$2x = 150 \Rightarrow x = \frac{150}{2} = 75$$

      75 pounds of Earl Gray tea must be blended with 25 pounds of Orange Pekoe.

33.   Let x represent the number of pounds of cashews.
      Then $x + 60$ represents the number of pounds in the mixture.

	No. of pounds	Price per pound	Total Value
cashews	x	$4.00	$4x$
peanuts	60	$1.50	$1.50(60)$
mixture	$x + 60$	$2.50	$2.50(x + 60)$

$$4x + 1.50(60) = 2.50(x + 60)$$

$$4x + 90 = 2.50x + 150$$

$$1.5x = 60 \Rightarrow x = \frac{60}{1.5} = 40$$

      40 pounds of cashews must be added to the 60 pounds of peanuts.

35.   Let x represent the number of ounces of pure water.

	No. of ounces	Conc. of water	Pure water
Pure water	x	1.00	x
40% solution	20	0.60	$(20)(0.60)$
30% solution	$20 + x$	0.70	$(20 + x)(0.70)$

$$x + (20)(0.60) = (20 + x)(0.70) \Rightarrow x + 12 = 14 + 0.70x$$

$$0.3x = 2 \Rightarrow x = \frac{2}{0.3} \Rightarrow x \approx 6.67$$

      Approximately 6.67 ounces of pure water should be added.

37.   Let r represent the rate of the Metra commuter train.
      Then $r + 50$ represents the rate of the Amtrak train.

	Rate	Time	Distance
Metra train	r	3	$3r$
Amtrak train	$r + 50$	1	$r + 50$

      Amtrak distance $=$ Metra distance $- 10$

$$r + 50 = 3r - 10$$

$$60 = 2r \Rightarrow r = 30$$

      The Metra commuter train travels at a rate of 30 miles per hour.
      The Amtrak train travels at a rate of 80 miles per hour.

39. Let r represent the speed of the current.

	Rate	Time	Distance
Upstream	$16 - r$	$\dfrac{20}{60} = \dfrac{1}{3}$	$\dfrac{16 - r}{3}$
Downstream	$16 + r$	$\dfrac{15}{60} = \dfrac{1}{4}$	$\dfrac{16 + r}{4}$

Since the distance is the same in each direction:

$$\frac{16 - r}{3} = \frac{16 + r}{4} \Rightarrow 4(16 - r) = 3(16 + r)$$

$$64 - 4r = 48 + 3r \Rightarrow 16 = 7r \Rightarrow r = \frac{16}{7} \approx 2.286$$

The speed of the current is approximately 2.286 miles per hour.

41. Let t represent the time it takes to do the job together.

	Time to do job	Part of job done in one minute
Trent	30	$\dfrac{1}{30}$
Lois	20	$\dfrac{1}{20}$
Together	t	$\dfrac{1}{t}$

$$\frac{1}{30} + \frac{1}{20} = \frac{1}{t} \Rightarrow 2t + 3t = 60 \Rightarrow 5t = 60 \Rightarrow t = 12$$

Working together, the job can be done in 12 minutes.

43. Let t represent the time the auxiliary pump needs to run.

	Time to do job alone	Part of job done in one hour	Time on Job	Part of total job done by each pump
Main Pump	4	$\dfrac{1}{4}$	3	$\dfrac{3}{4}$
Auxiliary Pump	9	$\dfrac{1}{9}$	t	$\dfrac{1}{9}t$

Since the two pumps are emptying one tanker, we have:

$$\frac{3}{4} + \frac{1}{9}t = 1 \Rightarrow 27 + 4t = 36 \Rightarrow 4t = 9 \Rightarrow t = \frac{9}{4} = 2.25$$

The auxiliary pump must run for 2.25 hours. It must be started at 9:45 a.m.

45. Let w represent the width of window.

Then $l = w + 2$ represents the length of the window.

Since the area is 143 square feet, we have: $w(w + 2) = 143$

$$w^2 + 2w - 143 = 0 \Rightarrow (w + 13)(w - 11) = 0 \Rightarrow w = -13 \text{ which is not practical}$$

or $w = 11$

The width of the rectangular window is 11 feet and the length is 13 feet.

47.   Let l represent the length of the rectangle.
Let w represent the width of the rectangle.
The perimeter is 26 meters and the area is 40 square meters.
$$2l + 2w = 26 \implies l + w = 13 \implies w = 13 - l$$
$$lw = 40$$
$$l(13 - l) = 40 \implies 13l - l^2 = 40 \implies l^2 - 13l + 40 = 0 \implies (l - 8)(l - 5) = 0$$
$$l = 8 \text{ or } l = 5$$
$$w = 5 \qquad w = 8$$
The dimensions are 5 meters by 8 meters.

49.   Let r represent the speed of the current.

	Rate	Time	Distance
Upstream	$15 - r$	$\dfrac{10}{15 - r}$	10
Downstream	$15 + r$	$\dfrac{10}{15 + r}$	10

Since the total time is 1.5 hours, we have:
$$\frac{10}{15 - r} + \frac{10}{15 + r} = 1.5$$
$$10(15 + r) + 10(15 - r) = 1.5(15 - r)(15 + r)$$
$$150 + 10r + 150 - 10r = 1.5(225 - r^2)$$
$$300 = 1.5(225 - r^2)$$
$$200 = 225 - r^2$$
$$r^2 - 25 = 0 \implies (r - 5)(r + 5) = 0 \implies r = 5 \text{ or } r = -5$$
The speed of the current is 5 miles per hour.

51. l = length of the garden
w = width of the garden
(a)   The length of the garden is to be twice its width. Thus, $l = 2w$.
The dimensions of the fence are $l + 4$ and $w + 4$.
The perimeter is 46 feet, so:
$$2(l + 4) + 2(w + 4) = 46 \implies 2(2w + 4) + 2(w + 4) = 46$$
$$4w + 8 + 2w + 8 = 46 \implies 6w + 16 = 46$$
$$6w = 30 \implies w = 5$$
The dimensions of the garden are 5 feet by 10 feet.
(b)   Area $= l \cdot w = 5 \cdot 10 = 50$ square feet
(c)   If the dimensions of the garden are the same, then the length and width of the fence
are also the same $(l + 4)$. The perimeter is 46 feet, so:
$$2(l + 4) + 2(l + 4) = 46 \implies 2l + 8 + 2l + 8 = 46$$
$$4l + 16 = 46 \implies 4l = 30 \implies l = 7.5$$
The dimensions of the garden are 7.5 feet by 7.5 feet.
(d)   Area $= l \cdot w = 7.5(7.5) = 56.25$ square feet.

53.   Let x represent the width of the border measured in feet.
The radius of the pool is 5 feet.
Then $x + 5$ represents the radius of the circle, including both the pool and the border.
The total area of the pool and border is $A_T = \pi(x + 5)^2$.
The area of the pool is $A_P = \pi(5)^2 = 25\pi$.
The area of the border is $A_B = A_T - A_P = \pi(x + 5)^2 - 25\pi$.
Since the concrete is 3 inches or 0.25 feet thick, the volume of the concrete in the border is
$$0.25A_B = 0.25\left(\pi(x + 5)^2 - 25\pi\right)$$
Solving the volume equation:
$$0.25\left(\pi(x+5)^2 - 25\pi\right) = 27 \Rightarrow \pi\left(x^2 + 10x + 25 - 25\right) = 108 \Rightarrow \pi x^2 + 10\pi x - 108 = 0$$
$$x = \frac{-10\pi \pm \sqrt{(10\pi)^2 - 4(\pi)(-108)}}{2(\pi)}$$
$$\approx \frac{-31.42 \pm \sqrt{2344.1285}}{6.28} \approx \frac{-31.42 \pm 48.42}{6.28} \approx 2.71 \text{ or } -12.71$$
The width of the border is approximately 2.71 feet.

55.   Let x represent the width of the border measured in feet.
The total area is $A_T = (6 + 2x)(10 + 2x)$.
The area of the garden is $A_G = 6 \cdot 10 = 60$.
The area of the border is $A_B = A_T - A_G = (6 + 2x)(10 + 2x) - 60$.
Since the concrete is 3 inches or 0.25 feet thick, the volume of the concrete in the border is
$$0.25A_B = 0.25((6 + 2x)(10 + 2x) - 60)$$
Solving the volume equation:
$$0.25((6 + 2x)(10 + 2x) - 60) = 27$$
$$60 + 32x + 4x^2 - 60 = 108$$
$$4x^2 + 32x - 108 = 0 \Rightarrow x^2 + 8x - 27 = 0$$
$$x = \frac{-8 \pm \sqrt{8^2 - 4(1)(-27)}}{2(1)} = \frac{-8 \pm \sqrt{172}}{2}$$
$$\approx \frac{-8 \pm 13.11}{2} \approx 2.56 \text{ or } -10.56 \text{ which is not practical.}$$
The width of the border is approximately 2.56 feet.

57.   Let x represent the number of ounces of pure water.
Then $x + 1$ represents the number of gallons in the 60% solution.

	No. of gallons	Conc. of Antifreeze	Pure Antifreeze
water	x	0	0
100% antifreeze	1	1.00	1(1)
60% antifreeze	$x+1$	0.60	$0.60(x + 1)$

$$0 + 1(1) = 0.60(x + 1)$$

$$1 = 0.6x + 0.6 \Rightarrow 0.4 = 0.6x \Rightarrow x = \frac{4}{6} = \frac{2}{3}$$

$\frac{2}{3}$ gallon of pure water should be added.

59. Let x represent the number of pounds of pure cement.
Then $x + 20$ represents the number of pounds in the 40% mixture.

	No. of pounds	Conc. of Cement	Pure Cement
Pure Cement	x	1.00	x
25% Cement	20	0.25	0.25(20)
40% Cement	$x + 20$	0.40	$0.40(x + 20)$

$$x + 0.25(20) = 0.40(x + 20)$$

$$x + 5 = 0.4x + 8 \Rightarrow 0.6x = 3 \Rightarrow x = \frac{30}{6} = 5$$

5 pounds of pure cement should be added.

61. Let x represent the number of centimeters the length and width should be reduced.
$12 - x =$ the new length, $7 - x =$ the new width.
The new volume is 90% of the old volume.

$$(12 - x)(7 - x)(3) = 0.9(12)(7)(3)$$

$$3x^2 - 57x + 252 = 226.8 \Rightarrow 3x^2 - 57x + 25.2 = 0 \Rightarrow x^2 - 19x + 8.4 = 0$$

$$x = \frac{-(-19) \pm \sqrt{(-19)^2 - 4(1)(8.4)}}{2(1)} = \frac{19 \pm \sqrt{327.4}}{2} \approx \frac{19 \pm 18.09}{2} \approx 0.45 \text{ or } 18.55$$

Since 18.55 exceeds the dimensions, it is discarded.
The dimensions of the new chocolate bar are: 11.55 cm by 6.55 cm by 3 cm.

63. Let x represent the number of grams of pure gold.
Then $60 - x$ represents the number of grams of 12 karat gold to be used.

	No. of grams	Conc. of gold	Pure gold
Pure gold	x	1.00	x
12 karat gold	$60 - x$	$\frac{1}{2}$	$\frac{1}{2}(60 - x)$
16 karat gold	60	$\frac{2}{3}$	$\frac{2}{3}(60)$

$$x + \frac{1}{2}(60 - x) = \frac{2}{3}(60) \Rightarrow x + 30 - 0.5x = 40 \Rightarrow 0.5x = 10 \Rightarrow x = 20$$

20 grams of pure gold should be mixed with 40 grams of 12 karat gold.

65. Let t represent the time it takes for Mike to catch up with Dan.

	Time to run mile	Time	Part of mile run in one minute	Distance
Mike	6	t	$\frac{1}{6}$	$\frac{1}{6}t$
Dan	9	$t + 1$	$\frac{1}{9}$	$\frac{1}{9}(t+1)$

Since the distances are the same, we have: $\frac{1}{6}t = \frac{1}{9}(t + 1) \Rightarrow 3t = 2t + 2 \Rightarrow t = 2$

Mike will pass Dan after 2 minutes, which is a distance of $\frac{1}{3}$ mile.

67. Let t represent the time for the tub to fill with the faucets on and the stopper removed.

	Time to do job alone	Part of job done in one minute	Time on Job	Part of total job done by each
Faucets open	15	$\dfrac{1}{15}$	t	$\dfrac{t}{15}$
Stopper removed	20	$-\dfrac{1}{20}$	t	$-\dfrac{t}{20}$

Since one tub is being filled, we have:

$$\frac{t}{15} + \left(-\frac{t}{20}\right) = 1$$

$$4t - 3t = 60 \qquad \therefore \ 60 \text{ minutes is required to fill the tub.}$$

$$t = 60$$

69. Let x represent the amount of money invested in a CD.
Then $100{,}000 - x$ represents the amount of money invested in the bond.

	Principle	Rate	Time (yrs)	Interest
CD	x	0.09	1	$0.09x$
Bond	$100{,}000 - x$	0.12	1	$0.12(100{,}000 - x)$

Since the total interest is to be $0.10(100{,}000) = \$10{,}000$, we have:

$$0.09x + 0.12(100{,}000 - x) = 10{,}000$$

$$9x + 12(100{,}000 - x) = 1{,}000{,}000$$

$$9x + 1{,}200{,}000 - 12x = 1{,}000{,}000 \Rightarrow -3x + 1{,}200{,}000 = 1{,}000{,}000$$

$$-3x = -200{,}000 \Rightarrow x = 66{,}667$$

The most money that can be invested in the CD is \$66,667 to ensure that the loan payment is made.

71. Let t_1 and t_2 represent the times for the two segments of the trip.

	Rate	Time	Distance
Chicago to Atlanta	45	t_1	$45t_1$
Atlanta to Miami	55	t_2	$55t_2$

Since Atlanta is halfway between Chicago and Miami, the distances are equal.

$$45t_1 = 55t_2 \ \Rightarrow \ t_1 = \frac{55}{45}t_2 = \frac{11}{9}t_2$$

Computing the average speed:

$$\text{Avg Speed} = \frac{\text{Distance}}{\text{Time}} = \frac{45t_1 + 55t_2}{t_1 + t_2} = \frac{45\left(\dfrac{11}{9}t_2\right) + 55t_2}{\dfrac{11}{9}t_2 + t_2}$$

$$= \frac{55t_2 + 55t_2}{\left(\dfrac{11t_2 + 9t_2}{9}\right)} = \frac{110t_2}{\left(\dfrac{20t_2}{9}\right)} = \frac{990t_2}{20t_2} = \frac{99}{2} = 49.5 \text{ miles per hour}$$

The average speed for the trip from Chicago to Miami is 49.5 miles per hour.

73. Let x be the original selling price of the shirt.

$$\text{Profit} = \text{Revenue} - \text{Cost}$$

$$4 = x - 0.40x - 20 \rightarrow 24 = 0.60x \rightarrow x = 40$$

The original price should be \$40 to ensure a profit of \$4 after the sale.

If the sale is 50% off, the profit is:

$$40 - 0.50(40) - 20 = 40 - 20 - 20 = 0$$

At 50% off there will be no profit.

75. It is impossible to mix two solutions with a lower concentration and end up with a new solution with a higher concentration.

Chapter 1

Graphs

1.5 Radical Equations; Equations Quadratic in Form; Absolute Value Equations

1. $\sqrt{x} = 3$
$\left(\sqrt{x}\right)^2 = 3^2$
$x = 9$
Check: $\sqrt{9} = 3$
The solution is $\{9\}$.

3. $\sqrt{y+3} = 5$
$\left(\sqrt{y+3}\right)^2 = 5^2$
$y + 3 = 25 \Rightarrow y = 22$
Check: $\sqrt{22+3} = \sqrt{25} = 5$
The solution is $\{22\}$.

5. $\sqrt{2t-1} = 1$
$\left(\sqrt{2t-1}\right)^2 = 1^2$
$2t - 1 = 1 \Rightarrow 2t = 2 \Rightarrow t = 1$
Check: $\sqrt{2(1)-1} = \sqrt{1} = 1$
The solution set is $\{1\}$.

7. $\sqrt{3t+1} = -6$

Since the principal square root is always a non-negative number, this equation has no real solution.

9. $\sqrt[3]{1-2x} - 3 = 0$
$\sqrt[3]{1-2x} = 3$
$\left(\sqrt[3]{1-2x}\right)^3 = 3^3$
$1 - 2x = 27 \Rightarrow -2x = 26 \Rightarrow x = -13$
Check: $\sqrt[3]{1-2(-13)} - 3 = \sqrt[3]{27} - 3 = 0$
The solution set is $\{-13\}$.

11. $x = 6\sqrt{x}$
$\left(x\right)^2 = \left(6\sqrt{x}\right)^2$
$x^2 = 36x \Rightarrow x^2 - 36x = 0$
$x(x-36) = 0 \Rightarrow x = 0$ or $x = 36$
Check
$x = 0$: $0 = 6\sqrt{0} \Rightarrow 0 = 0$
$x = 36$: $36 = 6\sqrt{36} \Rightarrow 36 = (6)(6) = 36$
The solution set is $\{0, 36\}$.

13. $\sqrt{15-2x} = x$
$\left(\sqrt{15-2x}\right)^2 = x^2$
$15 - 2x = x^2 \Rightarrow x^2 + 2x - 15 = 0$
$(x+5)(x-3) = 0 \Rightarrow x = -5$ or $x = 3$

Check -5: $\sqrt{15-2(-5)} = \sqrt{25}$
$= 5 \neq -5$
Check 3: $\sqrt{15-2(3)} = \sqrt{9} = 3 = 3$
The solution is $\{3\}$.

15.
$$x = 2\sqrt{x-1}$$
$$x^2 = \left(2\sqrt{x-1}\right)^2$$
$$x^2 = 4(x-1) \Rightarrow x^2 = 4x - 4$$
$$x^2 - 4x + 4 = 0 \Rightarrow (x-2)^2 = 0 \Rightarrow x = 2$$

Check: $2 = 2\sqrt{2-1} \Rightarrow 2 = 2$
The solution set is $\{2\}$.

17.
$$\sqrt{x^2 - x - 4} = x + 2$$
$$\left(\sqrt{x^2 - x - 4}\right)^2 = (x+2)^2$$
$$x^2 - x - 4 = x^2 + 4x + 4$$
$$-8 = 5x \Rightarrow -\frac{8}{5} = x$$

Check

$$x = -\frac{8}{5} : \sqrt{\left(-\frac{8}{5}\right)^2 - \left(-\frac{8}{5}\right) - 4} = \left(-\frac{8}{5}\right) + 2$$

$$\sqrt{\frac{64}{25} + \frac{8}{5} - 4} = \frac{2}{5} \Rightarrow \sqrt{\frac{64 + 40 - 100}{25}} = \frac{2}{5}$$

$$\sqrt{\frac{4}{25}} = \frac{2}{5} \Rightarrow \frac{2}{5} = \frac{2}{5} \text{ , The solution set is } \left\{-\frac{8}{5}\right\}.$$

19.
$$3 + \sqrt{3x+1} = x$$
$$\sqrt{3x+1} = x - 3$$
$$\left(\sqrt{3x+1}\right)^2 = (x-3)^2$$
$$3x + 1 = x^2 - 6x + 9$$
$$0 = x^2 - 9x + 8$$
$$(x-1)(x-8) = 0$$
$$x = 1 \text{ or } x = 8$$

Check 1: $3 + \sqrt{3(1)+1}$
$$= 3 + \sqrt{4} = 5 \neq 1$$
Check 8: $3 + \sqrt{3(8)+1}$
$$= 3 + \sqrt{25} = 8 = 8$$
The solution set is $\{8\}$.

21.
$$\sqrt{2x+3} - \sqrt{x+1} = 1$$
$$\sqrt{2x+3} = 1 + \sqrt{x+1}$$
$$\left(\sqrt{2x+3}\right)^2 = \left(1 + \sqrt{x+1}\right)^2$$
$$2x + 3 = 1 + 2\sqrt{x+1} + x + 1$$
$$x + 1 = 2\sqrt{x+1}$$
$$(x+1)^2 = \left(2\sqrt{x+1}\right)^2$$
$$x^2 + 2x + 1 = 4(x+1)$$
$$x^2 + 2x + 1 = 4x + 4$$
$$x^2 - 2x - 3 = 0$$
$$(x+1)(x-3) = 0 \Rightarrow x = -1 \text{ or } x = 3$$

Check -1: $\sqrt{2(-1)+3} - \sqrt{-1+1}$
$$= \sqrt{1} - \sqrt{0} = 1 - 0 = 1 = 1$$
Check 3: $\sqrt{2(3)+3} - \sqrt{3+1}$
$$= \sqrt{9} - \sqrt{4} = 3 - 2 = 1 = 1$$
The solution set is $\{-1, 3\}$.

23. $\sqrt{3x+1} - \sqrt{x-1} = 2$

$\sqrt{3x+1} = 2 + \sqrt{x-1}$

$\left(\sqrt{3x+1}\right)^2 = \left(2 + \sqrt{x-1}\right)^2$

$3x+1 = 4 + 4\sqrt{x-1} + x - 1$

$2x - 2 = 4\sqrt{x-1}$

$(2x-2)^2 = \left(4\sqrt{x-1}\right)^2$

$4x^2 - 8x + 4 = 16(x-1)$

$x^2 - 2x + 1 = 4x - 4$

$x^2 - 6x + 5 = 0$

$(x-1)(x-5) = 0 \Rightarrow x = 1 \ \text{or} \ x = 5$

Check 1: $\sqrt{3(1)+1} - \sqrt{1-1}$

$= \sqrt{4} - \sqrt{0} = 2 - 0 = 2 = 2$

Check 5: $\sqrt{3(5)+1} - \sqrt{5-1}$

$= \sqrt{16} - \sqrt{4} = 4 - 2 = 2 = 2$

The solution set is $\{1,5\}$.

25. $(3x+1)^{1/2} = 4$

$\left((3x+1)^{1/2}\right)^2 = (4)^2$

$3x + 1 = 16 \Rightarrow 3x = 15 \Rightarrow x = 5$

Check

$x = 5: \ (3(5)+1)^{1/2} = 4$

$16^{1/2} = 4 \Rightarrow 4 = 4$

The solution set is $\{5\}$.

27. $(5x-2)^{1/3} = 2$

$\left((5x-2)^{1/3}\right)^3 = (2)^3$

$5x - 2 = 8 \Rightarrow 5x = 10 \Rightarrow x = 2$

Check

$x = 2: \ (5(2)-2)^{1/3} = 2$

$8^{1/3} = 2 \Rightarrow 2 = 2$

The solution set is $\{2\}$.

29. $\left(x^2+9\right)^{1/2} = 5$

$\left(\left(x^2+9\right)^{1/2}\right)^2 = (5)^2$

$x^2 + 9 = 25 \Rightarrow x^2 = 16$

$x = -4 \ \text{or} \ x = 4$

Check

$x = -4: \ \left((-4)^2+9\right)^{1/2} = 5$

$25^{1/2} = 5 \Rightarrow 5 = 5$

$x = 4: \ \left((4)^2+9\right)^{1/2} = 5$

$25^{1/2} = 5 \Rightarrow 5 = 5$

The solution set is $\{-4,4\}$.

31. $t^4 - 16 = 0$

$\left(t^2+4\right)\left(t^2-4\right) = 0$

$\Rightarrow \left(t^2+4\right)(t+2)(t-2) = 0$

$t^2 + 4 = 0 \Rightarrow t^2 = -4$, which is impossible

or $(t+2)(t-2) = 0 \Rightarrow t = \pm 2$

Check : $t = -2: \ (-2)^4 - 16 = 0$

$16 - 16 = 0$

$0 = 0$

$t = 2: \ (2)^4 - 16 = 0$

$16 - 16 = 0$

$0 = 0$

The solution set is $\{-2,2\}$.

33.
$$x^4 - 5x^2 + 4 = 0$$
$$(x^2 - 4)(x^2 - 1) = 0$$
$$x^2 - 4 = 0 \text{ or } x^2 - 1 = 0$$
$$x = \pm 2 \text{ or } x = \pm 1$$
The solution set is $\{-2, -1, 1, 2\}$.

35.
$$3x^4 - 2x^2 - 1 = 0$$
$$(3x^2 + 1)(x^2 - 1) = 0$$
$$3x^2 + 1 = 0 \text{ or } x^2 - 1 = 0$$
$$3x^2 = -1 \text{ ,which is impossible}$$
or $x = \pm 1$
The solution set is $\{-1, 1\}$.

37.
$$x^6 + 7x^3 - 8 = 0$$
$$(x^3 + 8)(x^3 - 1) = 0$$
$$x^3 + 8 = 0 \text{ or } x^3 - 1 = 0$$
$$x^3 = -8 \Rightarrow x = -2$$
or $x^3 = 1 \Rightarrow x = 1$
The solution set is $\{-2, 1\}$.

39.
$$(x + 2)^2 + 7(x + 2) + 12 = 0$$
let $p = x + 2 \Rightarrow p^2 = (x + 2)^2$
$$p^2 + 7p + 12 = 0$$
$$(p + 3)(p + 4) = 0$$
$$p + 3 = 0 \text{ or } p + 4 = 0$$
$$p = -3 \Rightarrow x + 2 = -3 \Rightarrow x = -5$$
or $p = -4 \Rightarrow x + 2 = -4 \Rightarrow x = -6$
The solution set is $\{-6, -5\}$.

41.
$$(3x + 4)^2 - 6(3x + 4) + 9 = 0$$
let $p = 3x + 4 \Rightarrow p^2 = (3x + 4)^2$
$$p^2 - 6p + 9 = 0$$
$$(p - 3)(p - 3) = 0$$
$$p - 3 = 0$$
$$p = 3 \Rightarrow 3x + 4 = 3 \Rightarrow x = -\frac{1}{3}$$
The solution set is $\left\{-\frac{1}{3}\right\}$.

43.
$$2(s + 1)^2 - 5(s + 1) = 3$$
let $p = s + 1 \Rightarrow p^2 = (s + 1)^2$
$$2p^2 - 5p = 3$$
$$2p^2 - 5p - 3 = 0$$
$$(2p + 1)(p - 3) = 0$$
$$2p + 1 = 0 \text{ or } p - 3 = 0$$
$$p = -\frac{1}{2} \Rightarrow s + 1 = -\frac{1}{2} \Rightarrow s = -\frac{3}{2}$$
or $p = 3 \Rightarrow s + 1 = 3 \Rightarrow s = 2$
The solution set is $\left\{-\frac{3}{2}, 2\right\}$.

45.
$$x - 4\sqrt{x} = 0$$
$$x = 4\sqrt{x}$$
$$(x)^2 = \left(4\sqrt{x}\right)^2$$
$$x^2 = 16x \Rightarrow 0 = 16x - x^2$$
$$0 = x(16 - x) \Rightarrow x = 0$$
or $16 - x = 0 \Rightarrow x = 16$

Check
$$x = 0: \quad 0 - 4\sqrt{0} = 0$$
$$0 = 0$$
$$x = 16: \quad (16) - 4\sqrt{16} \neq 0$$
$$16 - 16 = 0$$
$$0 = 0$$
The solution set is $\{0, 16\}$.

47. $x + \sqrt{x} = 20$

    let $p = \sqrt{x} \Rightarrow p^2 = x$

    $p^2 + p = 20$

    $p^2 + p - 20 = 0$

    $(p+5)(p-4) = 0$

    $p + 5 = 0$ or $p - 4 = 0$

    $p = -5 \Rightarrow \sqrt{x} = -5 \Rightarrow x = 25$

    or $p = 4 \Rightarrow \sqrt{x} = 4 \Rightarrow x = 16$

Check

$x = 25:\ 25 + \sqrt{25} = 20$

         $25 + 5 \neq 20$

$x = 16:\ 16 + \sqrt{16} = 20$

         $16 + 4 = 20$

The solution set is $\{16\}$.

49. $t^{1/2} - 2t^{1/4} + 1 = 0$

    let $p = t^{1/4} \Rightarrow p^2 = t^{1/2}$

    $p^2 - 2p + 1 = 0$

    $(p-1)(p-1) = 0$

    $p - 1 = 0$

    $p = 1 \Rightarrow t^{1/4} = 1 \Rightarrow t = 1$

Check

$t = 1:\ 1^{1/2} - 2(1)^{1/4} + 1 = 0$

        $1 - 2 + 1 = 0 \Rightarrow 0 = 0$

The solution set is $\{1\}$.

51. $4x^{1/2} - 9x^{1/4} + 4 = 0$

    let $p = x^{1/4} \Rightarrow p^2 = x^{1/2}$

    $4p^2 - 9p + 4 = 0$

$$p = \frac{9 \pm \sqrt{81 - 64}}{8} = \frac{9 \pm \sqrt{17}}{8}$$

$$x^{1/4} = \frac{9 \pm \sqrt{17}}{8} \Rightarrow x = \left(\frac{9 \pm \sqrt{17}}{8}\right)^4$$

Check

$$x = \left(\frac{9 + \sqrt{17}}{8}\right)^4 :\ 4\left(\left(\frac{9 + \sqrt{17}}{8}\right)^4\right)^{1/2} - 9\left(\left(\frac{9 + \sqrt{17}}{8}\right)^4\right)^{1/4} + 4 = 0$$

$$4\left(\frac{9 + \sqrt{17}}{8}\right)^2 - 9\left(\frac{9 + \sqrt{17}}{8}\right) + 4 = 0$$

$$4\frac{\left(9 + \sqrt{17}\right)^2}{64} - 9\left(\frac{9 + \sqrt{17}}{8}\right) + 4 = 0$$

$$64\left(4\frac{\left(9 + \sqrt{17}\right)^2}{64} - 9\left(\frac{9 + \sqrt{17}}{8}\right) + 4\right) = (0)(64)$$

$$4\left(9+\sqrt{17}\right)^2 - 72\left(9+\sqrt{17}\right) + 256 = 0$$

$$4\left(81 + 18\sqrt{17} + 17\right) - 72\left(9 + \sqrt{17}\right) + 256 = 0$$

$$324 + 72\sqrt{17} + 68 - 648 - 72\sqrt{17} + 256 = 0$$

$$0 = 0$$

$$x = \left(\frac{9-\sqrt{17}}{8}\right)^4 : \quad 4\left(\left(\frac{9-\sqrt{17}}{8}\right)^4\right)^{1/2} - 9\left(\left(\frac{9-\sqrt{17}}{8}\right)^4\right)^{1/4} + 4 = 0$$

$$4\left(\frac{9-\sqrt{17}}{8}\right)^2 - 9\left(\frac{9-\sqrt{17}}{8}\right) + 4 = 0 \Rightarrow 4\left(81 - 18\sqrt{17} + 17\right) - 72\left(9 - \sqrt{17}\right) + 256 = (0)(64)$$

$$324 - 72\sqrt{17} + 68 - 648 + 72\sqrt{17} + 256 = 0$$

$$0 = 0$$

The solution set is $\left\{\left(\dfrac{9\pm\sqrt{17}}{8}\right)^4\right\}$.

53. $\quad \sqrt[4]{5x^2 - 6} = x$

$\left(\sqrt[4]{5x^2 - 6}\right)^4 = x^4$

$5x^2 - 6 = x^4$

$0 = x^4 - 5x^2 + 6$

let $p = x^2 \Rightarrow p^2 = x^4$

$0 = p^2 - 5p + 6 \Rightarrow (p-3)(p-2) = 0$

$p = 3 \Rightarrow x^2 = 3 \Rightarrow x = \pm\sqrt{3}$

or $p = 2 \Rightarrow x^2 = 2 \Rightarrow x = \pm\sqrt{2}$

Check

$x = -\sqrt{3}: \quad \sqrt[4]{5\left(-\sqrt{3}\right)^2 - 6} = -\sqrt{3}$

$\sqrt[4]{15 - 6} = -\sqrt{3} \Rightarrow \sqrt[4]{9} \neq -\sqrt{3}$

$x = \sqrt{3}: \quad \sqrt[4]{5\left(\sqrt{3}\right)^2 - 6} = \sqrt{3}$

$\sqrt[4]{15 - 6} = \sqrt{3} \Rightarrow \sqrt[4]{9} = \sqrt{3} \Rightarrow \sqrt{3} = \sqrt{3}$

$x = -\sqrt{2}: \quad \sqrt[4]{5\left(-\sqrt{2}\right)^2 - 6} = -\sqrt{2}$

$\sqrt[4]{10 - 6} = -\sqrt{2} \Rightarrow \sqrt[4]{4} \neq -\sqrt{2}$

$x = \sqrt{2}: \quad \sqrt[4]{5\left(\sqrt{2}\right)^2 - 6} = \sqrt{2}$

$\sqrt[4]{10 - 6} = \sqrt{2}$

$\sqrt[4]{4} = \sqrt{2} \Rightarrow \sqrt{2} = \sqrt{2}$

The solution set is $\left\{\sqrt{2}, \sqrt{3}\right\}$.

55. $\dfrac{1}{(x+1)^2} = \dfrac{1}{x+1} + 2$

let $p = \dfrac{1}{x+1} \Rightarrow p^2 = \left(\dfrac{1}{x+1}\right)^2$

$p^2 = p + 2 \Rightarrow p^2 - p - 2 = 0$

$(p+1)(p-2) = 0 \Rightarrow p = -1$ or $p = 2$

$p = -1 \Rightarrow \dfrac{1}{x+1} = -1 \Rightarrow 1 = -x - 1 \Rightarrow x = -2$

or

$\dfrac{1}{x+1} = 2 \Rightarrow 1 = 2x + 2 \Rightarrow x = -\dfrac{1}{2}$

Check

$x = -2: \quad \dfrac{1}{(-2+1)^2} = \dfrac{1}{-2+1} + 2$

$1 = -1 + 2 \Rightarrow 1 = 1$

$x = -\dfrac{1}{2}: \quad \dfrac{1}{\left(-\dfrac{1}{2}+1\right)^2} = \dfrac{1}{\left(-\dfrac{1}{2}+1\right)} + 2$

$4 = 2 + 2 \Rightarrow 4 = 4$

The solution set is $\left\{-2, -\dfrac{1}{2}\right\}$.

57. $3x^{-2} - 7x^{-1} - 6 = 0$

let $p = x^{-1} \Rightarrow p^2 = x^{-2}$

$3p^2 - 7p - 6 = 0$

$(3p+2)(p-3) = 0$

$p = -\dfrac{2}{3}$ or $p = 3$

$p = -\dfrac{2}{3} \Rightarrow x^{-1} = -\dfrac{2}{3} \Rightarrow \left(x^{-1}\right)^{-1}$

$= \left(-\dfrac{2}{3}\right)^{-1} \Rightarrow x = -\dfrac{3}{2}$

or

$p = 3 \Rightarrow x^{-1} = 3 \Rightarrow \left(x^{-1}\right)^{-1} = (3)^{-1} \Rightarrow x = \dfrac{1}{3}$

Check

$x = -\dfrac{3}{2}: \quad 3\left(-\dfrac{3}{2}\right)^{-2} - 7\left(-\dfrac{3}{2}\right)^{-1} - 6 = 0$

$3\left(\dfrac{4}{9}\right) - 7\left(-\dfrac{2}{3}\right) - 6 = 0$

$\dfrac{4}{3} + \dfrac{14}{3} - 6 = 0 \Rightarrow 6 - 6 = 0 \rightarrow 0 = 0$

$x = \dfrac{1}{3}: \quad 3\left(\dfrac{1}{3}\right)^{-2} - 7\left(\dfrac{1}{3}\right)^{-1} - 6 = 0$

$3(9) - 7(3) - 6 = 0$

$27 - 21 - 6 = 0 \Rightarrow 6 - 6 = 0 \Rightarrow 0 = 0$

The solution set is $\left\{-\dfrac{3}{2}, \dfrac{1}{3}\right\}$.

59. $2x^{2/3} - 5x^{1/3} - 3 = 0$

let $p = x^{1/3} \Rightarrow p^2 = x^{2/3}$

$2p^2 - 5p - 3 = 0 \Rightarrow (2p+1)(p-3) = 0$

$p = -\dfrac{1}{2}$ or $p = 3$

$p = -\dfrac{1}{2} \Rightarrow x^{1/3} = -\dfrac{1}{2}$

$\Rightarrow \left(x^{1/3}\right)^3 = \left(-\dfrac{1}{2}\right)^3 \Rightarrow x = -\dfrac{1}{8}$

or

$p = 3 \Rightarrow x^{1/3} = 3 \Rightarrow \left(x^{1/3}\right)^3 = (3)^3$

$\Rightarrow x = 27$

Check

$x = -\dfrac{1}{8}: \quad 2\left(-\dfrac{1}{8}\right)^{2/3} - 5\left(-\dfrac{1}{8}\right)^{1/3} - 3 = 0$

$2\left(\dfrac{1}{4}\right) - 5\left(-\dfrac{1}{2}\right) - 3 = 0$

$\dfrac{1}{2} + \dfrac{5}{2} - 3 = 0 \Rightarrow 3 - 3 = 0 \Rightarrow 0 = 0$

$x = 27: \quad 2(27)^{2/3} - 5(27)^{1/3} - 3 = 0$

$2(9) - 5(3) - 3 = 0$

$18 - 15 - 3 = 0 \Rightarrow 3 - 3 = 0 \Rightarrow 0 = 0$

The solution set is $\left\{-\dfrac{1}{8}, 27\right\}$.

61. $\left(\dfrac{v}{v+1}\right)^2 + \dfrac{2v}{v+1} = 8$

let $p = \dfrac{v}{v+1} \Rightarrow p^2 = \left(\dfrac{v}{v+1}\right)^2$

$\left(\dfrac{v}{v+1}\right)^2 + \dfrac{2v}{v+1} = 8 \Rightarrow \left(\dfrac{v}{v+1}\right)^2 + 2\left(\dfrac{v}{v+1}\right) = 8$

$p^2 + 2p = 8 \Rightarrow p^2 + 2p - 8 = 0$

$(p+4)(p-2) = 0 \Rightarrow p = -4 \ \text{ or } \ p = 2$

$p = -4 \Rightarrow \dfrac{v}{v+1} = -4$

$\Rightarrow v = -4v - 4 \Rightarrow v = -\dfrac{4}{5}$

or

$p = 2 \Rightarrow \dfrac{v}{v+1} = 2 \Rightarrow v = 2v + 2 \Rightarrow v = -2$

Check

$v = -\dfrac{4}{5}: \ \left(\dfrac{-\dfrac{4}{5}}{-\dfrac{4}{5}+1}\right)^2 + \dfrac{2\left(-\dfrac{4}{5}\right)}{\left(-\dfrac{4}{5}\right)+1} = 8$

$\dfrac{\left(\dfrac{16}{25}\right)}{\left(\dfrac{1}{25}\right)} + \dfrac{\left(-\dfrac{8}{5}\right)}{\left(\dfrac{1}{5}\right)} = 8$

$16 - 8 = 8 \Rightarrow 8 = 8$

$v = -2: \ \left(\dfrac{-2}{-2+1}\right)^2 + \dfrac{2(-2)}{(-2)+1} = 8$

$4 + 4 = 8 \Rightarrow 8 = 8$

The solution set is $\left\{-\dfrac{4}{5}, -2\right\}$.

63. $|x| = 6$

$x = 6 \ \text{ or } \ x = -6$

The solution set is $\{-6, 6\}$.

65. $|2x+3| = 5$

$2x+3 = 5 \ \text{ or } \ 2x+3 = -5$

$2x = 2 \ \text{ or } \qquad 2x = -8$

$x = 1 \ \text{ or } \qquad x = -4$

The solution set is $\{-4, 1\}$.

67. $|1-4t| + 8 = 13 \Rightarrow |1-4t| = 5$

$1-4t = 5 \ \text{ or } \ 1-4t = -5$

$-4t = 4 \ \text{ or } \qquad -4t = -6$

$t = -1 \ \text{ or } \qquad t = \dfrac{3}{2}$

The solution set is $\left\{-1, \dfrac{3}{2}\right\}$.

69. $|-2x| = 8$

$-2x = 8 \qquad \text{or} \qquad -2x = -8$

$x = -4 \ \text{ or } \qquad x = 4$

The solution set is $\{-4, 4\}$.

71. $4 - |2x| = 3 \Rightarrow |2x| = 1$

$2x = 1 \ \text{ or } \ 2x = -1$

$x = \dfrac{1}{2} \ \text{ or } \ x = -\dfrac{1}{2}$

The solution set is $\left\{-\dfrac{1}{2}, \dfrac{1}{2}\right\}$.

73. $\dfrac{2}{3}|x| = 9$

$|x| = \dfrac{27}{2} \Rightarrow x = \dfrac{27}{2} \ \text{ or } \ x = -\dfrac{27}{2}$

The solution set is $\left\{-\dfrac{27}{2}, \dfrac{27}{2}\right\}$.

75. $\left|\dfrac{x}{3}+\dfrac{2}{5}\right|=2$

$\dfrac{x}{3}+\dfrac{2}{5}=2$ or $\dfrac{x}{3}+\dfrac{2}{5}=-2$

$5x+6=30$ or $5x+6=-30$

$5x=24$ or $5x=-36$

$x=\dfrac{24}{5}$ or $x=-\dfrac{36}{5}$

The solution set is $\left\{-\dfrac{36}{5},\dfrac{24}{5}\right\}$.

77. $|u-2|=-\dfrac{1}{2}$

impossible, since absolute value always
yields a non-negative number.

79. $\left|x^2-9\right|=0$

$x^2-9=0$

$x^2=9$

$x=\pm3$

The solution set is $\{-3,3\}$.

81. $\left|x^2-2x\right|=3$

$x^2-2x=3$ or $x^2-2x=-3$

$x^2-2x-3=0$ or $x^2-2x+3=0$

$(x-3)(x+1)=0$ or $x=\dfrac{2\pm\sqrt{4-12}}{2}=\dfrac{2\pm\sqrt{-8}}{2}\Rightarrow$ no real solution

$x=3$ or $x=-1$
The solution set is $\{-1,3\}$.

83. $\left|x^2+x-1\right|=1$

$x^2+x-1=1$ or $x^2+x-1=-1$

$x^2+x-2=0$ or $x^2+x=0$

$(x-1)(x+2)=0$ or $x(x+1)=0$

$x=1,x=-2$ or $x=0,x=-1$
The solution set is $\{-2,-1,0,1\}$.

85. $x-4x^{1/2}+2=0$; Use ZERO (or ROOT)
on the graph of $y_1=x-4\sqrt{x}+2$.

The solution set is $\{0.34,11.66\}$.

87. $x^4 + \sqrt{3}x^2 - 3 = 0$; Use ZERO (or ROOT)
   on the graph of $y_1 = x^4 + \sqrt{3}x^2 - 3$.

The solution set is $\{-1.03, 1.03\}$.

89. $\pi(1+t)^2 = \pi + 1 + t$; Use ZERO (or ROOT)
   on the graph of $y_1 = \pi(1+x)\verb|^|2 - x - \pi - 1$.

The solution set is $\{-1.85, 0.17\}$.

91. $k^2 - k = 12 \Rightarrow k^2 - k - 12 = 0$
   $(k-4)(k+3) = 0$

   $k = 4$

   $\dfrac{x+3}{x-3} = 4 \Rightarrow x + 3 = 4x - 12$

   $\Rightarrow 3x = 15 \Rightarrow x = 5$

   or $k = -3$

   $\dfrac{x+3}{x-3} = -3 \Rightarrow x + 3 = -3x + 9 \Rightarrow x = \dfrac{3}{2}$

And since neither of these x values causes a
denominator to equal zero,

the solution set is $\left\{\dfrac{3}{2}, 5\right\}$.

93. Graph the equations
   $y_1 = \sqrt{x}/4 + x/1100$ and $y_2 = 4$;
   then use INTERSECT to find the
   x-coordinate of the points of
   intersection:

The distance to the water's surface is
approximately 229.94 feet.

95. Answers will vary, one example is $x - \sqrt{x} - 2 = 0$

Graphs

1.6 Solving Inequalities

1. $[0, 2]$ $0 \le x \le 2$

3. $(-1, 2)$ $-1 < x < 2$

5. $[0, 3)$ $0 \le x < 3$

7. (a) $6 < 8$
    (b) $-2 < 0$
    (c) $9 < 15$
    (d) $-6 > -10$

9. (a) $7 > 0$
    (b) $-1 > -8$
    (c) $12 > -9$
    (d) $-8 < 6$

11. (a) $2x + 4 < 5$
     (b) $2x - 4 < -3$
     (c) $6x + 3 < 6$
     (d) $-4x - 2 > -4$

13. $[0, 4]$

15. $[4, 6)$

17. $[4, \infty)$

19. $(-\infty, -4)$

21. $2 \le x \le 5$

23. $-3 < x < -2$

25. $x \ge 4$

27. $x < -3$

29. If $x < 5$, then $x - 5 < 0$.

31. If $x > -4$, then $x + 4 > 0$.

33. If $x \ge -4$, then $3x \ge -12$.

35. If $x > 6$, then $-2x < -12$.

37. If $x \le 5$, then $-4x \ge -20$.

39. If $2x < 6$, then $x < 3$.

41. If $-\dfrac{1}{2}x \le 3$, then $x \ge -6$.

43. $x+1<5$

$x+1-1<5-1 \Rightarrow x<4$

$\{x \mid x<4\}$ or $(-\infty, 4)$

4

45. $1-2x \le 3$

$-2x \le 2 \Rightarrow x \ge -1$

$\{x \mid x \ge -1\}$ or $[-1, +\infty)$

-1

47. $3x-7>2$

$3x>9 \Rightarrow x>3$

$\{x \mid x>3\}$ or $(3, +\infty)$

3

49. $3x-1 \ge 3+x$

$2x \ge 4 \Rightarrow x \ge 2$

$\{x \mid x \ge 2\}$ or $[2, +\infty)$

2

51. $-2(x+3)<8$
$-2x-6<8$

$-2x<14 \Rightarrow x>-7$

$\{x \mid x>-7\}$ or $(-7, +\infty)$

-7

53. $4-3(1-x) \le 3$
$4-3+3x \le 3$

$3x+1 \le 3$

$3x \le 2 \Rightarrow x \le \dfrac{2}{3}$

$\left\{x \mid x \le \dfrac{2}{3}\right\}$ or $\left(-\infty, \dfrac{2}{3}\right]$

$\dfrac{2}{3}$

55. $\dfrac{1}{2}(x-4)>x+8$

$\dfrac{1}{2}x-2>x+8$

$-\dfrac{1}{2}x>10 \Rightarrow x<-20$

$\{x \mid x<-20\}$ or $(-\infty, -20)$

-20

57. $\dfrac{x}{2} \ge 1-\dfrac{x}{4}$

$2x \ge 4-x$

$3x \ge 4 \Rightarrow x \ge \dfrac{4}{3}$

$\left\{x \mid x \ge \dfrac{4}{3}\right\}$ or $\left[\dfrac{4}{3}, +\infty\right)$

$\dfrac{4}{3}$

59. $0 \le 2x - 6 \le 4$
$6 \le 2x \le 10$

$3 \le x \le 5$
$\left\{x \mid 3 \le x \le 5\right\}$ or $[3, 5]$

61. $-5 \le 4 - 3x \le 2$
$-9 \le -3x \le -2$

$3 \ge x \ge \dfrac{2}{3}$

$\left\{x \mid \dfrac{2}{3} \le x \le 3\right\}$ or $\left[\dfrac{2}{3}, 3\right]$

63. $-3 < \dfrac{2x - 1}{4} < 0$
$-12 < 2x - 1 < 0$

$-11 < 2x < 1 \Rightarrow -\dfrac{11}{2} < x < \dfrac{1}{2}$

$\left\{x \mid -\dfrac{11}{2} < x < \dfrac{1}{2}\right\}$ or $\left(-\dfrac{11}{2}, \dfrac{1}{2}\right)$

65. $1 < 1 - \dfrac{1}{2}x < 4$

$0 < -\dfrac{1}{2}x < 3$

$0 > x > -6 \Rightarrow -6 < x < 0$
$\left\{x \mid -6 < x < 0\right\}$ or $(-6, 0)$

67. $(x + 2)(x - 3) > (x - 1)(x + 1)$
$x^2 - x - 6 > x^2 - 1$

$-x - 6 > -1$

$-x > 5 \Rightarrow x < -5$
$\left\{x \mid x < -5\right\}$ or $(-\infty, -5)$

69. $x(4x + 3) \le (2x + 1)^2$
$4x^2 + 3x \le 4x^2 + 4x + 1$

$3x \le 4x + 1$

$-x \le 1 \Rightarrow x \ge -1$
$\left\{x \mid x \ge -1\right\}$ or $[-1, +\infty)$

71. $\dfrac{1}{2} \le \dfrac{x + 1}{3} < \dfrac{3}{4}$
$6 \le 4x + 4 < 9$

$2 \le 4x < 5$

$\dfrac{1}{2} \le x < \dfrac{5}{4}$

$\left\{x \mid \dfrac{1}{2} \le x < \dfrac{5}{4}\right\}$ or $\left[\dfrac{1}{2}, \dfrac{5}{4}\right)$

73. $|x| < 6$
$-6 < x < 6$
$\left\{x \mid -6 < x < 6\right\}$ or $(-6, 6)$

75. $|x| > 4$
$x < -4$ or $x > 4$
$\left\{x \mid x < -4 \text{ or } x > 4\right\}$ or

$(-\infty, -4) \cup (4, +\infty)$

77. $|2x| < 8$
$-8 < 2x < 8$
$-4 < \quad x \quad < 4$
$\{x | -4 < x < 4\}$ or $(-4,4)$

79. $|3x| > 12$
$3x < -12$ or $3x > 12$
$x < -4$ or $x > 4$
$\{x | x < -4 \text{ or } x > 4\}$ or $(-\infty,-4) \cup (4,\infty)$

81. $|x-2| + 2 < 3 \Rightarrow |x-2| < 1$
$-1 < x - 2 < 1$
$1 < \quad x \quad < 3$
$\{x | 1 < x < 3\}$ or $(1,3)$

83. $|3t-2| \le 4$
$-4 \le 3t - 2 \le 4$
$-2 \le 3t \le 6 \Rightarrow -\dfrac{2}{3} \le t \le 2$
$\left\{t \left| -\dfrac{2}{3} \le t \le 2 \right.\right\}$ or $\left[-\dfrac{2}{3}, 2\right]$

85. $|x-3| \ge 2$
$x - 3 \le -2$ or $x - 3 \ge 2$
$x \le 1$ or $x \ge 5$
$\{x | x \le 1 \text{ or } x \ge 5\}$ or
$(-\infty,1] \cup [5,+\infty)$

87. $|1-4x| - 7 < -2 \Rightarrow |1-4x| < 5$
$-5 < 1 - 4x < 5$
$-6 < -4x < 4$
$\dfrac{-6}{-4} > x > \dfrac{4}{-4}$
$\dfrac{3}{2} > x > -1 \Rightarrow -1 < x < \dfrac{3}{2}$
$\{x | -1 < x < 1.5\}$ or $(-1,1.5)$

89. $|1-2x| > |-3| \Rightarrow |1-2x| > 3$
$1 - 2x < -3$ or $1 - 2x > 3$
$-2x < -4$ or $-2x > 2$
$x > 2$ or $x < -1$
$\{x | x < -1 \text{ or } x > 2\}$ or $(-\infty,-1) \cup (2,\infty)$

91. $|2x+1| < -1$
No solution since absolute value is
always non-negative.

93. $|x-2| < 0.5$
$-0.5 < x - 2 < 0.5$
$-0.5 + 2 < x < 0.5 + 2$
$1.5 < x < 2.5$
Solution set : $\{x | 1.5 < x < 2.5\}$

95. $|x-(-3)| > 2$
$x - (-3) < -2$ or $x - (-3) > 2$
$x + 3 < -2$ or $x + 3 > 2$
$x < -5$ or $x > -1$
Solution set : $\{x | x < -5 \text{ or } x > -1\}$

97. $21 <$ young adult's age < 30

99.   A temperature x that differs from $98.6°$F by at least $1.5°$
$$|x - 98.6°| \geq 1.5°$$
$$x - 98.6° \leq -1.5° \quad \text{or} \quad x - 98.6° \geq 1.5°$$
$$x \leq 97.1° \quad \text{or} \qquad x \geq 100.1°$$
The temperatures that are considered unhealthy are those that are less than $97.1°$F or greater than $100.1°$F, inclusive.

101. (a)   An average 25-year-old male can expect to live at least 48.4 more years.
$25 + 48.4 = 73.4$. Therefore, the average age of a 25-year-old male will be ≥ 73.4.
   (b)   An average 25-year-old female can expect to live at least 54.7 more years.
$25 + 54.7 = 79.7$. Therefore, the average age of a 25-year-old female will be ≥ 79.7.
   (c)   By the given information, a female can expect to live 6.3 years longer.

103.   Let P represent the selling price and C represent the commission.
Calculating the commission:
$$C = 45,000 + 0.25(P - 900,000) = 45,000 + 0.25P - 225,000 = 0.25P - 180,000$$
Calculate the commission range, given the price range:
$$900,000 \leq \qquad P \qquad \leq 1,100,000$$
$$0.25(900,000) \leq \quad 0.25P \quad \leq 0.25(1,100,000)$$
$$225,000 \leq \quad 0.25P \quad \leq 275,000$$
$$225,000 - 180,000 \leq 0.25P - 180,000 \leq 275,000 - 180,000$$
$$45,000 \leq \qquad C \qquad \leq 95,000$$
The agent's commission ranges from \$45,000 to \$95,000, inclusive.
$$\frac{45,000}{900,000} = 0.05 = 5\% \text{ to } \frac{95,000}{1,100,000} = 0.086 = 8.6\%, \text{ inclusive.}$$
As a percent of selling price, the commission ranges from 5% to 8.6%.

105.   Let W represent the weekly wage and T represent the withholding tax.
Calculating the tax:
$$T = 69.90 + 0.28(W - 517) = 69.90 + 0.28W - 144.76 = 0.28W - 74.86$$
Calculating the withholding tax range, given the range of weekly wages:
$$525 \leq \qquad W \qquad \leq 600$$
$$0.28(525) \leq \quad 0.28W \quad \leq 0.28(600)$$
$$147 \leq \quad 0.28W \quad \leq 168$$
$$147 - 74.86 \leq 0.28W - 74.86 \leq 168 - 74.86$$
$$72.14 \leq \qquad T \qquad \leq 93.14$$
The amount of withholding tax ranges from \$72.14 to \$93.14, inclusive.

107.   Let K represent the monthly usage in kilowatt-hours.
Let C represent the monthly customer bill.
Calculating the bill:
$$C = 0.10494K + 9.36$$

Calculating the range of kilowatt-hours, given the range of bills:

$$80.24 \leq \qquad C \qquad \leq 271.80$$
$$80.24 \leq 0.10494K + 9.36 \leq 271.80$$
$$70.88 \leq \qquad 0.10494K \qquad \leq 262.44$$
$$675.43 \leq \qquad K \qquad \leq 2500.86$$

The range of usage in kilowatt-hours varied from 675.43 to 2500.86.

109. Let C represent the dealer's cost and M represent the markup over dealer's cost.
     If the price is \$8800, then $8800 = C + MC = C(1 + M)$

Solving for C: $C = \dfrac{8800}{1 + M}$

Calculating the range of dealer costs, given the range of markups:

$$0.12 \leq \quad M \quad \leq 0.18$$
$$1.12 \leq 1 + M \leq 1.18$$
$$\frac{1}{1.12} \geq \frac{1}{1 + M} \geq \frac{1}{1.18}$$
$$\frac{8800}{1.12} \geq \frac{8800}{1 + M} \geq \frac{8800}{1.18}$$
$$7857.14 \geq \quad C \quad \geq 7457.63$$

The dealer's cost ranged from \$7457.63 to \$7857.14, inclusive.

111. Let T represent the score on the last test and G represent the course grade.
     Calculating the course grade and solving for the last test:

$$G = \frac{68 + 82 + 87 + 89 + T}{5} = \frac{326 + T}{5} \rightarrow T = 5G - 326$$

Calculating the range of scores on the last test, given the grade range:

$$80 \leq \qquad G \quad < 90$$
$$400 \leq \qquad 5G \quad < 450$$
$$74 \leq 5G - 326 < 124$$
$$74 \leq \qquad T \quad < 124$$

The fifth test must be greater than or equal to 74.

113. Let g represent the number of gallons of gasoline in the gas tank.
     Since the car averages 25 miles per gallon, a trip of at least 300 miles will require
     at least $\dfrac{300}{25} = 12$ gallons of gas.
     Therefore the range of the amount of gasoline is $12 \leq g \leq 20$.

115.   Since $a < b$

$$\frac{a}{2} < \frac{b}{2} \qquad\qquad\qquad \frac{a}{2} < \frac{b}{2}$$
$$\frac{a}{2} + \frac{a}{2} < \frac{a}{2} + \frac{b}{2} \qquad \frac{a}{2} + \frac{b}{2} < \frac{b}{2} + \frac{b}{2} \qquad \text{Thus, } a < \frac{a + b}{2} < b$$
$$a < \frac{a + b}{2} \qquad\qquad \frac{a + b}{2} < b$$

117.   If $0 < a < b$, then $0 < a^2 < ab$ and $0 < ab < b^2$

$$ab - a^2 > 0 \qquad\qquad\qquad b^2 - ab > 0$$

$$ab > a^2 > 0 \qquad\qquad\qquad b^2 > ab > 0$$

$$\left(\sqrt{ab}\right)^2 > a^2 \qquad\qquad\qquad b^2 > \left(\sqrt{ab}\right)^2$$

$$\sqrt{ab} > a \qquad\qquad\qquad b > \sqrt{ab}$$

Thus, $a < \sqrt{ab} < b$

119.   For $0 < a < b$, $\dfrac{1}{h} = \dfrac{1}{2}\left(\dfrac{1}{a} + \dfrac{1}{b}\right)$

$$h \cdot \dfrac{1}{h} = \dfrac{1}{2}\left(\dfrac{b+a}{ab}\right) \cdot h \;\Rightarrow\; 1 = \dfrac{1}{2}\left(\dfrac{b+a}{ab}\right) \cdot h \;\Rightarrow\; \dfrac{2ab}{a+b} = h$$

$$h - a = \dfrac{2ab}{a+b} - a \qquad\qquad\qquad b - h = b - \dfrac{2ab}{a+b}$$

$$= \dfrac{2ab - a(a+b)}{a+b} \qquad\qquad\qquad = \dfrac{b(a+b) - 2ab}{a+b}$$

$$= \dfrac{2ab - a^2 - ab}{a+b} = \dfrac{ab - a^2}{a+b} \qquad\qquad = \dfrac{ab + b^2 - 2ab}{a+b} = \dfrac{b^2 - ab}{a+b}$$

$$= \dfrac{a(b-a)}{a+b} > 0 \qquad\qquad\qquad = \dfrac{b(b-a)}{a+b} > 0$$

Therefore, $h > a$. $\qquad\qquad$ Therefore, $h < b$. $\qquad\qquad$ Thus, $a < h < b$.

Chapter 1

Graphs

1.7 Lines

1. (a) Slope $= \dfrac{1-0}{2-0} = \dfrac{1}{2}$

(b) If x increases by 2 units, y will increase by 1 unit.

3. (a) Slope $= \dfrac{1-2}{1-(-2)} = -\dfrac{1}{3}$

(b) If x increases by 3 units, y will decrease by 1 unit.

5. (x_1, y_1) (x_2, y_2)
    $(2,3)$ $(4,0)$

Slope $= \dfrac{y_2 - y_1}{x_2 - x_1} = \dfrac{0-3}{4-2} = \dfrac{-3}{2}$

7. (x_1, y_1) (x_2, y_2)
    $(-2,3)$ $(2,1)$

Slope $= \dfrac{y_2 - y_1}{x_2 - x_1} = \dfrac{1-3}{2-(-2)} = \dfrac{-2}{4} = -\dfrac{1}{2}$

9. (x_1, y_1) (x_2, y_2)
    $(-3,-1)$ $(2,-1)$

Slope $= \dfrac{y_2 - y_1}{x_2 - x_1} = \dfrac{-1-(-1)}{2-(-3)} = \dfrac{0}{5} = 0$

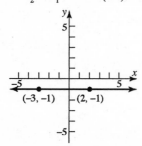

11. (x_1, y_1) (x_2, y_2)
     $(-1,2)$ $(-1,-2)$

Slope $= \dfrac{y_2 - y_1}{x_2 - x_1} = \dfrac{-2-2}{-1-(-1)} = \dfrac{-4}{0}$
Slope is undefined.

13.

15.

17.

19.

21. Slope $= 4 \Rightarrow$ if x increases by 1,
$\quad y$ increases by 4

$\quad$ original point $(1,2)$

Answers will vary. Three possible points are:
$\quad x = 1 + 1 = 2$ and $y = 2 + 4 = 6$

$\qquad (2,6)$

$\quad x = 2 + 1 = 3$ and $y = 6 + 4 = 10$

$\qquad (3,10)$

$\quad x = 3 + 1 = 4$ and $y = 10 + 4 = 14$

$\qquad (4,14)$

23. Slope $= -\dfrac{3}{2} \Rightarrow$ if x increases by 2,
$\quad y$ decreases by 3

$\quad$ original point $(2,-4)$

Answers will vary. Three possible points are:
$\quad x = 2 + 2 = 4$ and $y = -4 - 3 = -7$

$\qquad (4,-7)$

$\quad x = 4 + 2 = 6$ and $y = -7 - 3 = -10$

$\qquad (6,-10)$

$\quad x = 6 + 2 = 8$ and $y = -10 - 3 = -13$

$\qquad (8,-13)$

25. Slope $= -2 \Rightarrow$ if x increases by 1,
$\quad y$ decreases by 2

$\quad$ original point $(-2,-3)$

Answers will vary. Three possible points are:
$\quad x = -2 + 1 = -1$ and $y = -3 - 2 = -5$

$\qquad (-1,-5)$

$\quad x = -1 + 1 = 0$ and $y = -5 - 2 = -7$

$\qquad (0,-7)$

$\quad x = 0 + 1 = 1$ and $y = -7 - 2 = -9$

$\qquad (1,-9)$

27. $(0,0)$ and $(2,1)$ are points on the line.

$\quad$ Slope $= \dfrac{1 - 0}{2 - 0} = \dfrac{1}{2}$

$\quad y$ - intercept is 0; using $y = mx + b$:

$\qquad y = \dfrac{1}{2}x + 0$

$\qquad 2y = x$

$\qquad 0 = x - 2y$

$\quad x - 2y = 0$ or $y = \dfrac{1}{2}x$

29. (−1,3) and (1,1) are points on the line.

$$\text{Slope} = \frac{1-3}{1-(-1)} = \frac{-2}{2} = -1$$

Using $y - y_1 = m(x - x_1)$

$$y - 1 = -1(x - 1)$$
$$y - 1 = -x + 1$$
$$y = -x + 2$$
$$x + y = 2 \ \text{ or } \ y = -x + 2$$

31. $y - y_1 = m(x - x_1), \ \ m = 2$
$$y - 3 = 2(x - 3)$$
$$y - 3 = 2x - 6$$
$$y = 2x - 3$$
$$2x - y = 3 \ \text{ or } \ y = 2x - 3$$

33. $y - y_1 = m(x - x_1), \ \ m = -\dfrac{1}{2}$

$$y - 2 = -\frac{1}{2}(x - 1)$$
$$y - 2 = -\frac{1}{2}x + \frac{1}{2}$$
$$y = -\frac{1}{2}x + \frac{5}{2}$$
$$x + 2y = 5 \ \text{ or } \ y = -\frac{1}{2}x + \frac{5}{2}$$

35. Slope = 3; containing (−2,3)
$$y - y_1 = m(x - x_1)$$
$$y - 3 = 3(x - (-2))$$
$$y - 3 = 3x + 6$$
$$y = 3x + 9$$
$$3x - y = -9 \ \text{ or } \ y = 3x + 9$$

37. Slope $= -\dfrac{2}{3}$; containing (1,−1)

$$y - y_1 = m(x - x_1)$$
$$y - (-1) = -\frac{2}{3}(x - 1)$$
$$y + 1 = -\frac{2}{3}x + \frac{2}{3}$$
$$y = -\frac{2}{3}x - \frac{1}{3}$$
$$2x + 3y = -1 \ \text{ or } \ y = -\frac{2}{3}x - \frac{1}{3}$$

39. Containing (1,3) and (−1,2)
$$m = \frac{2-3}{-1-1} = \frac{-1}{-2} = \frac{1}{2}$$
$$y - y_1 = m(x - x_1)$$
$$y - 3 = \frac{1}{2}(x - 1)$$
$$y - 3 = \frac{1}{2}x - \frac{1}{2}$$
$$y = \frac{1}{2}x + \frac{5}{2}$$
$$x - 2y = -5 \ \text{ or } \ y = \frac{1}{2}x + \frac{5}{2}$$

41. Slope = −3; y-intercept =3
$$y = mx + b$$
$$y = -3x + 3$$
$$3x + y = 3 \ \text{ or } \ y = -3x + 3$$

43. x-intercept = 2; y-intercept = −1
Points are (2,0) and (0,−1)
$$m = \frac{-1-0}{0-2} = \frac{-1}{-2} = \frac{1}{2}$$
$$y = mx + b$$
$$y = \frac{1}{2}x - 1$$
$$x - 2y = 2 \ \text{ or } \ y = \frac{1}{2}x - 1$$

45. Slope undefined; passing through (2,4)
This is a vertical line.
$x = 2$
No slope intercept form.

47. Parallel to $y = 2x$; Slope = 2
Containing $(-1,2)$
$y - y_1 = m(x - x_1)$
$y - 2 = 2(x - (-1))$
$y - 2 = 2x + 2 \Rightarrow y = 2x + 4$
$2x - y = -4$ or $y = 2x + 4$

49. Parallel to $2x - y = -2$; Slope = 2
Containing the point (0,0)
$y - y_1 = m(x - x_1)$
$y - 0 = 2(x - 0)$
$y = 2x$ or $2x - y = 0$

51. Parallel to $x = 5$;
Containing (4,2)
This is a vertical line.
$x = 4$
No slope intercept form.

53. Perpendicular to $y = \frac{1}{2}x + 4$;
Slope of perpendicular = -2
Containing $(1,-2)$
$y - y_1 = m(x - x_1)$
$y - (-2) = -2(x - 1)$
$y + 2 = -2x + 2 \Rightarrow y = -2x$
$2x + y = 0$ or $y = -2x$

55. Perpendicular to $2x + y = 2$;
Containing $(-3,0)$
Slope of perpendicular = $\frac{1}{2}$
$y - y_1 = m(x - x_1)$
$y - 0 = \frac{1}{2}(x - (-3)) \Rightarrow y = \frac{1}{2}x + \frac{3}{2}$
$x - 2y = -3$ or $y = \frac{1}{2}x + \frac{3}{2}$

57. Perpendicular to $x = 8$;
Slope of perpendicular = 0
Containing (3,4)
$y - y_1 = m(x - x_1)$
$y - 4 = 0(x - 3) \Rightarrow y - 4 = 0 \Rightarrow y = 4$
$y = 4$ or $y = 0x + 4$

59. $y = 2x + 3$
Slope = 2; y-intercept = 3

61. $\frac{1}{2}y = x - 1$
$y = 2x - 2$
Slope = 2; y-intercept = -2

63. $y = \frac{1}{2}x + 2$
Slope = $\frac{1}{2}$; y-intercept = 2

85

65. $x + 2y = 4$

$2y = -x + 4 \Rightarrow y = -\dfrac{1}{2}x + 2$

Slope $= -\dfrac{1}{2}$; y-intercept $= 2$

67. $2x - 3y = 6$

$-3y = -2x + 6 \rightarrow y = \dfrac{2}{3}x - 2$

Slope $= \dfrac{2}{3}$; y-intercept $= -2$

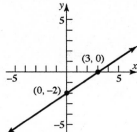

69. $x + y = 1$
$y = -x + 1$
Slope $= -1$; y-intercept $= 1$

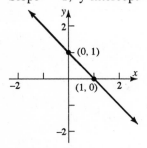

71. $x = -4$
Slope is undefined
y-intercept - none

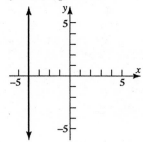

73. $y = 5$
Slope $= 0$
y-intercept $= 5$

75. $y - x = 0$
$y = x$
Slope $= 1$
y-intercept $= 0$

77. $2y - 3x = 0$

$2y = 3x \Rightarrow y = \dfrac{3}{2}x$

Slope $= \dfrac{3}{2}$; y-intercept $= 0$

79. The equation of the x-axis is $y = 0$.
     (The slope is 0 and the y-intercept is 0.)

81. (b)

83. (d)

85. Slope $= 1$; y-intercept $= 2$
     $y = x + 2$ or $x - y = -2$

87. Slope $= -\dfrac{1}{3}$; y-intercept $= 1$

$y = -\dfrac{1}{3}x + 1$ or $x + 3y = 3$

89. Let x = number of miles driven, and let C = cost in dollars.
     Total cost = (cost per mile)(number of miles) + fixed cost
     $C = 0.07x + 29$
     When $x = 110$, $C = (0.07)(110) + 29 = \$36.70$.
     When $x = 230$, $C = (0.07)(230) + 29 = \$45.10$.

91. $(^\circ C, ^\circ F) = (0, 32)$; $(^\circ C, ^\circ F) = (100, 212)$

slope $= \dfrac{212 - 32}{100 - 0} = \dfrac{180}{100} = \dfrac{9}{5}$

$^\circ F - 32 = \dfrac{9}{5}(^\circ C - 0)$

$^\circ F - 32 = \dfrac{9}{5}(^\circ C)$

$^\circ C = \dfrac{5}{9}(^\circ F - 32)$

If $^\circ F = 70$, then

$^\circ C = \dfrac{5}{9}(70 - 32) = \dfrac{5}{9}(38)$

$^\circ C \approx 21^\circ$

93. (a) Since there is only a profit of
          $0.50 per copy and the expense
          of $100 must be deducted, the
          profit is: $P = 0.50x - 100$
     (b) $P = 0.50(1000) - 100$
          $= 500 - 100 = \$400$
     (c) $P = 0.50(5000) - 100$
          $= 2500 - 100 = \$2400$

95. $C = 0.06543x + 5.65$
     For 300 kWh,

$C = 0.06543(300) + 5.65 = \$25.28$

For 750 kWh,

$C = 0.06543(750) + 5.65 = \$54.72$

87

97. $2x - y = C$

Graph the lines:

$$2x - y = -2$$
$$2x - y = 0$$
$$2x - y = 4$$

All the lines have the same slope, 2.
The lines are parallel.

99. (b), (c), (e) and (g)

101. (c)

103 – 105. Answers will vary.

Chapter 1

Graphs

1.8 Circles

1. Center = (2, 1)
   Radius = distance from (0,1) to (2,1)
   $$r = \sqrt{(2-0)^2 + (1-1)^2} = \sqrt{4} = 2$$
   $$(x-2)^2 + (y-1)^2 = 4$$

3. Center = midpoint of (1,2) and (4,2)
   $$= \left(\frac{1+4}{2}, \frac{2+2}{2}\right) = \left(\frac{5}{2}, 2\right)$$

   Radius = distance from $\left(\frac{5}{2}, 2\right)$ to (4,2)
   $$r = \sqrt{\left(4 - \frac{5}{2}\right)^2 + (2-2)^2} = \sqrt{\frac{9}{4}} = \frac{3}{2}$$
   $$\left(x - \frac{5}{2}\right)^2 + (y-2)^2 = \frac{9}{4}$$

5. $(x-h)^2 + (y-k)^2 = r^2$
   $(x-0)^2 + (y-0)^2 = 2^2$
   $$x^2 + y^2 = 4$$
   General form:
   $$x^2 + y^2 - 4 = 0$$

7. $(x-h)^2 + (y-k)^2 = r^2$
   $(x-0)^2 + (y-2)^2 = 2^2$
   $$x^2 + (y-2)^2 = 4$$
   General form:
   $$x^2 + y^2 - 4y + 4 = 4$$
   $$x^2 + y^2 - 4y = 0$$

9. $(x-h)^2 + (y-k)^2 = r^2$
    $(x-4)^2 + (y-(-3))^2 = 5^2$
    $(x-4)^2 + (y+3)^2 = 25$
    General form:
    $x^2 - 8x + 16 + y^2 + 6y + 9 = 25$
    $x^2 + y^2 - 8x + 6y = 0$

11. $(x-h)^2 + (y-k)^2 = r^2$
    $(x-(-2))^2 + (y-1)^2 = 4^2$
    $(x+2)^2 + (y-1)^2 = 16$
    General form:
    $x^2 + 4x + 4 + y^2 - 2y + 1 = 16$
    $x^2 + y^2 + 4x - 2y - 11 = 0$

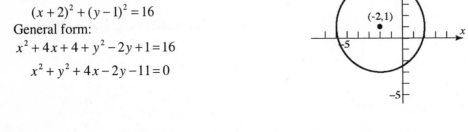

13. $(x-h)^2 + (y-k)^2 = r^2$
    $\left(x-\dfrac{1}{2}\right)^2 + (y-0)^2 = \left(\dfrac{1}{2}\right)^2$
    $\left(x-\dfrac{1}{2}\right)^2 + y^2 = \dfrac{1}{4}$
    General form:
    $x^2 - x + \dfrac{1}{4} + y^2 = \dfrac{1}{4}$
    $x^2 + y^2 - x = 0$

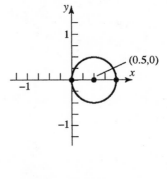

15. $x^2 + y^2 = 25$
    $x^2 + y^2 = 5^2$
    Center : (0,0)
    Radius = 5

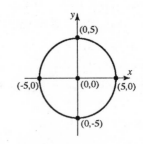

17. $(x-2)^2 + y^2 = 4$

$(x-2)^2 + y^2 = 2^2$
Center: (2,0)
Radius = 2

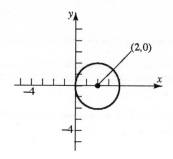

19. $x^2 + y^2 + 4x - 4y - 1 = 0$

$$x^2 + 4x + y^2 - 4y = 1$$
$$(x^2 + 4x + 4) + (y^2 - 4y + 4) = 1 + 4 + 4$$
$$(x+2)^2 + (y-2)^2 = 3^2$$
Center: (−2,2)
Radius = 3

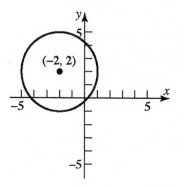

21. $x^2 + y^2 - x + 2y + 1 = 0$

$$x^2 - x + y^2 + 2y = -1$$
$$\left(x^2 - x + \frac{1}{4}\right) + (y^2 + 2y + 1) = -1 + \frac{1}{4} + 1$$
$$\left(x - \frac{1}{2}\right)^2 + (y+1)^2 = \left(\frac{1}{2}\right)^2$$
Center: $\left(\frac{1}{2}, -1\right)$

Radius = $\frac{1}{2}$

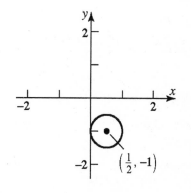

23. $2x^2 + 2y^2 - 12x + 8y - 24 = 0$

$$x^2 + y^2 - 6x + 4y = 12$$
$$x^2 - 6x + y^2 + 4y = 12$$
$$(x^2 - 6x + 9) + (y^2 + 4y + 4) = 12 + 9 + 4$$
$$(x-3)^2 + (y+2)^2 = 5^2$$
Center: (3,−2)
Radius = 5

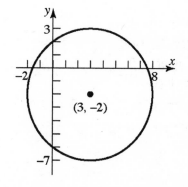

25. Center at (0,0); containing point (–2, 3).
$$r = \sqrt{(-2-0)^2 + (3-0)^2} = \sqrt{4+9} = \sqrt{13}$$
Equation: $(x-0)^2 + (y-0)^2 = \left(\sqrt{13}\right)^2$
$$x^2 + y^2 = 13 \Rightarrow x^2 + y^2 - 13 = 0$$

27. Center at (2,3); tangent to the x-axis.
$$r = 3$$
Equation: $(x-2)^2 + (y-3)^2 = 3^2$
$$x^2 - 4x + 4 + y^2 - 6y + 9 = 9 \Rightarrow x^2 + y^2 - 4x - 6y + 4 = 0$$

29. Endpoints of a diameter are (1,4) and (–3,2).
The center is at the midpoint of that diameter:
Center: $\left(\dfrac{1+(-3)}{2}, \dfrac{4+2}{2}\right) = (-1,3)$
Radius: $r = \sqrt{(1-(-1))^2 + (4-3)^2} = \sqrt{4+1} = \sqrt{5}$
Equation: $(x-(-1))^2 + (y-3)^2 = \left(\sqrt{5}\right)^2$
$$x^2 + 2x + 1 + y^2 - 6y + 9 = 5 \Rightarrow x^2 + y^2 + 2x - 6y + 5 = 0$$

31. (c)   33.   (b)   35. $(x+3)^2 + (y-1)^2 = 16$

37. $(x-2)^2 + (y-2)^2 = 9$ 39. (b), (c), (e) and (g)

41. $x^2 + y^2 + 2x + 4y - 4091 = 0$
$x^2 + 2x + y^2 + 4y - 4091 = 0$
$$x^2 + 2x + 1 + y^2 + 4y + 4 = 4091 + 5 \Rightarrow (x+1)^2 + (y+2)^2 = 4096$$
The circle representing Earth has center $(-1,-2)$ and radius $= \sqrt{4096} = 64$
So the radius of the satellite's orbit is $64 + 0.6 = 64.6$ units.
The equation of the orbit is $(x+1)^2 + (y+2)^2 = (64.6)^2 \Rightarrow x^2 + y^2 + 2x + 4y - 4168.6 = 0$

43. $x^2 + y^2 = 9$
Center: (0, 0)
Slope from center to $\left(1, 2\sqrt{2}\right)$ is $\dfrac{2\sqrt{2} - 0}{1-0} = \dfrac{2\sqrt{2}}{1} = 2\sqrt{2}$.
Slope of the tangent line is $\dfrac{-1}{2\sqrt{2}} = -\dfrac{\sqrt{2}}{4}$.
Equation of the tangent line is:
$$y - 2\sqrt{2} = -\dfrac{\sqrt{2}}{4}(x-1) \Rightarrow y - 2\sqrt{2} = -\dfrac{\sqrt{2}}{4}x + \dfrac{\sqrt{2}}{4}$$
$$4y - 8\sqrt{2} = -\sqrt{2}\,x + \sqrt{2} \Rightarrow \sqrt{2}\,x + 4y = 9\sqrt{2}$$

45.   Let (h, k) be the center of the circle.

$$x - 2y + 4 = 0 \Rightarrow 2y = x + 4 \Rightarrow y = \frac{1}{2}x + 2$$

The slope of the tangent line is $\frac{1}{2}$. The slope from (h, k) to $(0, 2)$ is -2.

$$\frac{2-k}{0-h} = -2 \;\Rightarrow\; 2 - k = 2h$$

The other tangent line is $y = 2x - 7$. Its slope is 2.

The slope from (h, k) to $(3, -1)$ is $-\frac{1}{2}$.

$$\frac{-1-k}{3-h} = -\frac{1}{2} \;\Rightarrow\; 2 + 2k = 3 - h \;\Rightarrow\; 2k = 1 - h \;\Rightarrow\; h = 1 - 2k$$

Solve the two equations in h and k:

$$2 - k = 2(1 - 2k) \;\Rightarrow\; 2 - k = 2 - 4k \;\Rightarrow\; 3k = 0 \;\Rightarrow\; k = 0$$

$$h = 1 - 2(0) = 1$$

The center of the circle is $(1, 0)$.

47.   Consider the following diagram:

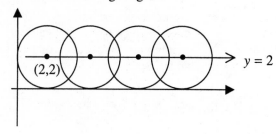

Graphs

1.R Chapter Review

1. $2 - \dfrac{x}{3} = 8$

$6 - x = 24 \Rightarrow x = -18$
The solution set is $\{-18\}$.

3. $-2(5 - 3x) + 8 = 4 + 5x$
$-10 + 6x + 8 = 4 + 5x$
$6x - 2 = 4 + 5x$
$x = 6$
The solution set is $\{6\}$.

5. $\dfrac{3x}{4} - \dfrac{x}{3} = \dfrac{1}{12}$

$9x - 4x = 1 \Rightarrow 5x = 1 \Rightarrow x = \dfrac{1}{5}$
The solution set is $\left\{\dfrac{1}{5}\right\}$.

7. $\dfrac{x}{x-1} = \dfrac{6}{5}$
$5x = 6x - 6$
$6 = x$
and since $x = 6$ does not cause a denominator to equal zero, the solution set is $\{6\}$.

9. $x(1 - x) = 6$
$x - x^2 = 6$
$0 = x^2 - x + 6$
$b^2 - 4ac = (-1)^2 - 4(1)(6) = 1 - 24 = -23 < 0$
No real solution.

11. $\dfrac{1}{2}\left(x - \dfrac{1}{3}\right) = \dfrac{3}{4} - \dfrac{x}{6}$
$\dfrac{x}{2} - \dfrac{1}{6} = \dfrac{3}{4} - \dfrac{x}{6}$
$6x - 2 = 9 - 2x$
$8x = 11$
$x = \dfrac{11}{8}$

13. $(x - 1)(2x + 3) = 3$
$2x^2 + x - 3 = 3$
$2x^2 + x - 6 = 0$
$(2x - 3)(x + 2) = 0$
$x = \dfrac{3}{2}$ or $x = -2$

15. $2x + 3 = 4x^2$
$0 = 4x^2 - 2x - 3$
$x = \dfrac{2 \pm \sqrt{4 + 48}}{8} = \dfrac{2 \pm \sqrt{52}}{8}$
$= \dfrac{2 \pm 2\sqrt{13}}{8} = \dfrac{1 \pm \sqrt{13}}{4}$

17. $\sqrt[3]{x^2-1}=2$
$$\left(\sqrt[3]{x^2-1}\right)^3=(2)^3$$
$$x^2-1=8$$
$$x^2=9$$
$$x=\pm3$$

Check:

$x=-3$ $x=3$

$\sqrt[3]{(-3)^2-1}=2$ $\sqrt[3]{(3)^2-1}=2$

$\sqrt[3]{9-1}=2$ $\sqrt[3]{9-1}=2$

$\sqrt[3]{8}=2$ $\sqrt[3]{8}=2$

$2=2$ $2=2$

so the solution set is $\{-3,3\}$.

19. $x(x+1)+2=0$
$$x^2+x+2=0$$
$$x=\frac{-1\pm\sqrt{1-8}}{2}=\frac{-1\pm\sqrt{-7}}{2}$$
no real solutions

21. $x^4-5x^2+4=0$
$$\left(x^2-4\right)\left(x^2-1\right)=0$$
$$x^2-4=0 \text{ or } x^2-1=0$$
$$x=\pm2 \text{ or } x=\pm1$$

23. $\sqrt{2x-3}+x=3$
$$\sqrt{2x-3}=3-x$$
$$2x-3=9-6x+x^2$$
$$x^2-8x+12=0$$
$$(x-2)(x-6)=0$$
$$x=2 \text{ or } x=6$$

Check $x=2$: $\sqrt{2(2)-3}+2=\sqrt{1}+2=3$

Check $x=6$: $\sqrt{2(6)-3}+6=\sqrt{9}+6$
$$=9\neq3$$

The solution set is $\{2\}$.

25. $x^{3/2}+5x^{1/2}=0$
$$x^{3/2}=-5x^{1/2}$$
$$\left(x^{3/2}\right)^2=\left(-5x^{1/2}\right)^2$$
$$x^3=25x$$
$$x^3-25x=0$$
$$x\left(x^2-25\right)=0$$
$$x(x-5)(x+5)=0$$
$$x=0$$
$$x-5=0\Rightarrow x=5$$
$$x+5=0\Rightarrow x=-5$$

Check $x=0$:

$0^{3/2}+5(0)^{1/2}=0$

$0+0=0$

$0=0$

Check $x=5$:

$5^{3/2}+5(5)^{1/2}=0$

$5^{3/2}+5^{3/2}=0$

$2\left(5^{3/2}\right)\neq0$

Check $x=-5$:

$(-5)^{3/2}+5(-5)^{1/2}=0$

$\left(\sqrt{-5}\right)^3+5\sqrt{-5}=0$

but $\sqrt{-5}$ is undefined.
The solution set is $\{0\}$.

27. $\sqrt{x+1}+\sqrt{x-1}=\sqrt{2x+1}$

$$\left(\sqrt{x+1}+\sqrt{x-1}\right)^2=\left(\sqrt{2x+1}\right)^2$$
$$x+1+2\sqrt{x+1}\sqrt{x-1}+x-1=2x+1$$
$$2x+2\sqrt{x+1}\sqrt{x-1}=2x+1$$
$$2\sqrt{x+1}\sqrt{x-1}=1$$
$$\left(2\sqrt{x+1}\sqrt{x-1}\right)^2=(1)^2$$
$$4(x+1)(x-1)=1\rightarrow 4x^2-4=1$$
$$4x^2=5\Rightarrow x^2=\frac{5}{4}\Rightarrow x=\pm\frac{\sqrt{5}}{2}$$

Check :

$$x=\frac{\sqrt{5}}{2}\Rightarrow\sqrt{\frac{\sqrt{5}}{2}+1}+\sqrt{\frac{\sqrt{5}}{2}-1}=\sqrt{2\left(\frac{\sqrt{5}}{2}\right)+1}$$

$$1.79890743995=1.79890743995$$

$$x=-\frac{\sqrt{5}}{2}\Rightarrow\sqrt{-\frac{\sqrt{5}}{2}+1}+\sqrt{-\frac{\sqrt{5}}{2}-1}=\sqrt{2\left(-\frac{\sqrt{5}}{2}\right)+1}$$

impossible since $-\frac{\sqrt{5}}{2}-1<0$

The solution set is $\left\{\frac{\sqrt{5}}{2}\right\}$.

29. $2\sqrt[3]{x^2}-\sqrt[3]{x}=1$

$$2\sqrt[3]{x^2}-\sqrt[3]{x}-1=0\Rightarrow 2x^{2/3}-x^{1/3}-1=0$$
$$\text{let } p=x^{1/3}\Rightarrow p^2=x^{2/3}$$
$$2p^2-p-1=0\Rightarrow(2p+1)(p-1)=0$$
$$p=-\frac{1}{2}\quad\text{or}\quad p=1$$

$$p=-\frac{1}{2}\Rightarrow x^{1/3}=-\frac{1}{2}\qquad\qquad p=1\rightarrow x^{1/3}=1$$
$$\Rightarrow\left(x^{1/3}\right)^3=\left(-\frac{1}{2}\right)^3\Rightarrow x=-\frac{1}{8}\qquad\Rightarrow\left(x^{1/3}\right)^3=(1)^3\Rightarrow x=1$$

Check

$$x=-\frac{1}{8}:2\sqrt[3]{\left(-\frac{1}{8}\right)^2}-\sqrt[3]{-\frac{1}{8}}-1=0$$

$$2\left(\frac{1}{4}\right)-\left(-\frac{1}{2}\right)-1=0\Rightarrow\frac{1}{2}+\frac{1}{2}-1=0\Rightarrow 0=0$$

$$x=1:2\sqrt[3]{1^2}-\sqrt[3]{1}-1=0$$

$$2-1-1=0\Rightarrow 2-2=0\Rightarrow 0=0$$

the solution set is $\left\{-\frac{1}{8},1\right\}$.

31. $x^{-6} - 7x^{-3} - 8 = 0$

$$\text{let } p = x^{-3} \Rightarrow p^2 = x^{-6}$$

$$p^2 - 7p - 8 = 0 \Rightarrow (p - 8)(p + 1) = 0$$

$$p = 8 \quad \text{or} \quad p = -1$$

$$p = 8 \Rightarrow x^{-3} = 8 \Rightarrow \left(x^{-3}\right)^{-1/3} = (8)^{-1/3} \Rightarrow x = \frac{1}{2}$$

$$p = -1 \Rightarrow x^{-3} = -1 \Rightarrow \left(x^{-3}\right)^{-1/3} = (-1)^{-1/3} \Rightarrow x = -1$$

Check :

$$x = \frac{1}{2} : \left(\frac{1}{2}\right)^{-6} - 7(p)^{-3} - 8 = 0 \Rightarrow 64 - 56 - 8 = 0 \Rightarrow 0 = 0 \qquad \text{the solution set is } \left\{\frac{1}{2}, -1\right\}.$$

$$x = -1 : (-1)^{-6} - 7(-1)^{-3} - 8 = 0 \Rightarrow 1 + 7 - 8 = 0 \Rightarrow 0 = 0$$

33. $\sqrt{x^2 + 3x + 7} - \sqrt{x^2 - 3x + 9} + 2 = 0$

$$\sqrt{x^2 + 3x + 7} = \sqrt{x^2 - 3x + 9} - 2 \Rightarrow \left(\sqrt{x^2 + 3x + 7}\right)^2 = \left(\sqrt{x^2 - 3x + 9} - 2\right)^2$$

$$x^2 + 3x + 7 = x^2 - 3x + 9 - 4\sqrt{x^2 - 3x + 9} + 4 \Rightarrow 6x - 6 = -4\sqrt{x^2 - 3x + 9}$$

$$\left(6(x - 1)\right)^2 = \left(-4\sqrt{x^2 - 3x + 9}\right)^2 \Rightarrow 36\left(x^2 - 2x + 1\right) = 16\left(x^2 - 3x + 9\right)$$

$$36x^2 - 72x + 36 = 16x^2 - 48x + 144 \Rightarrow 20x^2 - 24x - 108 = 0 \rightarrow 5x^2 - 6x - 27 = 0$$

$$(5x + 9)(x - 3) = 0 \Rightarrow x = -\frac{9}{5} \quad \text{or} \quad x = 3$$

Check $x = -\frac{9}{5}$:

$$\sqrt{\left(-\frac{9}{5}\right)^2 + 3\left(-\frac{9}{5}\right) + 7} - \sqrt{\left(-\frac{9}{5}\right)^2 - 3\left(-\frac{9}{5}\right) + 9} + 2 = 0$$

$$\sqrt{\frac{81}{25} - \frac{27}{5} + 7} - \sqrt{\frac{81}{25} + \frac{27}{5} + 9} + 2 = 0$$

$$\sqrt{\frac{81 - 135 + 175}{25}} - \sqrt{\frac{81 + 135 + 225}{25}} + 2 = 0$$

$$\sqrt{\frac{121}{25}} - \sqrt{\frac{441}{25}} + 2 = 0$$

$$\frac{11}{5} - \frac{21}{5} + 2 = 0$$

$$0 = 0$$

Check :

$$x = 3 : \sqrt{(3)^2 + 3(3) + 7} - \sqrt{(3)^2 - 3(3) + 9} + 2 = 0$$

$$\sqrt{9+9+7} - \sqrt{9-9+9} + 2 = 0 \Rightarrow \sqrt{25} - \sqrt{9} + 2 = 0$$

$$2 + 2 = 0 \Rightarrow 4 \neq 0$$

the solution set is $\left\{-\dfrac{9}{5}\right\}$.

35. $|2x + 3| = 7$
$2x + 3 = 7$ or $2x + 3 = -7$
$2x = 4$ or $2x = -10$
$x = 2$ or $x = -5$
The solution set is $\{-5, 2\}$.

37. $|2 - 3x| + 2 = 9 \rightarrow |2 - 3x| = 7$
$2 - 3x = 7$ or $2 - 3x = -7$
$3x = -5$ or $3x = 9$
$x = -\dfrac{5}{3}$ or $x = 3$
The solution set is $\left\{-\dfrac{5}{3}, 3\right\}$.

39. $x^3 - 5x + 3 = 0$; Use ZERO (or ROOT) on the graph of $y_1 = x^3 - 5x + 3$.

The solution set is $\{-2.49, 0.66, 1.83\}$.

41. $x^4 - 3 = 2x + 1$; Use ZERO (or ROOT) on the graph of $y_1 = x^4 - 2x - 4$.

The solution set is $\{-1.14, 1.64\}$.

43. $\dfrac{2x - 3}{5} + 2 \leq \dfrac{x}{2}$
$2(2x - 3) + 10(2) \leq 5x$
$4x - 6 + 20 \leq 5x \Rightarrow 14 \leq x \Rightarrow x \geq 14$
$\{x \mid x \geq 14\}$ or $[14, +\infty)$

45. $-9 \le \dfrac{2x+3}{-4} \le 7$

$36 \ge 2x+3 \ge -28$

$33 \ge \quad 2x \quad \ge -31$

$\dfrac{33}{2} \ge \quad x \quad \ge -\dfrac{31}{2}$

$-\dfrac{31}{2} \le \quad x \quad \le \dfrac{33}{2}$

$\{x \mid -15.5 \le x \le 16.5\}$ or $[-15.5, 16.5]$

47. $6 > \dfrac{3-3x}{12} > 2$

$72 > 3-3x > 24$

$69 > -3x > 21$

$-23 < \quad x \quad < -7$

$\{x \mid -23 < x < -7\}$ or $(-23, -7)$

49. $|3x+4| < \dfrac{1}{2}$

$\dfrac{-1}{2} < 3x+4 < \dfrac{1}{2}$

$-\dfrac{9}{2} < \quad 3x \quad < -\dfrac{7}{2}$

$-\dfrac{3}{2} < \quad x \quad < -\dfrac{7}{6}$

$\left\{x \mid -\dfrac{3}{2} < x < -\dfrac{7}{6}\right\}$ or $\left(-\dfrac{3}{2}, -\dfrac{7}{6}\right)$

51. $|2x-5| \ge 9$

$2x-5 \le -9$ or $2x-5 \ge 9$

$2x \le -4$ or $\quad 2x \ge 14$

$x \le -2$ or $\quad x \ge 7$

$\{x \mid x \le -2 \text{ or } x \ge 7\}$

or $(-\infty, -2] \cup [7, +\infty)$

53. $2 + |2-3x| \le 4$

$|2-3x| \le 2$

$-2 \le 2-3x \le 2$

$-4 \le -3x \le 0 \to \dfrac{4}{3} \ge x \ge 0$

$0 \le x \le \dfrac{4}{3}$

$\left\{x \mid 0 \le x \le \dfrac{4}{3}\right\}$ or $\left[0, \dfrac{4}{3}\right]$

55. $1 - |2-3x| < -4$

$-|2-3x| < -5 \to |2-3x| > 5$

$2-3x < -5$ or $2-3x > 5$

$7 < 3x$ or $\quad -3 > 3x$

$\dfrac{7}{3} < x$ or $\quad -1 > x$

$\to x < -1$ or $\quad x > \dfrac{7}{3}$

$\left\{x \mid x < -1 \text{ or } x > \dfrac{7}{3}\right\}$

or $(-\infty, -1) \cup \left(\dfrac{7}{3}, +\infty\right)$

57.

59.

61.

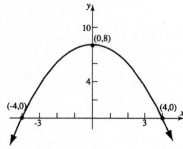

63. $x^2 + y^2 - 2x + 4y - 4 = 0$

$$x^2 - 2x + y^2 + 4y = 4$$

$$(x^2 - 2x + 1) + (y^2 + 4y + 4) = 4 + 1 + 4$$

$$(x-1)^2 + (y+2)^2 = 9$$

$$(x-1)^2 + (y+2)^2 = 3^2$$

Center: $(1,-2)$ Radius = 3

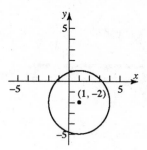

65. $3x^2 + 3y^2 - 6x + 12y = 0$

$$x^2 + y^2 - 2x + 4y = 0$$

$$x^2 - 2x + y^2 + 4y = 0$$

$$(x^2 - 2x + 1) + (y^2 + 4y + 4) = 1 + 4$$

$$(x-1)^2 + (y+2)^2 = 5$$

$$(x-1)^2 + (y+2)^2 = \left(\sqrt{5}\right)^2$$

Center: $(1,-2)$ Radius = $\sqrt{5}$

67. Slope = –2; containing (3,–1)
$$y - y_1 = m(x - x_1) \Rightarrow y - (-1) = -2(x - 3)$$
$$y + 1 = -2x + 6 \Rightarrow y = -2x + 5$$
$$2x + y = 5 \text{ or } y = -2x + 5$$

69. Slope undefined; containing (–3,4)
This is a vertical line.
$$x = -3 \Rightarrow \text{No slope intercept form.}$$

71. y-intercept = –2; containing (5,–3)
Points are (5,–3) and (0,–2)
$$m = \frac{-2 - (-3)}{0 - 5} = \frac{1}{-5} = -\frac{1}{5}$$
$$y = mx + b \Rightarrow y = -\frac{1}{5}x - 2$$
$$x + 5y = -10 \text{ or } y = -\frac{1}{5}x - 2$$

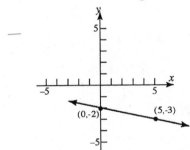

73. Parallel to $2x - 3y = -4$;
Slope $= \dfrac{2}{3}$; containing (–5,3)
$$y - y_1 = m(x - x_1)$$
$$y - 3 = \frac{2}{3}(x - (-5)) \Rightarrow y - 3 = \frac{2}{3}x + \frac{10}{3}$$
$$y = \frac{2}{3}x + \frac{19}{3}$$
$$2x - 3y = -19 \text{ or } y = \frac{2}{3}x + \frac{19}{3}$$

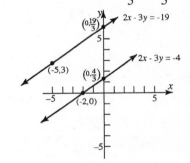

75. Perpendicular to $x + y = 2$;
Containing (4,–3)
Slope of perpendicular = 1
$$y - y_1 = m(x - x_1)$$
$$y - (-3) = 1(x - 4)$$
$$y + 3 = x - 4 \Rightarrow y = x - 7$$
$$x - y = 7 \text{ or } y = x - 7$$

77. Given the points $(7,4)$ and $(-3,2)$.

Slope: $m = \dfrac{2-4}{-3-7} = \dfrac{-2}{-10} = \dfrac{1}{5}$

Distance: $d = \sqrt{(-3-7)^2 + (2-4)^2}$
$$= \sqrt{100+4} = \sqrt{104} = 2\sqrt{26}$$

Midpoint: $\left(\dfrac{7+(-3)}{2}, \dfrac{4+2}{2}\right) = (2,3)$

79. Find the distance between each pair of points.

$d(A,B) = \sqrt{(1-3)^2 + (1-4)^2} = \sqrt{4+9} = \sqrt{13}$

$d(B,C) = \sqrt{(-2-1)^2 + (3-1)^2} = \sqrt{9+4} = \sqrt{13}$

$d(A,C) = \sqrt{(-2-3)^2 + (3-4)^2} = \sqrt{25+1} = \sqrt{26}$

Since $AB = BC$, triangle ABC is isosceles.

81. slope of $\overline{AB} = \dfrac{1-5}{6-2} = -1$; slope of $\overline{AC} = \dfrac{-1-5}{8-2} = -1$; slope of $\overline{BC} = \dfrac{-1-1}{8-6} = -1$

Therefore the points are collinear.

83. Endpoints of the diameter are $(-3, 2)$ and $(5, -6)$.
The center is at the midpoint of the diameter:

Center: $\left(\dfrac{-3+5}{2}, \dfrac{2+(-6)}{2}\right) = (1, -2)$

Radius: $r = \sqrt{(1-(-3))^2 + (-2-2)^2} = \sqrt{16+16} = \sqrt{32} = 4\sqrt{2}$

Equation:

$$(x-1)^2 + (y+2)^2 = \left(4\sqrt{2}\right)^2$$

$$x^2 - 2x + 1 + y^2 + 4y + 4 = 32 \Rightarrow x^2 + y^2 - 2x + 4y - 27 = 0$$

85. $P = 2l + 2w$

87. $I = P \cdot r \cdot t \Rightarrow I = (9000) \cdot (0.07) \cdot (1) = \$630.00$

89.

% acid	amount	amount of acid
40%	60	$(0.40)(60)$
15%	x	$(0.15)(x)$
25%	$60+x$	$(0.25)(60+x)$

$(0.40)(60) + (0.15)(x) = (0.25)(60+x)$

$24 + .15x = 15 + .25x \Rightarrow 9 = 0.1x \Rightarrow x = 90$

90 cubic centimeters of the 15% solution must be added, producing 150 cubic centimeters of the 25% solution.

91.

% salt	amount	amount of salt
10%	64	$(0.10)(64)$
0%	x	$(0.00)(x)$
2%	$64+x$	$(0.02)(64+x)$

$(0.10)(64) + (0.00)(x) = (0.02)(64+x)$

$6.4 = 1.28 + .02x \Rightarrow 5.12 = 0.2x \Rightarrow x = 256$

256 ounces of water must be added.

93. Let s represent the distance the plane can travel.

	Rate	Time	Distance
With wind	$250 + 30 = 280$	$\dfrac{\left(\dfrac{s}{2}\right)}{280}$	$\dfrac{s}{2}$
Against wind	$250 - 30 = 220$	$\dfrac{\left(\dfrac{s}{2}\right)}{220}$	$\dfrac{s}{2}$

Since the total time is at most 5 hours, we have:

$$\frac{\left(\dfrac{s}{2}\right)}{280} + \frac{\left(\dfrac{s}{2}\right)}{220} \leq 5 \Rightarrow \frac{s}{560} + \frac{s}{440} \leq 5$$

$$11s + 14s \leq 5(6160) \Rightarrow 25s \leq 30800 \Rightarrow s \leq 1232$$

The plane can travel at most 1232 miles or 616 miles one way and return 616 miles.

95. Let t represent the time it takes the helicopter to reach the raft.

	Rate	Time	Distance
Raft	5	t	$5t$
Helicopter	90	t	$90t$

Since the total distance is 150 miles, we have:

$$5t + 90t = 150 \Rightarrow 95t = 150 \Rightarrow t = 1.58 \text{ hours } = 1 \text{ hour and } 35 \text{ minutes}$$

The helicopter will reach the raft in 1 hour and 35 minutes.

97. Let t represent the time it takes Clarissa to complete the job by herself.

	Time to do job alone	Part of job done in one day	Time on Job	Part of total job done by each person
Clarissa	t	$\dfrac{1}{t}$	6	$\dfrac{6}{t}$
Shawna	$t + 5$	$\dfrac{1}{t+5}$	6	$\dfrac{6}{t+5}$

Since the two people paint one house, we have:

$$\frac{6}{t} + \frac{6}{t+5} = 1 \Rightarrow 6(t+5) + 6t = t(t+5)$$

$$6t + 30 + 6t = t^2 + 5t \Rightarrow t^2 - 7t - 30 = 0 \Rightarrow (t-10)(t+3) = 0$$

$$t = 10 \text{ or } t = -3, \text{ discard the negative value.}$$

It takes Clarissa 10 days to paint the house when working by herself.

99. The effective speed of the train (i.e., relative to the man) is $30 - 4 = 26$ miles per hour. The time is 5 seconds $= \dfrac{5}{60}$ minutes $= \dfrac{5}{3600}$ hours $= \dfrac{1}{720}$ hours.

$$s = vt = 26\left(\frac{1}{720}\right) = \frac{26}{720} \text{ miles } = \frac{26}{720} \cdot 5280 = 190.67 \text{ feet}$$

The freight train is 190.67 feet long

101. Let t represent the time it takes the smaller pump to fill the tank.

	Time to do job alone	Part of job done in one hour	Time on Job	Part of total job done by each pump
3hp Pump	12	$\dfrac{1}{12}$	$t+4$	$\dfrac{t+4}{12}$
8hp Pump	8	$\dfrac{1}{8}$	4	$\dfrac{4}{8}$

Since the two pumps fill one tank, we have:

$$\frac{t+4}{12}+\frac{4}{8}=1\Rightarrow\frac{t+4}{12}=\frac{1}{2}$$

$$2t+8=12\Rightarrow 2t=4\Rightarrow t=2$$

It takes the small pump a total of 2 more hours to fill the tank.

103. Let x represent the number of passengers over 20.
Then $20+x$ represents the total number of passengers.
$15-0.1x$ represents the fare for each passenger.
Solving the equation for total cost ($482.40), we have:

$$(20+x)(15-0.1x)=482.40$$

$$300+13x-0.1x^2=482.40\Rightarrow -0.1x^2+13x-182.40=0$$

$$x^2-130x+1824=0\Rightarrow(x-114)(x-16)=0\Rightarrow x=114 \ \text{ or } \ x=16$$

Since the capacity of the bus is 44, we discard the 114. The total number of passengers is
20 + 16 = 36, and the ticket price per passenger is 15 – 0.1(16) = $13.40.
So 36 people went on the trip; each person paid $13.40.

105. length of leg $1=x$; length of leg $2=17-x$; length of hypotenuse = 13
Using the Pythagorean Theorem yields the following

$$x^2+\left(17-x\right)^2=13^2$$

$$x^2+289-34x+x^2=169\Rightarrow 2x^2-34x+120=0$$

$$x^2-17x+60=0\Rightarrow\left(x-5\right)\left(x-12\right)=0\Rightarrow x=5 \ \text{ or } \ x=12$$

Therefore the legs of the triangle have length 5 cm and 12 cm.

107.   Answers will vary.

109. Let r_S represent Scott's rate and let r_T represent Todd's rate.
The time for Scott to run 95 meters is the same as for Todd to run 100 meters.

$$\frac{95}{r_S}=\frac{100}{r_T}\Rightarrow r_S=0.95r_T \ \text{ and } \ d_S=0.95d_T$$

If Todd starts from 5 meters behind the start:

$$d_T=105$$
$$d_S=0.95d_T=0.95(105)=99.75$$

(a)   The race does not end in a tie.   (b)   Todd wins the race.
(c)   Todd wins by 0.25 meters.

(d)   To end in a tie:

$$100 = 0.95(100 + x)$$

$$100 = 95 + 0.95x$$

$$5 = 0.95x$$

$$x = 5.263 \text{ meters}$$

(e) - (h) $95 = 0.95(100)$, Therefore, the race ends in a tie.

Chapter 2

Linear and Quadratic Functions

2.1 Functions

1. Function
   Domain: {Dad, Colleen, Kaleigh, Marissa}
   Range: {Jan. 8, Mar. 15, Sept. 17}

3. Not a function

5. Not a function.

7. Function
   Domain: {1, 2, 3, 4}
   Range: {3}

9. Not a function

11. Function
    Domain: {−2, −1, 0, 1}
    Range: {4, 1, 0}

13. $f(x) = 2x + 5$
    (a) $f(0) = 2(0) + 5 = 5$
    (b) $f(1) = 2(1) + 5 = 7$
    (c) $f(-1) = 2(-1) + 5 = 3$
    (d) $f(-x) = 2(-x) + 5 = -2x + 5$
    (e) $-f(x) = -(2x + 5) = -2x - 5$
    (f) $f(x + 1) = 2(x + 1) + 5 = 2x + 2 + 5 = 2x + 7$
    (g) $f(2x) = 2(2x) + 5 = 4x + 5$
    (h) $f(x + h) = 2(x + h) + 5 = 2x + 2h + 5$

15. $f(x) = 3x^2 + 2x - 4$
    (a) $f(0) = 3(0)^2 + 2(0) - 4 = -4$
    (b) $f(1) = 3(1)^2 + 2(1) - 4 = 3 + 2 - 4 = 1$
    (c) $f(-1) = 3(-1)^2 + 2(-1) - 4 = 3 - 2 - 4 = -3$
    (d) $f(-x) = 3(-x)^2 + 2(-x) - 4 = 3x^2 - 2x - 4$
    (e) $-f(x) = -(3x^2 + 2x - 4) = -3x^2 - 2x + 4$
    (f) $f(x + 1) = 3(x + 1)^2 + 2(x + 1) - 4 = 3(x^2 + 2x + 1) + 2x + 2 - 4$
    $= 3x^2 + 6x + 3 + 2x + 2 - 4 = 3x^2 + 8x + 1$
    (g) $f(2x) = 3(2x)^2 + 2(2x) - 4 = 12x^2 + 4x - 4$
    (h) $f(x + h) = 3(x + h)^2 + 2(x + h) - 4 = 3(x^2 + 2xh + h^2) + 2x + 2h - 4$
    $= 3x^2 + 6xh + 3h^2 + 2x + 2h - 4$

17. $f(x) = \dfrac{x}{x^2 + 1}$

   (a) $f(0) = \dfrac{0}{0^2 + 1} = \dfrac{0}{1} = 0$

   (b) $f(1) = \dfrac{1}{1^2 + 1} = \dfrac{1}{2}$

   (c) $f(-1) = \dfrac{-1}{(-1)^2 + 1} = \dfrac{-1}{1 + 1} = -\dfrac{1}{2}$

   (d) $f(-x) = \dfrac{-x}{(-x)^2 + 1} = \dfrac{-x}{x^2 + 1}$

   (e) $-f(x) = -\dfrac{x}{x^2 + 1} = \dfrac{-x}{x^2 + 1}$

   (f) $f(x+1) = \dfrac{x+1}{(x+1)^2 + 1} = \dfrac{x+1}{x^2 + 2x + 1 + 1} = \dfrac{x+1}{x^2 + 2x + 2}$

   (g) $f(2x) = \dfrac{2x}{(2x)^2 + 1} = \dfrac{2x}{4x^2 + 1}$

   (h) $f(x+h) = \dfrac{x+h}{(x+h)^2 + 1} = \dfrac{x+h}{x^2 + 2xh + h^2 + 1}$

19. $f(x) = |x| + 4$

   (a) $f(0) = |0| + 4 = 0 + 4 = 4$

   (b) $f(1) = |1| + 4 = 1 + 4 = 5$

   (c) $f(-1) = |-1| + 4 = 1 + 4 = 5$

   (d) $f(-x) = |-x| + 4 = |x| + 4$

   (e) $-f(x) = -\left(|x| + 4\right) = -|x| - 4$

   (f) $f(x+1) = |x+1| + 4$

   (g) $f(2x) = |2x| + 4 = 2|x| + 4$

   (h) $f(x+h) = |x+h| + 4$

21. Graph $y = x^2$. The graph passes the vertical line test. Thus, the equation represents a function.

23. Graph $y = \dfrac{1}{x}$. The graph passes the vertical line test. Thus, the equation represents a function.

25. $y^2 = 4 - x^2$
     Solve for y: $y = \pm\sqrt{4 - x^2}$
     For $x = 0$, $y = \pm 2$. Thus, (0,2) and (0,–2) are on the graph. This is not a function, since a distinct x corresponds to two different y's.

27. $x = y^2$
     Solve for y: $y = \pm\sqrt{x}$
     For $x = 1$, $y = \pm 1$. Thus, (1,1) and (1,–1) are on the graph. This is not a function, since a distinct x corresponds to two different y's.

29. Graph $y = 2x^2 - 3x + 4$. The graph passes the vertical line test. Thus, the equation represents a function.

31. $2x^2 + 3y^2 = 1$
     Solve for y:

$$2x^2 + 3y^2 = 1 \rightarrow 3y^2 = 1 - 2x^2 \rightarrow y^2 = \frac{1-2x^2}{3} \rightarrow y = \pm\sqrt{\frac{1-2x^2}{3}}$$

For $x = 0$, $y = \pm\sqrt{\frac{1}{3}}$. Thus, $\left(0, \sqrt{\frac{1}{3}}\right)$ and $\left(0, -\sqrt{\frac{1}{3}}\right)$ are on the graph. This is not a function, since a distinct x corresponds to two different y's.

33. $f(x) = -5x + 4$

Domain: {Real Numbers}

35. $f(x) = \dfrac{x}{x^2 + 1}$

Domain: {Real Numbers}

37. $g(x) = \dfrac{x}{x^2 - 16}$

$x^2 - 16 \neq 0$

$x^2 \neq 16 \Rightarrow x \neq \pm 4$

Domain: $\{x | x \neq -4, x \neq 4\}$

39. $F(x) = \dfrac{x-2}{x^3 + x}$

$x^3 + x \neq 0$

$x(x^2 + 1) \neq 0$

$x \neq 0, \quad x^2 \neq -1$

Domain: $\{x | x \neq 0\}$

41. $h(x) = \sqrt{3x - 12}$

$3x - 12 \geq 0$

$3x \geq 12$

$x \geq 4$

Domain: $\{x | x \geq 4\}$

43. $f(x) = \dfrac{4}{\sqrt{x-9}}$

$x - 9 > 0$

$x > 9$

Domain: $\{x | x > 9\}$

45. $p(x) = \sqrt{\dfrac{2}{x-1}}$

$\dfrac{2}{x-1} \geq 0 \Rightarrow x - 1 > 0 \Rightarrow x > 1$

Domain: $\{x | x > 1\}$

47. (a) $f(0) = 3$ since $(0, 3)$ is on the graph.
          $f(-6) = -3$ since $(-6, -3)$ is on the graph.
     (b) $f(6) = 0$ since $(6, 0)$ is on the graph.
          $f(11) = 1$ since $(11, 1)$ is on the graph.
     (c) $f(3)$ is positive since $f(3) \approx 3.7$.
     (d) $f(-4)$ is negative since $f(-4) = -1$.
     (e) $f(x) = 0$ when $x = -3$, $x = 6$, and $x = 10$.
     (f) $f(x) > 0$ when $-3 < x < 6$, and $10 < x \leq 11$.
     (g)   The domain of f is $\{x | -6 \leq x \leq 11\}$ or $[-6, 11]$.

(h)   The range of f is $\{y|-3 \le y \le 4\}$ or $[-3, 4]$
(i)   The x-intercepts are $(-3, 0)$, $(6, 0)$, and $(11, 0)$.
(j)   The y-intercept is $(0, 3)$
(k)   The line $y = \dfrac{1}{2}$ intersect the graph 3 times.
(l)   The line $x = 5$ intersects the graph 1 time
(m) $f(x) = 3$ when $x = 0$ and $x = 4$.
(n) $f(x) = -2$ when $x = -5$ and $x = 8$.

49.   Not a function since vertical lines will intersect the graph in more than one point.

51.   Function   (a)   Domain: $\{x|-\pi \le x \le \pi\}$;   Range: $\{y|-1 \le y \le 1\}$

(b) $\left(-\dfrac{\pi}{2}, 0\right)$, $\left(\dfrac{\pi}{2}, 0\right)$, $(0, 1)$

53.   Not a function since vertical lines will intersect the graph in more than one point.

55.   Function   (a)   Domain: $\{x|x > 0\}$;   Range: $\{y|y \in \text{Real Numbers}\}$
                   (b) $(1, 0)$

57.   Function   (a)   Domain: $\{x|x \in \text{Real Numbers}\}$;   Range: $\{y|y \le 2\}$
                   (b) $(-3, 0), (3, 0), (0, 2)$

59.   Function   (a)   Domain: $\{x|x \in \text{Real Numbers}\}$;   Range: $\{y|y \ge -3\}$
                   (b) $(1, 0), (3, 0), (0, 9)$

61. $f(x) = 2x^2 - x - 1$
(a) $f(-1) = 2(-1)^2 - (-1) - 1 = 2$ $(-1, 2)$ is on the graph of f.
(b) $f(-2) = 2(-2)^2 - (-2) - 1 = 9$ $(-2, 9)$ is on the graph of f.
(c)   Solve for x:
$$-1 = 2x^2 - x - 1 \Rightarrow 0 = 2x^2 - x$$
$$0 = x(2x - 1) \Rightarrow x = 0, x = \frac{1}{2}$$
$(0, -1)$ and $\left(\dfrac{1}{2}, -1\right)$ are points on the graph of f.
(d)   The domain of f is: $\{x|x \text{ is any real number}\}$.
(e)   x-intercepts:
$$f(x) = 0 \Rightarrow 2x^2 - x - 1 = 0$$
$$(2x + 1)(x - 1) = 0 \Rightarrow x = -\frac{1}{2}, x = 1$$
$\left(-\dfrac{1}{2}, 0\right)$ and $(1, 0)$
(f)   y-intercept: $f(0) = 2(0)^2 - 0 - 1 = -1 \to (0, -1)$

63. $f(x) = \dfrac{x+2}{x-6}$

(a) $f(3) = \dfrac{3+2}{3-6} = -\dfrac{5}{3} \neq 14$ (3,14) is not on the graph of f.

(b) $f(4) = \dfrac{4+2}{4-6} = \dfrac{6}{-2} = -3$ (4,−3) is the point on the graph of f.

(c) Solve for x:

$$2 = \dfrac{x+2}{x-6}$$
$$2x - 12 = x + 2$$
$$x = 14$$

(14, 2) is a point on the graph of f.

(d) The domain of f is: $\{x \mid x \neq 6\}$.

(e) x-intercepts:

$$f(x) = 0 \Rightarrow \dfrac{x+2}{x-6} = 0$$
$$x + 2 = 0 \Rightarrow x = -2$$
$$(-2,0)$$

(f) y-intercept: $f(0) = \dfrac{0+2}{0-6} = -\dfrac{1}{3} \rightarrow \left(0, -\dfrac{1}{3}\right)$

65. $f(x) = \dfrac{2x^2}{x^4 + 1}$

(a) $f(-1) = \dfrac{2(-1)^2}{(-1)^4 + 1} = \dfrac{2}{2} = 1$ (−1,1) is a point on the graph of f.

(b) $f(2) = \dfrac{2(2)^2}{(2)^4 + 1} = \dfrac{8}{17}$ $\left(2, \dfrac{8}{17}\right)$ is a point on the graph of f.

(c) Solve for x:

$$1 = \dfrac{2x^2}{x^4 + 1}$$
$$x^4 + 1 = 2x^2$$
$$x^4 - 2x^2 + 1 = 0$$
$$(x^2 - 1)^2 = 0$$
$$x^2 - 1 = 0 \Rightarrow x = \pm 1$$

(1,1) and (−1,1) are points on the graph of f.

(d) The domain of f is: $\{\text{Real Numbers}\}$.

(e) x-intercepts:

$$f(x) = 0 \Rightarrow \dfrac{2x^2}{x^4 + 1} = 0$$
$$2x^2 = 0 \Rightarrow x = 0$$
$$(0,0)$$

(f) y-intercept: $f(0) = \dfrac{2x^2}{x^4 + 1} = \dfrac{0}{0+1} = 0 \Rightarrow (0,0)$

67. Solving for C:

$f(x) = 2x^3 - 4x^2 + 4x + C$ and $f(2) = 5$

$f(2) = 2(2)^3 - 4(2)^2 + 4(2) + C$

$5 = 16 - 16 + 8 + C$

$-3 = C$

69. Solving for A:

$f(x) = \dfrac{3x + 8}{2x - A}$ and $f(0) = 2$

$f(0) = \dfrac{3(0) + 8}{2(0) - A}$

$2 = \dfrac{8}{-A} \Rightarrow -2A = 8 \Rightarrow A = -4$

71. Solving for A:

$f(x) = \dfrac{2x - A}{x - 3}$ and $f(4) = 0$

$f(4) = \dfrac{2(4) - A}{4 - 3}$

$0 = \dfrac{8 - A}{1}$

$0 = 8 - A$

$A = 8$

f is undefined when $x = 3$.

73. $f(x) = 4x + 3$

$\dfrac{f(x + h) - f(x)}{h} = \dfrac{4(x + h) + 3 - 4x - 3}{h} = \dfrac{4x + 4h + 3 - 4x - 3}{h} = \dfrac{4h}{h} = 4$

75. $f(x) = x^2 - x + 4$

$\dfrac{f(x + h) - f(x)}{h} = \dfrac{(x + h)^2 - (x + h) + 4 - (x^2 - x + 4)}{h}$

$= \dfrac{x^2 + 2xh + h^2 - x - h + 4 - x^2 + x - 4}{h} =$

$= \dfrac{2xh + h^2 - h}{h} = 2x + h - 1$

77. $f(x) = x^3 - 2$

$\dfrac{f(x + h) - f(x)}{h} = \dfrac{(x + h)^3 - 2 - (x^3 - 2)}{h}$

$= \dfrac{x^3 + 3x^2h + 3xh^2 + h^3 - 2 - x^3 + 2}{h}$

$= \dfrac{3x^2h + 3xh^2 + h^3}{h} = 3x^2 + 3xh + h^2$

79. (a) III   (b) IV   (c) I   (d) V   (e) II

81.

83. (a) 2 hours elapsed; $0 \leq d \leq 3$ miles.
    (b) 0.5 hours elapsed; $d = 3$ miles.
    (c) 0.3 hours elapsed; $0 \leq d \leq 3$ miles.
    (d) 0.2 hours elapsed; $d = 0$ miles.
    (e) 0.9 hours elapsed; $0 \leq d \leq 2.8$ miles.
    (f) 0.3 hours elapsed; $d = 2.8$ miles.
    (g) 1.1 hours elapsed; $0 \leq d \leq 2.8$ miles.
    (h) The furthest distance Kevin is from home is 3 miles.
    (i) 2 times.

85. (a) Graphing: $H(x) = 20 - 4.9x^2$

(b) $H(1) = 20 - 4.9(1)^2 = 20 - 4.9 = 15.1$ meters
$H(1.1) = 20 - 4.9(1.1)^2 = 20 - 4.9(1.21) = 20 - 5.929 = 14.071$ meters
$H(1.2) = 20 - 4.9(1.2)^2 = 20 - 4.9(1.44) = 20 - 7.056 = 12.944$ meters
$H(1.3) = 20 - 4.9(1.3)^2 = 20 - 4.9(1.69) = 20 - 8.281 = 11.719$ meters

(c)
$H(x) = 15$ $\qquad$ $H(x) = 10$ $\qquad$ $H(x) = 5$

$15 = 20 - 4.9x^2$ $\qquad$ $10 = 20 - 4.9x^2$ $\qquad$ $5 = 20 - 4.9x^2$

$-5 = -4.9x^2$ $\qquad$ $-10 = -4.9x^2$ $\qquad$ $-15 = -4.9x^2$

$x^2 \approx 1.0204$ $\qquad$ $x^2 \approx 2.0408$ $\qquad$ $x^2 \approx 3.0612$

$x \approx 1.01$ seconds $\qquad$ $x \approx 1.43$ seconds $\qquad$ $x \approx 1.75$ seconds

(d) $H(x) = 0$

$0 = 20 - 4.9x^2$

$-20 = -4.9x^2$

$x^2 \approx 4.0816$

$x \approx 2.02$ seconds

87. Let x represent the length of the rectangle.

Then $\dfrac{x}{2}$ represents the width of the rectangle, since the length is twice the width.

The function for the area is: $A(x) = x \cdot \dfrac{x}{2} = \dfrac{x^2}{2} = \dfrac{1}{2}x^2$

89. Let x represent the number of hours worked.
The function for the gross salary is: $G(x) = 10x$

91. $h(x) = \dfrac{-32x^2}{130^2} + x$

(a) $h(100) = \dfrac{-32(100)^2}{130^2} + 100 = \dfrac{-320000}{16900} + 100 \approx -18.93 + 100 = 81.07$ feet

(b) $h(300) = \dfrac{-32(300)^2}{130^2} + 300 = \dfrac{-2880000}{16900} + 300 \approx -170.41 + 300 = 129.59$ feet

(c) $h(500) = \dfrac{-32(500)^2}{130^2} + 500 = \dfrac{-8000000}{16900} + 500 \approx -473.37 + 500 = 26.63$ feet

(d) Graphing $h(x) = \dfrac{-32x^2}{130^2} + x$

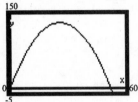

(e) Solve $h(x) = \dfrac{-32x^2}{130^2} + x = 90$

$$\left(-\dfrac{32}{130^2}\right)x^2 + x - 90 = 0$$

$$x = \dfrac{-1 \pm \sqrt{1^2 - 4\left(-\dfrac{32}{130^2}\right)(-90)}}{2\left(-\dfrac{32}{130^2}\right)} \approx \dfrac{-1 \pm \sqrt{1 - 0.68166}}{-0.00379} \approx \dfrac{-1 \pm 0.5642}{-0.00379}$$

$$x = \dfrac{-1 + 0.5642}{-0.00379} \approx 115 \quad \text{feet} \quad \text{or} \quad x = \dfrac{-1 - 0.5642}{-0.00379} \approx 413 \text{ feet}$$

Therefore, the ball reaches a height of 90 feet twice. The first time is when the ball has traveled 115 feet, and the second time is when the ball has traveled 413 feet.

(f) The ball travels approximately 275 feet before it reaches its maximum height of approximately 131.8 feet.

X	Y1
0	0
25	23.817
50	45.266
75	64.349
100	81.065
125	95.414
150	107.4

X=0

X	Y1
200	124.26
225	129.14
250	131.66
275	131.8
300	129.59
325	125
350	118.05

X=350

(g) The ball travels approximately 265.5 feet before it reaches its maximum height of approximately 132.03 feet.

X	Y1
263.5	132.03
264	132.03
264.5	132.03
265	132.03
265.5	132.03
266	132.02
266.5	132.02

X=265.5

(h) Solving $h(x) = \dfrac{-32x^2}{130^2} + x = 0$

$\dfrac{-32x^2}{130^2} + x = 0 \Rightarrow x\left(\dfrac{-32x}{130^2} + 1\right) = 0 \Rightarrow x = 0$ or $\dfrac{-32x}{130^2} + 1 = 0$

$\dfrac{-32x}{130^2} + 1 = 0 \Rightarrow 1 = \dfrac{32x}{130^2} \Rightarrow 130^2 = 32x \Rightarrow x = \dfrac{130^2}{32} \approx 528.125$ feet

Therefore, the domain of h is $\{x \mid 0 \le x \le 528.125\}$.

93. $C(x) = 100 + \dfrac{x}{10} + \dfrac{36000}{x}$

(a) $C(500) = 100 + \dfrac{500}{10} + \dfrac{36000}{500} = 100 + 50 + 72 = \$222$

(b) $C(450) = 100 + \dfrac{450}{10} + \dfrac{36000}{450} = 100 + 45 + 80 = \$225$

(c) $C(600) = 100 + \dfrac{600}{10} + \dfrac{36000}{600} = 100 + 60 + 60 = \$220$

(d) $C(400) = 100 + \dfrac{400}{10} + \dfrac{36000}{400} = 100 + 40 + 90 = \$230$

(e) Graphing:

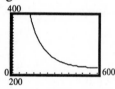

(f) As x varies from 400 to 600 mph, the cost decreases from $230 to $220.

95. (a) $h(x) = 2x$
     $h(a+b) = 2(a+b) = 2a + 2b = h(a) + h(b);$ $h(x) = 2x$ has the property.

(b) $g(x) = x^2$
     $g(a+b) = (a+b)^2 = a^2 + 2ab + b^2 \ne a^2 + b^2 = h(a) + h(b)$
     $g(x) = x^2$ does not have the property.

(c) $F(x) = 5x - 2$
     $F(a+b) = 5(a+b) - 2 = 5a + 5b - 2 \ne 5a - 2 + 5b - 2 = h(a) + h(b)$
     $F(x) = 5x - 2$ does not have the property.

(d) $G(x) = \dfrac{1}{x}$

     $G(a+b) = \dfrac{1}{a+b} \ne \dfrac{1}{a} + \dfrac{1}{b} = h(a) + h(b) \Rightarrow G(x) = \dfrac{1}{x}$ does not have the property.

97. No, $x = -1$ is not in the domain of g, but it is in the domain of f.

Linear and Quadratic Functions

2.2   Linear Functions and Models

1. $f(x) = 2x + 3$
     Slope = 2; y-intercept = 3

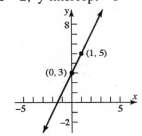

3. $h(x) = -3x + 4$
     Slope = –3; y-intercept = 4

5. $f(x) = \dfrac{1}{4}x - 3$

     Slope $= \dfrac{1}{4}$; y-intercept = –3

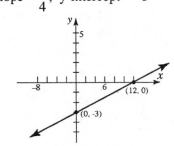

7. $F(x) = 4$
     Slope = 0; y-intercept = 4

9. (a) Consider the data points (x, y), where x = the age in years of the computer and y = the value in dollars of the computer. So we have the points $(0, 3000)$ and $(3, 0)$.

   The slope formula yields: slope $= \dfrac{\Delta y}{\Delta x} = \dfrac{0 - 3000}{3 - 0} = \dfrac{-3000}{3} = -1000 = m$

   $(0, 3000)$ is the y-intercept, so $b = 3000$
   Therefore, the linear function is $f(x) = mx + b = -1000x + 3000$.

   (b) The graph of $f(x) = -1000x + 3000$

   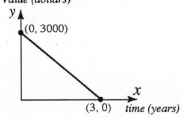

   (c) The computer's value after 2 years is given by
   $$f(2) = -1000(2) + 3000$$
   $$= -2000 + 3000 = \$1000$$

115

11.(a) Let x = the number of bicycles manufactured. We can use the cost function
$C(x) = mx + b$, with $m = 90$ and $b = 1800$.
Therefore $C(x) = 90x + 1800$

  (b)   The graph of $C(x) = 90x + 1800$

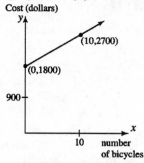

  (c)   The cost of manufacturing 14 bicycles is given by $C(14) = 90(14) + 1800 = \$3060$.

13.   Linear, $m > 0$ 15.   Linear, $m < 0$ 17.   Nonlinear

19.   (a)

  (b)   Answers will vary. We select (3,4) and (9,16). The slope of the line containing these points is:
$$m = \frac{16-4}{9-3} = \frac{12}{6} = 2$$
The equation of the line is:
$$y - y_1 = m(x - x_1)$$
$$y - 4 = 2(x - 3)$$
$$y - 4 = 2x - 6$$
$$y = 2x - 2$$

  (c)

  (d)   Using the LINear REGresssion program, the line of best fit is:
$$y = 2.0357x - 2.3571$$

  (e)

21.   (a)

(b)   Answers will vary. We select (–2,–4) and (2,5). The slope of the line containing these points is:

$$m = \frac{5-(-4)}{2-(-2)} = \frac{9}{4} = 2.25$$

The equation of the line is:

$$y - y_1 = m(x - x_1)$$
$$y - (-4) = 2.25(x - (-2))$$
$$y + 4 = 2.25x + 4.5$$
$$y = 2.25x + 0.5$$

(c)

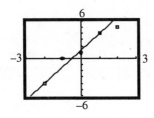

(d)   Using the LINear REGresssion program, the line of best fit is:
$$y = 2.2x + 1.2$$

(e)

23.   (a)

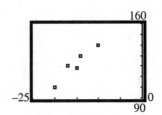

(b)   Answers will vary. We select (–20,100) and (–10,140). The slope of the line containing these points is:

$$m = \frac{140-100}{-10-(-20)} = \frac{40}{10} = 4$$

The equation of the line is:

$$y - y_1 = m(x - x_1)$$
$$y - 100 = 4(x - (-20))$$
$$y - 100 = 4x + 80$$
$$y = 4x + 180$$

(c)

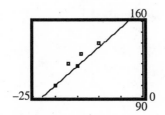

(d)   Using the LINear REGresssion program, the line of best fit is:
$$y = 3.8613x + 180.2920$$

(e)

117

25. (a)

(b) Using the LINear REGression program, the line of best fit is:
$$C = 1.038I - 1897.507$$

(c) For each $1 increase in disposable income, the per capita consumption increases by $1.04

(d) $C = 1.038(21500) - 1897.507$
$$\approx \$20419.49$$

27. (a)

(b) Using the LINear REGression program, the line of best fit is:
$$L = 0.026G + 7.874$$

(c) For each 1 day increase in Gestation period, the life expectancy increases by 0.026 years.

(d) $L = 0.026(89) + 7.874$
$$\approx 10.188 \text{ years}$$

29. (a) The relation is not a function because 23 is paired with both 56 and 53.

(b)

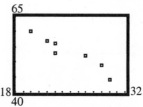

(c) Using the LINear REGression program, the line of best fit is:
$$D = -1.3355p + 86.1974$$

(d) As the price of the jeans increases by $1, the demand for the jeans decreases by 1.3355.

(e) $D(p) = -1.3355p + 86.1974$

(f) Domain: $\{p \mid p > 0\}$

(g) $D(28) = -1.3355(28) + 86.1974$
$$\approx 48.8034$$
Demand is about 49 pairs.

31. Let $p =$ the monthly payment and $B =$ the amount borrowed.
Consider the ordered pair (B, p). We can use the points $(0,0)$ and $(1000, 6.49)$.
Now compute the slope: slope $= \dfrac{\Delta y}{\Delta x} = \dfrac{6.49 - 0}{1000 - 0} = \dfrac{6.49}{1000} = 0.00649$
Therefore we have the linear function $p(B) = 0.00649B + 0 = 0.00649B$.
If $B = 145000$, then $p = (0.00649)(145000) = \$941.05$.

33. Let R = the revenue and g = the number of gallons of gasoline sold.
    Consider the ordered pair (g,R).
    We can use the points $(0,0)$ and $(12,15.84)$.
    Now compute the slope:
    $$\text{slope} = \frac{\Delta y}{\Delta x} = \frac{15.84 - 0}{12 - 0} = \frac{15.84}{12} = 1.32$$
    Therefore we have the linear function $R(g) = 1.32g + 0 = 1.32g$.
    If $g = 10.5$, then $R = (1.32)(10.5) \approx \$13.86$.

35. $s = kt^2$
    $16 = k(1)^2 \Rightarrow k = 16$
    in 3 seconds $s = (16)(9) = 144$ feet

    $64 = 16t^2 \Rightarrow t^2 = 4 \Rightarrow t = \pm 2$
    so it takes 2 seconds to fall 64 feet.

Chapter 2

Linear and Quadratic Functions

2.3 Quadratic Functions

1. C   3. F   5. G   7. H   9. B   11. D

13. $f(x) = x^2 + 2x$

  $a = 1, b = 2, c = 0$. Since $a = 1 > 0$, the graph opens up.

  The x-coordinate of the vertex is $x = \dfrac{-b}{2a} = \dfrac{-(2)}{2(1)} = \dfrac{-2}{2} = -1$.

  The y-coordinate of the vertex is $f\left(\dfrac{-b}{2a}\right) = f(-1) = (-1)^2 + 2(-1) = 1 - 2 = -1$.

  Thus, the vertex is $(-1, -1)$.
  The axis of symmetry is the line $x = -1$.
  The discriminant is:

  $\quad b^2 - 4ac = (2)^2 - 4(1)(0) = 4 > 0$,

  so the graph has two x-intercepts.
  The x-intercepts are found by solving:

  $\quad x^2 + 6x = 0$

  $\quad x(x + 2) = 0$

  $\quad x = 0 \text{ or } x = -2$

  The x-intercepts are -2 and 0.
  The y-intercept is $f(0) = 0$.

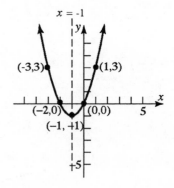

15. $f(x) = -x^2 - 6x$; $a = -1, b = -6, c = 0$. Since $a = -1 < 0$, the graph opens down.

  The x-coordinate of the vertex is $x = \dfrac{-b}{2a} = \dfrac{-(-6)}{2(-1)} = \dfrac{6}{-2} = -3$.

  The y-coordinate of the vertex is $f\left(\dfrac{-b}{2a}\right) = f(-3) = -(-3)^2 - 6(-3) = -9 + 18 = 9$.

  Thus, the vertex is $(-3, 9)$.
  The axis of symmetry is the line $x = -3$.
  The discriminant is:

  $\quad b^2 - 4ac = (-6)^2 - 4(-1)(0) = 36 > 0$,

  so the graph has two x-intercepts.
  The x-intercepts are found by solving:

  $\quad -x^2 - 6x = 0$

  $\quad -x(x + 6) = 0$

  $\quad x = 0 \text{ or } x = -6$

  The x-intercepts are -6 and 0.
  The y-intercept is $f(0) = 0$.

17. $f(x) = 2x^2 - 8x$; $a = 2, b = -8, c = 0$. Since $a = 2 > 0$, the graph opens up.

The x-coordinate of the vertex is $x = \dfrac{-b}{2a} = \dfrac{-(-8)}{2(2)} = \dfrac{8}{4} = 2$.

The y-coordinate of the vertex is $f\left(\dfrac{-b}{2a}\right) = f(2) = 2(2)^2 - 8(2) = 8 - 16 = -8$.

Thus, the vertex is $(2, -8)$.
The axis of symmetry is the line $x = 2$.
The discriminant is:

$\qquad b^2 - 4ac = (-8)^2 - 4(2)(0) = 64 > 0$,

so the graph has two x-intercepts.
The x-intercepts are found by solving:

$\qquad 2x^2 - 8x = 0$
$\qquad 2x(x - 4) = 0$
$\qquad x = 0 \ \text{ or } \ x = 4$

The x-intercepts are 0 and 4.
The y-intercept is $f(0) = 0$.

19. $f(x) = x^2 + 2x - 8$; $a = 1, b = 2, c = -8$. Since $a = 1 > 0$, the graph opens up.

The x-coordinate of the vertex is $x = \dfrac{-b}{2a} = \dfrac{-2}{2(1)} = \dfrac{-2}{2} = -1$.

The y-coordinate of the vertex is $f\left(\dfrac{-b}{2a}\right) = f(-1) = (-1)^2 + 2(-1) - 8 = 1 - 2 - 8 = -9$.

Thus, the vertex is $(-1, -9)$.
The axis of symmetry is the line $x = -1$.
The discriminant is:

$\qquad b^2 - 4ac = 2^2 - 4(1)(-8) = 4 + 32 = 36 > 0$,

so the graph has two x-intercepts.
The x-intercepts are found by solving:

$\qquad x^2 + 2x - 8 = 0$
$\qquad (x + 4)(x - 2) = 0$
$\qquad x = -4 \ \text{ or } \ x = 2$

The x-intercepts are –4 and 2.
The y-intercept is $f(0) = -8$.

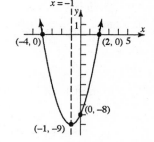

21. $f(x) = x^2 + 2x + 1$; $a = 1, b = 2, c = 1$. Since $a = 1 > 0$, the graph opens up.

The x-coordinate of the vertex is $x = \dfrac{-b}{2a} = \dfrac{-2}{2(1)} = \dfrac{-2}{2} = -1$.

The y-coordinate of the vertex is $f\left(\dfrac{-b}{2a}\right) = f(-1) = (-1)^2 + 2(-1) + 1 = 1 - 2 + 1 = 0$.

Thus, the vertex is $(-1, 0)$.
The axis of symmetry is the line $x = -1$.
The discriminant is: $b^2 - 4ac = 2^2 - 4(1)(1) = 4 - 4 = 0$, so the graph has one x-intercept.

The x-intercept is found by solving:
$$x^2 + 2x + 1 = 0$$
$$(x+1)^2 = 0$$
$$x = -1$$
The x-intercept is -1.
The y-intercept is $f(0) = 1$.

23. $f(x) = 2x^2 - x + 2$; $a = 2, b = -1, c = 2$. Since $a = 2 > 0$, the graph opens up.

The x-coordinate of the vertex is $x = \dfrac{-b}{2a} = \dfrac{-(-1)}{2(2)} = \dfrac{1}{4}$.

The y-coordinate of the vertex is $f\left(\dfrac{-b}{2a}\right) = f\left(\dfrac{1}{4}\right) = 2\left(\dfrac{1}{4}\right)^2 - \dfrac{1}{4} + 2 = \dfrac{1}{8} - \dfrac{1}{4} + 2 = \dfrac{15}{8}$.

Thus, the vertex is $\left(\dfrac{1}{4}, \dfrac{15}{8}\right)$.

The axis of symmetry is the line $x = \dfrac{1}{4}$.

The discriminant is:
$$b^2 - 4ac = (-1)^2 - 4(2)(2) = 1 - 16 = -15,$$
so the graph has no x-intercepts.
The y-intercept is $f(0) = 2$.

25. $f(x) = -2x^2 + 2x - 3$; $a = -2, b = 2, c = -3$. Since $a = -2 < 0$, the graph opens down.

The x-coordinate of the vertex is $x = \dfrac{-b}{2a} = \dfrac{-(2)}{2(-2)} = \dfrac{-2}{-4} = \dfrac{1}{2}$.

The y-coordinate of the vertex is $f\left(\dfrac{-b}{2a}\right) = f\left(\dfrac{1}{2}\right) = -2\left(\dfrac{1}{2}\right)^2 + 2\left(\dfrac{1}{2}\right) - 3 = -\dfrac{1}{2} + 1 - 3 = -\dfrac{5}{2}$.

Thus, the vertex is $\left(\dfrac{1}{2}, -\dfrac{5}{2}\right)$.

The axis of symmetry is the line $x = \dfrac{1}{2}$.

The discriminant is:
$$b^2 - 4ac = 2^2 - 4(-2)(-3) = 4 - 24 = -20,$$
so the graph has no x-intercepts.
The y-intercept is $f(0) = -3$.

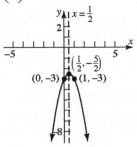

27. $f(x) = 3x^2 + 6x + 2$; $a = 3, b = 6, c = 2$. Since $a = 3 > 0$, the graph opens up.

The x-coordinate of the vertex is $x = \dfrac{-b}{2a} = \dfrac{-6}{2(3)} = \dfrac{-6}{6} = -1$.

The y-coordinate of the vertex is $f\left(\dfrac{-b}{2a}\right) = f(-1) = 3(-1)^2 + 6(-1) + 2 = 3 - 6 + 2 = -1$.

Thus, the vertex is $(-1, -1)$.
The axis of symmetry is the line $x = -1$.
The discriminant is:
$$b^2 - 4ac = 6^2 - 4(3)(2) = 36 - 24 = 12,$$
so the graph has two x-intercepts.
The x-intercepts are found by solving:
$$x = \frac{-b \pm \sqrt{b^2 - 4ac}}{2a} = \frac{-6 \pm \sqrt{12}}{2(3)}$$
$$= \frac{-6 \pm 2\sqrt{3}}{6} = \frac{-3 \pm \sqrt{3}}{3} \approx \frac{-3 \pm 1.732}{3}$$
The x-intercepts are approximately -0.42 and -1.58.
The y-intercept is $f(0) = 2$.

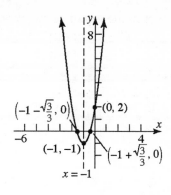

29. $f(x) = -4x^2 - 6x + 2$; $a = -4, b = -6, c = 2$. Since $a = -4 < 0$, the graph opens down.

The x-coordinate of the vertex is $x = \dfrac{-b}{2a} = \dfrac{-(-6)}{2(-4)} = \dfrac{6}{-8} = -\dfrac{3}{4}$. The y-coordinate of the

vertex is $f\left(\dfrac{-b}{2a}\right) = f\left(-\dfrac{3}{4}\right) = -4\left(-\dfrac{3}{4}\right)^2 - 6\left(-\dfrac{3}{4}\right) + 2 = -\dfrac{9}{4} + \dfrac{9}{2} + 2 = \dfrac{17}{4}$.

Thus, the vertex is $\left(-\dfrac{3}{4}, \dfrac{17}{4}\right)$.

The axis of symmetry is the line $x = -\dfrac{3}{4}$.

The discriminant is:
$$b^2 - 4ac = (-6)^2 - 4(-4)(2) = 36 + 32 = 68,$$
so the graph has two x-intercepts.
The x-intercepts are found by solving:
$$x = \frac{-b \pm \sqrt{b^2 - 4ac}}{2a} = \frac{-(-6) \pm \sqrt{68}}{2(-4)}$$
$$= \frac{6 \pm 2\sqrt{17}}{-8} = \frac{-3 \pm \sqrt{17}}{4} \approx \frac{-3 \pm 4.123}{4}$$

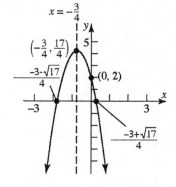

The x-intercepts are approximately -1.78 and 0.28.
The y-intercept is $f(0) = 2$.

31. Given that the graph of $f(x) = ax^2 + bx + c$ has vertex $(-1, -2)$ and passes through
the point $(0, -1)$, we can conclude
$$\frac{-b}{2a} = -1, \qquad f(-1) = -2, \quad \text{and} \qquad f(0) = -1$$
Notice that $f(0) = -1 \Rightarrow a(0)^2 + b(0) + c = -1 \Rightarrow c = -1$
Therefore $f(x) = ax^2 + bx + c = ax^2 + bx - 1$.
Furthermore, $\dfrac{-b}{2a} = -1 \Rightarrow b = 2a$
$\qquad$ and $f(-1) = -2 \Rightarrow a(-1)^2 + b(-1) - 1 = -2 \Rightarrow a - b - 1 = -2$
$\qquad\qquad \Rightarrow a - b = -1$

Replacing b with $2a$ in this equation yields
$$a - 2a = -1 \Rightarrow -a = -1 \Rightarrow a = 1.$$
So $b = 2a = 2(1) = 2$.
Therefore, we have the function $f(x) = x^2 + 2x - 1$.

33.   Given that the graph of $f(x) = ax^2 + bx + c$ has vertex $(-3, 5)$ and passes through the point $(0, -4)$, we can conclude

$$\frac{-b}{2a} = -3, \qquad f(-3) = 5, \qquad \text{and} \qquad f(0) = -4$$

Notice that $f(0) = -4 \Rightarrow a(0)^2 + b(0) + c = -4 \Rightarrow c = -4$
Therefore $f(x) = ax^2 + bx + c = ax^2 + bx - 4$.
Furthermore, $\dfrac{-b}{2a} = -3 \Rightarrow b = 6a$
and $f(-3) = 5 \Rightarrow a(-3)^2 + b(-3) - 4 = 5 \Rightarrow 9a - 3b - 4 = 5 \Rightarrow 9a - 3b = 9$
$$\Rightarrow 3a - b = 3$$
Replacing b with $6a$ in this equation yields
$$3a - 6a = 3 \Rightarrow -3a = 3 \Rightarrow a = -1.$$
So $b = 6a = 6(-1) = -6$.
Therefore, we have the function $f(x) = -x^2 - 6x - 4$.

35.   Given that the graph of $f(x) = ax^2 + bx + c$ has vertex $(1, -3)$ and passes through the point $(3, 5)$, we can conclude

$$\frac{-b}{2a} = 1, \qquad f(1) = -3, \qquad \text{and} \qquad f(3) = 5$$

Notice that $f(3) = 5 \Rightarrow a(3)^2 + b(3) + c = 5 \Rightarrow 9a + 3b + c = 5$
Furthermore, $\dfrac{-b}{2a} = 1 \Rightarrow b = -2a$
and $f(1) = -3 \Rightarrow a(1)^2 + b(1) + c = -3 \Rightarrow a + b + c = -3$
Replacing b with $-2a$ in each of these equations yields
$$9a + 3b + c = 5 \rightarrow 9a + 3(-2a) + c = 5 \rightarrow 9a - 6a + c = 5$$
$$\Rightarrow 3a + c = 5 \Rightarrow c = 5 - 3a$$
$$a + (-2a) + c = -3 \rightarrow a - 2a + c = -3$$
$$\Rightarrow -a + c = -3 \Rightarrow c = -3 + a$$
Finally, since $c = 5 - 3a$ and $c = -3 + a$, setting these two expressions equal and solving for a yields
$$5 - 3a = -3 + a$$
$$8 = 4a$$
$$2 = a$$
So $c = 5 - 3a = 5 - 3 \cdot 2 = 5 - 6 = -1$.
And $b = -2a = (-2)(2) = -4$.
Therefore, we have the function $f(x) = 2x^2 - 4x - 1$.

37. (a) $f(x) = 1(x-(-3))(x-1) = 1(x+3)(x-1) = 1(x^2+2x-3) = x^2+2x-3$

$f(x) = 2(x-(-3))(x-1) = 2(x+3)(x-1) = 2(x^2+2x-3) = 2x^2+4x-6$

$f(x) = -2(x-(-3))(x-1) = -2(x+3)(x-1) = -2(x^2+2x-3) = -2x^2-4x+6$

$f(x) = 5(x-(-3))(x-1) = 5(x+3)(x-1) = 5(x^2+2x-3) = 5x^2+10x-15$

(b) The value of a multiplies the value of the y-intercept by the value of a. The values of the x-intercepts are not changed.

(c) The axis of symmetry is unaffected by the value of a.

(d) The y-coordinate of the vertex is multiplied by the value of a.

(e) The x-coordinate of the vertex is the midpoint of the x-intercepts.

39. Given that the graph of $f(x) = ax^2 + bx + c$ has vertex $(0,2)$ and passes through the point $(1,8)$, we can conclude

$$\frac{-b}{2a} = 0, \qquad f(0) = 2, \qquad \text{and} \qquad f(1) = 8$$

Notice that $\dfrac{-b}{2a} = 0 \Rightarrow b = 0$

and $f(0) = 2 \Rightarrow a(0)^2 + b(0) + c = 2 \Rightarrow c = 2$

Therefore $f(x) = ax^2 + bx + c = ax^2 + 2$.

And since $f(1) = 8$, we have

$$f(1) = a(1)^2 + 2 = 8 \Rightarrow a + 2 = 8 \rightarrow a = 6$$

So we have the function $f(x) = 6x^2 + 2$.

41. $R(x) = x\left(-\dfrac{1}{6}x + 100\right) = -\dfrac{1}{6}x^2 + 100x$

43. If $x = -5p + 100$, then $p = \dfrac{100-x}{5}$. $R(x) = x\left(\dfrac{100-x}{5}\right) = -\dfrac{1}{5}x^2 + 20x$

45. Let x = width and y = length of the rectangular area.

$P = 2x + 2y = 400$

$y = \dfrac{400-2x}{2} = 200 - x$

Then $A(x) = (200-x)x = 200x - x^2 = -x^2 + 200x$

47. $f(x) = -(x+2)^2 = -x^2 - 4x - 4$ opens down and has only one x-intercept $(-2, 0)$.

In general, a quadratic function that has only one x-intercept must have the form $f(x) = ax^2 + bx + c$ such that $b^2 - 4ac = 0$, since discriminant $= 0$ means the associated quadratic equation has exactly one real solution. Also, we must have $a < 0$ in order for the parabola to open downwards.

49. $y = x^2 - 4x + 1;$ $y = x^2 + 1;$ $y = x^2 + 4x + 1$

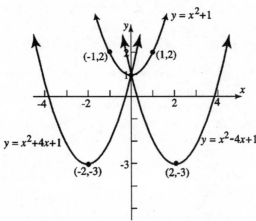

Each member of this family will be a parabola with the following characteristics:
- opens upwards since $a > 0$
- y-intercept occurs at $(0, 1)$

Linear and Quadratic Functions

2.4 Quadratic Models

1. $f(x) = x^2 + 2$, $a = 1, b = 0, c = 2$. Since $a = 1 > 0$, the graph opens up, so the vertex is a minimum point. The minimum occurs at $x = \dfrac{-b}{2a} = \dfrac{-(0)}{2(1)} = \dfrac{0}{2} = 0$.

    The minimum value is $f\left(\dfrac{-b}{2a}\right) = f(0) = (0)^2 + 2 = 0 + 2 = 2$.

X	Y1
-3	11
-2	6
-1	3
0	2
1	3
2	6
3	11

    X=0

3. $f(x) = -x^2 - 4x$, $a = -1, b = -4, c = 0$. Since $a = -1 < 0$, the graph opens down, so the vertex is a maximum point. The maximum occurs at $x = \dfrac{-b}{2a} = \dfrac{-(-4)}{2(-1)} = \dfrac{4}{-2} = -2$.

    The maximum value is $f\left(\dfrac{-b}{2a}\right) = f(-2) = -(-2)^2 - 4(-2) = -4 + 8 = 4$.

X	Y1
-5	-5
-4	0
-3	3
-2	4
-1	3
0	0
1	-5

    X=-2

5. $f(x) = 2x^2 + 12x$, $a = 2, b = 12, c = 0$. Since $a = 2 > 0$, the graph opens up, so the vertex is a minimum point. The minimum occurs at $x = \dfrac{-b}{2a} = \dfrac{-12}{2(2)} = \dfrac{-12}{4} = -3$.

    The minimum value is $f\left(\dfrac{-b}{2a}\right) = f(-3) = 2(-3)^2 + 12(-3) = 18 - 36 = -18$.

X	Y1
-5	-10
-4	-16
-3	-18
-2	-16
-1	-10
0	0
1	14

    X=-3

7. $f(x) = 2x^2 + 12x - 3$, $a = 2$, $b = 12$, $c = -3$. Since $a = 2 > 0$, the graph opens up,
    so the vertex is a minimum point. The minimum occurs at $x = \dfrac{-b}{2a} = \dfrac{-12}{2(2)} = \dfrac{-12}{4} = -3$.

    The minimum value is $f\left(\dfrac{-b}{2a}\right) = f(-3) = 2(-3)^2 + 12(-3) - 3 = 18 - 36 - 3 = -21$.

9. $f(x) = -x^2 + 10x - 4$; $a = -1$, $b = 10$, $c = -4$. Since $a = -1 < 0$, the graph opens down, so
    the vertex is a maximum point. The maximum occurs at $x = \dfrac{-b}{2a} = \dfrac{-10}{2(-1)} = \dfrac{-10}{-2} = 5$.

    The maximum value is $f\left(\dfrac{-b}{2a}\right) = f(5) = -(5)^2 + 10(5) - 4 = -25 + 50 - 4 = 21$.

11. $f(x) = -3x^2 + 12x + 1$; $a = -3$, $b = 12$, $c = 1$. Since $a = -3 < 0$, the graph opens down,
    so the vertex is a maximum point. The maximum occurs at $x = \dfrac{-b}{2a} = \dfrac{-12}{2(-3)} = \dfrac{-12}{-6} = 2$.

    The maximum value is $f\left(\dfrac{-b}{2a}\right) = f(2) = -3(2)^2 + 12(2) + 1 = -12 + 24 + 1 = 13$.

13. $R(p) = -4p^2 + 4000p$, $a = -4$, $b = 4000$, $c = 0$. Since $a = -4 < 0$, the graph is a parabola
    that opens down, so the vertex is a maximum point. The maximum occurs at
    $$p = \dfrac{-b}{2a} = \dfrac{-4000}{2(-4)} = 500.$$
    Thus, the unit price should be \$500 for maximum revenue.
    The maximum revenue is $R(500) = -4(500)^2 + 4000(500) = -1000000 + 2000000 = \$1,000,000$

15. $C(x) = x^2 - 80x + 2000$, $a = 1$, $b = -80$, $c = 2000$. Since $a = 1 > 0$, the graph opens up,
    so the vertex is a minimum point.

    The minimum cost occurs at $x = \dfrac{-b}{2a} = \dfrac{-(-80)}{2(1)} = \dfrac{80}{2} = 40$ televisions produced.

The minimum cost is

$$f\left(\frac{-b}{2a}\right) = f(40) = (40)^2 - 80(40) + 2000 = 1600 - 3200 + 2000 = \$400.$$

17. (a) $R(x) = x\left(-\frac{1}{6}x + 100\right) = -\frac{1}{6}x^2 + 100x$

(b) $R(200) = -\frac{1}{6}(200)^2 + 100(200) = \frac{-20000}{3} + 20000 = \frac{40000}{3} \approx \$13,333$

(c) $x = \frac{-b}{2a} = \frac{-100}{2\left(-\frac{1}{6}\right)} = \frac{-100}{\left(-\frac{1}{3}\right)} = \frac{300}{1} = 300$ maximizes revenue

$$R(300) = -\frac{1}{6}(300)^2 + 100(300) = -15000 + 30000 = \$15,000 = \text{maximum revenue}$$

(d) $p = -\frac{1}{6}(300) + 100 = -50 + 100 = \$50$ maximizes revenue

19. (a)   If $x = -5p + 100$, then $p = \frac{100 - x}{5}$. $R(x) = x\left(\frac{100 - x}{5}\right) = -\frac{1}{5}x^2 + 20x$

(b) $R(15) = -\frac{1}{5}(15)^2 + 20(15) = -45 + 300 = \$255$

(c) $x = \frac{-b}{2a} = \frac{-20}{2\left(-\frac{1}{5}\right)} = \frac{-20}{\left(-\frac{2}{5}\right)} = \frac{100}{2} = 50$ maximizes revenue

$$R(50) = -\frac{1}{5}(50)^2 + 20(50) = -500 + 1000 = \$500 = \text{maximum revenue}$$

(d) $p = \frac{100 - 50}{5} = \frac{50}{5} = \$10$ maximizes revenue

21. (a)   Let $x =$ width and $y =$ length of the rectangular area.

$$P = 2x + 2y = 400 \Rightarrow y = \frac{400 - 2x}{2} = 200 - x$$

Then $A(x) = (200 - x)x = 200x - x^2 = -x^2 + 200x$

(b) $x = \frac{-b}{2a} = \frac{-200}{2(-1)} = \frac{-200}{-2} = 100$ yards maximizes area

(c) $A(100) = -100^2 + 200(100) = -10000 + 20000 = 10,000$ sq yds. = maximum area

23. Let $x =$ width and $y =$ length of the rectangular area.

$$2x + y = 4000 \quad \Rightarrow \quad y = 4000 - 2x$$

Then $A(x) = (4000 - 2x)x = 4000x - 2x^2 = -2x^2 + 4000x$

$$x = \frac{-b}{2a} = \frac{-4000}{2(-2)} = \frac{-4000}{-4} = 1000 \text{ maximizes area}$$

$$A(1000) = -2(1000)^2 + 4000(1000) = -2000000 + 4000000 = 2,000,000$$

The largest area that can be enclosed is 2,000,000 square meters.

25. (a) $a = -\dfrac{32}{2500}, b = 1, c = 200.$ The maximum height occurs when

$$x = \frac{-b}{2a} = \frac{-1}{2\left(-\dfrac{32}{2500}\right)} = \frac{2500}{64} = 39.0625 \text{ feet from base of the cliff.}$$

   (b)   The maximum height is $h(39.0625) = \dfrac{-32(39.0625)^2}{2500} + 39.0625 + 200 \doteq 219.53$ feet.

   (c)   Solving when $h(x) = 0$:

$$-\frac{32}{2500}x^2 + x + 200 = 0$$

$$x = \frac{-1 \pm \sqrt{1^2 - 4\left(-\dfrac{32}{2500}\right)(200)}}{2\left(-\dfrac{32}{2500}\right)} = \frac{-1 \pm \sqrt{11.24}}{-0.0256} \rightarrow x \approx -91.90 \text{ or } x \approx 170.02$$

   Since the distance cannot be negative, the projectile strikes the water 170.02 feet from the base of the cliff.

   (d)   Graphing:

   (e) Using the MAXIMUM function

   (f)   Solving when $h(x) = 100$:

$$-\frac{32}{2500}x^2 + x + 200 = 100 \Rightarrow -\frac{32}{2500}x^2 + x + 100 = 0$$

$$x = \frac{-1 \pm \sqrt{1^2 - 4\left(-\dfrac{32}{2500}\right)(100)}}{2\left(-\dfrac{32}{2500}\right)} = \frac{-1 \pm \sqrt{6.12}}{-0.0256}; \quad x \approx -57.57 \text{ or } x \approx 135.70$$

   Since the distance cannot be negative, the projectile is 100 feet above the water 135.70 feet from the base of the cliff.

27. Locate the origin at the point where the cable touches the road. Then the equation of the parabola is of the form: $y = ax^2$, where $a > 0$. Since the point (200, 75) is on the parabola, we can find the constant a:

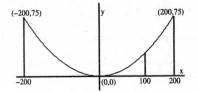

$$75 = a(200)^2 \implies a = \frac{75}{200^2} = 0.001875$$

When $x = 100$, we have:
$$y = 0.001875(100)^2 = 18.75 \text{ meters}.$$

29. Let x = the depth of the gutter and y = the width of the gutter.
     Then $A = xy$ is the cross-sectional area of the gutter.
     Since the aluminum sheets for the gutter are 12 inches wide, we have
     $$2x + y = 12 \implies y = 12 - 2x.$$
     The area is to be maximized, so: $A = xy = x(12 - 2x) = -2x^2 + 12x$.
     This equation is a parabola opening down; thus, it has a maximum when
     $$x = \frac{-b}{2a} = \frac{-12}{2(-2)} = \frac{-12}{-4} = 3.$$
     Thus, a depth of 3 inches produces a maximum cross-sectional area.

31. Let x = the width of the rectangle or the diameter of the semicircle.
     Let y = the length of the rectangle.

     The perimeter of each semicircle is $\dfrac{\pi x}{2}$.

     The perimeter of the track is given by: $\dfrac{\pi x}{2} + \dfrac{\pi x}{2} + y + y = 400$.

     Solving for x:

     $$\frac{\pi x}{2} + \frac{\pi x}{2} + y + y = 1500 \implies \pi x + 2y = 400 \implies \pi x = 400 - 2y \implies x = \frac{400 - 2y}{\pi}$$

     The area of the rectangle is: $A = xy = \left(\dfrac{400 - 2y}{\pi}\right) y = \dfrac{-2}{\pi} y^2 + \dfrac{400}{\pi} y$

     This equation is a parabola opening down; thus, it has a maximum when

     $$y = \frac{-b}{2a} = \frac{\frac{-400}{\pi}}{2\left(\frac{-2}{\pi}\right)} = \frac{-400}{-4} = 100. \quad \text{Thus, } x = \frac{400 - 2(100)}{\pi} = \frac{200}{\pi} \approx 63.66.$$

     The dimensions for the rectangle with maximum area are $\dfrac{200}{\pi} \approx 63.66$ meters

     by 100 meters.

Problems 33 – 35. The equations for the curves that are graphed on the screens use many more decimal places in order to get the desired accuracy.

33. (a) Graphing: The data appear to be quadratic with $a < 0$.

(b) Using the QUADratic REGression program, the quadratic function of best fit is:

$I(x) = -47.71x^2 + 4262.66x - 42777.73$

(c) $x = \dfrac{-b}{2a} = \dfrac{-4262.66}{2(-47.71)} \approx 44.673$

An individual will earn the most income at an age of 44.7 years.

(d) The maximum income will be:

$I(44.7) = -47.71(44.7)^2 + 4262.66(44.7) - 42777.73 = \$52,434.30$

(e) Graphing the quadratic function of best fit:

35. (a) Graphing: The data appears to be quadratic with $a < 0$.

(b) Using the QUADratic REGression program, the quadratic function of best fit is:

$M(s) = -0.0175s^2 + 1.93s - 25.34$

(c) $s = \dfrac{-b}{2a} = \dfrac{-1.93}{2(-0.0175)} = 55.14$ The speed that maximizes miles per gallon is about 55 miles per hour.

(d) The predicted miles per gallon when the speed is 63 miles per hour is:

$M(63) = -0.0175(63)^2 + 1.93(63) - 25.34 \approx 26.79$ miles per gallon.

(e)   Graphing the quadratic function of best fit:

37.   We are given: $V(x) = kx(a - x) = -kx^2 + akx$

The reaction rate is a maximum when: $x = \dfrac{-b}{2a} = \dfrac{-ak}{2(-k)} = \dfrac{ak}{2k} = \dfrac{a}{2}$

39. $f(x) = -5x^2 + 8 \quad h = 1$:

Area $= \dfrac{h}{3}\left(2ah^2 + 6c\right) = \dfrac{1}{3}\left(2(-5)(1)^2 + 6(8)\right) = \dfrac{1}{3}(-10 + 48) = \dfrac{38}{3} \approx 12.67$ sq. units

41. $f(x) = x^2 + 3x + 5, \quad h = 4$

Area $= \dfrac{h}{3}\left(2ah^2 + 6c\right) = \dfrac{4}{3}\left(2(1)(4)^2 + 6(5)\right) = \dfrac{4}{3}(32 + 30) = \dfrac{248}{3} \approx 82.67$ sq. units.

Linear and Quadratic Functions

2.R   Chapter Review

1. $f(4) = -5$ gives the ordered pair $(4, -5)$. $f(0) = 3$ gives $(0, 3)$.

Finding the slope: $m = \dfrac{3 - (-5)}{0 - 4} = \dfrac{8}{-4} = -2$

Using slope-intercept form: $f(x) = -2x + 3$

3. $f(x) = \dfrac{Ax + 5}{6x - 2}$ and $f(1) = 4$

Solving:
$$\dfrac{A(1) + 5}{6(1) - 2} = 4$$
$$\dfrac{A + 5}{4} = 4$$
$$A + 5 = 16$$
$$A = 11$$

5.   (b), (c), and (d) pass the vertical line test and therefore are functions.

7. $f(x) = \dfrac{3x}{x^2 - 4}$

(a) $f(-x) = \dfrac{3(-x)}{(-x)^2 - 4} = \dfrac{-3x}{x^2 - 4}$

(b) $-f(x) = -\left(\dfrac{3x}{x^2 - 4}\right) = \dfrac{-3x}{x^2 - 4}$

(c) $f(x + 2) = \dfrac{3(x + 2)}{(x + 2)^2 - 4} = \dfrac{3x + 6}{x^2 + 4x + 4 - 4} = \dfrac{3x + 6}{x^2 + 4x}$

(d) $f(x - 2) = \dfrac{3(x - 2)}{(x - 2)^2 - 4} = \dfrac{3x - 6}{x^2 - 4x + 4 - 4} = \dfrac{3x - 6}{x^2 - 4x}$

9. $f(x) = \sqrt{x^2 - 4}$

(a) $f(-x) = \sqrt{(-x)^2 - 4} = \sqrt{x^2 - 4}$

(b) $-f(x) = -\sqrt{x^2 - 4}$

(c) $f(x + 2) = \sqrt{(x + 2)^2 - 4} = \sqrt{x^2 + 4x + 4 - 4} = \sqrt{x^2 + 4x}$

(d) $f(x - 2) = \sqrt{(x - 2)^2 - 4} = \sqrt{x^2 - 4x + 4 - 4} = \sqrt{x^2 - 4x}$

11. $f(x) = \dfrac{x^2 - 4}{x^2}$

    (a) $f(-x) = \dfrac{(-x)^2 - 4}{(-x)^2} = \dfrac{x^2 - 4}{x^2}$

    (b) $-f(x) = -\left(\dfrac{x^2 - 4}{x^2}\right) = \dfrac{4 - x^2}{x^2}$

    (c) $f(x+2) = \dfrac{(x+2)^2 - 4}{(x+2)^2} = \dfrac{x^2 + 4x + 4 - 4}{x^2 + 4x + 4} = \dfrac{x^2 + 4x}{x^2 + 4x + 4}$

    (d) $f(x-2) = \dfrac{(x-2)^2 - 4}{(x-2)^2} = \dfrac{x^2 - 4x + 4 - 4}{x^2 - 4x + 4} = \dfrac{x^2 - 4x}{x^2 - 4x + 4}$

13. $f(x) = \dfrac{x}{x^2 - 9}$

The denominator cannot be zero:
$$x^2 - 9 \neq 0$$
$$(x+3)(x-3) \neq 0$$
$$x \neq -3 \text{ or } 3$$
Domain: $\{x \mid x \neq -3, x \neq 3\}$

15. $f(x) = \sqrt{2 - x}$

The radicand must be positive:
$$2 - x \geq 0$$
$$x \leq 2$$
Domain: $\{x \mid x \leq 2\}$ or $(-\infty, 2]$

17. $f(x) = \dfrac{\sqrt{x}}{|x|}$

The radicand must be positive and the
denominator cannot be zero: $x > 0$
Domain: $\{x \mid x > 0\}$ or $(0, +\infty)$

19. $f(x) = \dfrac{x}{x^2 + 2x - 3}$

The denominator cannot be zero:
$$x^2 + 2x - 3 \neq 0$$
$$(x+3)(x-1) \neq 0$$
$$x \neq -3 \text{ or } 1$$
Domain: $\{x \mid x \neq -3, x \neq 1\}$

21. $f(x) = 2x - 5$

23. $h(x) = \dfrac{4}{5}x - 6$

25. $f(x) = \dfrac{1}{4}x^2 - 16$, $a = \dfrac{1}{4}, b = 0, c = -16$. Since $a = \dfrac{1}{4} > 0$, the graph opens up.

The x-coordinate of the vertex is $x = \dfrac{-b}{2a} = \dfrac{-0}{2\left(\dfrac{1}{4}\right)} = \dfrac{0}{\left(\dfrac{1}{2}\right)} = 0.$

The y-coordinate of the vertex is $f\left(\dfrac{-b}{2a}\right) = f(0) = \dfrac{1}{4}(0)^2 - 16 = -16$.

Thus, the vertex is $(0, -16)$.
The axis of symmetry is the line $x = 0$.
The discriminant is:

$$b^2 - 4ac = (0)^2 - 4\left(\dfrac{1}{4}\right)(-16) = 16 > 0,$$

so the graph has two x-intercepts.
The x-intercepts are found by solving:

$$\dfrac{1}{4}x^2 - 16 = 0$$

$$x^2 - 64 = 0 \Rightarrow x^2 = 64 \Rightarrow x = 8 \ \text{ or } \ x = -8$$

The x-intercepts are −8 and 8.
The y-intercept is $f(0) = -16$.

Graphing Utility:

27. $f(x) = -4x^2 + 4x$, $a = -4$, $b = 4$, $c = 0$. Since $a = -4 < 0$, the graph opens down.

The x-coordinate of the vertex is $x = \dfrac{-b}{2a} = \dfrac{-4}{2(-4)} = \dfrac{-4}{-8} = \dfrac{1}{2}$.

The y-coordinate of the vertex is $f\left(\dfrac{-b}{2a}\right) = f\left(\dfrac{1}{2}\right) = -4\left(\dfrac{1}{2}\right)^2 + 4\left(\dfrac{1}{2}\right) = -1 + 2 = 1$.

Thus, the vertex is $\left(\dfrac{1}{2}, 1\right)$.

The axis of symmetry is the line $x = \dfrac{1}{2}$.

The discriminant is:
$$b^2 - 4ac = 4^2 - 4(-4)(0) = 16 > 0,$$
so the graph has two x-intercepts.
The x-intercepts are found by solving:
$-4x^2 + 4x = 0 \Rightarrow -4x(x-1) = 0 \Rightarrow x = 0 \ \text{ or } \ x = 1$
The x-intercepts are 0 and 1.
The y-intercept is $f(0) = -4(0)^2 + 4(0) = 0$.

Graphing Utility:

29. $f(x) = \dfrac{9}{2}x^2 + 3x + 1$, $a = \dfrac{9}{2}, b = 3, c = 1$. Since $a = \dfrac{9}{2} > 0$, the graph opens up.

The x - coordinate of the vertex is $x = \dfrac{-b}{2a} = \dfrac{-3}{2\left(\dfrac{9}{2}\right)} = \dfrac{-3}{9} = -\dfrac{1}{3}$.

The y-coordinate of the vertex is $f\left(\dfrac{-b}{2a}\right) = f\left(-\dfrac{1}{3}\right) = \dfrac{9}{2}\left(-\dfrac{1}{3}\right)^2 + 3\left(-\dfrac{1}{3}\right) + 1 = \dfrac{1}{2} - 1 + 1 = \dfrac{1}{2}$.

Thus, the vertex is $\left(-\dfrac{1}{3}, \dfrac{1}{2}\right)$. The axis of symmetry is the line $x = -\dfrac{1}{3}$.

The discriminant is: $b^2 - 4ac = 3^2 - 4\left(\dfrac{9}{2}\right)(1) = 9 - 18 = -9 < 0$, so the graph has

no x-intercepts. The y-intercept is $f(0) = \dfrac{9}{2}(0)^2 + 3(0) + 1 = 1$.

Graphing Utility:

31. $f(x) = 3x^2 + 4x - 1$, $a = 3, b = 4, c = -1$. Since $a = 3 > 0$, the graph opens up.

The x-coordinate of the vertex is $x = \dfrac{-b}{2a} = \dfrac{-4}{2(3)} = \dfrac{-4}{6} = -\dfrac{2}{3}$.

The y-coordinate of the vertex is $f\left(\dfrac{-b}{2a}\right) = f\left(-\dfrac{2}{3}\right) = 3\left(-\dfrac{2}{3}\right)^2 + 4\left(-\dfrac{2}{3}\right) - 1 = \dfrac{4}{3} - \dfrac{8}{3} - 1 = -\dfrac{7}{3}$.

Thus, the vertex is $\left(-\dfrac{2}{3}, -\dfrac{7}{3}\right)$.

The axis of symmetry is the line $x = -\dfrac{2}{3}$.

The discriminant is: $b^2 - 4ac = (4)^2 - 4(3)(-1) = 16 + 12 = 28 > 0$,
so the graph has two x-intercepts.

The x-intercepts are found by solving: $3x^2 + 4x - 1 = 0$

$$x = \dfrac{-b \pm \sqrt{b^2 - 4ac}}{2a} = \dfrac{-4 \pm \sqrt{28}}{2(3)} = \dfrac{-4 \pm 2\sqrt{7}}{6} = \dfrac{-2 \pm \sqrt{7}}{3} \approx \dfrac{-2 \pm 2.646}{3}$$

The x-intercepts are approximately 0.22 and −1.55.
The y-intercept is $f(0) = 3(0)^2 + 4(0) - 1 = -1$.

Graphing Utility:

33.　$f(x) = x^2 - 4x + 6$, $a = 1, b = -4, c = 6$.　Since $a = 1 > 0$, the graph opens up.

The x-coordinate of the vertex is $x = \dfrac{-b}{2a} = \dfrac{-(-4)}{2(1)} = \dfrac{4}{2} = 2$.

The y-coordinate of the vertex is $f\left(\dfrac{-b}{2a}\right) = f(2) = (2)^2 - 4(2) + 6 = 4 - 8 + 6 = 2$.

Thus, the vertex is $(2, 2)$.

The axis of symmetry is the line $x = 2$.

The discriminant is:

　　$b^2 - 4ac = (-4)^2 - 4(1)(6) = 16 - 24 = -8 < 0$,

so the graph has no x-intercepts.

The y-intercept is $f(0) = (0)^2 - 4(0) + 6 = 6$.

Graphing Utility:

35.　$f(x) = 3x^2 - 6x + 4$, $a = 3, b = -6, c = 4$.　Since $a = 3 > 0$, the graph opens up, so the vertex is a minimum point.　The minimum occurs at $x = \dfrac{-b}{2a} = \dfrac{-(-6)}{2(3)} = \dfrac{6}{6} = 1$.

The minimum value is $f\left(\dfrac{-b}{2a}\right) = f(1) = 3(1)^2 - 6(1) + 4 = 3 - 6 + 4 = 1$.

37.　$f(x) = -x^2 + 8x - 4$, $a = -1, b = 8, c = -4$.　Since $a = -1 < 0$, the graph opens down, so the vertex is a maximum point.　The maximum occurs at $x = \dfrac{-b}{2a} = \dfrac{-8}{2(-1)} = \dfrac{-8}{-2} = 4$.

The maximum value is $f\left(\dfrac{-b}{2a}\right) = f(4) = -(4)^2 + 8(4) - 4 = -16 + 32 - 4 = 12$.

39.　$f(x) = -3x^2 + 12x + 4$, $a = -3, b = 12, c = 4$.　Since $a = -3 < 0$, the graph opens down, so the vertex is a maximum point.　The maximum occurs at $x = \dfrac{-b}{2a} = \dfrac{-12}{2(-3)} = \dfrac{-12}{-6} = 2$.

The maximum value is $f\left(\dfrac{-b}{2a}\right) = f(2) = -3(2)^2 + 12(2) + 4 = -12 + 24 + 4 = 16$.

41. (a) The relation is a function. Each HS GPA value is paired with exactly one College GPA value.

(b)

(c) Using the LINear REGression program, the line of best fit is:
$$G = 0.964x + 0.072$$

(d) As the high school GPA increases by 1 point, the college GPA increases by 0.964 point.

(e) $G(x) = 0.964x + 0.072$

(f) Domain: $\{x | 0 \le x \le 4\}$

(g) $G(3.23) = (0.964)(3.23) + 0.072 \approx 3.186$
The college GPA is approximately 3.19.

43. Let R = the revenue in dollars, and g = the number of gallons of gasoline sold.
Consider the ordered pair (g, R).
We can use the points $(0,0)$ and $(13.5, 15.93)$.
Now compute the slope:
$$\text{slope} = \frac{\Delta y}{\Delta x} = \frac{15.93 - 0}{13.5 - 0} = \frac{15.93}{13.5} \approx 1.18$$
Therefore we have the linear function $R(g) = 1.18g + 0 = 1.18g$.
If $g = 11.2$, then $R = (1.18)(11.2) \approx \$13.22$.

45. Let x represent the length and y represent the width of the rectangle.
$2x + 2y = 20 \implies y = 10 - x$.
$x \cdot y = 16 \implies x(10 - x) = 16$.
Solving the area equation:
$$10x - x^2 = 16 \implies x^2 - 10x + 16 = 0$$
$$(x - 8)(x - 2) = 0 \implies x = 8 \text{ or } x = 2$$
The length and width of the rectangle are 8 feet by 2 feet.

47. $C(x) = 4.9x^2 - 617.40x + 19{,}600;$ $a = 4.9, b = -617.40, c = 19{,}600.$ Since $a = 4.9 > 0$, the graph opens up, so the vertex is a minimum point.

(a) The minimum marginal cost occurs at $x = \dfrac{-b}{2a} = \dfrac{-(-617.40)}{2(4.9)} = \dfrac{617.40}{9.8} = 63$.

(b) The minimum marginal cost is
$$C\left(\frac{-b}{2a}\right) = C(63) = 4.9(63)^2 - (617.40)(63) + 19600 = \$151.90$$

49.   (a)   Graphing, the data appear to be quadratic.

(b)   Using the QUADratic REGression program, the quadratic function of best fit is:
$R(A) = -7.76A^2 + 411.88A + 942.72$

(c)   The maximum revenue occurs at $A = \dfrac{-b}{2a} = \dfrac{-(411.88)}{2(-7.76)} = \dfrac{-411.88}{-15.52}$

≈ 26.53865979 thousand dollars $\approx \$26{,}538.66$

(d)   The maximum revenue is

$$R\left(\frac{-b}{2a}\right) = R(26.53866) = -7.76(26.53866)^2 + (411.88)(26.53866) + 942.72$$

≈ 6408.091683 thousand dollars $\approx \$6{,}408{,}091.68$

(e)   graphing:

Linear and Quadratic Functions

2.CR Cumulative Review

1. $d(P,Q) = \sqrt{(-1-4)^2 + (3-(-2))^2} = \sqrt{(-5)^2 + (5)^2} = \sqrt{25+25} = \sqrt{50} = 5\sqrt{2}$

3. $y = 3x^2 + 14x - 5$
    x-intercept(s): solve $3x^2 + 14x - 5 = 0$
    $(3x-1)(x+5) = 0 \Rightarrow x = \dfrac{1}{3}, x = -5$
    the x-intercepts are: $(-5,0); \left(\dfrac{1}{3}, 0\right)$

    y-intercept: let $x = 0$
    $\qquad\qquad y = 0^2 + 14(0) - 5 = -5$
    the y-intercept is: $(0,-5)$

5. $5x + 3 \geq 0$
    $5x \geq -3$

    $x \geq -\dfrac{3}{5}$

    $\left\{ x \middle| x \geq -\dfrac{3}{5} \right\}$ or $[-0.6, \infty)$

7. $(-1,4)$ and $(2,-2)$ are points on the line.
    $\text{Slope} = \dfrac{-2-4}{2-(-1)} = \dfrac{-6}{3} = -2$
    Using $y - y_1 = m(x - x_1)$
    $y - 4 = -2(x - (-1))$
    $y - 4 = -2(x + 1)$
    $\quad y = -2x - 2 + 4$
    $\quad y = -2x + 2$

9. $x^2 + y^2 - 4x + 8y - 5 = 0$
    $\qquad\quad x^2 - 4x + y^2 + 4y = 5$
    $(x^2 - 4x + 4) + (y^2 + 8y + 16) = 5 + 4 + 16$
    $\qquad\qquad (x-2)^2 + (y+4)^2 = 25$
    Center: $(2,-4)$
    Radius = 5

11. $f(x) = x^2 - 4x + 1$

(a) $f(2) = (2)^2 - 4(2) + 1 = 4 - 8 + 1 = -3$

(b) $f(x) + f(2) = x^2 - 4x + 1 + (2)^2 - 4(2) + 1 = x^2 - 4x + 1 + 4 - 8 + 1$
$$= x^2 - 4x - 2$$

(c) $f(-x) = (-x)^2 - 4(-x) + 1 = x^2 + 4x + 1$

(d) $-f(x) = -(x^2 - 4x + 1) = -x^2 + 4x - 1$

(e) $f(x + 2) = (x + 2)^2 - 4(x + 2) + 1 = x^2 + 4x + 4 - 4x - 8 + 1 = x^2 - 3$

(f) $\dfrac{f(x + h) - f(x)}{h}, h \neq 0$

$$\frac{f(x + h) - f(x)}{h} = \frac{(x + h)^2 - 4(x + h) + 1 - (x^2 - 4x + 1)}{h}$$

$$= \frac{x^2 + 2xh + h^2 - 4x - 4h + 1 - x^2 + 4x - 1}{h} = \frac{2xh + h^2 - 4h}{h}$$

$$= \frac{h(2x + h - 4)}{h} = 2x + h - 4$$

13.   Yes, since the graph passes the Vertical Line Test.

15. $f(x) = 3x^2 - 5x - 1$; $a = 3, b = -5, c = -1$. Since $a = 3 > 0$, the graph opens up.

The x-coordinate of the vertex is $x = \dfrac{-b}{2a} = \dfrac{-(-5)}{2(3)} = \dfrac{5}{6} = \dfrac{5}{6}$.

The y-coordinate of the vertex is $f\left(\dfrac{-b}{2a}\right) = f\left(\dfrac{5}{6}\right) = 3\left(\dfrac{5}{6}\right)^2 - 5\left(\dfrac{5}{6}\right) - 1 = \dfrac{25}{12} - \dfrac{25}{6} - 1 = -\dfrac{37}{12}$.

Thus, the vertex is $\left(\dfrac{5}{6}, -\dfrac{37}{12}\right)$.

The axis of symmetry is the line $x = \dfrac{5}{6}$.

The discriminant is:
$$b^2 - 4ac = (-5)^2 - 4(3)(-1) = 25 + 12 = 37 > 0.$$
So the graph has two x-intercepts.
The x-intercepts are found by solving:
$$3x^2 - 5x - 1 = 0$$
$$x = \frac{-b \pm \sqrt{b^2 - 4ac}}{2a} = \frac{5 \pm \sqrt{37}}{2(3)}$$

$$= \frac{5 \pm \sqrt{37}}{6} \approx \frac{5 \pm 6.08}{6}$$

The x-intercepts are −0.18 and 1.85.
The y-intercept is $f(0) = 3(0)^2 + 5 \cdot (0) - 1 = -1$.

Graphing utility:

17. (a) $x = -4p + 100 \Rightarrow p = -\dfrac{1}{4}x + 25$

$R(x) = x \cdot p = x\left(-\dfrac{1}{4}x + 25\right) = -\dfrac{1}{4}x^2 + 25x$

(b) $R(20) = -\dfrac{1}{4}(20)^2 + 25 \cdot 20 = \$400$

(c) $R(x) = -\dfrac{1}{4}x^2 + 25x$ $a = -4$, $b = 4000$, $c = 0$. Since $a = -\dfrac{1}{4} < 0$, the graph is a parabola that opens down, so the vertex is a maximum point.

The maximum revenue occurs at $x = \dfrac{-b}{2a} = \dfrac{-25}{2\left(-\dfrac{1}{4}\right)} = \dfrac{-25}{\left(-\dfrac{1}{2}\right)} = 50.$

$R(50) = -\dfrac{1}{4}(50)^2 + 25(50) = -625 + 1250 = \$625$.

Thus, the quantity sold should be 50 for maximum revenue. The maximum revenue is $625.

(d) When $x = 50$, $p = \left(-\dfrac{1}{4}\right)(50) + 25 = -12.5 + 25 = \$12.50$. Therefore, a selling price of $50 will yield the maximum revenue.

Functions and Their Graphs

3.1 Symmetry; Graphing Key Equations

1.

3.

5.

7.

9.

11. symmetric to the x-axis, y-axis and origin

13. symmetric to the y-axis

15. symmetric to the x-axis

17. not symmetric to x-axis, y-axis, or origin

19.

21.

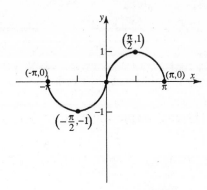

23. $x^2 = y + 5$

y - intercept : Let $x = 0$, then $y = -5$ $(0,-5)$

x - intercept : Let $y = 0$, then $x = \pm\sqrt{5}$ $\left(-\sqrt{5},0\right), \left(\sqrt{5},0\right)$

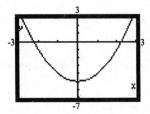

Test for symmetry:

x - axis :   Replace y by $-y$ so $x^2 = -y + 5$, which is not equivalent to $x^2 = y + 5$.

y - axis :   Replace x by $-x$ so $(-x)^2 = y$ or $x^2 = y + 5$, which is equivalent to $x^2 = y + 5$.

Origin :   Replace x by $-x$ and y by $-y$ so $(-x)^2 = -y + 5 \Rightarrow x^2 = -y + 5$,

which is not equivalent to $x^2 = y + 5$.

Therefore, the graph is symmetric with respect to the y - axis.

25. $y = 3x$

y - intercept: Let $x = 0$, then $y = 0$ $(0,0)$

x - intercept: Let $y = 0$, then $x = 0$ $(0,0)$

Test for symmetry:

x - axis :   Replace y by $-y$ so $-y = 3x$, which is not equivalent to $y = 3x$.

y - axis :   Replace x by $-x$ so $y = 3(-x)$ or $y = -3x$, which is not equivalent to $y = 3x$.

Origin :   Replace x by $-x$ and y by $-y$ so $-y = 3(-x) \Rightarrow y = 3x$,

which is equivalent to $y = 3x$.

Therefore, the graph is symmetric with respect to the origin.

27. $x^2 + y - 9 = 0$

y - intercept : Let $x = 0$, then $y = 9$ $(0,9)$

x - intercept : Let $y = 0$, then $x = \pm 3$ $(-3,0),(3,0)$

Test for symmetry:

x - axis :   Replace y by $-y$ so $x^2 + (-y) - 9 = 0 \implies x^2 - y - 9 = 0$,

which is not equivalent to $x^2 + y - 9 = 0$.

y - axis :   Replace x by $-x$ so $(-x)^2 + y - 9 = 0 \implies x^2 + y - 9 = 0$,

which is equivalent to $x^2 + y - 9 = 0$.

Origin :   Replace x by $-x$ and y by $-y$ so $(-x)^2 + (-y) - 9 = 0 \implies x^2 - y - 9 = 0$,

which is not equivalent to $x^2 + y - 9 = 0$.

Therefore, the graph is symmetric with respect to the y-axis.

29. $y = x^3 - 27$

y - intercept : Let $x = 0$, then $y = 0^3 - 27$

$$y = -27 \qquad (0, -27)$$

x - intercept : Let $y = 0$, then $0 = x^3 - 27$

$$x^3 = 27 \implies x = 3 \qquad (3, 0)$$

Test for symmetry:

x - axis :   Replace y by $-y$ so $-y = x^3 - 27$, which is not equivalent to $y = x^3 - 27$.

y - axis :   Replace x by $-x$ so $y = (-x)^3 - 27 \implies y = -x^3 - 27$,

which is not equivalent to $y = x^3 - 27$.

Origin :   Replace x by $-x$ and y by $-y$ so $-y = (-x)^3 - 27$

$$\implies y = x^3 + 27, \text{ which is not equivalent to } y = x^3 - 27.$$

Therefore, the graph is not symmetric to the x-axis, the y-axis, or the origin.

31. $y = x^2 - 3x - 4$

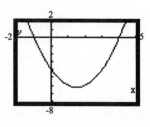

y - intercept: Let $x = 0$, then $y = 0^2 - 3(0) - 4$

$$y = -4 \qquad (0, -4)$$

x - intercept: Let $y = 0$, then $0 = x^2 - 3x - 4$

$$(x - 4)(x + 1) = 0$$

$$x = 4 \quad x = -1 \quad (4, 0), (-1, 0)$$

Test for symmetry:

x - axis :   Replace y by $-y$ so $-y = x^2 - 3x - 4$, which is not equivalent to $y = x^2 - 3x - 4$.

y - axis :   Replace x by $-x$ so $y = (-x)^2 - 3(-x) - 4 \implies y = x^2 + 3x - 4$,

which is not equivalent to $y = x^2 - 3x - 4$.

Origin :   Replace x by $-x$ and y by $-y$ so $-y = (-x)^2 - 3(-x) - 4$

$$\implies y = -x^2 - 3x + 4, \text{ which is not equivalent to } y = x^2 - 3x - 4.$$

Therefore, the graph is not symmetric to the x-axis, the y-axis, or the origin.

33. $y = \dfrac{3x}{x^2 + 9}$

y-intercept :   Let $x = 0$, then $y = \dfrac{0}{0 + 9}$

$$y = 0 \qquad (0, 0)$$

x-intercept :   Let $y = 0$, then $0 = \dfrac{3x}{x^2 + 9}$

$$3x = 0 \Rightarrow x = 0 \quad (0, 0)$$

Test for symmetry:

x-axis :   Replace y by $-y$ so $-y = \dfrac{3x}{x^2 + 9}$, which is not equivalent to $y = \dfrac{3x}{x^2 + 9}$.

y-axis :   Replace x by $-x$ so $y = \dfrac{3(-x)}{(-x)^2 + 9} \Rightarrow y = \dfrac{-3x}{x^2 + 9}$,

which is not equivalent to $y = \dfrac{3x}{x^2 + 9}$.

Origin :   Replace x by $-x$ and y by $-y$ so $-y = \dfrac{-3x}{(-x)^2 + 9}$

$\Rightarrow y = \dfrac{3x}{x^2 + 9}$, which is equivalent to $y = \dfrac{3x}{x^2 + 9}$.

Therefore, the graph is symmetric with respect to the origin.

35. $y = x^3$

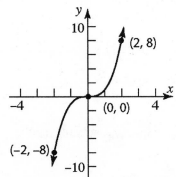

x-intercept : $(0,0)$;   y-intercept : $(0,0)$

37. $y = \sqrt{x}$

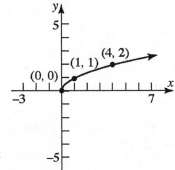

x-intercept : $(0,0)$;   y-intercept : $(0,0)$

Functions and Their Graphs

3.2 Properties of Functions

1. Yes

3. No It only increases on (5, 10).

5. f is increasing on the intervals: (–8, –2), (0, 2), (5, 10).

7. Yes. The local maximum at $x = 2$ is 10.

9. f has local maxima at $x = -2$ and $x = 2$. The local maxima are 6 and 10, respectively.

11. (a) Intercepts: (–2,0), (2,0), and (0,3).
    (b) Domain: $\{x \mid -4 \le x \le 4\}$; Range: $\{y \mid 0 \le y \le 3\}$.
    (c) Interval notation: Increasing: (–2, 0) and (2, 4); Decreasing: (–4, –2) and (0, 2).
        Inequality notation: Increasing: $-2 < x < 0$ and $2 < x < 4$
                    Decreasing: $-4 < x < -2$ and $0 < x < 2$
    (d) Since the graph is symmetric to the y-axis, the function is <u>even</u>.

13. (a) Intercepts: (0,1).
    (b) Domain: { Real Numbers }; Range: $\{y \mid y > 0\}$.
    (c) Interval notation: Increasing: $(-\infty, +\infty)$; Decreasing: never.
        Inequality notation: Increasing: $-\infty < x < +\infty$
                    Decreasing: never
    (d) Since the graph is not symmetric to the y-axis or the origin, the function is <u>neither</u> even nor odd.

15. (a) Intercepts: (–π,0), (0,0), and (π,0).
    (b) Domain: $\{x \mid -\pi \le x \le \pi\}$; Range: $\{y \mid -1 \le y \le 1\}$.
    (c) Interval notation: Increasing: $\left(-\dfrac{\pi}{2}, \dfrac{\pi}{2}\right)$; Decreasing: $\left(-\pi, -\dfrac{\pi}{2}\right)$ and $\left(\dfrac{\pi}{2}, \pi\right)$.

    Inequality notation: Increasing: $-\dfrac{\pi}{2} < x < \dfrac{\pi}{2}$

    Decreasing: $-\pi < x < -\dfrac{\pi}{2}$ and $\dfrac{\pi}{2} < x < \pi$
    (d) Since the graph is symmetric to the origin, the function is <u>odd</u>.

17. (a) Intercepts: $\left(0,\dfrac{1}{2}\right),\left(\dfrac{1}{2},0\right)$, and $\left(\dfrac{5}{2},0\right)$.

(b) Domain: $\{x\,|-3\le x\le 3\}$; Range: $\{y\,|-1\le y\le 2\}$.

(c) Interval notation: Increasing: $(2,3)$; Decreasing: $(-1,1)$;
Constant: $(-3,-1)$ and $(1,2)$.
Inequality notation: Increasing: $2<x<3$; Decreasing: $-1<x<1$;
Constant: $-3<x<-1$ and $1<x<2$.

(d) Since the graph is not symmetric to the y-axis or the origin, the function is <u>neither</u> even nor odd.

19. (a) Intercepts: $(0,2),(-2,0)$, and $(2,0)$.

(b) Domain: $\{x\,|-4\le x\le 4\}$; Range: $\{y\,|0\le y\le 2\}$.

(c) Interval notation: Increasing: $(-2,0)$ and $(2,4)$;
Decreasing: $(-4,-2)$ and $(0,2)$.
Inequality notation: Increasing: $-2<x<0$ and $2<x<4$;
Decreasing: $-4<x<-2$ and $0<x<2$.

(d) Since the graph is symmetric to the y-axis, the function is <u>even</u>.

21. (a) f has a local maximum of 3 at $x=0$.

(b) f has a local minimum of 0 at both $x=-2$ and $x=2$.

23. (a) f has a local maximum of 1 at $x=\dfrac{\pi}{2}$.

(b) f has a local minimum of -1 at $x=-\dfrac{\pi}{2}$.

25. $f(x)=5x$

(a) $\dfrac{f(x)-f(1)}{x-1}=\dfrac{5x-5}{x-1}=\dfrac{5(x-1)}{x-1}=5$

(b) $\dfrac{f(2)-f(1)}{2-1}=\dfrac{10-5}{2-1}=\dfrac{5}{1}=5$

(c) Slope $=5$; Containing $(1,5)$:
$y-5=5(x-1)$
$y-5=5x-5\Rightarrow y=5x$

27. $f(x)=1-3x$

(a) $\dfrac{f(x)-f(1)}{x-1}=\dfrac{1-3x-(-2)}{x-1}$
$=\dfrac{-3x+3}{x-1}=\dfrac{-3(x-1)}{x-1}=-3$

(b) $\dfrac{f(2)-f(1)}{2-1}=\dfrac{1-3(2)-(-2)}{2-1}=\dfrac{-3}{1}=-3$

(c) Slope $=-3$; Containing $(1,-2)$:
$y-(-2)=-3(x-1)$
$y+2=-3x+3\Rightarrow y=-3x+1$

29. $f(x) = x^2 - 2x$

(a) $\dfrac{f(x) - f(1)}{x-1} = \dfrac{x^2 - 2x - (-1)}{x-1}$

$= \dfrac{x^2 - 2x + 1}{x-1} = \dfrac{(x-1)^2}{x-1} = x - 1$

(b) $\dfrac{f(2) - f(1)}{2-1} = \dfrac{2^2 - 2(2) - (-1)}{2-1} = \dfrac{1}{1} = 1$

(c) Slope = 1; Containing $(1, -1)$:

$y - (-1) = 1(x-1)$

$y + 1 = 1x - 1 \Rightarrow y = x - 2$

31. $f(x) = x^3 - x$

(a) $\dfrac{f(x) - f(1)}{x-1} = \dfrac{x^3 - x - 0}{x-1} = \dfrac{x^3 - x}{x-1}$

$= \dfrac{x(x-1)(x+1)}{x-1} = x^2 + x$

(b) $\dfrac{f(2) - f(1)}{2-1} = \dfrac{2^3 - 2 - 0}{2-1} = \dfrac{6}{1} = 6$

(c) Slope = 6; Containing $(1, 0)$:

$y - 0 = 6(x-1) \Rightarrow y = 6x - 6$

33. $f(x) = \dfrac{2}{x+1}$

(a) $\dfrac{f(x) - f(1)}{x-1} = \dfrac{\left(\dfrac{2}{x+1} - 1\right)}{x-1} = \dfrac{\left(\dfrac{2-x-1}{x+1}\right)}{x-1}$

$= \dfrac{1-x}{(x-1)(x+1)} = \dfrac{-1}{x+1}$

(b) $\dfrac{f(2) - f(1)}{2-1} = \dfrac{\left(\dfrac{2}{2+1} - 1\right)}{2-1} = \dfrac{\left(-\dfrac{1}{3}\right)}{1} = -\dfrac{1}{3}$

(c) Slope $= -\dfrac{1}{3}$; Containing $(1, 1)$:

$y - 1 = -\dfrac{1}{3}(x-1)$

$y - 1 = -\dfrac{1}{3}x + \dfrac{1}{3} \Rightarrow y = -\dfrac{1}{3}x + \dfrac{4}{3}$

35. $f(x) = \sqrt{x}$

(a) $\dfrac{f(x) - f(1)}{x-1} = \dfrac{\sqrt{x} - 1}{x-1}$

(b) $\dfrac{f(2) - f(1)}{2-1} = \dfrac{\sqrt{2} - 1}{1} = \sqrt{2} - 1$

(c) Slope $= \sqrt{2} - 1$; Containing $(1, 1)$:

$y - 1 = \left(\sqrt{2} - 1\right)(x-1)$

$y - 1 = \left(\sqrt{2} - 1\right)x - \left(\sqrt{2} - 1\right)$

$y = \left(\sqrt{2} - 1\right)x - \sqrt{2} + 2$

37. $f(x) = 4x^3$
$$f(-x) = 4(-x)^3 = -4x^3$$
f is odd.

39. $g(x) = -3x^2 - 5$
$$g(-x) = -3(-x)^2 - 5 = -3x^2 - 5$$
g is even.

41. $F(x) = \sqrt[3]{x}$
$$F(-x) = \sqrt[3]{-x} = -\sqrt[3]{x}$$
F is odd.

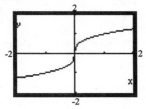

43. $f(x) = x + |x|$
$$f(-x) = -x + |-x| = -x + |x|$$
f is neither even nor odd.

45. $g(x) = \dfrac{1}{x^2}$
$$g(-x) = \frac{1}{(-x)^2} = \frac{1}{x^2}$$
g is even.

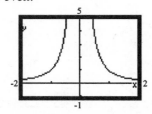

47. $h(x) = \dfrac{-x^3}{3x^2 - 9}$
$$h(-x) = \frac{-(-x)^3}{3(-x)^2 - 9} = \frac{x^3}{3x^2 - 9}$$
h is odd.

49. One at most because if f is increasing it could only cross the x-axis at most one time. It could not "turn" and cross it again or it would start to decrease.

51. $f(x) = x^3 - 3x + 2$ on the interval $(-2, 2)$
Use MAXIMUM and MINIMUM on the graph of $y_1 = x^3 - 3x + 2$.

local maximum at: $(-1, 4)$;   local minimum at: $(1, 0)$
f is increasing on: $(-2, -1) \cup (1, 2)$; f is decreasing on: $(-1, 1)$

53. $f(x) = x^5 - x^3$ on the interval $(-2,2)$

Use MAXIMUM and MINIMUM on the graph of $y_1 = x^5 - x^3$.

local maximum at: $(-0.78, 0.19)$;   local minimum at: $(0.78, -0.19)$

f is increasing on: $(-2, -0.78) \cup (0.78, 2)$; f is decreasing on: $(-0.78, 0.78)$

55. $f(x) = -0.2x^3 - 0.6x^2 + 4x - 6$ on the interval $(-6,4)$

Use MAXIMUM and MINIMUM on the graph of $y_1 = -0.2x^3 - 0.6x^2 + 4x - 6$.

local maximum at: $(1.77, -1.91)$;   local minimum at: $(-3.77, -18.89)$

f is increasing on: $(-3.77, 1.77)$; f is decreasing on: $(-6, -3.77) \cup (1.77, 4)$

57. $f(x) = 0.25x^4 + 0.3x^3 - 0.9x^2 + 3$ on the interval $(-3,2)$

Use MAXIMUM and MINIMUM on the graph of $y_1 = 0.25x^4 + 0.3x^3 - 0.9x^2 + 3$.

local maximum at: $(0,3)$; local minimum at: $(-1.86, 0.95)$, $(0.96, 2.65)$

f is increasing on: $(-1.86, 0) \cup (0.96, 2)$; f is decreasing on: $(-3, -1.86) \cup (0, 0.96)$

59. $f(x) = 2x + 5$

(a) $m_{sec} = \dfrac{f(x+h) - f(x)}{h} = \dfrac{2(x+h) + 5 - 2x - 5}{h} = \dfrac{2h}{h} = 2$

(b)   When $x = 1$,

$h = 0.5 \Rightarrow m_{sec} = 2$

$h = 0.1 \Rightarrow m_{sec} = 2$

$h = 0.01 \Rightarrow m_{sec} = 2$

as $h \to 0$, $m_{sec} \to 2$

(c)   Using point $(1, f(1)) = (1, 7)$ and slope $= 2$, we get the secant line:

$y - 7 = 2(x - 1) \Rightarrow y - 7 = 2x - 2 \Rightarrow y = 2x + 5$

(d)   Graphing:

61. $f(x) = x^2 + 2x$

(a) $m_{sec} = \dfrac{f(x+h) - f(x)}{h} = \dfrac{(x+h)^2 + 2(x+h) - (x^2 + 2x)}{h}$

$= \dfrac{x^2 + 2xh + h^2 + 2x + 2h - x^2 - 2x}{h} = \dfrac{2xh + h^2 + 2h}{h} = 2x + h + 2$

(b)   When $x = 1$,

$h = 0.5 \Rightarrow m_{sec} = 2 \cdot 1 + 0.5 + 2 = 4.5$

$h = 0.1 \Rightarrow m_{sec} = 2 \cdot 1 + 0.1 + 2 = 4.1$

$h = 0.01 \Rightarrow m_{sec} = 2 \cdot 1 + 0.01 + 2 = 4.01$

as $h \to 0$, $m_{sec} \to 2 \cdot 1 + 0 + 2 = 4$

(c)   Using point $(1, f(1)) = (1, 3)$ and slope = 4.01, we get the secant line:

$y - 3 = 4.01(x - 1) \Rightarrow y - 3 = 4.01x - 4.01 \Rightarrow y = 4.01x - 1.01$

(d)   Graphing:

63. $f(x) = 2x^2 - 3x + 1$

(a) $m_{sec} = \dfrac{f(x+h) - f(x)}{h} = \dfrac{2(x+h)^2 - 3(x+h) + 1 - (2x^2 - 3x + 1)}{h}$

$= \dfrac{2(x^2 + 2xh + h^2) - 3x - 3h + 1 - 2x^2 + 3x - 1}{h}$

$= \dfrac{2x^2 + 4xh + 2h^2 - 3x - 3h + 1 - 2x^2 + 3x - 1}{h}$

$= \dfrac{4xh + 2h^2 - 3h}{h} = 4x + 2h - 3$

(b)   When $x = 1$,

$h = 0.5 \Rightarrow m_{sec} = 4 \cdot 1 + 2(0.5) - 3 = 2$

$h = 0.1 \Rightarrow m_{sec} = 4 \cdot 1 + 2(0.1) - 3 = 1.2$

$h = 0.01 \Rightarrow m_{sec} = 4 \cdot 1 + 2(0.01) - 3 = 1.02$

as $h \to 0$, $m_{sec} \to 4 \cdot 1 + 2(0) - 3 = 1$

(c)   Using point $(1, f(1)) = (1, 0)$ and slope = 1.02, we get the secant line:

$y - 0 = 1.02(x - 1) \Rightarrow y = 1.02x - 1.02$

(d)　Graphing:

65.　　　$f(x) = \dfrac{1}{x}$

(a)

$$m_{sec} = \frac{f(x+h) - f(x)}{h} = \frac{\left(\dfrac{1}{x+h} - \dfrac{1}{x}\right)}{h}$$

$$= \frac{\left(\dfrac{x - (x+h)}{(x+h)x}\right)}{h} = \left(\frac{x - x - h}{(x+h)x}\right)\left(\frac{1}{h}\right) = \left(\frac{-h}{(x+h)x}\right)\left(\frac{1}{h}\right) = -\frac{1}{(x+h)x}$$

(b)　When $x = 1$,

$$h = 0.5 \Rightarrow m_{sec} = -\frac{1}{(1+0.5)(1)} = -\frac{1}{1.5} \approx -0.667$$

$$h = 0.1 \Rightarrow m_{sec} = -\frac{1}{(1+0.1)(1)} = -\frac{1}{1.1} \approx -0.909$$

$$h = 0.01 \Rightarrow m_{sec} = -\frac{1}{(1+0.01)(1)} = -\frac{1}{1.01} \approx -0.990$$

as $h \to 0$, $m_{sec} \to -\dfrac{1}{(1+0)(1)} = -\dfrac{1}{1} = -1$

(c)　Using point $(1, f(1)) = (1,1)$ and slope $= -0.990$, we get the secant line:

$y - 1 = -0.99(x - 1) \Rightarrow y - 1 = -0.99x + 0.99 \Rightarrow y = -0.99x + 1.99$

(d)　Graphing:

67.　Graphing: $V(x) = x(24 - 2x^2)$

Use MAXIMUM.
The volume is largest when $x = 4$ inches.

69. $s(t) = -16t^2 + 80t + 6$

    (a) Graphing:

    (b) The graph of $s(t) = -16t^2 + 80t + 6$ is a parabola that opens up since $a = -16 < 0$. The maximum value for s occurs at the vertex. That is when

$$t = \frac{-b}{2a} = \frac{-80}{(2)(-16)} = 2.5 \text{ seconds.}$$

    (c) The maximum height is $s(2.5) = -16(2.5)^2 + (80)(2.5) + 6 = -100 + 200 + 6 = 106$ feet.

71.   (a), (b), (e)

    (c) Average rate of change $= \dfrac{28000 - 0}{25 - 0} = \dfrac{28000}{25} = 1120$

    (d) For each additional bicycle sold between 0 and 25, the total revenue increases by \$1120.

    (f) Average rate of change $= \dfrac{64835 - 62360}{223 - 190} = \dfrac{2475}{33} = 75$

    (g) For each additional bicycle sold between 190 and 223, the total revenue increases by \$75.

73.   (a), (b), (e)

    (c) Average rate of change $= \dfrac{234 - 50}{2 - 0} = \dfrac{184}{2} = 92$

    (d) The population is increasing at a rate of 92 per day between day 0 and day 2.

    (f) Average rate of change $= \dfrac{1280 - 547}{6 - 4} = \dfrac{733}{2} = 366.5$

    (g) The population is increasing at a rate of 366.5 per day between day 4 and day 6.

    (h) As time passes, the average rate of change of the population is increasing.

Functions and Their Graphs

3.3   Library of Functions; Piecewise-Defined Functions

1. C   3.   E   5. B   7.   F

9.

11.

13.

15. (a) $f(-2) = (-2)^2 = 4$
    (b) $f(0) = 2$
    (c) $f(2) = 2(2) + 1 = 5$

17. (a) $f(1.2) = \text{int}(2(1.2)) = \text{int}(2.4) = 2$
    (b) $f(1.6) = \text{int}(2(1.6)) = \text{int}(3.2) = 3$
    (c) $f(-1.8) = \text{int}(2(-1.8))$
          $\qquad\quad = \text{int}(-3.6) = -4$

19. $f(x) = \begin{cases} 2x & \text{if } x \neq 0 \\ 1 & \text{if } x = 0 \end{cases}$

    (a)   Domain: {Real Numbers}
    (b)   x-intercept: none
          y-intercept: (0,1)
    (c)

    (d)   Range: $\{y \mid y \neq 0\}$
    (e)   graphing utility:

21. $f(x) = \begin{cases} -2x+3 & \text{if } x < 1 \\ 3x-2 & \text{if } x \geq 1 \end{cases}$

(a) Domain: {Real Numbers}
(b) x-intercept: none
     y-intercept: (0,3)
(c)

(d) Range: $\{y \mid y \geq 1\}$
(e) graphing utility:

23. $f(x) = \begin{cases} x+3 & \text{if } -2 \leq x < 1 \\ 5 & \text{if } x = 1 \\ -x+2 & \text{if } x > 1 \end{cases}$

(a) Domain: $\{x \mid x \geq -2\}$
(b) x-intercept: (2, 0)
     y-intercept: (0, 3)
(c)

(d) Range: $\{y \mid y < 4\} \cup \{5\}$
(e) graphing utility:

25. $f(x) = \begin{cases} 1+x & \text{if } x < 0 \\ x^2 & \text{if } x \geq 0 \end{cases}$

(a) Domain: {Real Numbers}
(b) x-intercept: (−1,0), (0,0)
     y-intercept: (0,0)
(c)

(d) Range: {Real Numbers}
(e) graphing utility:

157

27. $f(x) = \begin{cases} |x| & \text{if } -2 \le x < 0 \\ 1 & \text{if } x = 0 \\ x^3 & \text{if } x > 0 \end{cases}$

(d) Range: $\{y \mid y > 0\}$

(e) graphing utility:

(a) Domain: $\{x \mid x \ge -2\}$

(b) x-intercept: none
y-intercept: (0, 1)

(c)

29. $h(x) = 2 \operatorname{int}(x)$

(a) Domain: {Real Numbers}

(b) x-intercept: all ordered pairs
$(x, 0)$ when $0 \le x < 1$.

y-intercept: (0,0)

(c)

(d) Range: {Even Integers}

(e) graphing utility:

31. $f(x) = \begin{cases} -x & \text{if } -1 \le x \le 0 \\ \dfrac{1}{2}x & \text{if } 0 < x \le 2 \end{cases}$

33. $f(x) = \begin{cases} -x & \text{if } x \le 0 \\ -x + 2 & \text{if } 0 < x \le 2 \end{cases}$

35. (a) Let x represent the number of miles and C be the cost of transportation.

$$C(x) = \begin{cases} 0.50x & \text{if } 0 \le x \le 100 \\ 0.50(100) + 0.40(x - 100) & \text{if } 100 < x \le 400 \\ 0.50(100) + 0.40(300) + 0.25(x - 400) & \text{if } 400 < x \le 800 \\ 0.50(100) + 0.40(300) + 0.25(400) + 0(x - 800) & \text{if } 800 < x \le 960 \end{cases}$$

$$C(x) = \begin{cases} 0.50x & \text{if } 0 \le x \le 100 \\ 10 + 0.40x & \text{if } 100 < x \le 400 \\ 70 + 0.25x & \text{if } 400 < x \le 800 \\ 270 & \text{if } 800 < x \le 960 \end{cases}$$

Graphing:

(b)   For hauls between 100 and 400 miles the cost is: $C(x) = 10 + 0.40x$.

(c)   For hauls between 400 and 800 miles the cost is: $C(x) = 70 + 0.25x$.

37.   Let x = the amount of the bill in dollars. The minimum payment due is given by

$$f(x) = \begin{cases} x & \text{if } x < 10 \\ 10 & \text{if } 10 \le x < 500 \\ 30 & \text{if } 500 \le x < 1000 \\ 50 & \text{if } 1000 \le x < 1500 \\ 70 & \text{if } 1500 \le x \end{cases}$$

39.   For schedule X:

$$f(x) = \begin{cases} 0.15x & \text{if } 0 < x \le 27{,}050 \\ 4057.50 + 0.28(x - 27{,}050) & \text{if } 27{,}050 < x \le 65{,}550 \\ 14{,}837.50 + 0.31(x - 65{,}550) & \text{if } 65{,}550 < x \le 136{,}750 \\ 36{,}909.50 + 0.36(x - 136{,}750) & \text{if } 136{,}750 < x \le 297{,}300 \\ 94{,}707.50 + 0.396(x - 297{,}300) & \text{if } x > 297{,}300 \end{cases}$$

For Schedule Y-1:

$$f(x) = \begin{cases} 0.15x & \text{if } 0 < x \le 45{,}200 \\ 6{,}780.00 + 0.28(x - 45{,}200) & \text{if } 45{,}200 < x \le 109{,}250 \\ 24{,}714.00 + 0.31(x - 109{,}250) & \text{if } 109{,}250 < x \le 166{,}450 \\ 42{,}446.00 + 0.36(x - 166{,}450) & \text{if } 166{,}450 < x \le 297{,}300 \\ 89{,}552.00 + 0.396(x - 297{,}300) & \text{if } x > 297{,}300 \end{cases}$$

41.   (a)   Charge for 40 therms:
           $C = 6.45 + 0.2012(20) + 0.1117(20) + 0.3209(40) = \$25.54$

(b)   Charge for 202 therms:
           $C = 6.45 + 0.2012(20) + 0.1117(30) + 0.0374(152) + 0.3209(202) = \$84.33$

(c)   The monthly charge function:

$$C = \begin{cases} 6.45 + 0.2012x + 0.3209x & \text{for } 0 \le x \le 20 \\ 6.45 + 0.2012(20) + 0.1117(x-20) + 0.3209x & \text{for } 20 < x \le 50 \\ 6.45 + 0.2012(20) + 0.1117(30) + 0.0374(x-50) + 0.3209x & \text{for } x > 50 \end{cases}$$

$$= \begin{cases} 6.45 + 0.5221x & \text{for } 0 \le x \le 20 \\ 6.45 + 4.024 + 0.1117x - 2.234 + 0.3209x & \text{for } 20 < x \le 50 \\ 6.45 + 4.024 + 3.351 + 0.0374x - 1.87 + 0.3209x & \text{for } x > 50 \end{cases}$$

$$= \begin{cases} 6.45 + 0.5221x & \text{for } 0 \le x \le 20 \\ 8.24 + 0.4326x & \text{for } 20 < x \le 50 \\ 11.955 + 0.3583x & \text{for } x > 50 \end{cases}$$

(d)

43.   Each graph is that of $y = x^2$, but shifted vertically.

If $y = x^2 + k$, $k > 0$, the shift is up k units; if $y = x^2 + k$, $k < 0$, the shift is down $|k|$ units. The graph of $y = x^2 - 4$ is the same as the graph of $y = x^2$, but shifted down 4 units. The graph of $y = x^2 + 5$ is the graph of $y = x^2$, but shifted up 5 units.

45.   Each graph is that of $y = |x|$, but either compressed or stretched vertically.

If $y = k|x|$ and $k > 1$, the graph is stretched; if $y = k|x|$ and $0 < k < 1$, the graph is compressed. The graph of $y = \frac{1}{4}|x|$ is the same as the graph of $y = |x|$, but compressed. The graph of $y = 5|x|$ is the same as the graph of $y = |x|$, but stretched.

47.   The graph of $y = \sqrt{-x}$ is the reflection about the y-axis of the graph of $y = \sqrt{x}$.

The same type of reflection occurs when graphing $y = 2x + 1$ and $y = 2(-x) + 1$.

The conclusion is that the graph of $y = f(-x)$ is the reflection about the y-axis of the graph of $y = f(x)$.

49.   For the graph of $y = x^n$, n a positive even integer, as n increases, the graph of the function is narrower for $|x| > 1$ and flatter for $|x| < 1$.

51. $f(x) = \begin{cases} 1 & \text{if } x \text{ is rational} \\ 0 & \text{if } x \text{ is irrational} \end{cases}$ Domain = { all real numbers}   Range = $\{0,1\}$

y-intercept: $x = 0 \Rightarrow x$ is rational $\Rightarrow y = 1$, so the y-intercept is (0, 1).
x-intercept: $y = 0 \Rightarrow x$ is irrational, so the graph has infinitely many x-intercepts, namely, there is an x-intercept at each irrational value for x.
$f(-x) = 1 = f(x)$ when x is rational; $f(-x) = 0 = f(x)$ when x is irrational $\therefore f$ is even.
The graph of f consists of 2 infinite clusters of distinct points, extending horizontally in both directions.
One cluster is located 1 unit above the x-axis, and the other is located along the x-axis.

Functions and Their Graphs

3.4   Graphing Techniques; Transformations

1.   B   3.   H   5.   I   7.   L

9.   F   11.   G   13.   C   15.   B

17. $y = (x-4)^3$ 19. $y = x^3 + 4$ 21. $y = -x^3$ 23. $y = 4x^3$

25.   (1) $y = \sqrt{x} + 2$ 27.   (1) $y = -\sqrt{x}$
     (2) $y = -\left(\sqrt{x} + 2\right)$ (2) $y = -\sqrt{x} + 2$
     (3) $y = -\left(\sqrt{-x} + 2\right)$ (3) $y = -\sqrt{x+3} + 2$

29.   c   31.   c

33. $f(x) = x^2 - 1$ 35. $g(x) = x^3 + 1$
     Using the graph of $y = x^2$, vertically   Using the graph of $y = x^3$, vertically
     shift downward 1 unit.   shift upward 1 unit.

37. $h(x) = \sqrt{x-2}$ 39. $f(x) = (x-1)^3 + 2$
     Using the graph of $y = \sqrt{x}$, horizontally   Using the graph of $y = x^3$, horizontally
     shift to the right 2 units.   shift to the right 1 unit, then vertically
                                                    shift up 2 units.

41. $g(x) = 4\sqrt{x}$

Using the graph of $y = \sqrt{x}$, vertically stretch by a factor of 4.

43. $h(x) = \dfrac{1}{2x} = \left(\dfrac{1}{2}\right)\left(\dfrac{1}{x}\right)$

Using the graph of $y = \dfrac{1}{x}$, vertically compress by a factor of $\dfrac{1}{2}$.

45. $f(x) = -\dfrac{1}{x}$

Reflect the graph of $y = \dfrac{1}{x}$, about the x-axis.

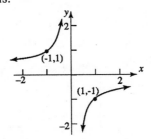

47. $g(x) = \left|-x\right|$

Reflect the graph of $y = |x|$, about the y-axis.

49. $h(x) = -x^3 + 2$

Reflect the graph of $y = x^3$ on the x-axis, vertically shift upward 2 units.

51. $f(x) = 2(x+1)^2 - 3$

Using the graph of $y = x^2$, horizontally shift to the left 1 unit, vertically stretch by a factor of 2, and vertically shift downward 3 units.

53. $g(x) = \sqrt{x-2} + 1$

Using the graph of $y = \sqrt{x}$, horizontally shift to the right 2 units and vertically shift upward 1 unit.

55. $h(x) = \sqrt{-x} - 2$

Reflect the graph of $y = \sqrt{x}$, about the y-axis and vertically shift downward 2 units.

57. $f(x) = -(x+1)^3 - 1$

Using the graph of $y = x^3$, horizontally shift to the left 1 units, reflect the graph on the x-axis, and vertically shift downward 1 unit.

59. $g(x) = 2\left|1 - x\right| = 2\left|-(-1+x)\right| = 2\left|x-1\right|$

Using the graph of $y = |x|$, horizontally shift to the right 1 unit, and vertically stretch by a factor or 2.

61. $h(x) = 2\,\text{int}(x-1)$

Using the graph of $y = \text{int}(x)$, horizontally shift to the right 1 unit, and vertically stretch by a factor of 2.

164

63. (a) $F(x) = f(x) + 3$
Shift up 3 units.

(b) $G(x) = f(x+2)$
Shift left 2 units.

(c) $P(x) = -f(x)$
Reflect about the x-axis.

(d) $H(x) = f(x+1) - 2$
Shift left 1 unit and shift down 2 units.

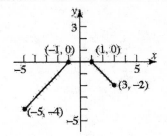

(e) $Q(x) = \dfrac{1}{2} f(x)$

Compress vertically by a factor of $\dfrac{1}{2}$.

(f) $g(x) = f(-x)$
Reflect about y-axis.

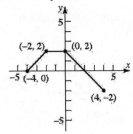

(g) $h(x) = f(2x)$
Compress horizontally by a factor of $\dfrac{1}{2}$.

65.   (a) $F(x) = f(x) + 3$
Shift up 3 units.

(b) $G(x) = f(x + 2)$
Shift left 2 units.

(c) $P(x) = -f(x)$
Reflect about the x-axis.

(d) $H(x) = f(x + 1) - 2$
Shift left 1 unit and shift down 2 units.

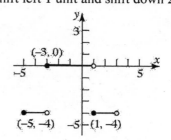

(e) $Q(x) = \dfrac{1}{2} f(x)$

Compress vertically by a factor of $\dfrac{1}{2}$.

(f) $g(x) = f(-x)$
Reflect about y-axis.

(g) $h(x) = f(2x)$

Compress horizontally by a factor of $\dfrac{1}{2}$.

67. (a) $F(x) = f(x) + 3$
Shift up 3 units.

(b) $G(x) = f(x + 2)$
Shift left 2 units.

(c) $P(x) = -f(x)$
Reflect about the x-axis.

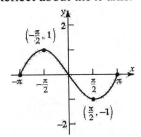

(d) $H(x) = f(x + 1) - 2$
Shift left 1 unit and shift down 2 units.

(e) $Q(x) = \dfrac{1}{2} f(x)$

Compress vertically by a factor of $\dfrac{1}{2}$.

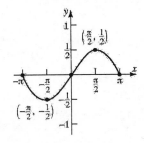

(f) $g(x) = f(-x)$
Reflect about y-axis.

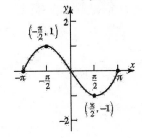

(g) $h(x) = f(2x)$

Compress horizontally by a factor of $\dfrac{1}{2}$.

167

69. (a) $y = |x+1|$

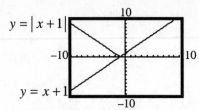

$y = x+1$

(b) $y = |4-x^2|$

$y = 4-x^2$

(c) $y = |x^3+x|$

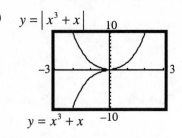

$y = x^3+x$

(d) Any part of the graph of $y = f(x)$ that lies below the x-axis is reflected about the x-axis to obtain the graph of $y = |f(x)|$.

71. (a) $y = |f(x)|$

(b) $y = f(|x|)$

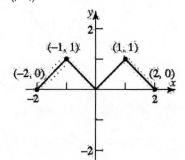

73. $f(x) = x^2 + 2x$

$f(x) = (x^2 + 2x + 1) - 1$

$f(x) = (x+1)^2 - 1$

Using $f(x) = x^2$, shift left 1 unit and shift down 1 unit.

75. $f(x) = x^2 - 8x + 1$

$f(x) = (x^2 - 8x + 16) + 1 - 16$

$f(x) = (x-4)^2 - 15$

Using $f(x) = x^2$, shift right 4 units and shift down 15 units.

77. $f(x) = x^2 + x + 1$

$$f(x) = \left(x^2 + x + \frac{1}{4}\right) + 1 - \frac{1}{4}$$

$$f(x) = \left(x + \frac{1}{2}\right)^2 + \frac{3}{4}$$

Using $f(x) = x^2$, shift left $\dfrac{1}{2}$ unit and

shift up $\dfrac{3}{4}$ unit.

79. $y = (x - c)^2$

If $c = 0$, $y = x^2$.

If $c = 3$, $y = (x - 3)^2$; shift right 3 units.

If $c = -2$, $y = (x + 2)^2$; shift left 2 units.

81. $F = \dfrac{9}{5}C + 32$

$F = \dfrac{9}{5}(K - 273) + 32$

Shift the graph 273 units to the right.

83. (a)

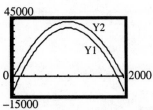

(b) Select the 10% tax since the profits are higher.

(c) The graph of Y1 is obtained by shifting the graph of $p(x)$ vertically down 10,000. The graph of Y2 is obtained by multiplying the y-coordinate of the graph of $p(x)$ by 0.9. Thus, Y2 is the graph of $p(x)$ vertically compressed by a factor of 0.9.

(d) Select the 10% tax since the graph of $Y1 = 0.9p(x) \geq Y2 = -0.05x^2 + 100x - 6800$ for all x in the domain.

Functions and Their Graphs

3.5 Operations on Functions; Composite Functions

1. $f(x) = 3x + 4$ $g(x) = 2x - 3$
    (a) $(f + g)(x) = 3x + 4 + 2x - 3 = 5x + 1$ The domain is all real numbers.
    (b) $(f - g)(x) = (3x + 4) - (2x - 3) = 3x + 4 - 2x + 3 = x + 7$
         The domain is all real numbers.
    (c) $(f \cdot g)(x) = (3x + 4)(2x - 3) = 6x^2 - 9x + 8x - 12 = 6x^2 - x - 12$
         The domain is all real numbers.
    (d) $\left(\dfrac{f}{g}\right)(x) = \dfrac{3x + 4}{2x - 3}$ The domain is all real numbers except $\dfrac{3}{2}$.

3. $f(x) = x - 1$ $g(x) = 2x^2$
    (a) $(f + g)(x) = x - 1 + 2x^2 = 2x^2 + x - 1$ The domain is all real numbers.
    (b) $(f - g)(x) = (x - 1) - (2x^2) = x - 1 - 2x^2 = -2x^2 + x - 1$
         The domain is all real numbers.
    (c) $(f \cdot g)(x) = (x - 1)(2x^2) = 2x^3 - 2x^2$ The domain is all real numbers.
    (d) $\left(\dfrac{f}{g}\right)(x) = \dfrac{x - 1}{2x^2}$ The domain is all real numbers except 0.

5. $f(x) = \sqrt{x}$ $g(x) = 3x - 5$
    (a) $(f + g)(x) = \sqrt{x} + 3x - 5$ The domain is $\{x \mid x \geq 0\}$.
    (b) $(f - g)(x) = \sqrt{x} - (3x - 5) = \sqrt{x} - 3x + 5$ The domain is $\{x \mid x \geq 0\}$.
    (c) $(f \cdot g)(x) = \sqrt{x}(3x - 5) = 3x\sqrt{x} - 5\sqrt{x}$ The domain is $\{x \mid x \geq 0\}$.
    (d) $\left(\dfrac{f}{g}\right)(x) = \dfrac{\sqrt{x}}{3x - 5}$ The domain is $\left\{x \mid x \geq 0 \text{ and } x \neq \dfrac{5}{3}\right\}$.

7. $f(x) = 1 + \dfrac{1}{x}$ $g(x) = \dfrac{1}{x}$
    (a) $(f + g)(x) = 1 + \dfrac{1}{x} + \dfrac{1}{x} = 1 + \dfrac{2}{x}$ The domain is $\{x \mid x \neq 0\}$.
    (b) $(f - g)(x) = 1 + \dfrac{1}{x} - \dfrac{1}{x} = 1$ The domain is $\{x \mid x \neq 0\}$.
    (c) $(f \cdot g)(x) = \left(1 + \dfrac{1}{x}\right)\dfrac{1}{x} = \dfrac{1}{x} + \dfrac{1}{x^2}$ The domain is $\{x \mid x \neq 0\}$.
    (d) $\left(\dfrac{f}{g}\right)(x) = \dfrac{\left(1 + \dfrac{1}{x}\right)}{\left(\dfrac{1}{x}\right)} = \dfrac{\left(\dfrac{x + 1}{x}\right)}{\left(\dfrac{1}{x}\right)} = \dfrac{x + 1}{x} \cdot \dfrac{x}{1} = x + 1$ The domain is $\{x \mid x \neq 0\}$.

9. $f(x) = \dfrac{2x+3}{3x-2}$ $g(x) = \dfrac{4x}{3x-2}$

(a) $(f+g)(x) = \dfrac{2x+3}{3x-2} + \dfrac{4x}{3x-2} = \dfrac{2x+3+4x}{3x-2} = \dfrac{6x+3}{3x-2}$

The domain is $\left\{ x \mid x \neq \dfrac{2}{3} \right\}$.

(b) $(f-g)(x) = \dfrac{2x+3}{3x-2} - \dfrac{4x}{3x-2} = \dfrac{2x+3-4x}{3x-2} = \dfrac{-2x+3}{3x-2}$

The domain is $\left\{ x \mid x \neq \dfrac{2}{3} \right\}$.

(c) $(f \cdot g)(x) = \left(\dfrac{2x+3}{3x-2} \right)\left(\dfrac{4x}{3x-2} \right) = \dfrac{8x^2+12x}{(3x-2)^2}$

The domain is $\left\{ x \mid x \neq \dfrac{2}{3} \right\}$.

(d) $\left(\dfrac{f}{g} \right)(x) = \dfrac{\left(\dfrac{2x+3}{3x-2} \right)}{\left(\dfrac{4x}{3x-2} \right)} = \dfrac{2x+3}{3x-2} \cdot \dfrac{3x-2}{4x} = \dfrac{2x+3}{4x}$

The domain is $\left\{ x \mid x \neq \dfrac{2}{3} \text{ and } x \neq 0 \right\}$.

11. $f(x) = 3x+1$ $(f+g)(x) = 6 - \dfrac{1}{2}x$

$6 - \dfrac{1}{2}x = 3x+1+g(x) \Rightarrow 5 - \dfrac{7}{2}x = g(x) \Rightarrow g(x) = 5 - \dfrac{7}{2}x$

13. $f(x) = 2x$ $g(x) = 3x^2+1$

(a) $(f \circ g)(4) = f(g(4)) = f\left(3(4)^2+1\right) = f(49) = 2(49) = 98$

(b) $(g \circ f)(2) = g(f(2)) = g(2 \cdot 2) = g(4) = 3(4)^2+1 = 48+1 = 49$

(c) $(f \circ f)(1) = f(f(1)) = f(2(1)) = f(2) = 2(2) = 4$

(d) $(g \circ g)(0) = g(g(0)) = g\left(3(0)^2+1\right) = g(1) = 3(1)^2+1 = 4$

15. $f(x) = 4x^2-3$ $g(x) = 3 - \dfrac{1}{2}x^2$

(a) $(f \circ g)(4) = f(g(4)) = f\left(3 - \dfrac{1}{2}(4)^2\right) = f(-5) = 4(-5)^2-3 = 97$

(b) $(g \circ f)(2) = g(f(2)) = g(4(2)^2-3) = g(13) = 3 - \dfrac{1}{2}(13)^2 = 3 - \dfrac{169}{2} = -\dfrac{163}{2}$

(c) $(f \circ f)(1) = f(f(1)) = f(4(1)^2-3) = f(1) = 4(1)^2-3 = 1$

(d) $(g \circ g)(0) = g(g(0)) = g\left(3 - \dfrac{1}{2}(0)^2\right) = g(3) = 3 - \dfrac{1}{2}(3)^2 = 3 - \dfrac{9}{2} = -\dfrac{3}{2}$

17. $f(x) = \sqrt{x}$ $g(x) = 2x$

(a) $(f \circ g)(4) = f(g(4)) = f(2(4)) = f(8) = \sqrt{8} = 2\sqrt{2}$

(b) $(g \circ f)(2) = g(f(2)) = g\left(\sqrt{2}\right) = 2\sqrt{2}$

(c) $(f \circ f)(1) = f(f(1)) = f\left(\sqrt{1}\right) = f(1) = \sqrt{1} = 1$

(d) $(g \circ g)(0) = g(g(0)) = g(2(0)) = g(0) = 2(0) = 0$

19. $f(x) = |x|$ $g(x) = \dfrac{1}{x^2 + 1}$

(a) $(f \circ g)(4) = f(g(4)) = f\left(\dfrac{1}{4^2 + 1}\right) = f\left(\dfrac{1}{17}\right) = \left|\dfrac{1}{17}\right| = \dfrac{1}{17}$

(b) $(g \circ f)(2) = g(f(2)) = g(|2|) = g(2) = \dfrac{1}{2^2 + 1} = \dfrac{1}{5}$

(c) $(f \circ f)(1) = f(f(1)) = f(|1|) = f(1) = |1| = 1$

(d) $(g \circ g)(0) = g(g(0)) = g\left(\dfrac{1}{0^2 + 1}\right) = g(1) = \dfrac{1}{1^2 + 1} = \dfrac{1}{2}$

21. $f(x) = \dfrac{3}{x + 1}$ $g(x) = \sqrt[3]{x}$

(a) $(f \circ g)(4) = f(g(4)) = f\left(\sqrt[3]{4}\right) = \dfrac{3}{\sqrt[3]{4} + 1}$

(b) $(g \circ f)(2) = g(f(2)) = g\left(\dfrac{3}{2 + 1}\right) = g\left(\dfrac{3}{3}\right) = \sqrt[3]{1} = 1$

(c) $(f \circ f)(1) = f(f(1)) = f\left(\dfrac{3}{1 + 1}\right) = f\left(\dfrac{3}{2}\right) = \dfrac{3}{\left(\dfrac{3}{2}\right) + 1} = \dfrac{3}{\left(\dfrac{5}{2}\right)} = \dfrac{6}{5}$

(d) $(g \circ g)(0) = g(g(0)) = g\left(\sqrt[3]{0}\right) = g(0) = \sqrt[3]{0} = 0$

23. The domain of g is $\{x \mid x \neq 0\}$. The domain of f is $\{x \mid x \neq 1\}$.
Thus, $g(x) \neq 1$, so we solve:
$g(x) = 1$

$\dfrac{2}{x} = 1$ Thus, $x \neq 2$; so the domain of $f \circ g$ is $\{x \mid x \neq 0, x \neq 2\}$.

$x = 2$

25. The domain of g is $\{x \mid x \neq 0\}$. The domain of f is $\{x \mid x \neq 1\}$.
Thus, $g(x) \neq 1$, so we solve:
$g(x) = 1$

$-\dfrac{4}{x} = 1$ Thus, $x \neq -4$; so the domain of $f \circ g$ is $\{x \mid x \neq -4, x \neq 0\}$.

$x = -4$

27. The domain of g is {Real Numbers}. The domain of f is $\{x \mid x \geq 0\}$.
Thus, $g(x) \geq 0$, so we solve:

$$g(x) \geq 0$$
$$2x + 3 \geq 0$$
$$x \geq -\frac{3}{2}$$

Thus, the domain of $f \circ g$ is $\left\{x \mid x \geq -\frac{3}{2}\right\}$.

29. The domain of g is $\{x \mid x \geq 1\}$. The domain of f is {Real Numbers}.
Thus, the domain of $f \circ g$ is $\{x \mid x \geq 1\}$.

31. $f(x) = 2x + 3 \qquad g(x) = 3x$
The domain of f is all real numbers. The domain of g is all real numbers.
(a) $(f \circ g)(x) = f(g(x)) = f(3x) = 2(3x) + 3 = 6x + 3$ Domain: All real numbers.
(b) $(g \circ f)(x) = g(f(x)) = g(2x + 3) = 3(2x + 3) = 6x + 9$
    Domain: All real numbers.
(c) $(f \circ f)(x) = f(f(x)) = f(2x + 3) = 2(2x + 3) + 3 = 4x + 6 + 3 = 4x + 9$
    Domain: All real numbers.
(d) $(g \circ g)(x) = g(g(x)) = g(3x) = 3(3x) = 9x$ Domain: All real numbers.

33. $f(x) = 3x + 1 \qquad g(x) = x^2$
The domain of f is all real numbers. The domain of g is all real numbers.
(a) $(f \circ g)(x) = f(g(x)) = f(x^2) = 3x^2 + 1$ Domain: All real numbers.
(b) $(g \circ f)(x) = g(f(x)) = g(3x + 1) = (3x + 1)^2 = 9x^2 + 6x + 1$
    Domain: All real numbers.
(c) $(f \circ f)(x) = f(f(x)) = f(3x + 1) = 3(3x + 1) + 1 = 9x + 3 + 1 = 9x + 4$
    Domain: All real numbers.
(d) $(g \circ g)(x) = g(g(x)) = g(x^2) = (x^2)^2 = x^4$ Domain: All real numbers.

35. $f(x) = x^2 \qquad g(x) = x^2 + 4$
The domain of f is all real numbers. The domain of g is all real numbers.
(a) $(f \circ g)(x) = f(g(x)) = f(x^2 + 4) = (x^2 + 4)^2 = x^4 + 8x^2 + 16$
    Domain: All real numbers.
(b) $(g \circ f)(x) = g(f(x)) = g(x^2) = (x^2)^2 + 4 = x^4 + 4$ Domain: All real numbers.
(c) $(f \circ f)(x) = f(f(x)) = f(x^2) = (x^2)^2 = x^4$ Domain: All real numbers.
(d) $(g \circ g)(x) = g(g(x)) = g(x^2 + 4) = (x^2 + 4)^2 + 4 = x^4 + 8x^2 + 16 + 4$
    $= x^4 + 8x^2 + 20$ Domain: All real numbers.

37. $f(x) = \dfrac{3}{x - 1} \qquad g(x) = \dfrac{2}{x}$ The domain of f is $\{x \mid x \neq 1\}$.
The domain of g is $\{x \mid x \neq 0\}$.

(a) $(f \circ g)(x) = f(g(x)) = f\left(\dfrac{2}{x}\right) = \dfrac{3}{\left(\dfrac{2}{x}-1\right)} = \dfrac{3}{\left(\dfrac{2-x}{x}\right)} = \dfrac{3x}{2-x}$

Domain of $f \circ g$ is $\{x \mid x \ne 0,\ x \ne 2\}$.

(b) $(g \circ f)(x) = g(f(x)) = g\left(\dfrac{3}{x-1}\right) = \dfrac{2}{\left(\dfrac{3}{x-1}\right)} = \dfrac{2(x-1)}{3}$

Domain of $g \circ f$ is $\{x \mid x \ne 1\}$

(c) $(f \circ f)(x) = f(f(x)) = f\left(\dfrac{3}{x-1}\right) = \dfrac{3}{\left(\dfrac{3}{x-1}-1\right)} = \dfrac{3}{\left(\dfrac{3-(x-1)}{x-1}\right)} = \dfrac{3(x-1)}{4-x}$

Domain of $f \circ f$ is $\{x \mid x \ne 1,\ x \ne 4\}$.

(d) $(g \circ g)(x) = g(g(x)) = g\left(\dfrac{2}{x}\right) = \dfrac{2}{\left(\dfrac{2}{x}\right)} = \dfrac{2x}{2} = x$

Domain of $g \circ g$ is $\{x \mid x \ne 0\}$.

39. $f(x) = \dfrac{x}{x-1}$ $g(x) = -\dfrac{4}{x}$

The domain of f is $\{x \mid x \ne 1\}$. The domain of g is $\{x \mid x \ne 0\}$.

(a) $(f \circ g)(x) = f(g(x)) = f\left(-\dfrac{4}{x}\right) = \dfrac{\left(-\dfrac{4}{x}\right)}{\left(-\dfrac{4}{x}-1\right)} = \dfrac{\left(-\dfrac{4}{x}\right)}{\left(\dfrac{-4-x}{x}\right)} = \dfrac{-4}{-4-x} = \dfrac{4}{4+x}$

Domain of $f \circ g$ is $\{x \mid x \ne -4,\ x \ne 0\}$.

(b) $(g \circ f)(x) = g(f(x)) = g\left(\dfrac{x}{x-1}\right) = -\dfrac{4}{\left(\dfrac{x}{x-1}\right)} = \dfrac{-4(x-1)}{x}$

Domain of $g \circ f$ is $\{x \mid x \ne 0,\ x \ne 1\}$.

(c) $(f \circ f)(x) = f(f(x)) = f\left(\dfrac{x}{x-1}\right) = \dfrac{\left(\dfrac{x}{x-1}\right)}{\left(\dfrac{x}{x-1}-1\right)} = \dfrac{\left(\dfrac{x}{x-1}\right)}{\left(\dfrac{x-(x-1)}{x-1}\right)} = \dfrac{x}{1} = x$

Domain of $f \circ f$ is $\{x \mid x \ne 1\}$.

(d) $(g \circ g)(x) = g(g(x)) = g\left(\dfrac{-4}{x}\right) = -\dfrac{4}{\left(-\dfrac{4}{x}\right)} = \dfrac{-4x}{-4} = x$

Domain of $g \circ g$ is $\{x \mid x \ne 0\}$.

41. $f(x) = \sqrt{x}$ $g(x) = 2x + 3$
The domain of f is $\{x \mid x \geq 0\}$. The domain of g is {Real Numbers}.

(a) $(f \circ g)(x) = f(g(x)) = f(2x + 3) = \sqrt{2x + 3}$ Domain of $f \circ g$ is $\left\{ x \mid x \geq -\dfrac{3}{2} \right\}$.

(b) $(g \circ f)(x) = g(f(x)) = g(\sqrt{x}) = 2\sqrt{x} + 3$ Domain of $g \circ f$ is $\{x \mid x \geq 0\}$.

(c) $(f \circ f)(x) = f(f(x)) = f(\sqrt{x}) = \sqrt{\sqrt{x}} = x^{1/4} = \sqrt[4]{x}$
     Domain of $f \circ f$ is $\{x \mid x \geq 0\}$.

(d) $(g \circ g)(x) = g(g(x)) = g(2x + 3) = 2(2x + 3) + 3 = 4x + 6 + 3 = 4x + 9$
     Domain of $g \circ g$ is {Real Numbers}.

43. $f(x) = x^2 + 1$ $g(x) = \sqrt{x - 1}$
The domain of f is {Real Numbers}. The domain of g is $\{x \mid x \geq 1\}$.

(a) $(f \circ g)(x) = f(g(x)) = f(\sqrt{x - 1}) = (\sqrt{x - 1})^2 + 1 = x - 1 + 1 = x$
     Domain of $f \circ g$ is $\{x \mid x \geq 1\}$.

(b) $(g \circ f)(x) = g(f(x)) = g(x^2 + 1) = \sqrt{x^2 + 1 - 1} = \sqrt{x^2} = |x|$
     Domain of $g \circ f$ {Real Numbers}.

(c) $(f \circ f)(x) = f(f(x)) = f(x^2 + 1) = (x^2 + 1)^2 + 1 = x^4 + 2x^2 + 1 + 1 = x^4 + 2x^2 + 2$
     Domain of $f \circ f$ is {Real Numbers}.

(d) $(g \circ g)(x) = g(g(x)) = g(\sqrt{x - 1}) = \sqrt{\sqrt{x - 1} - 1}$ Domain of $g \circ g$ is $\{x \mid x \geq 2\}$.

45. $f(x) = ax + b$ $g(x) = cx + d$ The domain of f is {Real Numbers}.
           The domain of g is {Real Numbers}.

(a) $(f \circ g)(x) = f(g(x)) = f(cx + d) = a(cx + d) + b = acx + ad + b$
     Domain of $f \circ g$ is {Real Numbers}.

(b) $(g \circ f)(x) = g(f(x)) = g(ax + b) = c(ax + b) + d = acx + bc + d$
     Domain of $g \circ f$ is {Real Numbers}.

(c) $(f \circ f)(x) = f(f(x)) = f(ax + b) = a(ax + b) + b = a^2 x + ab + b$
     Domain of $f \circ f$ is {Real Numbers}.

(d) $(g \circ g)(x) = g(g(x)) = g(cx + d) = c(cx + d) + d = c^2 x + cd + d$
     Domain of $g \circ g$ is {Real Numbers}.

47. $(f \circ g)(x) = f(g(x)) = f\left(\dfrac{1}{2}x\right) = 2\left(\dfrac{1}{2}x\right) = x$

     $(g \circ f)(x) = g(f(x)) = g(2x) = \dfrac{1}{2}(2x) = x$

49. $(f \circ g)(x) = f(g(x)) = f(\sqrt[3]{x}) = (\sqrt[3]{x})^3 = x$
     $(g \circ f)(x) = g(f(x)) = g(x^3) = \sqrt[3]{x^3} = x$

51. $(f \circ g)(x) = f(g(x)) = f\left(\frac{1}{2}(x+6)\right) = 2\left(\frac{1}{2}(x+6)\right) - 6 = x + 6 - 6 = x$

$(g \circ f)(x) = g(f(x)) = g(2x-6) = \frac{1}{2}((2x-6)+6) = \frac{1}{2}(2x) = x$

53. $(f \circ g)(x) = f(g(x)) = f\left(\frac{1}{a}(x-b)\right) = a\left(\frac{1}{a}(x-b)\right) + b = x - b + b = x$

$(g \circ f)(x) = g(f(x)) = g(ax+b) = \frac{1}{a}((ax+b)-b) = \frac{1}{a}(ax) = x$

55. $H(x) = (2x+3)^4$ $\qquad$ $f(x) = x^4, \quad g(x) = 2x+3$

57. $H(x) = \sqrt{x^2+1}$ $\qquad$ $f(x) = \sqrt{x}, \quad g(x) = x^2+1$

59. $H(x) = |2x+1|$ $\qquad$ $f(x) = |x|, \quad g(x) = 2x+1$

61. $f(x) = 2x^3 - 3x^2 + 4x - 1$ $\qquad$ $g(x) = 2$
$(f \circ g)(x) = f(g(x)) = f(2) = 2(2)^3 - 3(2)^2 + 4(2) - 1 = 16 - 12 + 8 - 1 = 11$
$(g \circ f)(x) = g(f(x)) = g(2x^3 - 3x^2 + 4x - 1) = 2$

63. $f(x) = 2x^2 + 5$ $\qquad$ $g(x) = 3x + a$
$(f \circ g)(x) = f(g(x)) = f(3x+a) = 2(3x+a)^2 + 5$
When $x = 0$, $(f \circ g)(0) = 23$
Solving: $2(3 \cdot 0 + a)^2 + 5 = 23 \Rightarrow 2a^2 + 5 = 23 \Rightarrow 2a^2 = 18 \Rightarrow a^2 = 9 \Rightarrow a = -3 \text{ or } 3$

65. $S(r) = 4\pi r^2$ $\qquad$ $r(t) = \frac{2}{3}t^3, \ t \geq 0$

$S(r(t)) = S\left(\frac{2}{3}t^3\right) = 4\pi\left(\frac{2}{3}t^3\right)^2 = 4\pi\left(\frac{4}{9}t^6\right) = \frac{16}{9}\pi t^6$

67. $N(t) = 100t - 5t^2, \ 0 \leq t \leq 10$ $\qquad$ $C(N) = 15000 + 8000N$
$C(N(t)) = C(100t - 5t^2) = 15000 + 8000(100t - 5t^2)$
$\qquad\qquad = 15,000 + 800,000t - 40,000t^2$

69. $p = -\frac{1}{4}x + 100$ $\qquad$ $0 \leq x \leq 400$

$\frac{1}{4}x = 100 - p \Rightarrow x = 4(100 - p)$

$C = \frac{\sqrt{x}}{25} + 600 = \frac{\sqrt{4(100-p)}}{25} + 600 = \frac{2\sqrt{100-p}}{25} + 600, \quad 0 \leq p \leq 100$

71. $V = \pi r^2 h$ $\qquad$ $h = 2r$ $\qquad$ $\Rightarrow V(r) = \pi r^2 (2r) = 2\pi r^3$

73. $R(x) = \left(\dfrac{L}{P}\right)(x) = \dfrac{L(x)}{P(x)}$

75. $H(x) = (P \cdot I)(x) = P(x) \cdot I(x)$

77. $f(x) =$ number of Euros bought for x dollars; $g(x) =$ number of Yen bought for x Euros
    (a) $f(x) = 1.136235x$
    (b) $g(x) = 109.846x$
    (c) $g(f(x)) = 109.846(1.136235x) = 124.8108698x$
    (d) $g(f(1000)) = 124.8108698(1000) = 124810.8698$ Yen

79. Given that f is odd and g is even, we know that
    $f(-x) = -f(x)$ and $g(-x) = g(x)$ for all x in the domain of f and g respectively.
    The composite function $f \circ g = f(g(x))$ has the following property:
    $f(g(-x)) = f(g(x))$ since g is even, $\therefore f \circ g$ is even
    The composite function $g \circ f = g(f(x))$ has the following property:
    $g(f(-x)) = g(-f(x))$ since f is odd
    $= g(f(x))$ since g is even, $\therefore g \circ f$ is even

Chapter 3

Functions and Their Graphs

3.6 Mathematical Models; Constructing Functions

1. (a) The distance d from P to the origin is $d = \sqrt{x^2 + y^2}$. Since P is a point on the graph of $y = x^2 - 8$, we have:
$$d(x) = \sqrt{x^2 + (x^2 - 8)^2} = \sqrt{x^4 - 15x^2 + 64}$$

(b) $d(0) = \sqrt{0^4 - 15(0)^2 + 64} = \sqrt{64} = 8$

(c) $d(1) = \sqrt{(1)^4 - 15(1)^2 + 64} = \sqrt{1 - 15 + 64} = \sqrt{50} = 5\sqrt{2} \approx 7.07$

(d) Graphing:

(e) d is smallest when $x \approx -2.74$ and when $x \approx 2.74$.

3. (a) The distance d from P to the point $(1, 0)$ is $d = \sqrt{(x - 1)^2 + y^2}$. Since P is a point on the graph of $y = \sqrt{x}$, we have: $d(x) = \sqrt{(x - 1)^2 + \left(\sqrt{x}\right)^2} = \sqrt{x^2 - x + 1}$

(b) Graphing: (c) d is smallest when x is 0.50.

5. By definition, a triangle has area $A = \dfrac{1}{2}bh, b =$ base, $h =$ height. Because a vertex of the triangle is at the origin, we know that $b = x$ and $h = y$. Expressing the area of the triangle as a function of x, we have: $A(x) = \dfrac{1}{2}xy = \dfrac{1}{2}x\left(x^3\right) = \dfrac{1}{2}x^4$.

7. (a) $A(x) = xy = x(16 - x^2) = -x^3 + 16x$ (b)   Domain: $\{x \mid 0 < x < 4\}$

   (c) Graphing: The area is largest when x is approximately 2.31.

9. (a) $A(x) = (2x)(2y) = 4x(4 - x^2)^{1/2}$ (b) $p(x) = 2(2x) + 2(2y) = 4x + 4(4 - x^2)^{1/2}$

   (c) Graphing: (d) Graphing:

   The area is largest when x is   The perimeter is largest when x is
   approximately 1.41.   approximately 1.41.

11. (a) $C =$ circumference, $A =$ area, $r =$ radius, $x =$ side of square

   $$C = 2\pi r = 10 - 4x \quad \Rightarrow \quad r = \frac{5 - 2x}{\pi}$$

   $$A(x) = x^2 + \pi r^2 = x^2 + \pi\left(\frac{5 - 2x}{\pi}\right)^2 = x^2 + \frac{25 - 20x + 4x^2}{\pi}$$

   (b) Since the lengths must be positive, we have:
   $$10 - 4x > 0 \quad \text{and} \ x > 0$$
   $$-4x > -10 \Rightarrow x < 2.5 \ \text{and} \ x > 0$$
   Domain: $\{x \mid 0 < x < 2.5\}$

   (c) Graphing: The area is smallest when x is approximately 1.40 meters.

13. (a) Since the wire of length x is bent into a circle, the circumference is x.
   Therefore, $C(x) = x$.

   (b) Since $C = x = 2\pi r$, $r = \dfrac{x}{2\pi}$.

   $$A(x) = \pi r^2 = \pi\left(\frac{x}{2\pi}\right)^2 = \frac{x^2}{4\pi}.$$

15. (a)　A = area, r = radius;　diameter = $2r$
$$A(r) = (2r)(r) = 2r^2$$
　(b)　p = perimeter
$$p(r) = 2(2r) + 2r = 6r$$

17.　Area of the equilateral triangle $= \dfrac{1}{2}x \cdot \dfrac{\sqrt{3}}{2}x = \dfrac{\sqrt{3}}{4}x^2$

Area of $\dfrac{1}{3}$ of the equilateral triangle $= \dfrac{1}{2}x\sqrt{r^2 - \left(\dfrac{x}{2}\right)^2} = \dfrac{1}{2}x\sqrt{r^2 - \dfrac{x^2}{4}} = \dfrac{1}{3} \cdot \dfrac{\sqrt{3}}{4}x^2$

Solving for r^2:

$$\dfrac{1}{2}x\sqrt{r^2 - \dfrac{x^2}{4}} = \dfrac{1}{3} \cdot \dfrac{\sqrt{3}}{4}x^2 \Rightarrow \sqrt{r^2 - \dfrac{x^2}{4}} = \dfrac{2}{x} \cdot \dfrac{\sqrt{3}}{12}x^2$$

$$\sqrt{r^2 - \dfrac{x^2}{4}} = \dfrac{\sqrt{3}}{6}x \Rightarrow r^2 - \dfrac{x^2}{4} = \dfrac{3}{36}x^2 \Rightarrow r^2 = \dfrac{x^2}{3}$$

Area inside the circle, but outside the triangle:

$$A(x) = \pi r^2 - \dfrac{\sqrt{3}}{4}x^2 = \pi\dfrac{x^2}{3} - \dfrac{\sqrt{3}}{4}x^2 = \left(\dfrac{\pi}{3} - \dfrac{\sqrt{3}}{4}\right)x^2$$

19. (a)　The total cost of installing the cable along the road is $10x$. If cable is installed x miles along the road, there are $5 - x$ miles left from the road to the house and where the cable ends.

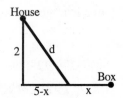

$$d = \sqrt{(5-x)^2 + 2^2} = \sqrt{25 - 10x + x^2 + 4}$$
$$= \sqrt{x^2 - 10x + 29}$$

The total cost of installing the cable is:

$$C(x) = 100x + 140\sqrt{x^2 - 10x + 29}$$

Domain: $\{x \mid 0 < x < 5\}$

(b)　$C(1) = 100(1) + 140\sqrt{1^2 - 10(1) + 29} = 100 + 140\sqrt{20} \approx 100 + 626.10 = \$726.10$

(c)　$C(3) = 100(3) + 140\sqrt{3^2 - 10(3) + 29} = 300 + 140\sqrt{8} \approx 300 + 396.00 = \$696.00$

(d)　

(e)　

The table indicates that $x = 2.93$ results in the least cost.

(f)　Using MINIMUM, the graph indicates that $x = 2.96$ results in the least cost.

21.　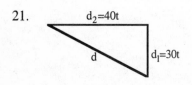

$$d^2 = d_1^2 + d_2^2$$
$$d^2 = (30t)^2 + (40t)^2$$
$$d(t) = \sqrt{900t^2 + 1600t^2}$$
$$d(t) = \sqrt{2500t^2} = 50t$$

23. (a)   length $= 24 - 2x$; width $= 24 - 2x$; height $= x$
        $V(x) = x(24 - 2x)(24 - 2x) = x(24 - 2x)^2$
    (b) $V(3) = 3(24 - 2(3))^2 = 3(18)^2 = 3(324) = 972$ cu. in.
    (c) $V(10) = 10(24 - 2(10))^2 = 10(4)^2 = 10(16) = 160$ cu. in.
    (d)

The volume is largest when $x = 4$ inches.

25. $r =$ radius of cylinder, $h =$ height of cylinder, $V =$ volume of cylinder

$$r^2 + \left(\frac{h}{2}\right)^2 = R^2 \Rightarrow r^2 + \frac{h^2}{4} = R^2$$

$$r^2 = R^2 - \frac{h^2}{4} \Rightarrow r^2 = \frac{4R^2 - h^2}{4}$$

$$V = \pi r^2 h \Rightarrow V(h) = \pi \left(\frac{4R^2 - h^2}{4}\right) h = \frac{\pi}{4}\left(4R^2 h - h^3\right)$$

Functions and Their Graphs

3.R Chapter Review

1.   (a)   Domain: $\left\{ x \mid -4 \le x \le 4 \right\}$ Range: $\left\{ y \mid -3 \le y \le 1 \right\}$

       (b)   Increasing: $(-4,-1) \cup (3,4)$;   Decreasing: $(-1, 3)$;   Constant: $(-5,-1)$

       (c)   Local minimum $(3,-3)$; Local maximum $(-1,1)$

       (d)   The graph is not symmetric to the x-axis, the y-axis or the origin.

       (e)   The function is neither even nor odd.

       (f)   x-intercepts: $-2, 0, 4$;   y-intercept: 0

3.   Test for symmetry:

       x - axis :   Replace y by $-y$ so $2x = 3(-y)^2 \implies 2x = 3y^2$, which is

                      equivalent to $2x = 3y^2$.

       y - axis :   Replace x by $-x$ so $2(-x) = 3y^2 \implies -2x = 3y^2$,

                      which is not equivalent to $2x = 3y^2$.

       Origin :   Replace x by $-x$ and y by $-y$ so $2(-x) = 3(-y)^2$

                      $\implies -2x = 3y^2$, which is not equivalent to $2x = 3y^2$.

     Therefore, the graph is symmetric with respect to the x - axis.

5.   Test for symmetry:

       x - axis :   Replace y by $-y$ so $x^2 + 4(-y)^2 = 16 \implies x^2 + 4y^2 = 16$,

                      which is equivalent to $x^2 + 4y^2 = 16$.

       y - axis :   Replace x by $-x$ so $(-x)^2 + 4y^2 = 16 \implies x^2 + 4y^2 = 16$,

                      which is equivalent to $x^2 + 4y^2 = 16$.

       Origin :   Replace x by $-x$ and y by $-y$ so $(-x)^2 + 4(-y)^2 = 16 \implies x^2 + 4y^2 = 16$,

                      which is equivalent to $x^2 + 4y^2 = 16$.

     Therefore, the graph is symmetric with respect to the x-axis, the y-axis and the origin.

7.   Test for symmetry:

x-axis: Replace y by $-y$ so $-y = x^4 + 2x^2 + 1$,

which is not equivalent to $y = x^4 + 2x^2 + 1$.

y-axis: Replace x by $-x$ so $y = (-x)^4 + 2(-x)^2 + 1 \implies y = x^4 + 2x^2 + 1$,

which is equivalent to $y = x^4 + 2x^2 + 1$.

Origin: Replace x by $-x$ and y by $-y$ so $-y = (-x)^4 + 2(-x)^2 + 1 \implies -y = x^4 + 2x^2 + 1$,

which is not equivalent to $y = x^4 + 2x^2 + 1$.

Therefore, the graph is symmetric with respect to the y-axis.

9.   Test for symmetry:

x-axis: Replace y by $-y$ so $x^2 + x + (-y)^2 + 2(-y) = 0 \implies x^2 + x + y^2 - 2y = 0$,

which is not equivalent to $x^2 + x + y^2 + 2y = 0$.

y-axis: Replace x by $-x$ so $(-x)^2 + (-x) + y^2 + 2y = 0 \implies x^2 - x + y^2 + 2y = 0$,

which is not equivalent to $x^2 + x + y^2 + 2y = 0$.

Origin: Replace x by $-x$ and y by $-y$ so $(-x)^2 + (-x) + (-y)^2 + 2(-y) = 0$

$\implies x^2 - x + y^2 - 2y = 0$, which is not equivalent to $x^2 + x + y^2 + 2y = 0$.

Therefore, the graph is not symmetric to the x-axis, the y-axis, or the origin.

11.

13. $f(x) = \begin{cases} 3x & \text{if } -2 < x \le 1 \\ x+1 & \text{if } x > 1 \end{cases}$

(a)   Domain: $\{ x \mid x > -2 \}$

(b)   x-intercept: $(0,0)$
      y-intercept: $(0,0)$

(c)

(d)   Range: $\{ y > -6 \}$

(e)   Graphing utility:

15. $f(x) = \begin{cases} x & \text{if } -4 \le x < 0 \\ 1 & \text{if } x = 0 \\ 3x & \text{if } x > 0 \end{cases}$

(a)　Domain: $\{x \mid x \ge -4\}$

(b)　x-intercept: none

y-intercept: (0, 1)

(c)

(d)　Range: $\{y \mid y \ge -4,\ y \ne 0\}$

(e)　Graphing utility:

17.　$f(x) = 2 - 5x$

$$\frac{f(x) - f(2)}{x - 2} = \frac{2 - 5x - (-8)}{x - 2} = \frac{-5x + 10}{x - 2} = \frac{-5(x - 2)}{x - 2} = -5$$

19.　$f(x) = 3x - 4x^2$

$$\frac{f(x) - f(2)}{x - 2} = \frac{3x - 4x^2 - (-10)}{x - 2} = \frac{-4x^2 + 3x + 10}{x - 2}$$
$$= \frac{-(4x^2 - 3x - 10)}{x - 2} = \frac{-(4x + 5)(x - 2)}{x - 2} = -4x - 5$$

21.　$f(x) = x^3 - 4x$

$$f(-x) = (-x)^3 - 4(-x) = -x^3 + 4x = -\left(x^3 - 4x\right) = -f(x) \Rightarrow f \text{ is odd.}$$

23.　$h(x) = \dfrac{1}{x^4} + \dfrac{1}{x^2} + 1$

$$h(-x) = \frac{1}{(-x)^4} + \frac{1}{(-x)^2} + 1 = \frac{1}{x^4} + \frac{1}{x^2} + 1 = h(x) \Rightarrow h \text{ is even.}$$

25.　$G(x) = 1 - x + x^3$

$$G(-x) = 1 - (-x) + (-x)^3 = 1 + x - x^3 \ne -G(x) \ne G(x)$$

G is neither even nor odd.

27.　$f(x) = \dfrac{x}{1 + x^2}$

$$f(-x) = \frac{-x}{1 + (-x)^2} = \frac{-x}{1 + x^2} = -f(x) \Rightarrow f \text{ is odd.}$$

29. $F(x) = |x| - 4$

Using the graph of $y = |x|$, vertically shift the graph downward 4 units.

Intercepts: (–4,0), (4,0), (0,–4)
Domain: {Real Numbers}
Range: $\{y \mid y \geq -4\}$

31. $g(x) = -2|x|$

Reflect the graph of $y = |x|$ about the x-axis and vertically stretch the graph by a factor of 2.

Intercepts: (0,0)
Domain: {Real Numbers}
Range: $\{y \mid y \leq 0\}$

33. $h(x) = \sqrt{x - 1}$

Using the graph of $y = \sqrt{x}$, horizontally shift the graph to the right 1 unit.

Intercepts: (1,0)
Domain: $\{x \mid x \geq 1\}$
Range: $\{y \mid y \geq 0\}$

35. $f(x) = \sqrt{1 - x} = \sqrt{-1(x - 1)}$

Reflect the graph of $y = \sqrt{x}$ about the y-axis and horizontally shift the graph to the right 1 unit..

Intercepts: (1,0), (0,1)
Domain: $\{x \mid x \leq 1\}$
Range: $\{y \mid y \geq 0\}$

37. $h(x) = (x-1)^2 + 2$

Using the graph of $y = x^2$, horizontally shift the graph to the right 1 unit and vertically shift the graph up 2 units.

Intercepts: $(0,3)$
Domain: {Real Numbers}
Range: $\{y \mid y \geq 2\}$

39. $g(x) = 3(x-1)^3 + 1$

Using the graph of $y = x^3$, horizontally shift the graph to the right 1 unit, vertically stretch the graph by a factor of 3, and vertically shift the graph up 1 unit.

Intercepts: $(0,-2)$, $\left(1 - \dfrac{\sqrt[3]{3}}{3}, 0\right)$

Domain: {Real Numbers}
Range: {Real Numbers}

41. $f(x) = 2x^3 - 5x + 1$ on the interval $(-3,3)$

Use MAXIMUM and MINIMUM on the graph of $y_1 = 2x^3 - 5x + 1$.

local maximum at: $(-0.91, 4.04)$;   local minimum at: $(0.91, -2.04)$
f is increasing on: $(-3, -0.91) \cup (0.91, 3)$; f is decreasing on: $(-0.91, 0.91)$

43. $f(x) = 2x^4 - 5x^3 + 2x + 1$ on the interval $(-2,3)$

Use MAXIMUM and MINIMUM on the graph of $y_1 = 2x^4 - 5x^3 + 2x + 1$.

local maximum at: $(0.41, 1.53)$; local minimum at: $(-0.34, 0.54)$, $(1.80, -3.56)$
f is increasing on: $(-0.34, 0.41) \cup (1.80, 3)$;
f is decreasing on: $(-2, -0.34) \cup (0.41, 1.80)$

45. $f(x) = 2 - x \quad g(x) = 3x + 1$

(a) $(f + g)(x) = f(x) + g(x) = 2 - x + 3x + 1 = 2x + 3$, Domain: {Real Numbers}

(b) $(f - g)(x) = f(x) - g(x) = 2 - x - (3x + 1) = 2 - x - 3x - 1 = -4x + 1$
     Domain: {Real Numbers}

(c) $(f \cdot g)(x) = f(x) \cdot g(x) = (2 - x)(3x + 1) = 6x + 2 - 3x^2 - x = -3x^2 + 5x + 2$
     Domain: {Real Numbers}

(d) $\left(\dfrac{f}{g}\right)(x) = \dfrac{f(x)}{g(x)} = \dfrac{2 - x}{3x + 1}$, Domain: $\left\{x \,\middle|\, x \neq -\dfrac{1}{3}\right\}$

47. $f(x) = 3x^2 + x + 1 \qquad g(x) = 3x$

(a) $(f + g)(x) = f(x) + g(x) = 3x^2 + x + 1 + 3x = 3x^2 + 4x + 1$
     Domain: {Real Numbers}

(b) $(f - g)(x) = f(x) - g(x) = 3x^2 + x + 1 - 3x = 3x^2 - 2x + 1$
     Domain: {Real Numbers}

(c) $(f \cdot g)(x) = f(x) \cdot g(x) = (3x^2 + x + 1)(3x) = 9x^3 + 3x^2 + 3x$
     Domain: {Real Numbers}

(d) $\left(\dfrac{f}{g}\right)(x) = \dfrac{f(x)}{g(x)} = \dfrac{3x^2 + x + 1}{3x}$, Domain: $\{x \,|\, x \neq 0\}$

49. $f(x) = \dfrac{x + 1}{x - 1} \qquad g(x) = \dfrac{1}{x}$

(a) $(f + g)(x) = f(x) + g(x) = \dfrac{x + 1}{x - 1} + \dfrac{1}{x} = \dfrac{x(x + 1) + 1(x - 1)}{x(x - 1)} = \dfrac{x^2 + x + x - 1}{x(x - 1)}$
     $$= \dfrac{x^2 + 2x - 1}{x(x - 1)}$$

     Domain: $\{x \,|\, x \neq 0, x \neq 1\}$

(b) $(f - g)(x) = f(x) - g(x) = \dfrac{x + 1}{x - 1} - \dfrac{1}{x} = \dfrac{x(x + 1) - 1(x - 1)}{x(x - 1)} = \dfrac{x^2 + x - x + 1}{x(x - 1)}$
     $$= \dfrac{x^2 + 1}{x(x - 1)}$$

     Domain: $\{x \,|\, x \neq 0, x \neq 1\}$

(c) $(f \cdot g)(x) = f(x) \cdot g(x) = \left(\dfrac{x + 1}{x - 1}\right)\left(\dfrac{1}{x}\right) = \dfrac{x + 1}{x(x - 1)}$

     Domain: $\{x \,|\, x \neq 0, x \neq 1\}$

(d) $\left(\dfrac{f}{g}\right)(x) = \dfrac{f(x)}{g(x)} = \dfrac{\left(\dfrac{x + 1}{x - 1}\right)}{\left(\dfrac{1}{x}\right)} = \left(\dfrac{x + 1}{x - 1}\right)\left(\dfrac{x}{1}\right) = \dfrac{x^2 + x}{x - 1}$

     Domain: $\{x \,|\, x \neq 0, x \neq 1\}$

51. $f(x) = 3x - 5$ $g(x) = 1 - 2x^2$
   (a) $(f \circ g)(2) = f(g(2)) = f(1 - 2(2)^2) = f(-7) = 3(-7) - 5 = -26$
   (b) $(g \circ f)(-2) = g(f(-2)) = g(3(-2) - 5) = g(-11) = 1 - 2(-11)^2 = -241$
   (c) $(f \circ f)(4) = f(f(4)) = f(3(4) - 5) = f(7) = 3(7) - 5 = 16$
   (d) $(g \circ g)(-1) = g(g(-1)) = g(1 - 2(-1)^2) = g(-1) = 1 - 2(-1)^2 = -1$

53. $f(x) = \sqrt{x + 2}$ $g(x) = 2x^2 + 1$
   (a) $(f \circ g)(2) = f(g(2)) = f(2(2)^2 + 1) = f(9) = \sqrt{9 + 2} = \sqrt{11}$
   (b) $(g \circ f)(-2) = g(f(-2)) = g(\sqrt{-2 + 2}) = g(0) = 2(0)^2 + 1 = 1$
   (c) $(f \circ f)(4) = f(f(4)) = f(\sqrt{4 + 2}) = f(\sqrt{6}) = \sqrt{\sqrt{6} + 2}$
   (d) $(g \circ g)(-1) = g(g(-1)) = g(2(-1)^2 + 1) = g(3) = 2(3)^2 + 1 = 19$

55. $f(x) = \dfrac{1}{x^2 + 4}$ $g(x) = 3x - 2$
   (a) $(f \circ g)(2) = f(g(2)) = f(3(2) - 2) = f(4) = \dfrac{1}{4^2 + 4} = \dfrac{1}{20}$
   (b) $(g \circ f)(-2) = g(f(-2)) = g\left(\dfrac{1}{(-2)^2 + 4}\right) = g\left(\dfrac{1}{8}\right) = 3\left(\dfrac{1}{8}\right) - 2 = \dfrac{-13}{8}$
   (c) $(f \circ f)(4) = f(f(4)) = f\left(\dfrac{1}{4^2 + 4}\right) = f\left(\dfrac{1}{20}\right) = \dfrac{1}{\left(\dfrac{1}{20}\right)^2 + 4} = \dfrac{1}{\left(\dfrac{1601}{400}\right)} = \dfrac{400}{1601}$
   (d) $(g \circ g)(-1) = g(g(-1)) = g(3(-1) - 2) = g(-5) = 3(-5) - 2 = -17$

57. $f(x) = 2 - x$ $g(x) = 3x + 1$
   The domain of f is all real numbers. The domain of g is all real numbers.
   (a) $(f \circ g)(x) = f(g(x)) = f(3x + 1) = 2 - (3x + 1) = 2 - 3x - 1 = 1 - 3x$
          Domain: All real numbers.
   (b) $(g \circ f)(x) = g(f(x)) = g(2 - x) = 3(2 - x) + 1 = 6 - 3x + 1 = 7 - 3x$
          Domain: All real numbers.
   (c) $(f \circ f)(x) = f(f(x)) = f(2 - x) = 2 - (2 - x) = 2 - 2 + x = x$
          Domain: All real numbers.
   (d) $(g \circ g)(x) = g(g(x)) = g(3x + 1) = 3(3x + 1) + 1 = 9x + 3 + 1 = 9x + 4$
          Domain: All real numbers.

59. $f(x) = 3x^2 + x + 1$ $g(x) = |3x|$
   The domain of f is all real numbers. The domain of g is all real numbers.
   (a) $(f \circ g)(x) = f(g(x)) = f(|3x|) = 3(|3x|)^2 + (|3x|) + 1 = 27x^2 + 3|x| + 1$
          Domain: All real numbers.
   (b) $(g \circ f)(x) = g(f(x)) = g(3x^2 + x + 1) = |3(3x^2 + x + 1)| = |9x^2 + 3x + 3|$
          Domain: All real numbers.

(c) $(f \circ f)(x) = f(f(x)) = f\left(3x^2 + x + 1\right) = 3\left(3x^2 + x + 1\right)^2 + \left(3x^2 + x + 1\right) + 1$

$\quad = 3\left(9x^4 + 6x^3 + 7x^2 + 2x + 1\right) + 3x^2 + x + 1 + 1$

$\quad = 27x^4 + 18x^3 + 24x^2 + 7x + 5$

Domain: All real numbers.

(d) $(g \circ g)(x) = g(g(x)) = g\left(|3x|\right) = \left|3\,|3x|\right| = 9|x|$

Domain: All real numbers.

61. $f(x) = \dfrac{x+1}{x-1} \qquad g(x) = \dfrac{1}{x}$

The domain of f is $\{x \mid x \neq 1\}$. The domain of g is $\{x \mid x \neq 0\}$.

(a) $(f \circ g)(x) = f\left(g(x)\right) = f\left(\dfrac{1}{x}\right) = \dfrac{\left(\dfrac{1}{x}+1\right)}{\left(\dfrac{1}{x}-1\right)} = \dfrac{\left(\dfrac{1+x}{x}\right)}{\left(\dfrac{1-x}{x}\right)} = \left(\dfrac{1+x}{x}\right)\left(\dfrac{x}{1-x}\right) = \left(\dfrac{1+x}{1-x}\right)$

Domain of $f \circ g$ is $\{x \mid x \neq 0,\ x \neq 1\}$.

(b) $(g \circ f)(x) = g\left(f(x)\right) = g\left(\dfrac{x+1}{x-1}\right) = \dfrac{1}{\left(\dfrac{x+1}{x-1}\right)} = \left(\dfrac{x-1}{x+1}\right)$

Domain of $g \circ f$ is $\{x \mid x \neq -1,\ x \neq 1\}$.

(c) $(f \circ f)(x) = f\left(f(x)\right) = f\left(\dfrac{x+1}{x-1}\right) = \dfrac{\left(\dfrac{x+1}{x-1}+1\right)}{\left(\dfrac{x+1}{x-1}-1\right)} = \dfrac{\left(\dfrac{x+1+1(x-1)}{x-1}\right)}{\left(\dfrac{x+1-1(x-1)}{x-1}\right)}$

$\quad = \dfrac{\left(\dfrac{x+1+x-1}{x-1}\right)}{\left(\dfrac{x+1-x+1}{x-1}\right)} = \dfrac{\left(\dfrac{2x}{x-1}\right)}{\left(\dfrac{2}{x-1}\right)} = \left(\dfrac{2x}{x-1}\right)\left(\dfrac{x-1}{2}\right) = x$

Domain of $f \circ f$ is $\{x \mid x \neq 1\}$.

(d) $(g \circ g)(x) = g\left(g(x)\right) = g\left(\dfrac{1}{x}\right) = \dfrac{1}{\left(\dfrac{1}{x}\right)} = x$, Domain of $g \circ g$ is $\{x \mid x \neq 0\}$.

63. (a) $y = f(-x)$
       Reflect about the y-axis.

(b) $y = -f(x)$
       Reflect about the x-axis.

(c) $y = f(x + 2)$

Horizontally shift left 2 units.

(d) $y = f(x) + 2$

Vertically shift up 2 units.

(e) $y = 2f(x)$

Vertical stretch by a factor of 2.

(f) $y = f(3x)$

Horizontal compression by $\dfrac{1}{3}$.

65.

$$d(P,Q) = \sqrt{(x-3)^2 + (x-1)^2}$$
$$\rightarrow d^2(x) = (x-3)^2 + (x-1)^2 = x^2 - 6x + 9 + x^2 - 2x + 1$$
$$\therefore d^2(x) = 2x^2 - 8x + 10$$

Since $d^2(x) = 2x^2 - 8x + 10$ is a quadratic function with $a = 2 > 0,$ the vertex corresponds to the minimum value for the function.

The vertex occurs at $x = -\dfrac{b}{2a} = -\dfrac{-8}{2(2)} = 2.$ Therefore the point Q on the line $y = x$ will be closest to the point $P = (3,1)$ when $Q = (2,2).$

67. The area function is: $A(x) = x(10 - x^2) = -x^3 + 10x$
     Use MAXIMUM on the graph of $y_1 = -x^3 + 10x$.

The maximum area is:

$$A(1.83) = -(1.83)^3 + 10(1.83) \approx 12.17 \text{ square units.}$$

69. $S = 4\pi r^2 \rightarrow r = \sqrt{\dfrac{S}{4\pi}}$ $V(S) = \dfrac{4}{3}\pi r^3 = \dfrac{4\pi}{3}\left(\sqrt{\dfrac{S}{4\pi}}\right)^3 = \dfrac{4\pi}{3} \cdot \dfrac{S}{4\pi}\sqrt{\dfrac{S}{4\pi}} = \dfrac{S}{6}\sqrt{\dfrac{S}{\pi}}$

$V(2S) = \dfrac{2S}{6}\sqrt{\dfrac{2S}{\pi}} = 2\sqrt{2}\left(\dfrac{S}{6}\sqrt{\dfrac{S}{\pi}}\right) \Rightarrow$ The volume is $2\sqrt{2}$ times as large.

Functions and Their Graphs

3.CR Cumulative Review

1. $x^3 - 6x^2 + 8x = 0$
$x(x^2 - 6x + 8) = 0$
$x(x-4)(x-2) = 0$
$x = 0$ or $x = 4$ or $x = 2$

3. $x^2 + 4x + y^2 - 2y - 4 = 0$
$(x^2 + 4x + 4) + (y^2 - 2y + 1) = 4 + 4 + 1$
$\qquad (x+2)^2 + (y-1)^2 = 9$
Center: $(-2,1)$
Radius $= 3$

5. Perpendicular to $3x - 2y = 7 \Rightarrow y = \dfrac{3}{2}x - \dfrac{7}{2}$;

Slope of perpendicular $= -\dfrac{2}{3}$

Containing $(1,5)$

$y - y_1 = m(x - x_1) \Rightarrow y - 5 = -\dfrac{2}{3}(x-1)$

$y - 5 = -\dfrac{2}{3}x + \dfrac{2}{3} \Rightarrow y = -\dfrac{2}{3}x + \dfrac{17}{3}$

7. $f(x) = x^2 + 5x - 2$

   (a) $f(3) = 3^2 + 5 \cdot 3 - 2 = 9 + 15 - 2 = 22$

   (b) $f(-x) = (-x)^2 + 5(-x) - 2 = x^2 - 5x - 2$

   (c) $-f(x) = -(x^2 + 5x - 2) = -x^2 - 5x + 2$

   (d) $f(3x) = (3x)^2 + 5(3x) - 2 = 9x^2 + 15x - 2$

   (e) $\dfrac{f(x+h) - f(x)}{h} = \dfrac{(x+h)^2 + 5(x+h) - 2 - (x^2 + 5x - 2)}{h}$

   $= \dfrac{x^2 + 2xh + h^2 + 5x + 5h - 2 - x^2 - 5x + 2}{h} = \dfrac{2xh + h^2 + 5h}{h} = 2x + h + 5$

9. $f(x) = -3x + 7$

11. $f(x) = x^2 + 3x + 1$

$$\text{avg rate of change of } f \atop \text{from 1 to } x = \frac{f(x) - f(1)}{x - 1}$$

$$= \frac{x^2 + 3x + 1 - (1^2 + 3 \cdot 1 + 1)}{x - 1}$$

$$= \frac{x^2 + 3x + 1 - 5}{x - 1} = \frac{x^2 + 3x - 4}{x - 1} \quad \text{when}$$

$$= \frac{(x + 4)(x - 1)}{x - 1} = x + 4 = m_{\text{sec}}$$

when $x = 2, \quad m_{\text{sec}} = 2 + 4 = 6.$

13. $f(x) = -x^3 + 7x - 2$, for $-3 < x < 3$

Use MAXIMUM and MINIMUM on the graph of $y_1 = -x^3 + 7x - 2$.

local maximum at: $(1.53, 5.13)$;   local minimum at: $(-1.53, -9.13)$

f is increasing on: $(-1.53, 1.53)$ f is decreasing on: $(-3, 1.53) \cup (1.53, 3)$

15. $f(x) = \begin{cases} 2x + 1 & \text{if } -3 < x < 2 \\ -3x + 4 & \text{if } x \geq 2 \end{cases}$

(a) Domain: $(-3, \infty)$

(b) x-intercept: $\left(-\frac{1}{2}, 0\right)$

y-intercept: $(0, 1)$

(c)

(d) Range: $\{y < 5\}$

(e) Graphing Utility:

17. $f(x) = x^2 - 5x + 1 \qquad g(x) = -4x - 7$

(a) $(f + g)(x) = x^2 - 5x + 1 + (-4x - 7) = x^2 - 9x - 6$

The domain is all real numbers.

(b) $\left(\dfrac{f}{g}\right)(x) = \dfrac{f(x)}{g(x)} = \dfrac{x^2 - 5x + 1}{-4x - 7}$

The domain is all real numbers except $-\dfrac{7}{4}$.

(c) $(f \circ g)(2) = f\big(g(2)\big) = f\big(-4(2) - 7\big) = f(-15) = (-15)^2 - 5(-15) + 1$

$\qquad\qquad\qquad\qquad\qquad\qquad = 225 + 75 + 1 = 301$

(d) $(f \circ g)(x) = f\big(g(x)\big) = f(-4x - 7) = (-4x - 7)^2 - 5(-4x - 7) + 1$

$\qquad\qquad\qquad\qquad = 16x^2 + 56x + 49 + 20x + 35 + 1 = 16x^2 + 76x + 85$

Domain: All real numbers.

19. (a) $R(x) = x \cdot p = x\left(-\dfrac{1}{10}x + 150\right) = -\dfrac{1}{10}x^2 + 150x$

(b) $R(100) = -\dfrac{1}{10}(100)^2 + 150(100) = -1000 + 15000 = \$14000$

(c) $x = \dfrac{-b}{2a} = \dfrac{-150}{2\left(-\dfrac{1}{10}\right)} = \dfrac{-150}{\left(-\dfrac{1}{5}\right)} = 750$ maximizes revenue

$R(750) = -\dfrac{1}{10}(750)^2 + 150(750) = -56250 + 112500 = \$56250 =$ maximum revenue

(d) $p = -\dfrac{1}{10}(750) + 150 = -75 + 150 = \$75$ maximizes revenue

Polynomial and Rational Functions

4.1 Power Functions and Models

1. $f(x) = (x+1)^4$

Using the graph of $y = x^4$, shift the graph horizontally, 1 unit to the left.

3. $f(x) = x^5 - 3$

Using the graph of $y = x^5$, shift the graph vertically, 3 units down.

5. $f(x) = \dfrac{1}{2}x^4$

Using the graph of $y = x^4$, compress the graph vertically by a factor of $\dfrac{1}{2}$.

7. $f(x) = -x^5$

Using the graph of $y = x^5$, reflect the graph about the x-axis.

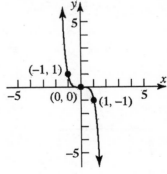

9.　　$f(x) = (x-1)^5 + 2$

Using the graph of $y = x^5$, shift the graph horizontally, 1 unit to the right, and shift vertically 2 units up.

11.　　$f(x) = 2(x+1)^4 + 1$

Using the graph of $y = x^4$, shift the graph horizontally, 1 unit to the left, stretch vertically by a factor of 2, and shift vertically 1 unit up.

13.　　$f(x) = 4 - (x-2)^5 = -(x-2)^5 + 4$

Using the graph of $y = x^5$, shift the graph horizontally, 2 units to the right, reflect about the x-axis, and shift vertically 4 units up.

15.　　$f(x) = -\dfrac{1}{2}(x-2)^4 - 1$

Using the graph of $y = x^4$, shift the graph horizontally, 2 units to the right, reflect about the x-axis, compress vertically by a factor of $\dfrac{1}{2}$ and shift vertically 1 unit down.

17.　(a)

(b)　　$s = 15.973t^{2.002}$

(c)

(d)　Solve $s = 15.973t^{2.002} = 100$ for t.

$15.973t^{2.002} = 100$

$t^{2.002} = \dfrac{100}{15.973} \approx 6.261$

$t \approx (6.261)^{1/2.002} \approx 2.4998$ seconds

(e)　$s = 15.973t^2 = \dfrac{1}{2}gt^2$

$15.973 = \dfrac{1}{2}g \Rightarrow g = 31.946$

$s = \left(\dfrac{1}{2}\right)(31.946)t^2$

Chapter 4

Polynomial and Rational Functions

4.2 Polynomial Functions and Models

1. $f(x) = 4x + x^3$ is a polynomial function of degree 3.

3. $g(x) = \dfrac{1-x^2}{2} = \dfrac{1}{2} - \dfrac{1}{2}x^2$ is a polynomial function of degree 2.

5. $f(x) = 1 - \dfrac{1}{x} = 1 - x^{-1}$ is not a polynomial function because it contains a negative exponent.

7. $g(x) = x^{3/2} - x^2 + 2$ is not a polynomial function because it contains a fractional exponent.

9. $F(x) = 5x^4 - \pi x^3 + \dfrac{1}{2}$ is a polynomial function of degree 4.

11. $f(x) = a(x - (-1))(x - 1)(x - 3)$
    For $a = 1$: $f(x) = (x+1)(x-1)(x-3) = (x^2 - 1)(x-3) = x^3 - 3x^2 - x + 3$

13. $f(x) = a(x - (-3))(x - 0)(x - 4)$
    For $a = 1$: $f(x) = (x+3)(x)(x-4)$
    $$f(x) = (x^2 + 3x)(x - 4) = x^3 - 4x^2 + 3x^2 - 12x = x^3 - x^2 - 12x$$

15. $f(x) = a(x - (-4))(x - (-1))(x - 2)(x - 3)$
    For $a = 1$: $f(x) = (x+4)(x+1)(x-2)(x-3)$
    $$f(x) = (x^2 + 5x + 4)(x^2 - 5x + 6)$$
    $$f(x) = x^4 - 5x^3 + 6x^2 + 5x^3 - 25x^2 + 30x + 4x^2 - 20x + 24$$
    $$f(x) = x^4 - 15x^2 + 10x + 24$$

17. $f(x) = a(x - (-1))(x - 3)^2$
    For $a = 1$: $f(x) = (x+1)(x-3)^2$
    $$f(x) = (x+1)(x^2 - 6x + 9)$$
    $$f(x) = x^3 - 6x^2 + 9x + x^2 - 6x + 9 = x^3 - 5x^2 + 3x + 9$$

19. The real zeros of $f(x) = 3(x-7)(x+3)^2$ are: 7, with multiplicity one; and –3, with multiplicity two. The graph crosses the x-axis at 7 and touches it at –3.
The function resembles $y = 3x^3$ for large values of $|x|$.

21. The real zeros of $f(x) = 4(x^2+1)(x-2)^3$ is: 2, with multiplicity three. $x^2+1 = 0$ has no real solution. The graph crosses the x-axis at 2.
The function resembles $y = 4x^5$ for large values of $|x|$.

23. The real zeros of $f(x) = -2\left(x+\dfrac{1}{2}\right)^2(x^2+4)^2$ is: $-\dfrac{1}{2}$, with multiplicity two. $x^2+4 = 0$ has no real solution. The graph touches the x-axis at $-\dfrac{1}{2}$.
The function resembles $y = -2x^6$ for large values of $|x|$.

25. The real zeros of $f(x) = (x-5)^3(x+4)^2$ are: 5, with multiplicity three; and –4, with multiplicity two. The graph crosses the x-axis at 5 and touches it at –4.
The function resembles $y = x^5$ for large values of $|x|$.

27. $f(x) = 3(x^2+8)(x^2+9)^2$ has no real zeros. $x^2+8 = 0$ and $x^2+9 = 0$ have no real solutions. The graph neither touches nor crosses the x-axis. The function resembles $y = 3x^6$ for large values of $|x|$.

29. The real zeros of $f(x) = -2x^2(x^2-2)$ are: $-\sqrt{2}$ and $\sqrt{2}$ with multiplicity one; and 0, with multiplicity two. The graph touches the x-axis at 0 and crosses the x-axis at $-\sqrt{2}$ and $\sqrt{2}$. The function resembles $y = -2x^4$ for large values of $|x|$.

31. $f(x) = (x-1)^2$
(a)   x-intercept: 1; y-intercept: 1
(b)   touches x-axis at x = 1
(c) $y = x^2$
(d)   graphing utility:

(e)   1 turning point; local minimum $(1,0)$

(f)   graphing by hand

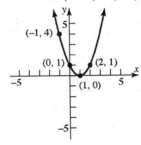

Interval	$(-\infty, 1)$	$(1, \infty)$
Number Chosen	-1	2
Value of f	$f(-1) = 4$	$f(2) = 1$
Location of Graph	Above x-axis	Above x-axis
Point on Graph	(-1, 4)	(2, 1)

f is above the x-axis for $(-\infty, 1) \cup (1, \infty)$

33. $f(x) = x^2(x - 3)$

(a)   x-intercepts: 0, 3; y-intercept: 0

(b)   touches x-axis at x = 0 ; crosses x-axis at x = 3

(c) $y = x^3$

(d)   graphing utility:

(e)   2 turning points; local maximum: (0, 0); local minimum: (2, –4)

(f)   graphing by hand

Interval	$(-\infty, 0)$	$(0, 3)$	$(3, \infty)$
Number Chosen	-1	2	4
Value of f	$f(-1) = -4$	$f(2) = -4$	$f(4) = 16$
Location of Graph	Below x-axis	Below x-axis	Above x-axis
Point on Graph	(-1, -4)	(2, -4)	(4, 16)

f is below the x-axis for $(-\infty, 0) \cup (0, 3)$; f is above the x-axis for $(3, \infty)$

199

35.　　　$f(x) = 6x^3(x+4)$

(a)　x-intercepts: –4, 0; y-intercept: 0　　　(b)　crosses x-axis at x = –4 and x = 0

(c)　$y = 6x^4$

(d)　graphing utility:

(e)　1 turning point; local minimum: (–3, –162)

(f)　graphing by hand

Interval	(–∞, –4)	(–4, 0)	(0, ∞)
Number Chosen	–5	–2	1
Value of f	f(–5) = 750	f(–2) = –96	f(1) = 30
Location of Graph	Above x-axis	Below x-axis	Above x-axis
Point on Graph	(–5, 750)	(–2, –96)	(1, 30)

f　is above the x-axis for $(-\infty,-4)\cup(0,\infty)$;　f is below the x-axis for $(-4,0)$

37.　　　$f(x) = -4x^2(x+2)$

(a)　x-intercepts: 0, –2; y-intercept: 0

(b)　crosses x-axis at $x = -2$; touches x-axis at $x = 0$

(c)　$y = -4x^3$

(d)　graphing utility:

(e)　2 turning points;　local maximum: (0, 0); local minimum: (–1.33, –4.74)

(f)   graphing by hand

Interval	$(-\infty, -2)$	$(-2, 0)$	$(0, \infty)$
Number Chosen	-3	-1	1
Value of f	$f(-3) = 36$	$f(-1) = -4$	$f(1) = -12$
Location of Graph	Above x-axis	Below x-axis	Below x-axis
Point on Graph	$(-3, 36)$	$(-1, -4)$	$(1, -12)$

f is above the x-axis for $(-\infty, -2)$; f is below the x-axis for $(-2, 0) \cup (0, \infty)$

39. $f(x) = (x+1)(x-2)(x+4)$

(a)   x-intercepts: $-1, 2, -4$; y-intercept: -8

(b)   crosses x-axis at $x = -1, 2, -4$

(c) $y = x^3$

(d)   graphing utility:

(e)   2 turning points; local maximum: $(-2.73, 10.39)$; local minimum: $(0.73, -10.39)$

(f)   graphing by hand

Interval	$(-\infty, -4)$	$(-4, -1)$	$(-1, 2)$	$(2, \infty)$
Number Chosen	-5	-2	0	3
Value of f	$f(-5) = -28$	$f(-2) = 8$	$f(0) = -8$	$f(3) = 28$
Location of Graph	Below x-axis	Above x-axis	Below x-axis	Above x-axis
Point on Graph	$(-5, -28)$	$(-2, 8)$	$(0, -8)$	$(3, 28)$

f is above the x-axis for $(-4, -1) \cup (2, \infty)$; f is below the x-axis for $(-\infty, -4) \cup (-1, 2)$

41. $f(x) = 4x - x^3 = x(4 - x^2) = x(2 + x)(2 - x)$

(a)   x-intercepts: $0, -2, 2$; y-intercept: 0

(b)   crosses x-axis at $x = 0, x = -2, x = 2$

(c) $y = -x^3$

(d)   graphing utility:

(e)   2 turning points; local maximum: $(1.15, 3.08)$;
local minimum: $(-1.15, -3.08)$

(f)   graphing by hand

Interval	$(-\infty, -2)$	$(-2, 0)$	$(0, 2)$	$(2, \infty)$
Number Chosen	-3	-1	1	3
Value of f	$f(-3) = 15$	$f(-1) = -3$	$f(1) = 3$	$f(3) = -15$
Location of Graph	Above x-axis	Below x-axis	Above x-axis	Below x-axis
Point on Graph	$(-3, 15)$	$(-1, -3)$	$(1, 3)$	$(3, -15)$

f is above the x-axis for $(-\infty, -2) \cup (0, 2)$; f is below the x-axis for $(-2, 0) \cup (2, \infty)$

43. $f(x) = x^2(x - 2)(x + 2)$

(a)   x-intercepts: $0, 2, -2$; y-intercept: 0

(b)   crosses x-axis at $x = 2, x = -2$; touches x-axis at $x = 0$

(c) $y = x^4$

(d)   graphing utility:

(e)   3 turning points; local maximum: $(0, 0)$; local minima: $(-1.41, -4), (1.41, -4)$

(f)   graphing by hand

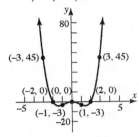

Interval	$(-\infty, -2)$	$(-2, 0)$	$(0, 2)$	$(2, \infty)$
Number Chosen	-3	-1	1	3
Value of f	$f(-3) = 45$	$f(-1) = -3$	$f(1) = -3$	$f(3) = 45$
Location of Graph	Above x-axis	Below x-axis	Below x-axis	Above x-axis
Point on Graph	$(-3, 45)$	$(-1, -3)$	$(1, -3)$	$(3, 45)$

f is above the x-axis for $(-\infty, -2) \cup (2, \infty)$; f is below the x-axis for $(-2, 0) \cup (0, 2)$

45. $f(x) = (x+1)^2 (x-2)^2$

(a)   x-intercepts: $-1, 2$; y-intercept: 4   (b)   touches x-axis at $x = -1, x = 2$

(c) $y = x^4$

(d)   graphing utility:

(e)   3 turning points; local maximum: $(0.5, 5.06)$; local minima: $(-1, 0), (2, 0)$

(f)   graphing by hand

Interval	$(-\infty, -1)$	$(-1, 2)$	$(2, \infty)$
Number Chosen	-2	0	3
Value of f	$f(-2) = 16$	$f(0) = 4$	$f(3) = 16$
Location of Graph	Above x-axis	Above x-axis	Above x-axis
Point on Graph	$(-2, 16)$	$(0, 4)$	$(3, 16)$

f is above the x-axis for $(-\infty, -1) \cup (-1, 2) \cup (2, \infty)$

47. $f(x) = x^2(x-3)(x+1)$
   (a)   x-intercepts: 0,3,−1; y-intercept: 0
   (b)   crosses x-axis at $x = -1, x = 3$; touches x-axis at x = 0
   (c) $y = x^4$
   (d)   graphing utility:

   (e)   3 turning points; local maximum: (0, 0); local minima: (−0.69, -0.54), (2.19, −12.39)
   (f)   graphing by hand

Interval	$(-\infty, -1)$	$(-1, 0)$	$(0, 3)$	$(3, \infty)$
Number Chosen	-2	$-\frac{1}{2}$	2	4
Value of f	$f(-2) = 20$	$f(-\frac{1}{2}) = -\frac{7}{16}$	$f(2) = -12$	$f(4) = 80$
Location of Graph	Above x-axis	Below x-axis	Below x-axis	Above x-axis
Point on Graph	(-2, 20)	$(-\frac{1}{2}, -\frac{7}{16})$	(2, -12)	(4, 80)

f is above the x-axis for $(-\infty,-1)\cup(3,\infty)$; f is below the x-axis for $(-1,0)\cup(0,3)$

49. $f(x) = (x+2)^2(x-4)^2$
   (a)   x-intercepts: −2,4; y-intercept: 64
   (b)   touches x-axis at $x = -2, x = 4$
   (c) $y = x^4$
   (d)   graphing utility:

   (e)   3 turning points; local maximum $(1,81)$; local minima $(-2,0)$ and $(4,0)$

(f)   graphing by hand

Interval	$(-\infty, -2)$	$(-2, 4)$	$(4, \infty)$
Number Chosen	-3	0	5
Value of f	$f(-3) = 49$	$f(0) = 64$	$f(5) = 49$
Location of Graph	Above x-axis	Above x-axis	Above x-axis
Point on Graph	(-3, 49)	(0, 64)	(5, 49)

f is above the x-axis for $(-\infty, -2) \cup (-2, 4) \cup (4, \infty)$

51. $f(x) = x^2(x-2)(x^2+3)$

(a)   x-intercepts: 0, 2; y-intercept: 0

(b)   crosses x-axis at x = 2 ; touches x-axis at x = 0

(c) $y = x^5$

(d)   graphing utility:

(e)   2 turning points; local maximum: (0, 0); local minimum: (1.48, –5.91)

(f)   graphing by hand

Interval	$(-\infty, 0)$	$(0, 2)$	$(2, \infty)$
Number Chosen	-1	1	3
Value of f	$f(-1) = -12$	$f(1) = -4$	$f(3) = 108$
Location of Graph	Below x-axis	Below x-axis	Above x-axis
Point on Graph	(-1, -12)	(1, -4)	(3, 108)

f is above the x-axis for $(2, \infty)$; f is below the x-axis for $(-\infty, 0) \cup (0, 2)$

53. $f(x) = -x^2(x^2-1)(x+1) = -x^2(x-1)(x+1)(x+1) = -x^2(x-1)(x+1)^2$

(a) x-intercepts: $0,1,-1$; y-intercept: 0

(b) crosses x-axis at $x = 1$; touches x-axis at $x = 0$ and $x = -1$

(c) $y = -x^5$

(d) graphing utility:

(e) 4 turning points; local maxima: $(-0.52, 0.10), (0.74, 0.43)$; local minima: $(-1,0), (0,0)$

(f) graphing by hand

Interval	$(-\infty, -1)$	$(-1, 0)$	$(0, 1)$	$(1, \infty)$
Number Chosen	-2	$-\frac{1}{2}$	$\frac{1}{2}$	2
Value of f	$f(-2) = 12$	$f(-\frac{1}{2}) = \frac{3}{32}$	$f(\frac{1}{2}) = \frac{9}{32}$	$f(2) = -36$
Location of Graph	Above x-axis	Above x-axis	Above x-axis	Below x-axis
Point on Graph	$(-2, 12)$	$(-\frac{1}{2}, \frac{3}{32})$	$(\frac{1}{2}, \frac{9}{32})$	$(2, -36)$

f is above the x-axis for $(-\infty,-1) \cup (-1,0) \cup (0,1)$; f is below the x-axis for $(1,\infty)$

55. $f(x) = x^3 + 0.2x^2 - 1.5876x - 0.31752$

(a) graphing utility:

(b) x-intercepts: $-1.26, -0.2, 1.26$;
y-intercept: -0.31752

(c) $y = x^3$

(d) 2 turning points;
local maximum: $(-0.80, 0.57)$
local minimum: $(0.66, -0.99)$

57. $f(x) = x^3 + 2.56x^2 - 3.31x + 0.89$

(a) graphing utility

(b) x-intercepts: $-3.56, 0.50$;
y-intercept: 0.89

(c) $y = x^3$

(d) 2 turning points;
local maximum: $(-2.21, 9.91)$
local minimum: $(0.50, 0)$

59. $f(x) = x^4 - 2.5x^2 + 0.5625$
   (a)   graphing utility:

   (b)   x-intercepts: $-1.50, -0.50, 0.50, 1.50$;
        y-intercept: 0.5625
   (c) $y = x^4$
   (d)   3 turning points:
        local maximum: $(0, 0.5625)$
        local minima: $(-1.12, -1), (1.12, -1)$

61. $f(x) = 2x^4 - \pi x^3 + \sqrt{5}x - 4$
   (a)   graphing utility:

   (b)   x-intercepts: $-1.07, 1.62$;
        y-intercept: -4
   (c) $y = 2x^4$
   (c)   1 turning point;
        local minimum: $(-0.42, -4.64)$

63. $f(x) = -2x^5 - \sqrt{2}x^2 - x - \sqrt{2}$
   (a)   graphing utility:

   (b)   x-intercept: -0.98;
        y-intercept: -1.41
   (c) $y = -2x^5$
   (d)   No turning points
        No local extrema

65.   Answers will vary. One possible
     answer is $f(x) = x(x-1)(x-2)$,
     since the graph crosses
     the x-axis at $x = 0, 1$ and 2.

67.   Answers will vary. One possible
     answer is
     $$f(x) = -\frac{1}{2}(x+1)(x-1)(x-2), \text{ since}$$
     the graph crosses the x-axis at
     $x = -1, 1$ and 2 and has a y-intercept
     at -1.

69.   (a)   Graphing, we see that the graph may be a cubic relation.

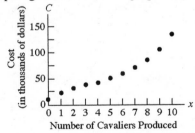

   (b)   Average rate of change $= \dfrac{50 - 43}{5 - 4} = \dfrac{7}{1} = 7$ thousand dollars per car

   (c)   Average rate of change $= \dfrac{105 - 85}{9 - 8} = \dfrac{20}{1} = 20$ thousand dollars per car

   (d) $C(x) = 0.2x^3 - 2.3x^2 + 14.3x + 10.2$
        $C(11) = 0.2(11)^3 - 2.3(11)^2 + 14.3(11) + 10.2 \approx 155.4$
        The cost of manufacturing 11 Cavaliers in 1 hour would be approximately $155,400.

(e) and (f)   Graphing the cubic function of best fit:

(g)   The y-intercept would indicate the fixed costs before any cars are made.

71. (a)   Graphing, we see that the graph may be a cubic relation..

(b) $T(x) = 1.52x^3 - 39.81x^2 + 282.29x + 1035.5$

(c)   Graphing the cubic function of best fit:

(d) $T(12) = 1.52(12)^3 - 39.81(12)^2 + 282.29(12) + 1035.5 = 1316.9$
       According to the function there would be approximately 1,316,900 motor vehicle
       thefts in 1998.

(e) answers will vary

73. Answers will vary

75. Answers will vary , $f(x) = (x+2)(x-1)^2$ and $g(x) = (x+2)^3(x-1)^2$ are two such
     polynomials.

Chapter 4

Polynomial and Rational Functions

4.3 Rational Functions I

1. In $R(x) = \dfrac{4x}{x-3}$, the denominator, $q(x) = x - 3$, has a zero at 3. Thus, the domain of $R(x)$ is all real numbers except 3.

3. In $H(x) = \dfrac{-4x^2}{(x-2)(x+4)}$, the denominator, $q(x) = (x-2)(x+4)$, has zeros at 2 and -4. Thus, the domain of $H(x)$ is all real numbers except 2 and -4.

5. In $F(x) = \dfrac{3x(x-1)}{2x^2 - 5x - 3}$, the denominator, $q(x) = 2x^2 - 5x - 3 = (2x+1)(x-3)$, has zeros at $-\dfrac{1}{2}$ and 3. Thus, the domain of $F(x)$ is all real numbers except $-\dfrac{1}{2}$ and 3.

7. In $R(x) = \dfrac{x}{x^3 - 8}$, the denominator, $q(x) = x^3 - 8 = (x-2)(x^2 + 2x + 4)$, has a zero at 2. ($x^2 + 2x + 4$ has no real zeros.) Thus, the domain of $R(x)$ is all real numbers except 2.

9. In $H(x) = \dfrac{3x^2 + x}{x^2 + 4}$, the denominator, $q(x) = x^2 + 4$, has no real zeros. Thus, the domain of $H(x)$ is all real numbers.

11. In $R(x) = \dfrac{3(x^2 - x - 6)}{4(x^2 - 9)}$, the denominator, $q(x) = 4(x^2 - 9) = 4(x-3)(x+3)$, has zeros at 3 and -3. Thus, the domain of $R(x)$ is all real numbers except 3 and -3.

13. (a) Domain: $\{x \mid x \neq 2\}$; Range: $\{y \mid y \neq 1\}$
    (b) Intercept: $(0, 0)$ (c) Horizontal Asymptote: $y = 1$
    (d) Vertical Asymptote: $x = 2$ (e) Oblique Asymptote: none

15. (a) Domain: $\{x \mid x \neq 0\}$; Range: all real numbers
    (b) Intercepts: $(-1, 0)$, $(1, 0)$ (c) Horizontal Asymptote: none
    (d) Vertical Asymptote: $x = 0$ (e) Oblique Asymptote: $y = 2x$

17. (a) Domain: $\{x \mid x \neq -2, x \neq 2\}$; Range: $\{y \mid y \leq 0 \text{ or } y > 1\}$
    (b) Intercept: $(0, 0)$ (c) Horizontal Asymptote: $y = 1$
    (d) Vertical Asymptotes: $x = -2, x = 2$ (e) Oblique Asymptote: none

19. (a) Domain: $\{x \mid x \neq -1\}$; Range: $\{y \mid y \neq 2\}$
    (b) Intercepts: $(-1.5, 0)$; $(0, 3)$ (c) Horizontal Asymptote: $y = 2$
    (d) Vertical Asymptote: $x = -1$ (e) Oblique Asymptote: none

21. (a) Domain: $\{x \mid x \neq -4, x \neq 3\}$; Range: all real numbers
    (b) Intercept: $(0, 0)$ (c) Horizontal Asymptote: $y = 0$
    (d) Vertical Asymptotes: $x = -4, x = 3$ (e) Oblique Asymptote: none

23. $R(x) = \dfrac{1}{(x-1)^2}$

Using the function, $y = \dfrac{1}{x^2}$, shift the
graph horizontally 1 unit to the right.

25. $H(x) = \dfrac{-2}{x+1} = -2\left(\dfrac{1}{x+1}\right)$

Using the function $y = \dfrac{1}{x}$, shift the graph
horizontally 1 unit to the left, reflect
about the x-axis, and stretch vertically by
a factor of 2.

27. $R(x) = \dfrac{1}{x^2 + 4x + 4} = \dfrac{1}{(x+2)^2}$

$\qquad = \dfrac{1}{(x+2)^2}$

Using the function $y = \dfrac{1}{x^2}$, shift the graph
horizontally 2 units to the left.

29. $F(x) = 1 - \dfrac{1}{x} = -\dfrac{1}{x} + 1$

Using the function, $y = \dfrac{1}{x}$, reflect the
graph across the x-axis and then shift the
graph vertically 1 unit up.

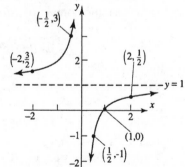

31. $R(x) = \dfrac{x^2 - 4}{x^2} = 1 - \dfrac{4}{x^2} = -4\left(\dfrac{1}{x^2}\right) + 1$

Using the function $y = \dfrac{1}{x^2}$, reflect about
the x-axis, stretch vertically by a factor of
4 and shift vertically 1 unit up.

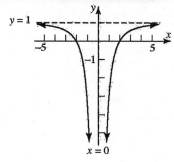

33. $G(x) = 1 + \dfrac{2}{(x-3)^2} = \dfrac{2}{(x-3)^2} + 1$

$= 2\left(\dfrac{1}{(x-3)^2}\right) + 1$

Using the function $y = \dfrac{1}{x^2}$, shift the

graph 3 units right, stretch vertically by a
factor of 2, and shift vertically 1 unit up.

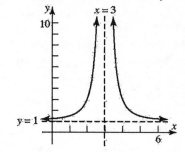

35. $R(x) = \dfrac{3x}{x+4}$

The degree of the numerator, $p(x) = 3x$, is $n = 1$. The degree of the denominator,

$q(x) = x + 4$, is $m = 1$. Since $n = m$, the line $y = \dfrac{3}{1} = 3$ is a horizontal asymptote. The

denominator is zero at $x = -4$, so $x = -4$ is a vertical asymptote.

37. $H(x) = \dfrac{x^4 + 2x^2 + 1}{x^2 - x + 1}$

The degree of the numerator, $p(x) = x^4 + 2x^2 + 1$, is $n = 4$. The degree of the
denominator, $q(x) = x^2 - x + 1$, is $m = 2$. Since $n > m + 1$, there is no horizontal
asymptote or oblique asymptote. The denominator has no real zeros, so there is no vertical
asymptote.

39. $T(x) = \dfrac{x^3}{x^4 - 1}$

The degree of the numerator, $p(x) = x^3$, is $n = 3$. The degree of the denominator,
$q(x) = x^4 - 1$ is $m = 4$. Since $n < m$, the line $y = 0$ is a horizontal asymptote. The
denominator is zero at $x = -1$ and $x = 1$, so $x = -1$ and $x = 1$ are vertical asymptotes.

41. $Q(x) = \dfrac{5 - x^2}{3x^4}$

The degree of the numerator, $p(x) = 5 - x^2$, is $n = 2$. The degree of the denominator,
$q(x) = 3x^4$ is $m = 4$. Since $n < m$, the line $y = 0$ is a horizontal asymptote. The
denominator is zero at $x = 0$, so $x = 0$ is a vertical asymptote.

43. $R(x) = \dfrac{3x^4 - 4}{x^3 + 3x}$

The degree of the numerator, $p(x) = 3x^4 - 4$, is $n = 4$. The degree of the denominator, $q(x) = x^3 + 3x$ is $m = 3$. Since $n = m + 1$, there is an oblique asymptote.
Dividing:

$$x^3 + 3x \overline{\smash{)}3x^4 + 0x^3 + 0x^2 + 0x - 4} \qquad\qquad R(x) = 3x + \dfrac{-9x^2 - 4}{x^3 + 3x}$$

$$\underline{3x^4 \qquad\ +9x^2}$$

$$-9x^2 + 0x - 4$$

with quotient $3x$ above.

Thus, the oblique asymptote is $y = 3x$.
The denominator is zero at $x = 0$, so $x = 0$ is a vertical asymptote.

45. $G(x) = \dfrac{x^3 - 1}{x - x^2}$, $x \neq 1$

The degree of the numerator, $p(x) = x^3 - 1$, is $n = 3$. The degree of the denominator, $q(x) = x - x^2$ is $m = 2$. Since $n = m + 1$, there is an oblique asymptote.
Dividing:

$$-x^2 + x \overline{\smash{)}x^3 + 0x^2 + 0x - 1} \qquad G(x) = -x - 1 + \dfrac{x - 1}{x - x^2} = -x - 1 - \dfrac{1}{x}, \ x \neq 1$$

$$\underline{x^3 - x^2}$$

$$x^2 + 0x \qquad\qquad\qquad\text{Thus, the oblique asymptote is } y = -x - 1.$$

$$\underline{x^2 - x}$$

$$x - 1$$

with quotient $-x - 1$ above.

$G(x)$ must be in lowest terms to find the vertical asymptote:

$$G(x) = \frac{x^3 - 1}{x - x^2} = \frac{(x - 1)(x^2 + x + 1)}{-x(x - 1)} = \frac{x^2 + x + 1}{-x}$$

The denominator is zero at $x = 0$, so $x = 0$ is a vertical asymptotes.

47.   A rational function $R(x) = \dfrac{p(x)}{q(x)}$ has a vertical asymptote at x = c in each of these cases:

Case 1: $R(c) = \dfrac{nonzero}{zero}$

That is, whenever x = c yields a zero in the denominator of the function formula. And the denominator will equal zero only if it contains the factor $(x - c)^n$, for some $n > 0$.

Case 2: $R(c) = \dfrac{(x - c)^m}{(x - c)^n}$, where $n > 0$, $m > 0$ and $n > m$.

That is, whenever x = c yields a zero in the numerator and denominator of the function formula such that the multiplicity is greater in the denominator.

49.   We need $R(x) = \dfrac{p(x)}{q(x)} = 2x + 1 + \dfrac{h(x)}{q(x)}$, with $h(x) \neq 0$ for some x.

Letting $q(x) = x + 1$, we have

$$2x + 1 + \frac{h(x)}{q(x)} = 2x + 1 + \frac{h(x)}{x+1} = \frac{(2x+1)(x+1) + h(x)}{x+1} = \frac{2x^2 + 3x + 1 + h(x)}{x+1}.$$

So choosing $h(x) = 1$, we get $R(x) = \dfrac{2x^2 + 3x + 1 + 1}{x+1} = \dfrac{2x^2 + 3x + 2}{x+1}$.

Polynomial and Rational Functions

4.4 Rational Functions II: Analyzing Graphs

In problems 1-37, we will use the terminology: $R(x) = \dfrac{p(x)}{q(x)}$, *where the degree of* $p(x) = n$ *and the degree of* $q(x) = m$.

1. $R(x) = \dfrac{x+1}{x(x+4)}$ $p(x) = x+1$; $q(x) = x(x+4) = x^2 + 4x$; $n = 1$; $m = 2$

    Step 1: Domain: $\{x \mid x \neq -4, x \neq 0\}$

    Step 2: (a) The x-intercept is the zero of $p(x)$: -1

    (b) There is no y-intercept; $R(0)$ is not defined, since $q(0) = 0$.

    Step 3: $R(-x) = \dfrac{-x+1}{-x(-x+4)} = \dfrac{-x+1}{x^2 - 4x}$; this is neither $R(x)$ nor $-R(x)$, so there is no symmetry.

    Step 4: The vertical asymptotes are the zeros of $q(x)$: $x = -4$ and $x = 0$

    Step 5: Since $n < m$, the line $y = 0$ is the horizontal asymptote.

    $R(x)$ intersects $y = 0$ at $(-1, 0)$.

    Step 6:

Interval	$(-\infty, -4)$	$(-4, -1)$	$(-1, 0)$	$(0, \infty)$
Number Chosen	-5	-2	$-\frac{1}{2}$	1
Value of R	$R(-5) = -\frac{4}{5}$	$R(-2) = \frac{1}{4}$	$R(-\frac{1}{2}) = -\frac{2}{7}$	$R(1) = \frac{2}{5}$
Location of Graph	Below x-axis	Above x-axis	Below x-axis	Above x-axis
Point on Graph	$(-5, -\frac{4}{5})$	$(-2, \frac{1}{4})$	$(-\frac{1}{2}, -\frac{2}{7})$	$(1, \frac{2}{5})$

Step 7: Graphing Utility:

Step 8: Graphing by hand:

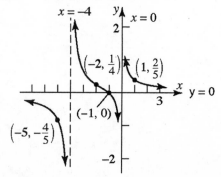

3. $R(x) = \dfrac{3x+3}{2x+4}$ $p(x) = 3x+3$; $q(x) = 2x+4$; $n=1$; $m=1$

Step 1:   Domain: $\{x \mid x \neq -2\}$

Step 2:   (a)   The x-intercept is the zero of $p(x)$: -1

(b)   The y-intercept is $R(0) = \dfrac{3(0)+3}{2(0)+4} = \dfrac{3}{4}$.

Step 3: $R(-x) = \dfrac{3(-x)+3}{2(-x)+4} = \dfrac{-3x+3}{-2x+4} = \dfrac{3x-3}{2x-4}$; this is neither $R(x)$ nor $-R(x)$, so there

is no symmetry.

Step 4:   The vertical asymptote is the zero of $q(x)$: $x = -2$

Step 5:   Since $n = m$, the line $y = \dfrac{3}{2}$ is the horizontal asymptote.

$R(x)$ does not intersect $y = \dfrac{3}{2}$.

Step 6:

Interval	$(-\infty, -2)$	$(-2, -1)$	$(-1, \infty)$
Number Chosen	-3	$-\frac{3}{2}$	0
Value of R	$R(-3) = 3$	$R(-\frac{3}{2}) = -\frac{3}{2}$	$R(0) = \frac{3}{4}$
Location of Graph	Above x-axis	Below x-axis	Above x-axis
Point on Graph	$(-3, 3)$	$(-\frac{3}{2}, -\frac{3}{2})$	$(0, \frac{3}{4})$

Step 7:   Graphing Utility: Step 8:   Graphing by hand:

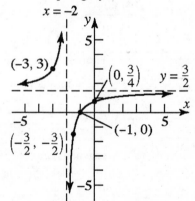

5. $R(x) = \dfrac{3}{x^2-4}$ $p(x) = 3$; $q(x) = x^2 - 4$; $n = 0$; $m = 2$

Step 1:   Domain: $\{x \mid x \neq -2, x \neq 2\}$

Step 2:   (a)   There is no x-intercept.

(b)   The y-intercept is $R(0) = \dfrac{3}{0^2-4} = \dfrac{3}{-4} = -\dfrac{3}{4}$.

Step 3: $R(-x) = \dfrac{3}{(-x)^2-4} = \dfrac{3}{x^2-4} = R(x)$; $R(x)$ is symmetric to the y-axis.

Step 4:   The vertical asymptotes are the zeros of $q(x)$: $x = -2$ and $x = 2$

215

Step 5:   Since $n < m$, the line $y = 0$ is the horizontal asymptote.
$R(x)$ does not intersect $y = 0$.

Step 6:

-2   2

Interval	$(-\infty, -2)$	$(-2, 2)$	$(2, \infty)$
Number Chosen	-3	0	3
Value of R	$R(-3) = \frac{3}{5}$	$R(0) = -\frac{3}{4}$	$R(3) = \frac{3}{5}$
Location of Graph	Above x-axis	Below x-axis	Above x-axis
Point on Graph	$(-3, \frac{3}{5})$	$(0, -\frac{3}{4})$	$(3, \frac{3}{5})$

Step 7:   Graphing Utility:

Step 8:   Graphing by hand:

7. $P(x) = \dfrac{x^4 + x^2 + 1}{x^2 - 1}$ $p(x) = x^4 + x^2 + 1$; $q(x) = x^2 - 1$; $n = 4$; $m = 2$

Step 1:   Domain: $\{x \mid x \neq -1, x \neq 1\}$

Step 2:   (a)   There is no x-intercept.

(b)   The y-intercept is $P(0) = \dfrac{0^4 + 0^2 + 1}{0^2 - 1} = \dfrac{1}{-1} = -1$.

Step 3: $P(-x) = \dfrac{(-x)^4 + (-x)^2 + 1}{(-x)^2 - 1} = \dfrac{x^4 + x^2 + 1}{x^2 - 1} = P(x)$; $P(x)$ is symmetric to the y - axis.

Step 4:   The vertical asymptotes are the zeros of $q(x)$: $x = -1$ and $x = 1$

Step 5:   Since $n > m + 1$, there is no horizontal asymptote and no oblique asymptote.

Step 6:

-1   1

Interval	$(-\infty, -1)$	$(-1, 1)$	$(1, \infty)$
Number Chosen	-2	0	2
Value of P	$P(-2) = 7$	$P(0) = -1$	$P(2) = 7$
Location of Graph	Above x-axis	Below x-axis	Above x-axis
Point on Graph	$(-2, 7)$	$(0, -1)$	$(2, 7)$

Step 7:   Graphing Utility:

Step 8:   Graphing by hand:

9. $H(x) = \dfrac{x^3 - 1}{x^2 - 9}$ $p(x) = x^3 - 1;\ q(x) = x^2 - 9;\ n = 3;\ m = 2$

Step 1:   Domain: $\{x \mid x \neq -3,\ x \neq 3\}$

Step 2:   (a)   The x-intercept is the zero of $p(x)$: 1.

(b)   The y-intercept is $H(0) = \dfrac{0^3 - 1}{0^2 - 9} = \dfrac{-1}{-9} = \dfrac{1}{9}$.

Step 3: $H(-x) = \dfrac{(-x)^3 - 1}{(-x)^2 - 9} = \dfrac{-x^3 - 1}{x^2 - 9}$; this is neither $H(x)$ nor $-H(x)$, so there is no symmetry.

Step 4:   The vertical asymptotes are the zeros of $q(x)$: $x = -3$ and $x = 3$

Step 5:   Since $n = m + 1$, there is an oblique asymptote. Dividing:

$$x^2 - 9\overline{)x^3 + 0x^2 + 0x - 1} \qquad H(x) = x + \dfrac{9x - 1}{x^2 - 9}$$
$$\underline{x^3\qquad -9x}$$
$$9x - 1$$

The oblique asymptote is $y = x$.

Solve to find intersection points:

$$\dfrac{x^3 - 1}{x^2 - 9} = x \Rightarrow x^3 - 1 = x^3 - 9x$$

$$-1 = -9x \Rightarrow x = \dfrac{1}{9}$$

The oblique asymptote intersects $H(x)$ at $\left(\dfrac{1}{9}, \dfrac{1}{9}\right)$.

Step 6:

Interval	$(-\infty, -3)$	$(23, 1)$	$(1, 3)$	$(3, \infty)$
Number Chosen	-4	0	2	4
Value of H	$H(-4) \approx -9.3$	$H(0) = \frac{1}{9}$	$H(2) = -1.4$	$H(4) = 9$
Location of Graph	Below x-axis	Above x-axis	Below x-axis	Above x-axis
Point on Graph	$(-4, -9.3)$	$(0, \frac{1}{9})$	$(2, -1.4)$	$(4, 9)$

217

Step 7:   Graphing Utility:

Step 8:   Graphing by hand:

11. $R(x) = \dfrac{x^2}{x^2 + x - 6} = \dfrac{x^2}{(x+3)(x-2)}$ $p(x) = x^2; \quad q(x) = x^2 + x - 6; \quad n = 2; \quad m = 2$

Step 1:   Domain: $\{x \mid x \neq -3, x \neq 2\}$

Step 2:   (a)   The x-intercept is the zero of $p(x)$: 0

(b)   The y-intercept is $R(0) = \dfrac{0^2}{0^2 + 0 - 6} = \dfrac{0}{-6} = 0$.

Step 3: $R(-x) = \dfrac{(-x)^2}{(-x)^2 + (-x) - 6} = \dfrac{x^2}{x^2 - x - 6}$; this is neither $R(x)$ nor $-R(x)$, so there

is no symmetry.

Step 4:   The vertical asymptotes are the zeros of $q(x)$: $x = -3$ and $x = 2$

Step 5:   Since $n = m$, the line $y = 1$ is the horizontal asymptote.

$R(x)$ intersects $y = 1$ at (6, 1), since:

$$\frac{x^2}{x^2 + x - 6} = 1 \Rightarrow x^2 = x^2 + x - 6 \Rightarrow 0 = x - 6 \Rightarrow x = 6$$

Step 6:

Interval	$(-\infty, -3)$	$(-3, 0)$	$(0, 2)$	$(2, \infty)$
Number Chosen	-6	-1	1	3
Value of R	$R(-6) = 1.5$	$R(-1) = -\frac{1}{6}$	$R(1) = -0.25$	$R(3) = 1.5$
Location of Graph	Above x-axis	Below x-axis	Below x-axis	Above x-axis
Point on Graph	(-6, 1.5)	$(-1, -\frac{1}{6})$	(1, -0.25)	(3, 1.5)

Step 7:   Graphing Utility:

Step 8:   Graphing by hand:

13. $G(x) = \dfrac{x}{x^2 - 4} = \dfrac{x}{(x+2)(x-2)}$ $p(x) = x$; $q(x) = x^2 - 4$; $n = 1$; $m = 2$

Step 1: Domain: $\{x \mid x \neq -2, x \neq 2\}$

Step 2: (a) The x-intercept is the zero of $p(x)$: 0

        (b) The y-intercept is $G(0) = \dfrac{0}{0^2 - 4} = \dfrac{0}{-4} = 0$.

Step 3: $G(-x) = \dfrac{-x}{(-x)^2 - 4} = \dfrac{-x}{x^2 - 4} = -G(x)$; $G(x)$ is symmetric to the origin.

Step 4: The vertical asymptotes are the zeros of $q(x)$: $x = -2$ and $x = 2$

Step 5: Since $n < m$, the line $y = 0$ is the horizontal asymptote.

        $G(x)$ intersects $y = 0$ at $(0, 0)$.

Step 6:

Interval	$(-\infty, -2)$	$(-2, 0)$	$(0, 2)$	$(2, \infty)$
Number Chosen	-3	-1	1	3
Value of G	$G(-3) = -\frac{3}{5}$	$G(-1) = \frac{1}{3}$	$G(1) = -\frac{1}{3}$	$G(3) = \frac{3}{5}$
Location of Graph	Below x-axis	Above x-axis	Below x-axis	Above x-axis
Point on Graph	$(-3, -\frac{3}{5})$	$(-1, \frac{1}{3})$	$(1, -\frac{1}{3})$	$(3, \frac{3}{5})$

Step 7:   Graphing Utility:

Step 8:   Graphing by hand:

15. $R(x) = \dfrac{3}{(x-1)(x^2 - 4)} = \dfrac{3}{(x-1)(x+2)(x-2)}$ $p(x) = 3$; $q(x) = (x-1)(x^2 - 4)$;

        $n = 0$; $m = 3$

Step 1: Domain: $\{x \mid x \neq -2, x \neq 1, x \neq 2\}$

Step 2: (a) There is no x-intercept.

        (b) The y-intercept is $R(0) = \dfrac{3}{(0-1)(0^2 - 4)} = \dfrac{3}{4}$.

Step 3: $R(-x) = \dfrac{3}{(-x-1)((-x)^2 - 4)} = \dfrac{3}{(-x-1)(x^2 - 4)}$; this is neither $R(x)$ nor $-R(x)$,

        so there is no symmetry.

Step 4: The vertical asymptotes are the zeros of $q(x)$: $x = -2$, $x = 1$, and $x = 2$

Step 5: Since $n < m$, the line $y = 0$ is the horizontal asymptote.

        $R(x)$ does not intersect $y = 0$.

Step 6:

Interval	$(-\infty, -2)$	$(-2, 1)$	$(1, 2)$	$(2, \infty)$
Number Chosen	-3	0	1.5	3
Value of R	$R(-3) = -\frac{3}{20}$	$R(0) = \frac{3}{4}$	$R(1.5) = -\frac{24}{7}$	$R(3) = \frac{3}{10}$
Location of Graph	Below x-axis	Above x-axis	Below x-axis	Above x-axis
Point on Graph	$(-3, -\frac{3}{20})$	$(0, \frac{3}{4})$	$(1.5, -\frac{24}{7})$	$(3, \frac{3}{10})$

Step 7:   Graphing Utility: Step 8:   Graphing by hand:

17. $H(x) = \dfrac{4(x^2 - 1)}{x^4 - 16} = \dfrac{4(x-1)(x+1)}{(x^2 + 4)(x+2)(x-2)}$ $p(x) = 4(x^2 - 1)$; $q(x) = x^4 - 16$;

                    $n = 2$; $m = 4$

Step 1:   Domain: $\{x \mid x \ne -2, x \ne 2\}$

Step 2:   (a)   The x-intercepts are the zeros of $p(x)$: -1 and 1

         (b)   The y-intercept is $H(0) = \dfrac{4(0^2 - 1)}{0^4 - 16} = \dfrac{-4}{-16} = \dfrac{1}{4}$.

Step 3: $H(-x) = \dfrac{4\left((-x)^2 - 1\right)}{(-x)^4 - 16} = \dfrac{4\left(x^2 - 1\right)}{x^4 - 16} = H(x)$; $H(x)$ is symmetric to the y-axis.

Step 4:   The vertical asymptotes are the zeros of $q(x)$: $x = -2$, and $x = 2$

Step 5:   Since $n < m$, the line $y = 0$ is the horizontal asymptote.

         $H(x)$ intersects $y = 0$ at $(-1, 0)$ and $(1, 0)$.

Step 6:

Interval	$(-\infty, -2)$	$(-2, -1)$	$(-1, 1)$	$(1, 2)$	$(2, \infty)$
Number Chosen	-3	-1.5	0	1.5	3
Value of H	$H(-3) \approx 0.49$	$H(-1.5) \approx -0.46$	$H(0) = \frac{1}{4}$	$H(1.5) \approx -0.46$	$H(3) \approx 0.49$
Location of Graph	Above x-axis	Below x-axis	Above x-axis	Below x-axis	Above x-axis
Point on Graph	$(-3, 0.49)$	$(-1.5, -0.46)$	$(0, \frac{1}{4})$	$(1.5, -0.46)$	$(3, 0.49)$

Step 7:   Graphing Utility:

Step 8:   Graphing by hand:

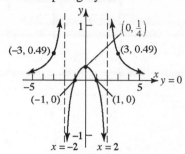

19. $F(x) = \dfrac{x^2 - 3x - 4}{x + 2} = \dfrac{(x+1)(x-4)}{x+2}$ $p(x) = x^2 - 3x - 4;\ q(x) = x + 2;\ n = 2;\ m = 1$

Step 1:   Domain: $\{x \mid x \neq -2\}$

Step 2:   (a)   The x-intercepts are the zeros of $p(x)$: -1 and 4.

(b)   The y-intercept is $F(0) = \dfrac{0^2 - 3(0) - 4}{0 + 2} = \dfrac{-4}{2} = -2$.

Step 3: $F(-x) = \dfrac{(-x)^2 - 3(-x) - 4}{-x + 2} = \dfrac{x^2 + 3x - 4}{-x + 2}$; this is neither $F(x)$ nor $-F(x)$, so there is no symmetry.

Step 4:   The vertical asymptote is the zero of $q(x)$: $x = -2$

Step 5:   Since $n = m + 1$, there is an oblique asymptote. Dividing:

$$\begin{array}{r} x - 5 \\ x+2\overline{)x^2 - 3x - 4} \\ \underline{x^2 + 2x} \\ -5x - 4 \\ \underline{-5x - 10} \\ 6 \end{array} \qquad F(x) = x - 5 + \dfrac{6}{x + 2}$$

The oblique asymptote is $y = x - 5$.

Solve to find intersection points:

$$\dfrac{x^2 - 3x - 4}{x + 2} = x - 5 \Rightarrow x^2 - 3x - 4 = x^2 - 3x - 10 \Rightarrow -4 = -10$$

Since there is no solution, the oblique asymptote does not intersect $F(x)$.

Step 6:

Interval	$(-\infty, -2)$	$(-2, -1)$	$(-1, 4)$	$(4, \infty)$
Number Chosen	-3	-1.5	0	5
Value of F	$F(-3) = -14$	$F(-1.5) = 5.5$	$F(0) = -2$	$F(5) \approx 0.86$
Location of Graph	Below x-axis	Above x-axis	Below x-axis	Above x-axis
Point on Graph	(-3, -14)	(-1.5, 5.5)	(0, -2)	(5, 0.86)

Step 7:   Graphing Utility: Step 8:   Graphing by hand:

21. $R(x) = \dfrac{x^2 + x - 12}{x - 4} = \dfrac{(x+4)(x-3)}{x-4}$ $p(x) = x^2 + x - 12;\ q(x) = x - 4;\ n = 2;\ m = 1$

Step 1:   Domain: $\{x \mid x \neq 4\}$

Step 2:   (a)   The x-intercepts are the zeros of $p(x)$: -4 and 3.

   (b)   The y-intercept is $R(0) = \dfrac{0^2 + 0 - 12}{0 - 4} = \dfrac{-12}{-4} = 3.$

Step 3: $R(-x) = \dfrac{(-x)^2 + (-x) - 12}{-x - 4} = \dfrac{x^2 - x - 12}{-x - 4}$; this is neither $R(x)$ nor $-R(x)$, so
there is no symmetry.

Step 4:   The vertical asymptote is the zero of $q(x)$: $x = 4$

Step 5:   Since $n = m + 1$, there is an oblique asymptote. Dividing:

$$
\begin{array}{r}
x + 5 \\
x - 4 \overline{)\, x^2 + x - 12} \\
\underline{x^2 - 4x} \\
5x - 12 \\
\underline{5x - 20} \\
8
\end{array}
\qquad R(x) = x + 5 + \dfrac{8}{x - 4}
$$

The oblique asymptote is $y = x + 5$.

Solve to find intersection points:

$$\dfrac{x^2 + x - 12}{x - 4} = x + 5$$

$$x^2 + x - 12 = x^2 + x - 20$$

$$-12 = -20$$

Since there is no solution, the oblique asymptote does not intersect $R(x)$.

Step 6:

	-4	3	4	

Interval	$(-\infty, -4)$	$(-4, 3)$	$(3, 4)$	$(4, \infty)$
Number Chosen	-5	0	3.5	5
Value of R	$R(-5) = -\frac{8}{9}$	$R(0) = 3$	$R(3.5) = -7.5$	$R(5) = 18$
Location of Graph	Below x-axis	Above x-axis	Below x-axis	Above x-axis
Point on Graph	$(-5, -\frac{8}{9})$	$(0, 3)$	$(3.5, -7.5)$	$(5, 18)$

Step 7:   Graphing Utility:

Step 8:   Graphing by hand:

23. $F(x) = \dfrac{x^2 + x - 12}{x + 2} = \dfrac{(x+4)(x-3)}{x+2}$ $p(x) = x^2 + x - 12;\ q(x) = x + 2;\ n = 2;\ m = 1$

Step 1:   Domain: $\{x \mid x \neq -2\}$

Step 2:   (a)   The x-intercepts are the zeros of $p(x)$: -4 and 3.

　　　　 (b)   The y-intercept is $F(0) = \dfrac{0^2 + 0 - 12}{0 + 2} = \dfrac{-12}{2} = -6$.

Step 3: $F(-x) = \dfrac{(-x)^2 + (-x) - 12}{-x + 2} = \dfrac{x^2 - x - 12}{-x + 2}$; this is neither $F(x)$ nor $-F(x)$, so there is no symmetry.

Step 4:   The vertical asymptote is the zero of $q(x)$: $x = -2$

Step 5:   Since $n = m + 1$, there is an oblique asymptote. Dividing:

$$
\begin{array}{r}
x - 1 \\
x + 2 \overline{) x^2 + x - 12} \\
\underline{x^2 + 2x} \\
-x - 12 \\
\underline{-x - 2} \\
-10
\end{array}
\qquad
F(x) = x - 1 + \dfrac{-10}{x + 2}
$$

The oblique asymptote is $y = x - 1$.

Solve to find intersection points:

$$\dfrac{x^2 + x - 12}{x + 2} = x - 1 \Rightarrow x^2 + x - 12 = x^2 + x - 2 \Rightarrow -12 = -2$$

Since there is no solution, the oblique asymptote does not intersect $F(x)$.

Step 6:

Interval	$(-\infty, -4)$	$(-4, -2)$	$(-2, 3)$	$(3, \infty)$
Number Chosen	-5	-3	0	4
Value of F	$F(-5) = -\frac{8}{3}$	$F(-3) = 6$	$F(0) = -6$	$F(4) = \frac{4}{3}$
Location of Graph	Below x-axis	Above x-axis	Below x-axis	Above x-axis
Point on Graph	$(-5, -\frac{8}{3})$	$(-3, 6)$	$(0, -6)$	$(4, \frac{4}{3})$

223

Step 7:   Graphing Utility:

Step 8:   Graphing by hand:

25. $R(x) = \dfrac{x(x-1)^2}{(x+3)^3}$ $p(x) = x(x-1)^2;\ \ q(x) = (x+3)^3;\ \ n = 3;\ \ m = 3$

Step 1:   Domain: $\{x \mid x \neq -3\}$

Step 2:   (a)   The x-intercepts are the zeros of $p(x)$: 0 and 1

(b)   The y-intercept is $R(0) = \dfrac{0(0-1)^2}{(0+3)^3} = \dfrac{0}{27} = 0$.

Step 3: $R(-x) = \dfrac{-x(-x-1)^2}{(-x+3)^3}$; this is neither $R(x)$ nor $-R(x)$, so there is no symmetry.

Step 4:   The vertical asymptote is the zero of $q(x)$: $x = -3$

Step 5:   Since $n = m$, the line $y = 1$ is the horizontal asymptote.

Solve to find intersection points:

$$\frac{x(x-1)^2}{(x+3)^3} = 1$$

$$x^3 - 2x^2 + x = x^3 + 9x^2 + 27x + 27$$

$$0 = 11x^2 + 26x + 27$$

Since there is no real solution, $R(x)$ does not intersect $y = 1$.

Step 6:

Interval	$(-\infty, -3)$	$(-3, 0)$	$(0, 1)$	$(1, \infty)$
Number Chosen	-4	-1	$\frac{1}{2}$	2
Value of R	$R(-4) = 100$	$R(-1) = -0.5$	$R(\frac{1}{2}) \approx 0.003$	$R(2) = 0.016$
Location of Graph	Above x-axis	Below x-axis	Above x-axis	Above x-axis
Point on Graph	$(-4, 100)$	$(-1, -0.5)$	$(\frac{1}{2}, 0.003)$	$(2, 0.016)$

Step 7:   Graphing Utility:

Step 8:   Graphing by hand:

Enlarged view

27. $R(x) = \dfrac{x^2 + x - 12}{x^2 - x - 6} = \dfrac{(x+4)(x-3)}{(x-3)(x+2)} = \dfrac{x+4}{x+2}$ $p(x) = x^2 + x - 12;$ $q(x) = x^2 - x - 6;$
$n = 2;$ $m = 2$

Step 1:   Domain: $\{x \mid x \neq -2, x \neq 3\}$

Step 2:   (a)   The x-intercept is the zero of $p(x)$: -4 ; 3 is not a zero because reduced form must be used to find the zeros.

(b)   The y-intercept is $R(0) = \dfrac{0^2 + 0 - 12}{0^2 - 0 - 6} = \dfrac{-12}{-6} = 2$.

Step 3: $R(-x) = \dfrac{(-x)^2 + (-x) - 12}{(-x)^2 - (-x) - 6} = \dfrac{x^2 - x - 12}{x^2 + x - 6}$; this is neither $R(x)$ nor $-R(x)$, so there is no symmetry.

Step 4:   The vertical asymptote is the zero of $q(x)$: $x = -2$; $x = 3$ is not a vertical asymptote because reduced form must be used to find the them. The graph has a hole at $\left(3, \dfrac{7}{5}\right)$.

Step 5:   Since $n = m$, the line $y = 1$ is the horizontal asymptote.
$R(x)$ does not intersect $y = 1$ because $R(x)$ is not defined at $x = 3$.
$$\dfrac{x^2 + x - 12}{x^2 - x - 6} = 1$$
$$x^2 + x - 12 = x^2 - x - 6$$
$$2x = 6$$
$$x = 3$$

Step 6:

Interval	$(-\infty, -4)$	$(-4, -2)$	$(-2, 3)$	$(3, \infty)$
Number Chosen	-5	-3	0	4
Value of R	$R(-5) = \frac{1}{3}$	$R(-3) = -1$	$R(0) = 2$	$R(4) = \frac{4}{3}$
Location of Graph	Above x-axis	Below x-axis	Above x-axis	Above x-axis
Point on Graph	$(-5, \frac{1}{3})$	$(-3, -1)$	$(0, 2)$	$(4, \frac{4}{3})$

225

Step 7:   Graphing Utility:

Step 8:   Graphing by hand:

29. $R(x) = \dfrac{6x^2 - 7x - 3}{2x^2 - 7x + 6} = \dfrac{(3x+1)(2x-3)}{(2x-3)(x-2)} = \dfrac{3x+1}{x-2}$ $p(x) = 6x^2 - 7x - 3;$

$q(x) = 2x^2 - 7x + 6;$ $n = 2;$ $m = 2$

Step 1:   Domain: $\left\{ x \mid x \neq \dfrac{3}{2},\ x \neq 2 \right\}$

Step 2:   (a)   The x-intercept is the zero of $p(x)$: $-\dfrac{1}{3}$; $x = \dfrac{3}{2}$ is not a zero because reduced form must be used to find the zeros.

(b)   The y-intercept is $R(0) = \dfrac{6(0)^2 - 7(0) - 3}{2(0)^2 - 7(0) + 6} = \dfrac{-3}{6} = -\dfrac{1}{2}$.

Step 3: $R(-x) = \dfrac{6(-x)^2 - 7(-x) - 3}{2(-x)^2 - 7(-x) + 6} = \dfrac{6x^2 + 7x - 3}{2x^2 + 7x + 6}$; this is neither $R(x)$ nor $-R(x)$, so there is no symmetry.

Step 4:   The vertical asymptote is the zero of $q(x)$: $x = 2$; $x = \dfrac{3}{2}$ is not a vertical asymptote because reduced form must be used to find the them. The graph has a hole at $\left(\dfrac{3}{2}, -11 \right)$.

Step 5:   Since $n = m$, the line $y = 3$ is the horizontal asymptote.

$R(x)$ does not intersect $y = 3$ because $R(x)$ is not defined at $x = \dfrac{3}{2}$.

$$\dfrac{6x^2 - 7x - 3}{2x^2 - 7x + 6} = 3$$

$$6x^2 - 7x - 3 = 6x^2 - 21x + 18$$

$$14x = 21$$

$$x = \dfrac{3}{2}$$

Step 6:

Interval	$(-\infty, -\frac{1}{3})$	$(-\frac{1}{3},\frac{3}{2})$	$(\frac{3}{2}, 2)$	$(2, \infty)$
Number Chosen	-1	0	1.7	6
Value of R	$R(-1) = \frac{2}{3}$	$R(0) = -\frac{1}{2}$	$R(1.7) \approx -20.3$	$R(6) = 4.75$
Location of Graph	Above x-axis	Below x-axis	Below x-axis	Above x-axis
Point on Graph	$(-1,\frac{2}{3})$	$(0, -\frac{1}{2})$	$(1.7, -20.3)$	$(6, 4.75)$

Step 7:   Graphing Utility:

Step 8:   Graphing by hand:

31. $R(x) = \dfrac{x^2+5x+6}{x+3} = \dfrac{(x+2)(x+3)}{x+3} = x+2$ $p(x) = x^2+5x+6; \quad q(x) = x+3;$

$n = 2; \ m = 1$

Step 1:   Domain: $\{x \mid x \neq -3\}$

Step 2:   (a)   The x-intercept is the zero of $p(x)$: -2 ; -3 is not a zero because reduced form must be used to find the zeros.

(b)   The y-intercept is $R(0) = \dfrac{0^2+5(0)+6}{0+3} = \dfrac{6}{3} = 2$.

Step 3: $R(-x) = \dfrac{(-x)^2+5(-x)+6}{-x+3} = \dfrac{x^2-5x+6}{-x+3}$; this is neither $R(x)$ nor $-R(x)$, so there is no symmetry.

Step 4:   There are no vertical asymptotes. $x = -3$ is not a vertical asymptote because reduced form must be used to find the them. The graph has a hole at $(-3,-1)$.

Step 5:   Since $n = m+1$ there is a oblique asymptote. The line $y = x+2$ is the oblique asymptote. The oblique asymptote intersects $R(x)$ at every point of the form $(x, x+2)$ except $(-3, -1)$.

Step 6:

Interval	$(-\infty, -3)$	$(-3, -2)$	$(-2, \infty)$
Number Chosen	-4	-2.5	0
Value of R	$R(-4) = -2$	$R(-2.5) = -\frac{1}{2}$	$R(0) = 2$
Location of Graph	Below x-axis	Below x-axis	Above x-axis
Point on Graph	$(-4, -2)$	$(-2.5, -\frac{1}{2})$	$(0, 2)$

227

Step 7:   Graphing Utility:

Step 8:   Graphing by hand:

33. $f(x) = x + \dfrac{1}{x} = \dfrac{x^2 + 1}{x}$ $p(x) = x^2 + 1;\ \ q(x) = x;\ \ n = 2;\ \ m = 1$

Step 1:   Domain: $\{x \mid x \neq 0\}$

Step 2:   (a)   There are no x-intercepts.

(b)   There is no y-intercept because 0 is not in the domain.

Step 3: $f(-x) = \dfrac{(-x)^2 + 1}{-x} = \dfrac{x^2 + 1}{-x} = -f(x)$; The graph of $f(x)$ is symmetric to the origin.

Step 4:   The vertical asymptote is the zero of $q(x)$: $x = 0$

Step 5:   Since $n = m + 1$, there is an oblique asymptote. Dividing:

$$\begin{array}{r} x \\ x\overline{)x^2 + 1} \\ \underline{x^2} \\ 1 \end{array}$$

$f(x) = x + \dfrac{1}{x}$

The oblique asymptote is $y = x$.

Solve to find intersection points: $\dfrac{x^2 + 1}{x} = x \Rightarrow x^2 + 1 = x^2 \Rightarrow 1 = 0$

Since there is no solution, the oblique asymptote does not intersect $f(x)$.

Step 6:

Interval	$(-\infty, 0)$	$(0, \infty)$
Number Chosen	-1	1
Value of f	$f(-1) = -2$	$f(1) = 2$
Location of Graph	Below x-axis	Above x-axis
Point on Graph	(-1, -2)	(1, 2)

Step 7:   Graphing Utility:

Step 8:   Graphing by hand:

228

35. $f(x) = x^2 + \dfrac{1}{x} = \dfrac{x^3 + 1}{x}$ $p(x) = x^3 + 1;\ q(x) = x;\ n = 3;\ m = 1$

Step 1: Domain: $\{x \mid x \neq 0\}$

Step 2: (a)   The x-intercept is the zero of $p(x)$: -1

   (b)   There is no y-intercept because 0 is not in the domain.

Step 3: $f(-x) = \dfrac{(-x)^3 + 1}{-x} = \dfrac{-x^3 + 1}{-x}$; this is neither $f(x)$ nor $-f(x)$, so there is no symmetry.

Step 4: The vertical asymptote is the zero of $q(x)$: $x = 0$

Step 5: Since $n > m + 1$, there is no horizontal or oblique asymptote.

Step 6:

Interval	$(-\infty, -1)$	$(-1, 0)$	$(0, \infty)$
Number Chosen	-2	$-\frac{1}{2}$	1
Value of f	$f(-2) = 3.5$	$f(-\frac{1}{2}) = -1.75$	$f(1) = 2$
Location of Graph	Above x-axis	Below x-axis	Above x-axis
Point on Graph	$(-2, 3.5)$	$(-\frac{1}{2}, -1.75)$	$(1, 2)$

Step 7: Graphing Utility:

Step 8: Graphing by hand:

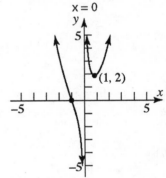

37. $f(x) = x + \dfrac{1}{x^3} = \dfrac{x^4 + 1}{x^3}$ $p(x) = x^4 + 1;\ q(x) = x^3;\ n = 4;\ m = 3$

Step 1: Domain: $\{x \mid x \neq 0\}$

Step 2: (a)   There are no x-intercepts.

   (b)   There is no y-intercept because 0 is not in the domain.

Step 3: $f(-x) = \dfrac{(-x)^4 + 1}{(-x)^3} = \dfrac{x^4 + 1}{-x^3} = -f(x)$; the graph of $f(x)$ is symmetric with respect to the origin.

Step 4: The vertical asymptote is the zero of $q(x)$: $x = 0$

Step 5: Since $n = m + 1$, there is an oblique asymptote. Dividing:

$$f(x) = x + \frac{1}{x^3}$$ The oblique asymptote is $y = x$.

Solve to find intersection points: $\dfrac{x^4+1}{x^3} = x \Rightarrow x^4+1 = x^4 \Rightarrow 1 = 0$

Since there is no solution, the oblique asymptote does not intersect $f(x)$.

Step 6:

Interval	$(-\infty, 0)$	$(0, \infty)$
Number Chosen	-1	1
Value of f	$f(-1) = -2$	$f(1) = 2$
Location of Graph	Below x-axis	Above x-axis
Point on Graph	$(-1, -2)$	$(1, 2)$

Step 7:   Graphing Utility:

Step 8:   Graphing by hand:

39. $f(x) = \dfrac{x^2}{x^2-4}$

41. $f(x) = \dfrac{(x-1)^3(x-3)}{(x+1)^2(x-2)^2}$

43.   Answers will vary, one example is $R(x) = \dfrac{3(x-2)(x+1)^2}{(x+5)(x-6)^2}$

45. $g(h) = \dfrac{3.99 \times 10^{14}}{\left(6.374 \times 10^6 + h\right)^2}$

(a) $g(0) = \dfrac{3.99 \times 10^{14}}{\left(6.374 \times 10^6 + 0\right)^2} \approx 9.821 \ m/s^2$

(b) $g(443) = \dfrac{3.99 \times 10^{14}}{\left(6.374 \times 10^6 + 443\right)^2} \approx 9.8195 \ m/s^2$

(c) $g(8848) = \dfrac{3.99 \times 10^{14}}{\left(6.374 \times 10^6 + 8848\right)^2} \approx 9.794 \ m/s^2$

(d) $g(h) = \dfrac{3.99 \times 10^{14}}{\left(6.374 \times 10^6 + h\right)^2} \approx \dfrac{3.99 \times 10^{14}}{h^2} \to 0 \ \text{as} \ h \to \infty$

$\therefore y = 0$ is the horizontal asymptote.

(e)

(f) $g(h) = \dfrac{3.99 \times 10^{14}}{\left(6.374 \times 10^6 + h\right)^2} = 0$, to solve this equation would require that

$3.99 \times 10^{14} = 0$, which is impossible. Therefore, there is no height above sea level at which $g = 0$. In other words, there is no point in the entire universe that is unaffected by the Earth's gravity!

47.   (a)   Graphing:

(b)   Using MAXIMUM, the concentration is highest when $t = 0.71$ hours.

(c) $C(t) = \dfrac{t}{2t^2 + 1} \approx \dfrac{t}{2t^2} = \dfrac{1}{2t} \to 0$ as $t \to \pm\infty$

therefore the horizontal asymptote is $y = 0$.

The concentration of the drug decreases to 0 as time increases.

49.   (a)   The average cost function is: $\overline{C}(x) = \dfrac{0.2x^3 - 2.3x^2 + 14.3x + 10.2}{x}$

(b) $\overline{C}(6) = \dfrac{0.2(6)^3 - 2.3(6)^2 + 14.3(6) + 10.2}{6} = \dfrac{56.4}{6} = 9.4$

The average cost of producing 6 Cavaliers per hour is $9400 per car.

(c) $\overline{C}(9) = \dfrac{0.2(9)^3 - 2.3(9)^2 + 14.3(9) + 10.2}{9} = \dfrac{98.4}{9} = 10.933$

The average cost of producing 9 Cavaliers per hour is $10,933 per car.

(d)   Graphing:

(e)   Using MINIMUM, the number of Cavaliers that should be produced per hour to minimize cost is 6.38 cars

(f)   The minimum average cost is

$\overline{C}(6.38) = \dfrac{0.2(6.38)^3 - 2.3(6.38)^2 + 14.3(6.38) + 10.2}{6.38} \approx \$9366$ per car.

51. (a) The surface area is the sum of the areas of the six sides.

$$S = xy + xy + xy + xy + x^2 + x^2 = 4xy + 2x^2$$

The volume is $x \cdot x \cdot y = x^2 y = 10{,}000 \implies y = \dfrac{10000}{x^2}$

Thus, $S(x) = 4x\left(\dfrac{10000}{x^2}\right) + 2x^2 = 2x^2 + \dfrac{40000}{x} = \dfrac{2x^3 + 40000}{x}$

(b) Graphing:

(c) Using MINIMUM, the minimum surface area (amount of cardboard) is 2,785 square inches.

(d) The surface area is a minimum when $x = 21.544$.

$$y = \dfrac{10000}{21.544^2} \approx 21.545$$

The dimensions of the box are: 21.544 in. by 21.544 in. by 21.545 in.

53. (a) $500 = \pi r^2 h \implies h = \dfrac{500}{\pi r^2}$

$$C(r) = 6(2\pi r^2) + 4(2\pi rh) = 12\pi r^2 + 8\pi r\left(\dfrac{500}{\pi r^2}\right) = 12\pi r^2 + \dfrac{4000}{r}$$

(b) Graphing:

Using MINIMUM, the cost is least for $r \approx 3.76$ cm.

55.   Answers will vary.

Polynomial and Rational Functions

4.5 Polynomial and Rational Inequalities

1. $(x-5)(x+2) < 0$ $f(x) = (x-5)(x+2)$
   $x = 5, x = -2$ are the zeros.

Interval	Test Number	$f(x)$	Positive/Negative
$-\infty < x < -2$	-3	8	Positive
$-2 < x < 5$	0	-10	Negative
$5 < x < \infty$	6	8	Positive

   The solution set is $\left\{ x \mid -2 < x < 5 \right\}$.

   Graph $f(x) = (x-5)(x+2)$.
   The x-intercepts are $x = -2$ and $x = 5$. The graph
   of f is below the x-axis for $-2 < x < 5$. Thus, the
   solution set is $\left\{ x \mid -2 < x < 5 \right\}$.

   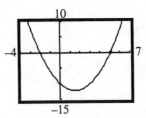

3. $x^2 - 4x > 0$ $f(x) = x^2 - 4x$
   $x(x-4) > 0$
   $x = 0, x = 4$ are the zeros.

Interval	Test Number	$f(x)$	Positive/Negative
$-\infty < x < 0$	-1	5	Positive
$0 < x < 4$	1	-3	Negative
$4 < x < \infty$	5	5	Positive

   The solution set is $\left\{ x \mid x < 0 \ \text{ or } \ x > 4 \right\}$.

   Graph $f(x) = x^2 - 4x$.
   The x-intercepts are $x = 0$ and $x = 4$. The graph of
   f is above the x-axis for $x < 0$ or $x > 4$. Thus,
   the solution set is $\left\{ x \mid x < 0 \text{ or } x > 4 \right\}$.

   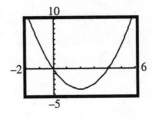

5. $x^2 - 9 < 0$ $f(x) = x^2 - 9$

$(x+3)(x-3) < 0$

$x = -3$, $x = 3$ are the zeros

Interval	Test Number	$f(x)$	Positive/Negative
$-\infty < x < -3$	-4	7	Positive
$-3 < x < 3$	0	-9	Negative
$3 < x < \infty$	4	7	Positive

The solution set is $\left\{ x \mid -3 < x < 3 \right\}$.

Graph $f(x) = x^2 - 9$.

The x-intercepts are $x = -3$ and $x = 3$. The graph of f is below the x-axis for $-3 < x < 3$. Thus, the solution set is $\left\{ x \mid -3 < x < 3 \right\}$.

7. $x^2 + x > 12$ $f(x) = x^2 + x - 12$

$x^2 + x - 12 > 0 \Rightarrow (x+4)(x-3) > 0$

$x = -4$, $x = 3$ are the zeros.

Interval	Test Number	$f(x)$	Positive/Negative
$-\infty < x < -4$	-5	8	Positive
$-4 < x < 3$	0	-12	Negative
$3 < x < \infty$	4	8	Positive

The solution set is $\left\{ x \mid x < -4 \text{ or } x > 3 \right\}$.

Graph $y_1 = x^2 + x$, $y_2 = 12$.

y_1 intersects y_2 at $x = -4$ and $x = 3$. $y_1 > y_2$ for $x < -4$ or $x > 3$. Thus, the solution set is $\left\{ x \mid x < -4 \text{ or } x > 3 \right\}$.

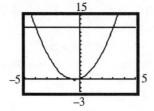

9. $2x^2 < 5x + 3$ $f(x) = 2x^2 - 5x - 3$

$2x^2 - 5x - 3 < 0 \Rightarrow (2x+1)(x-3) < 0$

$x = -\dfrac{1}{2}$, $x = 3$ are the zeros.

Interval	Test Number	$f(x)$	Positive/Negative
$-\infty < x < -1/2$	-1	4	Positive
$-1/2 < x < 3$	0	-3	Negative
$3 < x < \infty$	4	9	Positive

The solution set is $\left\{ x \mid -\dfrac{1}{2} < x < 3 \right\}$.

Graph $y_1 = 2x^2$, $y_2 = 5x + 3$.
y_1 intersects y_2 at $x = -0.50$ and $x = 3$.
$y_1 < y_2$ for $-0.50 < x < 3$. Thus, the solution set
is $\left\{ x \mid -0.50 < x < 3 \right\}$.

11. $x(x - 7) > 8$ $f(x) = x^2 - 7x - 8$

$x^2 - 7x > 8 \Rightarrow x^2 - 7x - 8 > 0 \rightarrow (x + 1)(x - 8) > 0$
$x = -1$, $x = 8$ are the zeros.

Interval	Test Number	$f(x)$	Positive/Negative
$-\infty < x < -1$	-2	10	Positive
$-1 < x < 8$	0	-8	Negative
$8 < x < \infty$	9	10	Positive

The solution set is $\left\{ x \mid x < -1 \text{ or } x > 8 \right\}$.

Graph $y_1 = x(x - 7)$, $y_2 = 8$.
y_1 intersects y_2 at $x = -1$ and $x = 8$.
$y_1 > y_2$ for $x < -1$ or $x > 8$. Thus, the solution set
is $\left\{ x \mid x < -1 \text{ or } x > 8 \right\}$.

13. $4x^2 + 9 < 6x$ $f(x) = 4x^2 - 6x + 9$
$4x^2 - 6x + 9 < 0$
$b^2 - 4ac = (-6)^2 - 4(4)(9) = 36 - 144 = -108$
Since the discriminant is negative, there are no real zeros.
There is only one interval, the entire number line; choose any value and test.
For $x = 0$, $4x^2 - 6x + 9 = 9 > 0$. Thus, there is no solution.

Graph $y_1 = 4x^2 + 9$, $y_2 = 6x$.
y_1 is always greater than y_2. Thus, there is no
solution.

15. $6\left(x^2 - 1\right) > 5x$ $f(x) = 6x^2 - 5x - 6$

$6x^2 - 6 > 5x \Rightarrow 6x^2 - 5x - 6 > 0 \Rightarrow (3x + 2)(2x - 3) > 0$
$x = -\dfrac{2}{3}$, $x = \dfrac{3}{2}$ are the zeros.

Interval	Test Number	$f(x)$	Positive/Negative
$-\infty < x < -2/3$	-1	5	Positive
$-2/3 < x < 3/2$	0	-6	Negative
$3/2 < x < \infty$	2	8	Positive

The solution set is $\left\{ x \middle| x < -\dfrac{2}{3} \text{ or } x > \dfrac{3}{2} \right\}$.

Graph $y_1 = 6(x^2 - 1)$, $y_2 = 5x$.

y_1 intersects y_2 at $x = -0.67$ and $x = 1.5$. $y_1 > y_2$ for $x < -0.67$ or $x > 1.5$. Thus, the solution set is $\left\{ x \middle| x < -0.67 \text{ or } x > 1.5 \right\}$.

17. $(x-1)(x^2 + x + 1) > 0$ $f(x) = (x-1)(x^2 + x + 1)$

      $x = 1$ is the zero. $x^2 + x + 1 = 0$ has no real zeros.

Interval	Test Number	$f(x)$	Positive/Negative
$-\infty < x < 1$	0	-1	Negative
$1 < x < \infty$	2	7	Positive

      The solution set is $\left\{ x \middle| x > 1 \right\}$.

Graph $f(x) = (x-1)(x^2 + x + 1)$.

The x-intercept is $x = 1$. The graph of f is above the x-axis for $x > 1$. Thus, the solution set is $\left\{ x \middle| x > 1 \right\}$.

19. $(x-1)(x-2)(x-3) < 0$ $f(x) = (x-1)(x-2)(x-3)$

      $x = 1$, $x = 2$, $x = 3$ are the zeros.

Interval	Test Number	$f(x)$	Positive/Negative
$-\infty < x < 1$	0	-6	Negative
$1 < x < 2$	1.5	0.375	Positive
$2 < x < 3$	2.5	-0.375	Negative
$3 < x < \infty$	4	6	Positive

      The solution set is $\left\{ x \middle| x < 1 \text{ or } 2 < x < 3 \right\}$.

Graph $f(x) = (x-1)(x-2)(x-3)$.

The x-intercepts are and $x = 3$. The graph of f is below the x-axis for $x < 1$ or $2 < x < 3$. Thus, the solution set is $\left\{ x \middle| x < 1 \text{ or } 2 < x < 3 \right\}$.

21. $x^3 - 2x^2 - 3x > 0$ $f(x) = x^3 - 2x^2 - 3x$

$x(x^2 - 2x - 3) > 0 \Rightarrow x(x+1)(x-3) > 0$

$x = -1$, $x = 0$, $x = 3$ are the zeros.

Interval	Test Number	$f(x)$	Positive/Negative
$-\infty < x < -1$	-2	-10	Negative
$-1 < x < 0$	-0.5	0.875	Positive
$0 < x < 3$	1	-4	Negative
$3 < x < \infty$	4	20	Positive

The solution set is $\{x \mid -1 < x < 0 \text{ or } x > 3\}$.

Graph $f(x) = x^3 - 2x^2 - 3x$.
The x-intercepts are $x = -1$, $x = 0$, and $x = 3$.
The graph of f is above the x-axis for
$-1 < x < 0$ or $x > 3$. Thus, the solution set is
$\{x \mid -1 < x < 0 \text{ or } x > 3\}$.

23. $x^4 > x^2$ $f(x) = x^4 - x^2$

$x^4 - x^2 > 0 \Rightarrow x^2(x^2 - 1) > 0 \Rightarrow x^2(x+1)(x-1) > 0$

$x = -1$, $x = 0$, $x = 1$ are the zeros.

Interval	Test Number	$f(x)$	Positive/Negative
$-\infty < x < -1$	-2	12	Positive
$-1 < x < 0$	-0.5	-0.1875	Negative
$0 < x < 1$	0.5	-0.1875	Negative
$1 < x < \infty$	2	12	Positive

The solution set is $\{x \mid x < -1 \text{ or } x > 1\}$.

Graph $y_1 = x^4$, $y_2 = x^2$.
y_1 intersects y_2 at $x = -1$, $x = 0$, and $x = 1$.
$y_1 > y_2$ for $x < -1$ or $x > 1$. Thus, the solution set
is $\{x \mid x < -1 \text{ or } x > 1\}$.

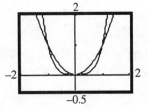

25. $x^3 > x^2$ $f(x) = x^3 - x^2$

$x^3 - x^2 > 0 \Rightarrow x^2(x-1) > 0$

$x = 0$, $x = 1$ are the zeros.

Interval	Test Number	$f(x)$	Positive/Negative
$-\infty < x < 0$	-1	-2	Negative
$0 < x < 1$	0.5	-0.125	Negative
$1 < x < \infty$	2	4	Positive

The solution set is $\{x \mid x > 1\}$.

Graph $y_1 = x^3$, $y_2 = x^2$.
y_1 intersects y_2 at $x = 0$ and $x = 1$. $y_1 > y_2$ for
$x > 1$. Thus, the solution set is $\{x \mid x > 1\}$.

27. $x^4 > 1$ $f(x) = x^4 - 1$

$x^4 - 1 > 0 \Rightarrow (x^2 + 1)(x^2 - 1) > 0 \Rightarrow (x^2 + 1)(x + 1)(x - 1) > 0$

$x = -1$, $x = 1$ are the zeros.

Interval	Test Number	$f(x)$	Positive/Negative
$-\infty < x < -1$	-2	15	Positive
$-1 < x < 1$	0	-1	Negative
$1 < x < \infty$	2	15	Positive

The solution set is $\{x \mid x < -1 \text{ or } x > 1\}$.

Graph $y_1 = x^4$, $y_2 = 1$.
y_1 intersects y_2 at $x = -1$ and $x = 1$. $y_1 > y_2$ for
$x < -1$ or $x > 1$. Thus, the solution set is
$\{x \mid x < -1 \text{ or } x > 1\}$.

29. $x^2 - 7x - 8 < 0$ $f(x) = x^2 - 7x - 8$

$(x + 1)(x - 8) < 0$

$x = -1$, $x = 8$ are the zeros.

Interval	Test Number	$f(x)$	Positive/Negative
$-\infty < x < -1$	-2	10	Positive
$-1 < x < 8$	0	-8	Negative
$8 < x < \infty$	9	10	Positive

The solution set is $\{x \mid -1 < x < 8\}$.

Graph $f(x) = x^2 - 7x - 8$.
The x-intercepts are $x = -1$ and $x = 8$. The graph
of f is below the x-axis for $-1 < x < 8$. Thus, the
solution set is $\{x \mid -1 < x < 8\}$.

31. Graph $f(x) = x^3 + x - 12$ and use ZERO to find the zero of the function.

$x = 2.14$ is the zero (rounded to two decimal places).

Interval	Test Number	$f(x)$	Positive/Negative
$-\infty < x < 2.14$	0	-12	Negative
$2.14 < x < \infty$	3	18	Positive

The solution set is $\{x \mid x \geq 2.14\}$.

Graph $f(x) = x^3 + x - 12$.
The x-intercept is $x = 2.14$. The graph of f is
above the x-axis for $x > 2.14$. Thus, the solution
set is $\left\{ x \middle| x \geq 2.14 \right\}$.

33. $x^4 - 3x^2 - 4 > 0$ $\qquad$ $f(x) = x^4 - 3x^2 - 4$
$\qquad$ $\left(x^2 - 4\right)\left(x^2 + 1\right) > 0 \Rightarrow (x+2)(x-2)\left(x^2+1\right) > 0$
$\qquad$ $x = -2, x = 2$ are the zeros.

Interval	Test Number	$f(x)$	Positive/Negative
$-\infty < x < -2$	-3	50	Positive
$-2 < x < 2$	0	-4	Negative
$2 < x < \infty$	3	50	Positive

$\qquad$ The solution set is $\left\{ x \middle| x < -2 \ \text{ or } \ x > 2 \right\}$.

Graph $f(x) = x^4 - 3x^2 - 4$.
The x-intercepts are $x = -2$, and $x = 2$. The graph
of f is above the x-axis for $x < -2$ or $x > 2$.
Thus, the solution set is $\left\{ x \middle| x < -2 \ \text{ or } \ x > 2 \right\}$.

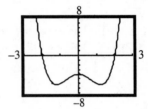

35. $x^3 - 4 \geq 3x^2 + 5x - 3$ $\qquad$ $f(x) = x^3 - 3x^2 - 5x - 1$
$\qquad$ $x^3 - 3x^2 - 5x - 1 \geq 0$
$\qquad$ Do synthetic division by -1:

$$
\begin{array}{r|rrrr}
-1 & 1 & -3 & -5 & -1 \\
   &   & -1 & 4 & 1 \\
\hline
   & 1 & -4 & -1 & 0 \\
\end{array}
$$

$\qquad$ $x = -1$ is a solution. Solving the remaining factor $x^2 - 4x - 1 = 0$:

$$x = \frac{-(-4) \pm \sqrt{(-4)^2 - 4(1)(-1)}}{2(1)} = \frac{4 \pm \sqrt{20}}{2} = \frac{4 \pm 2\sqrt{5}}{2} = 2 \pm \sqrt{5}$$

$\qquad$ $x = -1, x = 2 - \sqrt{5}, x = 2 + \sqrt{5}$ or $x = -1, x = -0.24, x = 4.24$ are the zeros.

Interval	Test Number	$f(x)$	Positive/Negative
$-\infty < x < -1$	-2	-11	Negative
$-1 < x < 2 - \sqrt{5}$	-0.5	0.625	Positive
$2 - \sqrt{5} < x < 2 + \sqrt{5}$	0	-1	Negative
$2 + \sqrt{5} < x < \infty$	5	24	Positive

$\qquad$ The solution set is $\left\{ x \middle| -1 \leq x \leq 2 - \sqrt{5} \text{ or } x \geq 2 + \sqrt{5} \right\}$.

Graph $y_1 = x^3 - 4$, $y_2 = 3x^2 + 5x - 3$.
y_1 intersects y_2 at $x = -1$, $x = -0.24$,
and $x = 4.24$. $y_1 \geq y_2$ for
$-1 \leq x \leq -0.24$ or $x \geq 4.24$. Thus, the solution set
is $\left\{ x \mid -1 \leq x \leq -0.24 \text{ or } x \geq 4.24 \right\}$.

37.　$\dfrac{x+1}{x-1} > 0$　　　　　　　　　　$f(x) = \dfrac{x+1}{x-1}$

The zeros and values where the expression is undefined are $x = -1$, and $x = 1$.

Interval	Test Number	$f(x)$	Positive/Negative
$-\infty < x < -1$	-2	$1/3$	Positive
$-1 < x < 1$	0	-1	Negative
$1 < x < \infty$	2	3	Positive

The solution set is $\left\{ x \mid x < -1 \text{ or } x > 1 \right\}$.

Graph $f(x) = \dfrac{x+1}{x-1}$.

The x-intercept is $x = -1$. The expression is
undefined at $x = 1$. The graph of f is above the
x-axis for $x < -1$ or $x > 1$. Thus, the solution set
is $\left\{ x \mid x < -1 \text{ or } x > 1 \right\}$.

39.　$\dfrac{(x-1)(x+1)}{x} < 0$　　　　　　　$f(x) = \dfrac{(x-1)(x+1)}{x}$

The zeros and values where the expression is undefined are $x = -1$, $x = 0$, and $x = 1$.

Interval	Test Number	$f(x)$	Positive/Negative
$-\infty < x < -1$	-2	-1.5	Negative
$-1 < x < 0$	-0.5	1.5	Positive
$0 < x < 1$	0.5	-1.5	Negative
$1 < x < \infty$	2	1.5	Positive

The solution set is $\left\{ x \mid x < -1 \text{ or } 0 < x < 1 \right\}$.

Graph $f(x) = \dfrac{(x-1)(x+1)}{x}$.

The x-intercepts are $x = -1$ and $x = 1$. The
expression is undefined at $x = 0$. The graph of f
is below the x-axis for $x < -1$ or $0 < x < 1$. Thus,
the solution set is $\left\{ x \mid x < -1 \text{ or } 0 < x < 1 \right\}$.

41. $\dfrac{(x-2)^2}{x^2-1} \geq 0$ $\qquad$ $f(x) = \dfrac{(x-2)^2}{x^2-1}$

$\dfrac{(x-2)^2}{(x+1)(x-1)} \geq 0$

The zeros and values where the expression is undefined are $x = -1$, $x = 1$, and $x = 2$.

Interval	Test Number	$f(x)$	Positive/Negative
$-\infty < x < -1$	-2	$16/3$	Positive
$-1 < x < 1$	0	-4	Negative
$1 < x < 2$	1.5	0.2	Positive
$2 < x < \infty$	3	0.125	Positive

The solution set is $\left\{ x \mid x < -1 \text{ or } x > 1 \right\}$.

Graph $f(x) = \dfrac{(x-2)^2}{x^2-1}$.

The x-intercept is $x = 2$. The expression is undefined at $x = -1$ and $x = 1$. The graph of f is above the x-axis for $x < -1$ or $x > 1$. Thus, the solution set is $\left\{ x \mid x < -1 \text{ or } x > 1 \right\}$.

43. $6x - 5 < \dfrac{6}{x}$ $\qquad$ $f(x) = 6x - 5 - \dfrac{6}{x}$

$6x - 5 - \dfrac{6}{x} < 0 \Rightarrow \dfrac{6x^2 - 5x - 6}{x} < 0 \Rightarrow \dfrac{(2x-3)(3x+2)}{x} < 0$

The zeros and values where the expression is undefined are $x = -\dfrac{2}{3}$, $x = 0$, and $x = \dfrac{3}{2}$.

Interval	Test Number	$f(x)$	Positive/Negative
$-\infty < x < -2/3$	-1	-5	Negative
$-2/3 < x < 0$	-0.5	4	Positive
$0 < x < 3/2$	1	-5	Negative
$3/2 < x < \infty$	2	4	Positive

The solution set is $\left\{ x \mid x < -\dfrac{2}{3} \text{ or } 0 < x < \dfrac{3}{2} \right\}$.

Graph $y_1 = 6x - 5$, $y_2 = \dfrac{6}{x}$.

y_1 intersects y_2 at $x = -0.67$ and $x = 1.5$. y_2 is undefined at $x = 0$. $y_1 < y_2$ for $x < -0.67$ or $0 < x < 1.5$. Thus, the solution set is $\left\{ x \mid x < -0.67 \text{ or } 0 < x < 1.5 \right\}$.

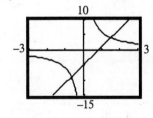

45. $\dfrac{x+4}{x-2} \le 1$ $f(x) = \dfrac{x+4}{x-2} - 1$

$\dfrac{x+4}{x-2} - 1 \le 0 \Rightarrow \dfrac{x+4-(x-2)}{x-2} \le 0 \Rightarrow \dfrac{6}{x-2} \le 0$

The value where the expression is undefined is $x = 2$.

Interval	Test Number	$f(x)$	Positive/Negative
$-\infty < x < 2$	0	-3	Negative
$2 < x < \infty$	3	6	Positive

The solution set is $\left\{ x \mid x < 2 \right\}$.

Graph $y_1 = \dfrac{x+4}{x-2}$, $y_2 = 1$.

y_1 is not defined at $x = 2$. $y_1 < y_2$ for $x < 2$. Thus, the solution set is $\left\{ x \mid x < 2 \right\}$.

47. $\dfrac{3x-5}{x+2} \le 2$ $f(x) = \dfrac{3x-5}{x+2} - 2$

$\dfrac{3x-5}{x+2} - 2 \le 0 \Rightarrow \dfrac{3x-5-2(x+2)}{x+2} \le 0 \Rightarrow \dfrac{x-9}{x+2} \le 0$

The zeros and values where the expression is undefined are $x = -2$, and $x = 9$.

Interval	Test Number	$f(x)$	Positive/Negative
$-\infty < x < -2$	-3	12	Positive
$-2 < x < 9$	0	-4.5	Negative
$9 < x < \infty$	10	$1/12$	Positive

The solution set is $\left\{ x \mid -2 < x \le 9 \right\}$.

Graph $y_1 = \dfrac{3x-5}{x+2}$, $y_2 = 2$.

y_1 is not defined at $x = -2$. y_1 intersects y_2 at $x = 9$. $y_1 < y_2$ for $-2 < x < 9$. Thus, the solution set is $\left\{ x \mid -2 < x \le 9 \right\}$.

49. $\dfrac{1}{x-2} < \dfrac{2}{3x-9}$ $f(x) = \dfrac{1}{x+2} - \dfrac{2}{3x-9}$

$\dfrac{1}{x-2} - \dfrac{2}{3x-9} < 0 \Rightarrow \dfrac{3x-9-2(x-2)}{(x-2)(3x-9)} < 0 \Rightarrow \dfrac{x-5}{(x-2)(3x-9)} < 0$

The zeros and values where the expression is undefined are $x = 2$, $x = 3$, and $x = 5$.

Interval	Test Number	$f(x)$	Positive/Negative
$-\infty < x < 2$	0	$-5/18$	Negative
$2 < x < 3$	2.5	$10/3$	Positive
$3 < x < 5$	4	$-1/6$	Negative
$5 < x < \infty$	6	$1/36$	Positive

The solution set is $\left\{ x \mid x < 2 \text{ or } 3 < x < 5 \right\}$.

Graph $y_1 = \dfrac{1}{x-2}$, $y_2 = \dfrac{2}{3x-9}$.

The undefined values are at $x = 2$, $x = 3$.

y_1 intersects y_2 at $x = 5$. $y_1 < y_2$ for $x < 2$ or $3 < x < 5$. Thus, the solution set is $\{x \mid x < 2 \text{ or } 3 < x < 5\}$.

51.
$$\frac{2x+5}{x+1} > \frac{x+1}{x-1}$$

$$f(x) = \frac{2x+5}{x+1} - \frac{x+1}{x-1}$$

$$\frac{2x+5}{x+1} - \frac{x+1}{x-1} > 0 \Rightarrow \frac{(2x+5)(x-1) - (x+1)(x+1)}{(x+1)(x-1)} > 0$$

$$\frac{2x^2 + 3x - 5 - (x^2 + 2x + 1)}{(x+1)(x-1)} > 0 \Rightarrow \frac{x^2 + x - 6}{(x+1)(x-1)} > 0 \Rightarrow \frac{(x+3)(x-2)}{(x+1)(x-1)} > 0$$

The zeros and values where the expression is undefined are

$x = -3$, $x = -1$, $x = 1$, and $x = 2$.

Interval	Test Number	$f(x)$	Positive/Negative
$-\infty < x < -3$	-4	2/5	Positive
$-3 < x < -1$	-2	$-4/3$	Negative
$-1 < x < 1$	0	6	Positive
$1 < x < 2$	1.5	$-9/5$	Negative
$2 < x < \infty$	3	3/4	Positive

The solution set is $\{x \mid x < -3, \ -1 < x < 1, \ x > 2\}$.

Graph $y_1 = \dfrac{2x+5}{x+1}$, $y_2 = \dfrac{x+1}{x-1}$.

The undefined values are at $x = -1$, $x = 1$.

y_1 intersects y_2 at $x = -3$ and $x = 2$. $y_1 > y_2$ for $x < -3$, $-1 < x < 1$, or $x > 2$. Thus, the solution set is $\{x \mid x < -3, \ -1 < x < 1, \ x > 2\}$.

53.
$$\frac{x^2(3+x)(x+4)}{(x+5)(x-1)} > 0$$

$$f(x) = \frac{x^2(3+x)(x+4)}{(x+5)(x-1)}$$

The zeros and values where the expression is undefined are

$x = -5$, $x = -4$, $x = -3$, $x = 0$ and $x = 1$.

Interval	Test Number	$f(x)$	Positive/Negative
$-\infty < x < -5$	-6	216/7	Positive
$-5 < x < -4$	-4.5	$-243/44$	Negative
$-4 < x < -3$	-3.5	49/108	Positive
$-3 < x < 0$	-1	$-3/4$	Negative
$0 < x < 1$	0.5	$-63/44$	Negative
$1 < x < \infty$	2	120/7	Positive

The solution set is $\{x \mid x < -5, \ -4 < x < -3, \ x > 1\}$.

Graph $f(x) = \dfrac{x^2(3+x)(x+4)}{(x+5)(x-1)}$.

The x-intercepts are $x = -4$, $x = -3$, and $x = 0$.
The expression is undefined at $x = -5$ and $x = 1$.
 The graph of f is above the x-axis for
$x < -5$, $-4 < x < -3$, or $x > 1$. Thus, the solution
set is $\left\{ x \mid x < -5, -4 < x < -3, x > 1 \right\}$.

55. $\dfrac{2x^2 - x - 1}{x - 4} \le 0$ $f(x) = \dfrac{2x^2 - x - 1}{x - 4}$

$\dfrac{(2x+1)(x-1)}{x-4} \le 0$

The zeros and values where the expression is undefined are $x = -\dfrac{1}{2}$, $x = 1$, and $x = 4$.

Interval	Test Number	$f(x)$	Positive/Negative
$-\infty < x < -1/2$	-1	$-2/5$	Negative
$-1/2 < x < 1$	0	$1/4$	Positive
$1 < x < 4$	2	$-5/2$	Negative
$4 < x < \infty$	5	44	Positive

The solution set is $\left\{ x \mid x \le -\dfrac{1}{2}, \text{ or } 1 \le x < 4 \right\}$.

Graph $f(x) = \dfrac{2x^2 - x - 1}{x - 4}$.

The x-intercepts are $x = -0.5$, and $x = 1$. The
expression is undefined at $x = 4$. The graph of f
is below the x-axis for $x < -0.5$, or $1 < x < 4$.
Thus, the solution set is
$\left\{ x \mid x \le -0.5, \text{ or } 1 \le x < 4 \right\}$.

57. $\dfrac{x^2 + 3x - 1}{x + 3} > 0$ $f(x) = \dfrac{x^2 + 3x - 1}{x + 3}$

Solving the numerator: $x = \dfrac{-3 \pm \sqrt{3^2 - 4(1)(-1)}}{2(1)} = \dfrac{-3 \pm \sqrt{13}}{2}$

The zeros and values where the expression is undefined are

$x = \dfrac{-3 - \sqrt{13}}{2}$, $x = \dfrac{-3 + \sqrt{13}}{2}$, and $x = -3$ or $x = -3.30$, $x = 0.30$, $x = -3$.

Interval	Test Number	$f(x)$	Positive/Negative
$-\infty < x < \dfrac{-3 - \sqrt{13}}{2}$	-4	-3	Negative
$\dfrac{-3 - \sqrt{13}}{2} < x < -3$	-3.2	$9/5$	Positive
$-3 < x < \dfrac{-3 + \sqrt{13}}{2}$	0	$-1/3$	Negative
$\dfrac{-3 + \sqrt{13}}{2} < x < \infty$	1	$3/4$	Positive

The solution set is $\left\{ x \middle| \dfrac{-3-\sqrt{13}}{2} < x < -3 \text{ or } x > \dfrac{-3+\sqrt{13}}{2} \right\}$.

Graph $f(x) = \dfrac{x^2 + 3x - 1}{x+3}$.

The x-intercepts are $x = -3.30$ and $x = 0.30$. The
expression is undefined at $x = -3$. The graph of
f is above the x-axis for
$-3.30 < x < -3$, or $x > 0.30$. Thus, the solution set
is $\left\{ x \middle| -3.30 < x < -3, \text{ or } x > 0.30 \right\}$.

59.   Let x be the positive number. Then

$$x^3 > 4x^2 \Rightarrow x^3 - 4x^2 > 0 \Rightarrow x^2(x-4) > 0$$

The zeros are $x = 0$ and $x = 4$. $f(x) = x^3 - 4x^2$

Interval	Test Number	$f(x)$	Positive/Negative
$-\infty < x < 0$	-1	-5	Negative
$0 < x < 4$	1	-3	Negative
$4 < x < \infty$	5	25	Positive

The solution set is $\left\{ x \middle| x > 4 \right\}$. All real number larger than 4 satisfy the condition.

61.   The domain of the expression includes all values for which

$$x^2 - 16 \geq 0 \Rightarrow (x+4)(x-4) \geq 0$$

The zeros are $x = -4$ and $x = 4$. $f(x) = x^2 - 16$

Interval	Test Number	$f(x)$	Positive/Negative
$-\infty < x < -4$	-5	9	Positive
$-4 < x < 4$	0	-16	Negative
$4 < x < \infty$	5	9	Positive

The solution or domain is $\left\{ x \middle| x \leq -4 \text{ or } x \geq 4 \right\}$.

63.   The domain of the expression includes all values for which

$$\frac{x-2}{x+4} \geq 0$$

The zeros and values where the expression is undefined are $x = -4$ and $x = 2$

$$f(x) = \frac{x-2}{x+4}$$

Interval	Test Number	$f(x)$	Positive/Negative
$-\infty < x < -4$	-5	7	Positive
$-4 < x < 2$	0	$-1/2$	Negative
$2 < x < \infty$	3	$1/7$	Positive

The solution or domain is $\left\{ x \middle| x < -4 \text{ or } x \geq 2 \right\}$.

65. (a) Find the values of t for which
$$80t - 16t^2 > 96 \Rightarrow -16t^2 + 80t - 96 > 0$$

$$16t^2 - 80t + 96 < 0 \Rightarrow 16(t^2 - 5t + 6) < 0 \Rightarrow 16(t-2)(t-3) < 0$$

The zeros are $t = 2$ and $t = 3$. $s(t) = 16t^2 - 80t + 96$

Interval	Test Number	$s(t)$	Positive/Negative
$-\infty < t < 2$	1	32	Positive
$2 < t < 3$	2.5	-4	Negative
$3 < t < \infty$	4	32	Positive

The solution set is $\{t \mid 2 < t < 3\}$. The ball is more than 96 feet above the ground for times between 2 and 3 seconds.

(b) Graphing: $s = 80t - 16t^2$

(c) Using MAXIMUM, the maximum height is 100 feet.
(d) The maximum height occurs at 2.5 seconds.

67. (a) Profit = Revenue − Cost
$$x(40 - 0.2x) - 32x \geq 50 \Rightarrow 40x - 0.2x^2 - 32x \geq 50$$

$$-0.2x^2 + 8x - 50 \geq 0 \Rightarrow 2x^2 - 80x + 500 \leq 0 \Rightarrow x^2 - 40x + 250 \leq 0$$

The zeros are approximately $x = 7.75$ and $x = 32.25$.
$$f(x) = x^2 - 40x + 250$$

Interval	Test Number	$f(x)$	Positive/Negative
$0 < x < 7.75$	7	19	Positive
$7.75 < x < 32.25$	10	-50	Negative
$32.25 < x < \infty$	40	250	Positive

The profit is at least $50 when at least 8 and no more than 32 watches are sold.

(b) Graphing the revenue function: $(R(x) = x(40 - 0.2x))$

(c) Using MAXIMUM, the maximum revenue is $2,000.
(d) Using MAXIMUM, the company should sell 100 wristwatches to maximize revenue.
(e) Graphing the profit function: $P(x) = x(40 - 0.2x) - 32x$

(f) Using MAXIMUM, the maximum profit is $80.
(g) Using MAXIMUM, the company should sell 20 watches for maximum profit.

69. The cost of manufacturing x Chevy Cavaliers in a day was found to be:
$$C(x) = 0.216x^3 - 2.347x^2 + 14.328x + 10.224$$
Since the budget constraints require that the cost must be less than or equal to $97,000, we need to solve: $C(x) \le 97$ or
$$0.216x^3 - 2.347x^2 + 14.328x + 10.224 \le 97$$
Graphing $y_1 = 0.216x^3 - 2.347x^2 + 14.328x + 10.224$ and $y_2 = 97$:

y_1 intersects y_2 at $x = 8.59$. $y_1 < y_2$ when $x < 8.59$. Chevy can produce at most eight Cavaliers in a day, assuming cars cannot be partially completed.

71. Prove that if a, b are real numbers and $a \ge 0$, $b \ge 0$, then $a \le b$ is equivalent to $\sqrt{a} \le \sqrt{b}$.
First note that if $a = 0$, then $a \le b \Rightarrow b = 0$.
Similarly, if $\sqrt{a} = 0$ then $a = 0$ and $\sqrt{a} \le \sqrt{b} \Rightarrow \sqrt{b} = 0 \Rightarrow b = 0$.
Therefore, $a \le b$ is equivalent to $\sqrt{a} \le \sqrt{b}$.
Now suppose $a \ne 0$.
We must show that $a \le b \Rightarrow \sqrt{a} \le \sqrt{b}$ and that $\sqrt{a} \le \sqrt{b} \Rightarrow a \le b$.

Assume $a \le b$, this means that $b - a \ge 0$. We can factor the left hand side by treating it as a difference of two perfect squares:
$$\left(\sqrt{b} - \sqrt{a}\right)\left(\sqrt{b} + \sqrt{a}\right) \ge 0$$
Case 1: $\sqrt{b} - \sqrt{a} \ge 0$ and $\sqrt{b} + \sqrt{a} \ge 0$
$$\Rightarrow \sqrt{b} \ge \sqrt{a} \text{ and } \sqrt{b} \ge -\sqrt{a}$$
$$\Rightarrow \sqrt{a} \le \sqrt{b} \text{ and } -\sqrt{a} \le \sqrt{b}$$

or

Case 2: $\sqrt{b} \le \sqrt{a}$ and $\sqrt{b} \le -\sqrt{a}$

this is impossible since $\sqrt{a} \ge 0$ and $\sqrt{b} \ge 0$ which means
$$\sqrt{b} \le -\sqrt{a} \text{ is impossible since } a \ne 0.$$
Since Case 2 is impossible, Case 1 must be true. Therefore, $a \le b \Rightarrow \sqrt{a} \le \sqrt{b}$.
Assume $\sqrt{a} \le \sqrt{b}$. This means that $\sqrt{a} - \sqrt{b} \le 0$. Since $\sqrt{a} \ge 0$ and $\sqrt{b} \ge 0$, we can conclude that $\sqrt{a} + \sqrt{b} \ge 0$. Therefore,
$$\left(\sqrt{a} - \sqrt{b}\right)\left(\sqrt{a} + \sqrt{b}\right) \le 0\left(\sqrt{a} + \sqrt{b}\right)$$
$$a - b \le 0$$
$$a \le b$$
Thus $\sqrt{a} \le \sqrt{b} \Rightarrow a \le b$.

Polynomial and Rational Functions

4.R   Chapter Review

1. $f(x) = 4x^5 - 3x^2 + 5x - 2$ is a polynomial function of degree 5.

3. $f(x) = 3x^2 + 5x^{1/2} - 1$ is not a polynomial function because there is a fractional exponent on the variable.

5. $f(x) = (x + 2)^3$
     Using the graph of $y = x^3$, shift the graph horizontally, 2 units to the left.

7. $f(x) = -(x - 1)^4$
     Using the graph of $y = x^4$, shift the graph horizontally, 1 unit right, and reflect about the x-axis.

9. $f(x) = (x - 1)^4 + 2$
     Using the graph of $y = x^4$, shift the graph horizontally, 1 unit to the right, and shift vertically 2 units up.

11. $f(x) = x(x + 2)(x + 4)$
     (a)   x-intercepts: –4, –2, 0;   y-intercept: 0
     (b)   crosses x axis at x = –4, –2, 0
     (c) $y = x^3$

(d)   graphing utility

(e)   2 turning points; Local maximum: (–3.15, 3.08)
       Local minimum: (–0.85, –3.08)

(f)   graphing by hand

Interval	(-∞, -4)	(-4, -2)	(-2, 0)	(0, ∞)
Number Chosen	-5	-3	-1	1
Value of f	$f(-5) = -15$	$f(-3) = 3$	$f(-1) = -3$	$f(1) = 15$
Location of Graph	Below x-axis	Above x-axis	Below x-axis	Above x-axis
Point on Graph	(-5, -15)	(-3, 3)	(-1, -3)	(1, 15)

Graph of f is above the x-axis for $(-4,-2) \cup (0,\infty)$

Graph of f is below the x-axis for $(-\infty,-4) \cup (-2,0)$

13. $f(x) = (x - 2)^2(x + 4)$

(a)   x-intercepts: - 4, 2;   y-intercept: 16

(b)   crosses x axis at x = - 4 and touches the x axis at x = 2

(c) $y = x^3$ (d)   graphing utility

(e)   2 turning points; Local maximum: (–2, 32)
       Local minimum: (2, 0)

(f)   graphing by hand

| | -4 | 2 | |

Interval	$(-\infty, -4)$	$(-4, 2)$	$(2, \infty)$
Number Chosen	-5	-2	3
Value of f	$f(-5) = -49$	$f(-2) = 32$	$f(3) = 7$
Location of Graph	Below x-axis	Above x-axis	Above x-axis
Point on Graph	(-5, -49)	(-2, 32)	(3, 7)

Graph of f is above the x-axis for $(-4,2) \cup (2,\infty)$; Graph of f is below the x-axis for $(-\infty,-4)$

15. $f(x) = x^3 - 4x^2 = x^2(x-4)$

   (a)   x-intercepts: 0, 4;   y-intercept: 0

   (b)   crosses x axis at x = 4 and touches the x axis at x = 0

   (c) $y = x^3$ (d)   graphing utility

   (e)   2 turning points; Local maximum: (0, 0)
         Local minimum: (2.67, –9.48)

   (f)   graphing by hand

| | 0 | 4 | |

Interval	$(-\infty, 0)$	$(0, 4)$	$(4, \infty)$
Number Chosen	-1	1	5
Value of f	$f(-1) = -5$	$f(1) = -3$	$f(5) = 25$
Location of Graph	Below x-axis	Below x-axis	Above x-axis
Point on Graph	(-1, -5)	(1, -3)	(5, 25)

Graph of f is above the x-axis for $(4,\infty)$; Graph of f is below the x-axis for $(-\infty,0) \cup (0,4)$

17. $f(x) = (x-1)^2(x+3)(x+1)$

(a)   x-intercepts: - 3, - 1, 1;   y-intercept: 3
(b)   crosses x axis at x = - 3, - 1 and touches x-axis at x = 1
(c) $y = x^4$ (d)   graphing utility

(e)   3 turning points; Local maximum: $(-0.22, 3.23)$
       Local minima: $(-2.28, -9.91)$, $(1,0)$
(f)   graphing by hand

Interval	$(-\infty, -3)$	$(-3, -1)$	$(-1, 1)$	$(1, \infty)$
Number Chosen	-4	-2	0	2
Value of f	$f(-4) = 75$	$f(-2) = -9$	$f(0) = 3$	$f(2) = 15$
Location of Graph	Above x-axis	Below x-axis	Above x-axis	Above x-axis
Point on Graph	$(-4, 75)$	$(-2, -9)$	$(0, 3)$	$(2, 15)$

Graph of f is above the x-axis for $(-\infty, -3) \cup (-1, 1) \cup (1, \infty)$
Graph of f is below the x-axis for $(-3, -1)$

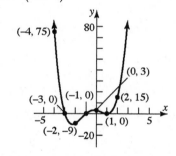

19. $R(x) = \dfrac{2x-6}{x}$ $p(x) = 2x-6$; $q(x) = x$; $n = 1$; $m = 1$

Step 1:   Domain: $\{x \mid x \neq 0\}$
Step 2: R is in lowest terms.
Step 3:   (a)   The x-intercept is the zero of $p(x)$: 3
          (b)   There is no y-intercept because 0 is not in the domain.
Step 4: $R(-x) = \dfrac{2(-x)-6}{-x} = \dfrac{-2x-6}{-x} = \dfrac{2x+6}{x}$; this is neither $R(x)$ nor $-R(x)$, so there is
          no symmetry.
Step 5:   The vertical asymptote is the zero of $q(x)$: $x = 0$
Step 6:   Since $n = m$, the line $y = 2$ is the horizontal asymptote.
          $R(x)$ does not intersect $y = 2$.

Step 7:   Graphing utility:

Step 8: Graphing by hand

Interval	$(-\infty, 0)$	$(0, 3)$	$(3, \infty)$
Number Chosen	-2	1	4
Value of R	$R(-2) = 5$	$R(1) = -4$	$R(4) = \frac{1}{2}$
Location of Graph	Above x-axis	Below x-axis	Above x-axis
Point on Graph	$(-2, 5)$	$(1, -4)$	$(4, \frac{1}{2})$

21. $H(x) = \dfrac{x+2}{x(x-2)}$ $p(x) = x+2;\ q(x) = x(x-2) = x^2 - 2x;\ n = 1;\ m = 2$

Step 1:   Domain: $\{x \mid x \neq 0,\ x \neq 2\}$

Step 2: H is in lowest terms.

Step 3:   (a)   The x-intercept is the zero of $p(x)$: -2

(b)   There is no y-intercept because 0 is not in the domain.

Step 4: $H(-x) = \dfrac{-x+2}{-x(-x-2)} = \dfrac{-x+2}{x^2+2x}$; this is neither $H(x)$ nor $-H(x)$, so there is no symmetry.

Step 5:   The vertical asymptotes are the zeros of $q(x)$: $x = 0$ and $x = 2$

Step 6:   Since $n < m$, the line $y = 0$ is the horizontal asymptote.

$R(x)$ intersects $y = 0$ at $(-2, 0)$.

Step 7:   Graphing utility:

Step 8: Graphing by hand:

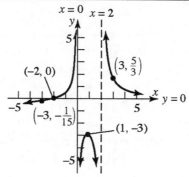

Interval	$(-\infty, -2)$	$(-2, 0)$	$(0, 2)$	$(2, \infty)$
Number Chosen	-3	-1	1	3
Value of H	$H(-3) = -\frac{1}{15}$	$H(-1) = \frac{1}{3}$	$H(1) = -3$	$H(3) = \frac{5}{3}$
Location of Graph	Below x-axis	Above x-axis	Below x-axis	Above x-axis
Point on Graph	$(-3, -\frac{1}{15})$	$(-1, \frac{1}{3})$	$(1, -3)$	$(3, \frac{5}{3})$

23. $R(x) = \dfrac{x^2 + x - 6}{x^2 - x - 6} = \dfrac{(x+3)(x-2)}{(x-3)(x+2)}$ $p(x) = x^2 + x - 6; \ q(x) = x^2 - x - 6;$

$n = 2; \ m = 2$

Step 1: Domain: $\{x \,|\, x \neq -2, \, x \neq 3\}$

Step 2: R is in lowest terms.

Step 3: (a) The x-intercepts are the zeros of $p(x)$: -3 and 2

(b) The y-intercept is $R(0) = \dfrac{0^2 + 0 - 6}{0^2 - 0 - 6} = \dfrac{-6}{-6} = 1.$

Step 4: $R(-x) = \dfrac{(-x)^2 + (-x) - 6}{(-x)^2 - (-x) - 6} = \dfrac{x^2 - x - 6}{x^2 + x - 6}$; this is neither $R(x)$ nor $-R(x)$, so there is no symmetry.

Step 5: The vertical asymptotes are the zeros of $q(x)$: $x = -2$ and $x = 3$

Step 6: Since $n = m$, the line $y = 1$ is the horizontal asymptote.

$R(x)$ intersects $y = 1$ at $(0, 1)$, since:

$$\dfrac{x^2 + x - 6}{x^2 - x - 6} = 1 \Rightarrow x^2 + x - 6 = x^2 - x - 6$$

$$2x = 0 \Rightarrow x = 0$$

Step 7: Graphing utility:

Step 8:　Graphing by hand:

Interval	$(-\infty, -3)$	$(-3, -2)$	$(-2, 2)$	$(2, 3)$	$(3, \infty)$
Number Chosen	-4	-2.5	0	2.5	4
Value of R	$R(-4) \approx 0.43$	$R(-2.5) \approx -0.82$	$R(0) = 1$	$R(2.5) \approx -1.22$	$R(4) = \frac{7}{3}$
Location of Graph	Above x-axis	Below x-axis	Above x-axis	Below x-axis	Above x-axis
Point on Graph	$(-4, 0.43)$	$(-2.5, -0.82)$	$(0, 1)$	$(2.5, -1.22)$	$(4, \frac{7}{3})$

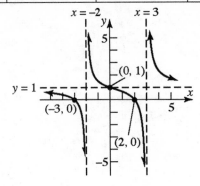

25.　$F(x) = \dfrac{x^3}{x^2 - 4}$　$p(x) = x^3$;　$q(x) = x^2 - 4$;　$n = 3$;　$m = 2$

Step 1:　Domain:　$\left\{ x \mid x \neq -2, x \neq 2 \right\}$

Step 2:　F is in lowest terms.

Step 3:　(a)　The x-intercept is the zero of $p(x)$:　0.

　　　　　(b)　The y-intercept is $F(0) = \dfrac{0^3}{0^2 - 4} = \dfrac{0}{-4} = 0$.

Step 4:　$F(-x) = \dfrac{(-x)^3}{(-x)^2 - 4} = \dfrac{-x^3}{x^2 - 4} = -F(x)$;　$F(x)$ is symmetric to the origin.

Step 5:　The vertical asymptotes are the zeros of $q(x)$:　$x = -2$ and $x = 2$

Step 6:　Since $n = m + 1$, there is an oblique asymptote.　Dividing:

$$
\begin{array}{r}
x \\
x^2 - 4 \overline{\smash{)}\, x^3 + 0x^2 + 0x + 0} \\
\underline{x^3 \qquad\; -4x} \\
4x
\end{array}
\qquad
F(x) = x + \dfrac{4x}{x^2 - 4}
$$

The oblique asymptote is　$y = x$.

Solve to find intersection points:

$$\dfrac{x^3}{x^2 - 4} = x \Rightarrow x^3 = x^3 - 4x \Rightarrow 0 = -4x \Rightarrow x = 0$$

The oblique asymptote intersects　$F(x)$ at $(0, 0)$.

Step 7:　Graphing utility:

Step 8: Graphing by hand:

Interval	$(-\infty, -2)$	$(-2, 0)$	$(0, 2)$	$(2, \infty)$
Number Chosen	-3	-1	1	3
Value of F	$F(-3) = -\frac{27}{5}$	$F(-1) = \frac{1}{3}$	$F(1) = -\frac{1}{3}$	$F(3) = \frac{27}{5}$
Location of Graph	Below x-axis	Above x-axis	Below x-axis	Above x-axis
Point on Graph	$(-3, -\frac{27}{5})$	$(-1, \frac{1}{3})$	$(1, -\frac{1}{3})$	$(3, \frac{27}{5})$

27. $R(x) = \dfrac{2x^4}{(x-1)^2}$ $p(x) = 2x^4;\ q(x) = (x-1)^2;\ n = 4;\ m = 2$

Step 1:   Domain: $\{x \mid x \neq 1\}$ Step 2: R is in lowest terms.

Step 3:   (a)   The x-intercept is the zero of $p(x)$: 0

　　　　　(b)   The y-intercept is $R(0) = \dfrac{2(0)^4}{(0-1)^2} = \dfrac{0}{1} = 0$.

Step 4: $R(-x) = \dfrac{2(-x)^4}{(-x-1)^2} = \dfrac{2x^4}{(x+1)^2}$; this is neither $R(x)$ nor $-R(x)$, so there is no
　　　　　symmetry.

Step 5:   The vertical asymptote is the zero of $q(x)$: $x = 1$

Step 6:   Since $n > m + 1$, there is no horizontal asymptote and no oblique asymptote.

Step 7:   Graphing utility:

Step 8: Graphing by hand:

Interval	$(-\infty, 0)$	$(0, 1)$	$(1, \infty)$
Number Chosen	-2	$\frac{1}{2}$	2
Value of R	$R(-2) \approx \frac{32}{9}$	$R(\frac{1}{2}) = \frac{1}{2}$	$R(2) = 32$
Location of Graph	Above x-axis	Above x-axis	Above x-axis
Point on Graph	$(-2, \frac{32}{9})$	$(\frac{1}{2}, \frac{1}{2})$	$(2, 32)$

29. $G(x) = \dfrac{x^2 - 4}{x^2 - x - 2}$ $p(x) = x^2 - 4$; $q(x) = x^2 - x - 2$;

$$n = 2; \quad m = 2$$

Step 1:   Domain: $\{x \mid x \neq -1, x \neq 2\}$

Step 2:   Write G in lowest terms: $G(x) = \dfrac{x^2 - 4}{x^2 - x - 2} = \dfrac{(x+2)(x-2)}{(x-2)(x+1)} = \dfrac{x+2}{x+1}$

Step 3:   (a)   The x-intercept is the zero of $p(x)$: -2 ; 2 is not a zero because reduced form must be used to find the zeros.

(b)   The y-intercept is $G(0) = \dfrac{0^2 - 4}{0^2 - 0 - 2} = \dfrac{-4}{-2} = 2$.

Step 4: $G(-x) = \dfrac{(-x)^2 - 4}{(-x)^2 - (-x) - 2} = \dfrac{x^2 - 4}{x^2 + x - 2}$; this is neither $G(x)$ nor $-G(x)$, so there is no symmetry.

Step 5:   The vertical asymptote is the zero of $q(x)$: $x = -1$; $x = 2$ is not a vertical asymptote because reduced form must be used to find the them. The graph has a hole at $\left(2, \dfrac{4}{3}\right)$.

Step 6:   Since $n = m$, the line $y = 1$ is the horizontal asymptote.

$G(x)$ does not intersect $y = 1$ because $G(x)$ is not defined at $x = 2$.

$$\dfrac{x^2 - 4}{x^2 - x - 2} = 1 \Rightarrow x^2 - 4 = x^2 - x - 2$$

$$-2 = -x \Rightarrow x = 2$$

Step 7:   Graphing utility:

Step 8:   Graphing by hand

Interval	$(-\infty, -2)$	$(-2, -1)$	$(-1, 2)$	$(2, \infty)$
Number Chosen	-3	-1.5	0	3
Value of G	$G(-3) = \frac{1}{2}$	$G(-1.5) = -1$	$G(0) = 2$	$G(3) = 1.25$
Location of Graph	Above x-axis	Below x-axis	Above x-axis	Above x-axis
Point on Graph	$(-3, \frac{1}{2})$	$(-1.5, -1)$	$(0, 2)$	$(3, 1.25)$

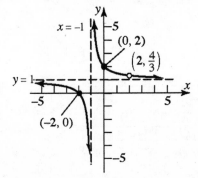

31. (a) $2x^2 + 5x - 12 < 0$ $f(x) = 2x^2 + 5x - 12$

$(x+4)(2x-3) < 0$

$x = -4, x = \dfrac{3}{2}$ are the zeros.

Interval	Test Number	$f(x)$	Positive/Negative
$-\infty < x < -4$	-5	13	Positive
$-4 < x < 3/2$	0	-12	Negative
$3/2 < x < \infty$	2	6	Positive

The solution set is $\left\{ x \middle| -4 < x < \dfrac{3}{2} \right\}$.

(b) $2x^2 + 5x - 12 < 0$

Graph $f(x) = 2x^2 + 5x - 12$.
The x-intercepts are $x = -4$ and $x = 1.5$. The graph of f is below the x-axis for $-4 < x < 1.5$.
Thus, the solution set is $\left\{ x \middle| -4 < x < 1.5 \right\}$.

33. (a) $\dfrac{6}{x+3} \geq 1$ $f(x) = \dfrac{6}{x+3} - 1$

$\dfrac{6}{x+3} - 1 \geq 0 \Rightarrow \dfrac{6 - 1(x+3)}{x+3} \geq 0 \Rightarrow \dfrac{-x+3}{x+3} \geq 0$

The zeros and values where the expression is undefined are $x = -3$, and $x = 3$.

Interval	Test Number	$f(x)$	Positive/Negative
$-\infty < x < -3$	-4	-7	Negative
$-3 < x < 3$	0	1	Positive
$3 < x < \infty$	4	$-1/7$	Negative

The solution set is $\left\{ x \middle| -3 < x \leq 3 \right\}$.

(b) $\dfrac{6}{x+3} \geq 1$

Graph $y_1 = \dfrac{6}{x+3}$, $y_2 = 1$.
y_1 is undefined at $x = -3$. y_1 intersects y_2 at $x = 3$. $y_1 > y_2$ for $-3 < x < 3$. Thus, the solution set is $\left\{ x \middle| -3 < x \leq 3 \right\}$.

35. (a) $\dfrac{2x-6}{1-x} < 2$ $f(x) = \dfrac{2x-6}{1-x} - 2$

$\dfrac{2x-6}{1-x} - 2 < 0 \Rightarrow \dfrac{2x - 6 - 2(1-x)}{1-x} < 0 \Rightarrow \dfrac{4x-8}{1-x} < 0$

The zeros and values where the expression is undefined are $x = 1$, and $x = 2$.

Interval	Test Number	$f(x)$	Positive/Negative
$-\infty < x < 1$	0	-8	Negative
$1 < x < 2$	1.5	4	Positive
$2 < x < \infty$	3	-2	Negative

The solution set is $\{x \mid x < 1 \text{ or } x > 2\}$.

(b) $\dfrac{2x-6}{1-x} < 2$

Graph $y_1 = \dfrac{2x-6}{1-x}, \ y_2 = 2$.

y_1 is undefined at $x = 1$. y_1 intersects y_2 at $x = 2$. $y_1 < y_2$ for $x < 1$ or $x > 2$. Thus, the solution set is $\{x \mid x < 1 \text{ or } x > 2\}$.

37. (a) $\dfrac{(x-2)(x-1)}{x-3} > 0$ 　　　 $f(x) = \dfrac{(x-2)(x-1)}{x-3}$

The zeros and values where the expression is undefined are $x = 1$, $x = 2$, and $x = 3$.

Interval	Test Number	$f(x)$	Positive/Negative
$-\infty < x < 1$	0	$-2/3$	Negative
$1 < x < 2$	1.5	$1/6$	Positive
$2 < x < 3$	2.5	$-3/2$	Negative
$3 < x < \infty$	4	6	Positive

The solution set is $\{x \mid 1 < x < 2 \text{ or } x > 3\}$.

(b) $\dfrac{(x-2)(x-1)}{x-3} > 0$

Graph $f(x) = \dfrac{(x-2)(x-1)}{x-3}$.
The x-intercepts are $x = 2$ and $x = 1$. The expression is undefined at $x = 3$. The graph of f is above the x-axis for $1 < x < 2$ or $x > 3$. Thus, the solution set is $\{x \mid 1 < x < 2 \text{ or } x > 3\}$.

39. (a) $\dfrac{x^2 - 8x + 12}{x^2 - 16} > 0$ 　　　 $f(x) = \dfrac{x^2 - 8x + 12}{x^2 - 16}$

$\dfrac{(x-2)(x-6)}{(x+4)(x-4)} > 0$

The zeros and values where the expression is undefined are $x = -4$, $x = 2$, $x = 4$, and $x = 6$.

Interval	Test Number	$f(x)$	Positive/Negative
$-\infty < x < -4$	-5	$77/9$	Positive
$-4 < x < 2$	0	$-3/4$	Negative
$2 < x < 4$	3	$3/7$	Positive
$4 < x < 6$	5	$-1/3$	Negative
$6 < x < \infty$	7	$5/33$	Positive

The solution set is $\{x \mid x < -4, \ 2 < x < 4, \ x > 6\}$.

(b) $\dfrac{x^2-8x+12}{x^2-16}>0$

Graph $f(x)=\dfrac{x^2-8x+12}{x^2-16}$.
The x-intercepts are $x=2$, and $x=6$. The
expression is undefined at $x=-4$ and $x=4$.
The graph of f is above the x-axis for
$x<-4$, $2<x<4$, or $x>6$. Thus, the solution
set is $\left\{x\mid x<-4,\,2<x<4,\,x>6\right\}$.

41. (a) Graphing:

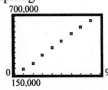

(b) $A(t)=-212.008t^3+2429.132t^2+59568.854t+130003.143$

(c) Graphing the cubic function of best fit:

(d) In the year 2000, $t=11$.
$A(11)=-212.008\cdot(11)^3+2429.132\cdot(11)^2+59568.845\cdot(11)+130003.143$
$\approx 797{,}003$ cases.

(e) Answers will vary.

43. Answers will vary, one example is $p(x)=-5\left(x^2+1\right)(x+1)^3\left(x-\dfrac{3}{5}\right)$

45. (a) The degree is even.
(b) The leading coefficient is positive.
(c) The function is even - it is symmetric to the y-axis.
(d) x^2 is a factor because the curve touches the x-axis at the origin.
(e) The minimum degree is 8.
(f) Answers will vary, 5 possibilities are:
$$p_1(x)=x^2(x+3)(x+2)(x+1)(x-1)(x-2)(x-3)$$
$$p_2(x)=x^4(x+3)(x+2)(x+1)(x-1)(x-2)(x-3)$$
$$p_3(x)=x^6(x+3)(x+2)(x+1)(x-1)(x-2)(x-3)$$
$$p_4(x)=x^8(x+3)(x+2)(x+1)(x-1)(x-2)(x-3)$$
$$p_5(x)=x^{10}(x+3)(x+2)(x+1)(x-1)(x-2)(x-3)$$

Polynomial and Rational Functions

4.CR   Cumulative Review

1. $4x^2 + 2x = 5 \Rightarrow 4x^2 + 2x - 5 = 0$
    $a = 4, b = 2, c = -5$

    $x = \dfrac{-b \pm \sqrt{b^2 - 4ac}}{2a} = \dfrac{-2 \pm \sqrt{2^2 - 4(4)(-5)}}{2(4)} = \dfrac{-2 \pm \sqrt{4 + 80}}{8}$

    $= \dfrac{-2 \pm \sqrt{84}}{8} = \dfrac{-2 \pm 2\sqrt{21}}{8} = \dfrac{-1 \pm \sqrt{21}}{4}$

    The solution set is $\left\{ \dfrac{-1 - \sqrt{21}}{4}, \dfrac{-1 + \sqrt{21}}{4} \right\}$.

3. $3x - 4y = 5 \Rightarrow y = \dfrac{3}{4}x - \dfrac{5}{4} \Rightarrow \text{slope} = \dfrac{3}{4}$

    $4x + 3y = 10 \Rightarrow y = -\dfrac{4}{3}x + \dfrac{10}{3} \Rightarrow \text{slope} = -\dfrac{4}{3}$

    Therefore, the lines are perpendicular since their slopes are negative reciprocals.

5. $g(t) = -16t^2 + 100t + 100 \Rightarrow g(4) = -16(4)^2 + 100(4) + 10 = -256 + 400 + 10 = 154$

7. $f(x) = -2(x + 3)^2 + 5$
    Using the graph of $y = x^2$, shift the graph
    horizontally, 3 units to the left, reflect about the
    x-axis, stretch vertically by a factor of 2 and
    shift vertically 3 units up.

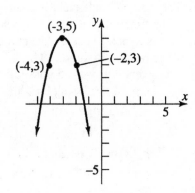

9. $f(x) = 0.2x^3 + x^2 + 1$
    Use MAXIMUM and MINIMUM on the graph of $y_1 = 0.2x^3 + x^2 + 1$.

local maximum at: $(-3.33, 4.70)$;   local minimum at: $(0,1)$
f is increasing on: $(-\infty, -3.33) \cup (0, \infty)$; f is decreasing on: $(-3.33, 0)$

11. $f(x) = (x+3)(x-4)^2$
    (a)   x-intercepts: –3, 4;   y-intercept: 48
    (b)   crosses x axis at x = –3, touches x-axis at $x = 4$
    (c) $y = x^3$
    (d)   graphing utility

    (e)   2 turning points; Local maximum: (–0.67, 50.81); Local minimum: (4, 0)
    (f)   graphing by hand

Interval	$(-\infty, -3)$	$(-3, 4)$	$(4, \infty)$
Number Chosen	-4	3.5	5
Value of f	$f(-4) = -64$	$f(3.5) = 1.625$	$f(5) = 8$
Location of Graph	Below x-axis	Above x-axis	Above x-axis
Point on Graph	(-4, -64)	(3.5, 1.625)	(5, 8)

Graph of f is above the x-axis for $(-3, 4) \cup (4, \infty)$
Graph of f is below the x-axis for $(-\infty, -3)$

13.   Let r = the radius of the circle after t seconds. Then $r(t) = 2t$.
    The area of the circle as a function of the radius is given by $A(r) = \pi \cdot r^2$.
    Therefore, we can express the area of the circle as a function of time:
$$(A \circ r)(t) = A(r(t)) = \pi \cdot (2t)^2 = 4\pi \cdot t^2$$

Chapter 5

The Zeros of a Polynomial Function

5.1   Synthetic Division

1. Use synthetic division:

$2\overline{)\begin{array}{ccc} 1 & -1 & 2 & 4 \\ & 2 & 2 & 8 \end{array}}$
$\overline{\begin{array}{cccc} 1 & 1 & 4 & 12 \end{array}}$

Quotient: $x^2 + x + 4$
Remainder: 12

3. Use synthetic division:

$3\overline{)\begin{array}{ccc} 3 & 2 & -1 & 3 \\ & 9 & 33 & 96 \end{array}}$
$\overline{\begin{array}{cccc} 3 & 11 & 32 & 99 \end{array}}$

Quotient: $3x^2 + 11x + 32$
Remainder: 99

5. Use synthetic division:

$-3\overline{)\begin{array}{cccccc} 1 & 0 & -4 & 0 & 1 & 0 \\ & -3 & 9 & -15 & 45 & -138 \end{array}}$
$\overline{\begin{array}{cccccc} 1 & -3 & 5 & -15 & 46 & -138 \end{array}}$

Quotient : $x^4 - 3x^3 + 5x^2 - 15x + 46$
Remainder : -138

7. Use synthetic division:

$1\overline{)\begin{array}{cccccc} 4 & 0 & -3 & 0 & 1 & 0 & 5 \\ & 4 & 4 & 1 & 1 & 2 & 2 \end{array}}$
$\overline{\begin{array}{ccccccc} 4 & 4 & 1 & 1 & 2 & 2 & 7 \end{array}}$

Quotient : $4x^5 + 4x^4 + x^3 + x^2 + 2x + 2$
Remainder : 7

9. Use synthetic division:

$-1.1\overline{)\begin{array}{cccc} 0.1 & 0 & 0.2 & 0 \\ & -0.11 & 0.121 & -0.3531 \end{array}}$
$\overline{\begin{array}{cccc} 0.1 & -0.11 & 0.321 & -0.3531 \end{array}}$

Quotient: $0.1x^2 - 0.11x + 0.321$
Remainder: –0.3531

11. Use synthetic division:

$1\overline{)\begin{array}{ccccc} 1 & 0 & 0 & 0 & 0 & -1 \\ & 1 & 1 & 1 & 1 & 1 \end{array}}$
$\overline{\begin{array}{cccccc} 1 & 1 & 1 & 1 & 1 & 0 \end{array}}$

Quotient: $x^4 + x^3 + x^2 + x + 1$
Remainder: 0

13. Use synthetic division:

$$2)\overline{\begin{array}{rrrr} 4 & -3 & -8 & 4 \\ & 8 & 10 & 4 \\ \hline 4 & 5 & 2 & 8 \end{array}}$$

Remainder = 8 ≠ 0.
Therefore $x-2$ is not a factor of $f(x)$.

15. Use synthetic division:

$$2)\overline{\begin{array}{rrrrr} 3 & -6 & 0 & -5 & 10 \\ & 6 & 0 & 0 & -10 \\ \hline 3 & 0 & 0 & -5 & 0 \end{array}}$$

Remainder = 0.
Therefore $x-2$ is a factor of $f(x)$.

17. Use synthetic division:

$$-3)\overline{\begin{array}{rrrrrr} 3 & 0 & 0 & 82 & 0 & 0 & 27 \\ & -9 & 27 & -81 & -3 & 9 & -27 \\ \hline 3 & -9 & 27 & 1 & -3 & 9 & 0 \end{array}}$$

Remainder = 0.
Therefore $x+3$ is a factor of $f(x)$.

19. Use synthetic division:

$$-4)\overline{\begin{array}{rrrrrrr} 4 & 0 & -64 & 0 & 1 & 0 & -15 \\ & -16 & 64 & 0 & 0 & -4 & 16 \\ \hline 4 & -16 & 0 & 0 & 1 & -4 & 1 \end{array}}$$

Remainder = 1 ≠ 0.
Therefore $x+3$ is not a factor of $f(x)$.

21. Use synthetic division:

$$\frac{1}{2})\overline{\begin{array}{rrrrr} 2 & -1 & 0 & 2 & -1 \\ & 1 & 0 & 0 & 1 \\ \hline 2 & 0 & 0 & 2 & 0 \end{array}}$$

Remainder = 0.

Therefore $x-\frac{1}{2}$ is a factor of $f(x)$.

23. Use synthetic division:

$$-2)\overline{\begin{array}{rrrr} 1 & -2 & 3 & 5 \\ & -2 & 8 & -22 \\ \hline 1 & -4 & 11 & -17 \end{array}}$$

$$\frac{x^3-2x^2+3x+5}{x+2} = x^2-4x+11+\frac{-17}{x+2}$$
$$a+b+c+d = 1-4+11-17 = -9$$

Chapter 5

The Zeros of a Polynomial Function

5.2 The Real Zeros of a Polynomial Function

1. $f(x) = 4x^3 - 3x^2 - 8x + 4; \quad c = 3$

$f(3) = 4(3)^3 - 3(3)^2 - 8(3) + 4 = 108 - 27 - 24 + 4 = 61 \neq 0$

Thus, 3 is not a zero of f ∴ $x - 3$ is not a factor of f.

3. $f(x) = 3x^4 - 6x^3 - 5x + 10; \quad c = 1$

$f(1) = 3(1)^4 - 6(1)^3 - 5(1) + 10 = 3 - 6 - 5 + 10 = 2 \neq 0$

Thus, 1 is not a zero of f ∴ $x - 1$ is not a factor of f.

5. $f(x) = 3x^6 + 2x^3 - 176; \quad c = -2$

$f(-2) = 3(-2)^6 + 2(-2)^3 - 176 = 192 - 16 - 176 = 0$

Thus, -2 is a zero of f ∴ $x + 2$ is a factor of f. Use synthetic division to find the factors.

$$
\begin{array}{r|rrrrrrr}
-2 & 3 & 0 & 0 & 2 & 0 & 0 & -176 \\
   &   & -6 & 12 & -24 & 44 & -88 & 176 \\
\hline
   & 3 & -6 & 12 & -22 & 44 & -88 & 0
\end{array}
$$

The factored form is: $f(x) = (x + 2)\left(3x^5 - 6x^4 + 12x^3 - 22x^2 + 44x - 88\right)$.

7. $f(x) = 4x^6 - 64x^4 + x^2 - 16; \quad c = 4$

$f(4) = 4(4)^6 - 64(4)^4 + (4)^2 - 16 = 16384 - 16384 + 16 - 16 = 0$

Thus, 4 is a zero of f ∴ $x - 4$ is a factor of f. Use synthetic division to find the factors.

$$
\begin{array}{r|rrrrrrr}
4 & 4 & 0 & -64 & 0 & 1 & 0 & -16 \\
  &   & 16 & 64 & 0 & 0 & 4 & 16 \\
\hline
  & 4 & 16 & 0 & 0 & 1 & 4 & 0
\end{array}
$$

The factored form is: $f(x) = (x - 4)\left(4x^5 + 16x^4 + x + 4\right)$.

We can use grouping to factor $4x^5 + 16x^4 + x + 4 = 4x^4(x + 4) + x + 4 = (x + 4)\left(4x^4 + 1\right)$

So $f(x) = (x - 4)(x + 4)\left(4x^4 + 1\right)$.

9. $f(x) = 2x^4 - x^3 + 2x - 1; \quad c = -\dfrac{1}{2}$

$f\left(-\dfrac{1}{2}\right) = 2\left(-\dfrac{1}{2}\right)^4 - \left(-\dfrac{1}{2}\right)^3 + 2\left(-\dfrac{1}{2}\right) - 1 = \dfrac{1}{8} + \dfrac{1}{8} - 1 - 1 = -\dfrac{7}{4} \neq 0$

Thus, $-\dfrac{1}{2}$ is not a zero of f ∴ $x + \dfrac{1}{2}$ is not a factor of f.

11. $f(x) = 3x^4 - 3x^3 + x^2 - x + 1$
The maximum number of zeros is the degree of the polynomial which is 4.
p must be a factor of 1: $p = \pm 1$
q must be a factor of 3: $q = \pm 1, \pm 3$

The possible rational zeros are: $\dfrac{p}{q} = \pm 1, \pm \dfrac{1}{3}$

13. $f(x) = x^5 - 6x^2 + 9x - 3$
The maximum number of zeros is the degree of the polynomial which is 5.
p must be a factor of -3: $p = \pm 1, \pm 3$
q must be a factor of 1: $q = \pm 1$

The possible rational zeros are: $\dfrac{p}{q} = \pm 1, \pm 3$

15. $f(x) = -4x^3 - x^2 + x + 2$
The maximum number of zeros is the degree of the polynomial which is 3.
p must be a factor of 2: $p = \pm 1, \pm 2$
q must be a factor of -4: $q = \pm 1, \pm 2, \pm 4$

The possible rational zeros are: $\dfrac{p}{q} = \pm 1, \pm 2, \pm \dfrac{1}{2}, \pm \dfrac{1}{4}$

17. $f(x) = 3x^4 - x^2 + 2$
The maximum number of zeros is the degree of the polynomial which is 4.
p must be a factor of 2: $p = \pm 1, \pm 2$
q must be a factor of 3: $q = \pm 1, \pm 3$

The possible rational zeros are: $\dfrac{p}{q} = \pm 1, \pm \dfrac{1}{3}, \pm 2, \pm \dfrac{2}{3}$

19. $f(x) = 2x^5 - x^3 + 2x^2 + 4$
The maximum number of zeros is the degree of the polynomial which is 5.
p must be a factor of 4: $p = \pm 1, \pm 2, \pm 4$
q must be a factor of 2: $q = \pm 1, \pm 2$

The possible rational zeros are: $\dfrac{p}{q} = \pm 1, \pm \dfrac{1}{2}, \pm 2, \pm 4$

21. $f(x) = 6x^4 + 2x^3 - x^2 + 2$
The maximum number of zeros is the degree of the polynomial which is 4.
p must be a factor of 2: $p = \pm 1, \pm 2$
q must be a factor of 6: $q = \pm 1, \pm 2, \pm 3, \pm 6$

The possible rational zeros are: $\dfrac{p}{q} = \pm 1, \pm \dfrac{1}{2}, \pm \dfrac{1}{3}, \pm \dfrac{1}{6}, \pm 2, \pm \dfrac{2}{3}$

23. $f(x) = 2x^3 + x^2 - 1 = 2\left(x^3 + \dfrac{1}{2}x^2 - \dfrac{1}{2}\right)$

Note: The leading coefficient must be 1.

$a_2 = \dfrac{1}{2}, a_1 = 0, a_0 = -\dfrac{1}{2}$

$Max\left\{1, \left|-\dfrac{1}{2}\right| + |0| + \left|\dfrac{1}{2}\right|\right\} = Max\left\{1, \dfrac{1}{2} + 0 + \dfrac{1}{2}\right\} = Max\{1,1\} = 1$

$1 + Max\left\{\left|-\dfrac{1}{2}\right|, |0|, \left|\dfrac{1}{2}\right|\right\} = 1 + Max\left\{\dfrac{1}{2}, 0, \dfrac{1}{2}\right\} = 1 + \dfrac{1}{2} = 1.5$

The smaller of the two numbers is 1. Thus, every zero of f lies between -1 and 1.
Graphing using the bounds and ZOOM-FIT:

25. $f(x) = x^3 - 5x^2 - 11x + 11$
$a_2 = -5, a_1 = -11, a_0 = 11$

$Max\{1, |-5| + |-11| + |11|\} = Max\{1, 5 + 11 + 11\} = Max\{1,27\} = 27$

$1 + Max\{|-5|, |-11|, |11|\} = 1 + Max\{1, 5, 11, 11\} = 1 + 11 = 12$

The smaller of the two numbers is 12. Thus, every zero of f lies between -12 and 12.
Graphing using the bounds and ZOOM-FIT: (Second graph has a better window.)

27. $f(x) = x^4 + 3x^3 - 5x^2 + 9$
$a_3 = 3, a_2 = -5, a_1 = 0, a_0 = 9$
$Max\{1, |9| + |0| + |-5| + |3|\} = Max\{1, 9 + 0 + 5 + 3\} = Max\{1,17\} = 17$

$1 + Max\{|9|, |0|, |-5|, |3|\} = 1 + Max\{9, 0, 5, 3\} = 1 + 9 = 10$

The smaller of the two numbers is 10. Thus, every zero of f lies between -10 and 10.
Graphing using the bounds and ZOOM-FIT: (Second graph has a better window.)

29. $f(x) = x^3 + 2x^2 - 5x - 6$

Step 1: $f(x)$ has at most 3 real zeros.

Step 2:   Possible rational zeros:

$$p = \pm 1, \pm 2, \pm 3, \pm 6; \quad q = \pm 1; \quad \frac{p}{q} = \pm 1, \pm 2, \pm 3, \pm 6$$

Step 3:   Using the Bounds on Zeros Theorem:

$$a_2 = 2, \quad a_1 = -5, \quad a_0 = -6$$

$$\text{Max} \left\{ 1, |-6| + |-5| + |2| \right\} = \text{Max} \left\{ 1, 13 \right\} = 13$$

$$1 + \text{Max} \left\{ |-6|, |-5|, |2| \right\} = 1 + 6 = 7$$

The smaller of the two numbers is 7. Thus, every zero of f lies between -7 and 7.

Graphing using the bounds and ZOOM-FIT: (Second graph has a better window.)

Step 4:   (a)   From the graph it appears that there are x-intercepts at $-3, -1,$ and 2.

(b)   Using synthetic division:

$$-3 \overline{)\begin{array}{rrrr} 1 & 2 & -5 & -6 \\ & -3 & 3 & 6 \\ \hline 1 & -1 & -2 & 0 \end{array}}$$

Since the remainder is 0, $x - (-3) = x + 3$ is a factor.

The other factor is the quotient: $x^2 - x - 2$.

(c)   Thus, $f(x) = (x + 3)(x^2 - x - 2) = (x + 3)(x + 1)(x - 2)$.

The zeros are $-3, -1,$ and 2.

31. $f(x) = 2x^3 - 13x^2 + 24x - 9$

Step 1: $f(x)$ has at most 3 real zeros.

Step 2:   Possible rational zeros:

$$p = \pm 1, \pm 3, \pm 9; \quad q = \pm 1, \pm 2; \quad \frac{p}{q} = \pm 1, \pm 3, \pm 9, \pm \frac{1}{2}, \pm \frac{3}{2}, \pm \frac{9}{2}$$

Step 3:   Using the Bounds on Zeros Theorem:

$$f(x) = 2 \left(x^3 - 6.5x^2 + 12x - 4.5 \right)$$

$$a_2 = -6.5, \quad a_1 = 12, \quad a_0 = -4.5$$

$$\text{Max} \left\{ 1, |-4.5| + |12| + |-6.5| \right\} = \text{Max} \left\{ 1, 23 \right\} = 23$$

$$1 + \text{Max} \left\{ |-4.5|, |12|, |-6.5| \right\} = 1 + 12 = 13$$

The smaller of the two numbers is 13. Thus, every zero of f lies between -13 and 13.

Graphing using the bounds and ZOOM-FIT: (Second graph has a better window.)

Step 4: (a) From the graph it appears that there are x-intercepts at 0.5 and 3.

(b) Using synthetic division:

$$3 \overline{)\begin{array}{rrrr} 2 & -13 & 24 & -9 \\ & 6 & -21 & 9 \\ \hline 2 & -7 & 3 & 0 \end{array}}$$

Since the remainder is 0, $x - 3$ is a factor.

The other factor is the quotient: $2x^2 - 7x + 3$.

(c) Thus, $f(x) = (x - 3)\left(2x^2 - 7x + 3\right) = (x - 3)(2x - 1)(x - 3)$.

The zeros are 0.5 and 3 (multiplicity 2).

33. $f(x) = 3x^3 + 4x^2 + 4x + 1$

Step 1: $f(x)$ has at most 3 real zeros..

Step 2: Possible rational zeros: $p = \pm 1$; $\quad q = \pm 1, \pm 3$; $\quad \dfrac{p}{q} = \pm 1, \pm \dfrac{1}{3}$

Step 3: Using the Bounds on Zeros Theorem:

$$f(x) = 3\left(x^3 + \frac{4}{3}x^2 + \frac{4}{3}x + \frac{1}{3}\right)$$

$$a_2 = \frac{4}{3}, \quad a_1 = \frac{4}{3}, \quad a_0 = \frac{1}{3}$$

$$\text{Max}\left\{1, \left|\frac{1}{3}\right| + \left|\frac{4}{3}\right| + \left|\frac{4}{3}\right|\right\} = \text{Max}\{1, 3\} = 3$$

$$1 + \text{Max}\left\{\left|\frac{1}{3}\right|, \left|\frac{4}{3}\right|, \left|\frac{4}{3}\right|\right\} = 1 + \frac{4}{3} = \frac{7}{3}$$

The smaller of the two numbers is $\dfrac{7}{3}$. Thus, every zero of f lies

between $-\dfrac{7}{3}$ and $\dfrac{7}{3}$.

Graphing using the bounds and ZOOM-FIT: (Second graph has a better window.)

Step 4: (a) From the graph it appears that there is an x-intercepts at $-\dfrac{1}{3}$.

(b)   Using synthetic division:

$$-\frac{1}{3})\overline{\begin{array}{cccc} 3 & 4 & 4 & 1 \\ & -1 & -1 & -1 \\ \hline 3 & 3 & 3 & 0 \end{array}}$$

Since the remainder is 0, $x - \left(-\frac{1}{3}\right) = x + \frac{1}{3}$ is a factor.

The other factor is the quotient: $3x^2 + 3x + 3$.

(c)   Thus, $f(x) = \left(x + \frac{1}{3}\right)\left(3x^2 + 3x + 3\right) = 3\left(x + \frac{1}{3}\right)\left(x^2 + x + 1\right)$.

$x^2 + x + 1 = 0$ has no real solution.

The zero is $-\frac{1}{3}$.

35. $f(x) = x^3 - 8x^2 + 17x - 6$

Step 1: $f(x)$ has at most 3 real zeros.

Step 2:   Possible rational zeros:

$$p = \pm 1, \pm 2, \pm 3, \pm 6; \quad q = \pm 1; \quad \frac{p}{q} = \pm 1, \pm 2, \pm 3, \pm 6$$

Step 3:   Using the Bounds on Zeros Theorem:

$a_2 = -8, \quad a_1 = 17, \quad a_0 = -6$

$\text{Max}\left\{1, |-6| + |17| + |-8|\right\} = \text{Max}\left\{1, 31\right\} = 31$

$1 + \text{Max}\left\{|-6|, |17|, |-8|\right\} = 1 + 17 = 18$

The smaller of the two numbers is 18. Thus, every zero of f lies between -18 and 18.

Graphing using the bounds and ZOOM-FIT: (Second graph has a better window.)

Step 4:   (a)   From the graph it appears that there are x-intercepts at 0.5, 3, and 4.5.

(b)   Using synthetic division:

$$3)\overline{\begin{array}{cccc} 1 & -8 & 17 & -6 \\ & 3 & -15 & 6 \\ \hline 1 & -5 & 2 & 0 \end{array}}$$

Since the remainder is 0, $x - 3$ is a factor.

The other factor is the quotient: $x^2 - 5x + 2$.

(c)   Thus, $f(x) = (x - 3)\left(x^2 - 5x + 2\right)$. Using the quadratic formula to find the solutions of the depressed equation $x^2 - 5x + 2 = 0$:

$$x = \frac{-(-5) \pm \sqrt{(-5)^2 - 4(1)(2)}}{2(1)} = \frac{5 \pm \sqrt{17}}{2}$$

Thus, $f(x) = (x-3)\left(x - \left(\dfrac{5+\sqrt{17}}{2}\right)\right)\left(x - \left(\dfrac{5-\sqrt{17}}{2}\right)\right)$.

The zeros are 3, $\dfrac{5+\sqrt{17}}{2}$, and $\dfrac{5-\sqrt{17}}{2}$ or $3, 4.56,$ and 0.44.

37. $f(x) = x^4 + x^3 - 3x^2 - x + 2$

Step 1: $f(x)$ has at most 4 real zeros.

Step 2:   Possible rational zeros:

$$p = \pm 1, \pm 2; \quad q = \pm 1; \quad \frac{p}{q} = \pm 1, \pm 2$$

Step 3:   Using the Bounds on Zeros Theorem:

$$a_3 = 1, \ a_2 = -3, \ a_1 = -1, \ a_0 = 2$$

$$\text{Max} \left\{1, |2| + |-1| + |-3| + |1|\right\} = \text{Max}\{1, 7\} = 7$$

$$1 + \text{Max}\left\{|2|, |-1|, |-3|, |1|\right\} = 1 + 3 = 4$$

The smaller of the two numbers is 4. Thus, every zero of f lies
between -4 and 4.

Graphing using the bounds and ZOOM-FIT: (Second graph has a better window.)

Step 4: (a)   From the graph it appears that there are x-intercepts at $-2, -1,$ and 1.

(b)   Using synthetic division:

$$
\begin{array}{r|rrrrr}
-2 & 1 & 1 & -3 & -1 & 2 \\
   &   & -2 & 2 & 2 & -2 \\
\hline
   & 1 & -1 & -1 & 1 & 0
\end{array}
\qquad
\begin{array}{r|rrrr}
-1 & 1 & -1 & -1 & 1 \\
   &   & -1 & 2 & -1 \\
\hline
   & 1 & -2 & 1 & 0
\end{array}
$$

Since the remainder is 0, $x+2$ and $x+1$ are factors.
The other factor is the quotient: $x^2 - 2x + 1$.

(c)   Thus, $f(x) = (x+2)(x+1)(x-1)^2$.
The zeros are $-2, -1,$ and 1 (multiplicity 2).

39. $f(x) = 2x^4 + 17x^3 + 35x^2 - 9x - 45$

Step 1: $f(x)$ has at most 4 real zeros.

Step 2:   Possible rational zeros:

$$p = \pm 1, \pm 3, \pm 5, \pm 9, \pm 15, \pm 45; \quad q = \pm 1, \pm 2;$$

$$\frac{p}{q} = \pm 1, \pm 3, \pm 5, \pm 9, \pm 15, \pm 45, \pm \frac{1}{2}, \pm \frac{3}{2}, \pm \frac{5}{2}, \pm \frac{9}{2}, \pm \frac{15}{2}, \pm \frac{45}{2}$$

Step 3:   Using the Bounds on Zeros Theorem:

$$f(x) = 2\left(x^4 + 8.5x^3 + 17.5x^2 - 4.5x - 22.5\right)$$

$$a_3 = 8.5, \ a_2 = 17.5, \ a_1 = -4.5, \ a_0 = -22.5$$

$$\text{Max}\left\{1, |-22.5| + |-4.5| + |17.5| + |8.5|\right\} = \text{Max}\{1, 53\} = 53$$

$$1 + \text{Max}\left\{|-22.5|, |-4.5|, |17.5|, |8.5|\right\} = 1 + 22.5 = 23.5$$

The smaller of the two numbers is 23.5. Thus, every zero of f lies between -23.5 and 23.5.

Graphing using the bounds and ZOOM-FIT: (Second graph has a better window.)

Step 4:   (a)   From the graph it appears that there are x-intercepts at $-5, -3, -1.5$, and 1.

(b)   Using synthetic division:

$$-5)\overline{\begin{array}{rrrrr} 2 & 17 & 35 & -9 & -45 \\ & -10 & -35 & 0 & 45 \\ \hline 2 & 7 & 0 & -9 & 0 \end{array}}$$

$$-3)\overline{\begin{array}{rrrr} 2 & 7 & 0 & -9 \\ & -6 & -3 & 9 \\ \hline 2 & 1 & -3 & 0 \end{array}}$$

Since the remainder is 0, $x + 5$ and $x + 3$ are factors.

The other factor is the quotient: $2x^2 + x - 3$.

(c)   Thus, $f(x) = (x + 5)(x + 3)(2x + 3)(x - 1)$.

The zeros are $-5, -3, -1.5$ and 1.

41. $f(x) = 2x^4 - 3x^3 - 21x^2 - 2x + 24$

Step 1: $f(x)$ has at most 4 real zeros.

Step 2:   Possible rational zeros:

$$p = \pm 1, \pm 2, \pm 3, \pm 4, \pm 6, \pm 8, \pm 12, \pm 24; \quad q = \pm 1, \pm 2;$$

$$\frac{p}{q} = \pm 1, \pm 2, \pm 3, \pm 4, \pm 6, \pm 8, \pm 12, \pm 24, \pm \frac{1}{2}, \pm \frac{3}{2}$$

Step 3:   Using the Bounds on Zeros Theorem:

$$f(x) = 2\left(x^4 - 1.5x^3 - 10.5x^2 - x + 12\right)$$

$$a_3 = -1.5, \ a_2 = -10.5, \ a_1 = -1, \ a_0 = 12$$

$$\text{Max}\left\{1, |12| + |-1| + |-10.5| + |-1.5|\right\} = \text{Max}\left\{1, 25\right\} = 25$$

$$1 + \text{Max}\left\{|12|, |-1|, |-10.5|, |-1.5|\right\} = 1 + 12 = 13$$

The smaller of the two numbers is 13. Thus, every zero of f lies between -13 and 13.

Graphing using the bounds and ZOOM-FIT: (Second graph has a better window.)

Step 4:   (a)   From the graph it appears that there are x-intercepts at $-2, -1.5, 1$, and 4.

(b)   Using synthetic division:

$$-2)\overline{\begin{array}{rrrrr} 2 & -3 & -21 & -2 & 24 \\ & -4 & 14 & 14 & -24 \\ \hline 2 & -7 & -7 & 12 & 0 \end{array}}$$

$$4)\overline{\begin{array}{rrrr} 2 & -7 & -7 & 12 \\ & 8 & 4 & -12 \\ \hline 2 & 1 & -3 & 0 \end{array}}$$

Since the remainder is 0, $x + 2$ and $x - 4$ are factors.
The other factor is the quotient: $2x^2 + x - 3$.

(c)   Thus, $f(x) = (x + 2)(2x + 3)(x - 1)(x - 4)$.

The zeros are –2, –1.5, 1 and 4.

43. $f(x) = 4x^4 + 7x^2 - 2$

Step 1: $f(x)$ has at most 4 real zeros.

Step 2:   Possible rational zeros: $p = \pm 1, \pm 2;$ $q = \pm 1, \pm 2, \pm 4;$ $\dfrac{p}{q} = \pm 1, \pm 2, \pm \dfrac{1}{2}, \pm \dfrac{1}{4}$

Step 3:   Using the Bounds on Zeros Theorem:

$$f(x) = 4\left(x^4 + 1.75x^2 - 0.5\right)$$

$$a_3 = 0, \quad a_2 = 1.75, \quad a_1 = 0, \quad a_0 = -0.5$$

$$\text{Max}\left\{1, \left|-0.5\right| + \left|0\right| + \left|1.75\right| + \left|0\right|\right\} = \text{Max}\left\{1, 2.25\right\} = 2.25$$

$$1 + \text{Max}\left\{\left|-0.5\right|, \left|0\right|, \left|1.75\right|, \left|0\right|\right\} = 1 + 1.75 = 2.75$$

The smaller of the two numbers is 2.25. Thus, every zero of f lies between –2.25 and 2.25.

Graphing using the bounds and ZOOM-FIT: (Second graph has a better window.)

Step 4:   (a)   From the graph it appears that there are x-intercepts at –0.5, and 0.5.

(b)   Using synthetic division:

$$-0.5)\overline{\begin{array}{ccccc} 4 & 0 & 7 & 0 & -2 \end{array}}$$
$$\begin{array}{ccccc} & -2 & 1 & -4 & 2 \end{array}$$
$$\overline{\begin{array}{ccccc} 4 & -2 & 8 & -4 & 0 \end{array}}$$

$$0.5)\overline{\begin{array}{cccc} 4 & -2 & 8 & -4 \end{array}}$$
$$\begin{array}{cccc} & 2 & 0 & 4 \end{array}$$
$$\overline{\begin{array}{cccc} 4 & 0 & 8 & 0 \end{array}}$$

Since the remainder is 0, $x + 0.5$ and $x - 0.5$ are factors.
The other factor is the quotient: $4x^2 + 8$.

(c)   Thus, $f(x) = 4(x + 0.5)(x - 0.5)\left(x^2 + 2\right) = (2x + 1)(2x - 1)\left(x^2 + 2\right)$.

The depressed equation has no real zeros.
The zeros are –0.5, and 0.5.

45. $f(x) = 4x^5 - 8x^4 - x + 2$

Step 1: $f(x)$ has at most 5 real zeros.

Step 2:   Possible rational zeros: $p = \pm 1, \pm 2;$ $q = \pm 1, \pm 2, \pm 4;$ $\dfrac{p}{q} = \pm 1, \pm 2, \pm \dfrac{1}{2}, \pm \dfrac{1}{4}$

Step 3:   Using the Bounds on Zeros Theorem:

$$f(x) = 4\left(x^5 - 2x^4 - 0.25x + 0.5\right)$$

$$a_4 = -2, \quad a_3 = 0, \quad a_2 = 0, \quad a_1 = -0.25, \quad a_0 = 0.5$$

$$\text{Max}\left\{1, \left|0.5\right| + \left|-0.25\right| + \left|0\right| + \left|0\right| + \left|-2\right|\right\} = \text{Max}\left\{1, 2.75\right\} = 2.75$$

$$1 + \text{Max}\left\{\left|0.5\right|, \left|-0.25\right|, \left|0\right|, \left|0\right|, \left|-2\right|\right\} = 1 + 2 = 3$$

The smaller of the two numbers is 2.75. Thus, every zero of f lies between -2.75 and 2.75.

Graphing using the bounds and ZOOM-FIT: (Second graph has a better window.)

Step 4:   (a)   From the graph it appears that there are x-intercepts at $-0.7, 0.7$ and 2.

(b)   Using synthetic division:

$$2 \overline{)\begin{array}{rrrrr} 4 & -8 & 0 & 0 & -1 & 2 \\ & 8 & 0 & 0 & 0 & -2 \\ \hline 4 & 0 & 0 & 0 & -1 & 0 \end{array}}$$

Since the remainder is 0, $x - 2$ is a factor.

The other factor is the quotient: $4x^4 - 1$.

(c)   Factoring,

$$f(x) = (x - 2)\left(4x^4 - 1\right) = (x - 2)(2x^2 - 1)(2x^2 + 1)$$

$$= (x - 2)\left(\sqrt{2}x - 1\right)\left(\sqrt{2}x + 1\right)\left(2x^2 + 1\right)$$

The zeros are $-\dfrac{\sqrt{2}}{2}, \dfrac{\sqrt{2}}{2}$, and 2 or $-0.71, -0.71$, and 2.

47. $f(x) = x^3 + 3.2x^2 - 16.83x - 5.31$

$f(x)$ has at most 3 real zeros.

Solving by graphing (using ZERO):

The zeros are approximately -5.9, -0.3, and 3.

49. $f(x) = x^4 - 1.4x^3 - 33.71x^2 + 23.94x + 292.41$

$f(x)$ has at most 4 real zeros.

Solving by graphing (using ZERO):

The zeros are approximately -3.80 and 4.50. These zeros are each of multiplicity 2.

51. $f(x) = x^3 + 19.5x^2 - 1021x + 1000.5$

$f(x)$ has at most 3 real zeros.

Solving by graphing (using ZERO):

The zeros are approximately $-43.5, 1$, and 23.

53. $x^4 - x^3 + 2x^2 - 4x - 8 = 0$

The solutions of the equation are the zeros of $f(x) = x^4 - x^3 + 2x^2 - 4x - 8$.

Step 1: $f(x)$ has at most 4 real zeros.

Step 2:   Possible rational zeros: $p = \pm 1, \pm 2, \pm 4, \pm 8; \quad q = \pm 1; \quad \dfrac{p}{q} = \pm 1, \pm 2, \pm 4, \pm 8$

Step 3:   Using the Bounds on Zeros Theorem:

$a_3 = -1, \ a_2 = 2, \ a_1 = -4, \ a_0 = -8$

$\text{Max}\left\{1, |-8| + |-4| + |2| + |-1|\right\} = \text{Max}\left\{1, 15\right\} = 15$

$1 + \text{Max}\left\{|-8|, |-4|, |2|, |-1|\right\} = 1 + 8 = 9$

The smaller of the two numbers is 9. Thus, every zero of f lies between –9 and 9.

Graphing using the bounds and ZOOM-FIT: (Second graph has a better window.)

 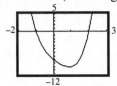

Step 4:   (a)   From the graph it appears that there are x-intercepts at –1 and 2.

       (b)   Using synthetic division:

$$-1\overline{)1 \ \ -1 \ \ \ 2 \ \ -4 \ \ -8}$$
$$\underline{\quad \ \ -1 \ \ \ 2 \ \ -4 \ \ \ \ 8}$$
$$\ \ \ \ 1 \ \ -2 \ \ \ 4 \ \ -8 \ \ \ \ \ 0$$

$$2\overline{)1 \ \ -2 \ \ \ 4 \ \ -8}$$
$$\underline{\qquad \ \ \ 2 \ \ \ 0 \ \ \ \ 8}$$
$$\ \ \ \ 1 \ \ \ \ 0 \ \ \ 4 \ \ \ \ 0$$

Since the remainder is 0, $x + 1$ and $x - 2$ are factors.

The other factor is the quotient: $x^2 + 4$.

       (c)   The zeros are –1 and 2. ($x^2 + 4 = 0$ has no real solutions.)

55. $3x^3 + 4x^2 - 7x + 2 = 0$

The solutions of the equation are the zeros of $f(x) = 3x^3 + 4x^2 - 7x + 2$.

Step 1: $f(x)$ has at most 3 real zeros.

Step 2:   Possible rational zeros: $p = \pm 1, \pm 2; \quad q = \pm 1, \pm 3; \quad \dfrac{p}{q} = \pm 1, \pm 2, \pm \dfrac{1}{3}, \pm \dfrac{2}{3}$

Step 3:   Using the Bounds on Zeros Theorem:

$$f(x) = 3\left(x^3 + \frac{4}{3}x^2 - \frac{7}{3}x + \frac{2}{3}\right)$$

$$a_2 = \frac{4}{3}, \ \ a_1 = -\frac{7}{3}, \ \ a_0 = \frac{2}{3}$$

$$\text{Max}\left\{1, \left|\frac{2}{3}\right| + \left|-\frac{7}{3}\right| + \left|\frac{4}{3}\right|\right\} = \text{Max}\left\{1, \frac{13}{3}\right\} = \frac{13}{3} \approx 4.333$$

$$1 + \text{Max}\left\{\left|\frac{2}{3}\right|, \left|-\frac{7}{3}\right|, \left|\frac{4}{3}\right|\right\} = 1 + \frac{7}{3} = \frac{10}{3} \approx 3.333$$

The smaller of the two numbers is 3.33. Thus, every zero of f lies between –3.33 and 3.33.

Graphing using the bounds and ZOOM-FIT: (Second graph has a better window.)

Step 4:   (a)   From the graph it appears that there are x-intercepts at $\frac{1}{3}, \frac{2}{3}$, and -2.4.

(b)   Using synthetic division:

$$\frac{2}{3}\overline{)\begin{array}{cccc} 3 & 4 & -7 & 2 \end{array}}$$
$$\begin{array}{cccc} & 2 & 4 & -2 \end{array}$$
$$\begin{array}{cccc} \hline 3 & 6 & -3 & 0 \end{array}$$

Since the remainder is 0, $x - \frac{2}{3}$ is a factor.

The other factor is the quotient: $3x^2 + 6x - 3$.

$$f(x) = \left(x - \frac{2}{3}\right)\left(3x^2 + 6x - 3\right) = 3\left(x - \frac{2}{3}\right)\left(x^2 + 2x - 1\right)$$

Using the quadratic formula to solve $x^2 + 2x - 1 = 0$:

$$x = \frac{-2 \pm \sqrt{4 - 4(1)(-1)}}{2(1)} = \frac{-2 \pm \sqrt{8}}{2} = \frac{-2 \pm 2\sqrt{2}}{2} = -1 \pm \sqrt{2}$$

(c)   The zeros are $\frac{2}{3}, -1 + \sqrt{2}$, and $-1 - \sqrt{2}$ or $0.67, 0.41$, and -2.41.

57. $3x^3 - x^2 - 15x + 5 = 0$

Solving by factoring: $x^2(3x - 1) - 5(3x - 1) = 0 \Rightarrow (3x - 1)(x^2 - 5) = 0$

$$(3x - 1)(x - \sqrt{5})(x + \sqrt{5}) = 0$$

The solutions of the equation are $\frac{1}{3}, \sqrt{5}$, and $-\sqrt{5}$ or $0.33, 2.24$, and -2.24.

59. $x^4 + 4x^3 + 2x^2 - x + 6 = 0$

The solutions of the equation are the zeros of $f(x) = x^4 + 4x^3 + 2x^2 - x + 6$.

Step 1: $f(x)$ has at most 4 real zeros.

Step 2:   Possible rational zeros: $p = \pm 1, \pm 2, \pm 3, \pm 6$; $q = \pm 1$; $\frac{p}{q} = \pm 1, \pm 2, \pm 3, \pm 6$

Step 3:   Using the Bounds on Zeros Theorem:

$a_3 = 4, \ a_2 = 2, \ a_1 = -1, \ a_0 = 6$

$\text{Max }\{1, |6| + |-1| + |2| + |4|\} = \text{Max }\{1, 13\} = 13$

$1 + \text{Max }\{|6|, |-1|, |2|, |4|\} = 1 + 6 = 7$

The smaller of the two numbers is 7. Thus, every zero of f lies between -7 and 7.

Graphing using the bounds and ZOOM-FIT: (Second graph has a better window.)

Step 4: (a) From the graph it appears that there are x-intercepts at –3 and –2.

(b) Using synthetic division:

$$-3\overline{\smash{)}1 \quad 4 \quad 2 \quad -1 \quad 6} \qquad\qquad -2\overline{\smash{)}1 \quad 1 \quad -1 \quad 2}$$
$$\underline{\quad -3 \;\; -3 \;\; 3 \;\; -6\quad} \qquad\qquad \underline{\quad -2 \;\; 2 \;\; -2\quad}$$
$$\;\; 1 \quad 1 \;\; -1 \quad 2 \quad 0 \qquad\qquad\quad 1 \;\; -1 \;\; 1 \quad 0$$

Since the remainder is 0, $x + 3$ and $x + 2$ are factors.

The other factor is the quotient: $x^2 - x + 1$.

(c) The zeros are –3 and –2. ($x^2 - x + 1 = 0$ has no real solutions.)

61. $x^3 - \dfrac{2}{3}x^2 + \dfrac{8}{3}x + 1 = 0$

The solutions of the equation are the zeros of $f(x) = x^3 - \dfrac{2}{3}x^2 + \dfrac{8}{3}x + 1 = 0$.

Step 1: $f(x)$ has at most 3 real zeros.

Step 2: Use the equivalent equation $3x^3 - 2x^2 + 8x + 3 = 0$ to find the possible rational

zeros: $p = \pm 1, \pm 3; \quad q = \pm 1, \pm 3; \quad \dfrac{p}{q} = \pm 1, \pm 3, \pm \dfrac{1}{3}$

Step 3: Using the Bounds on Zeros Theorem:

$$a_2 = -\frac{2}{3}, \quad a_1 = \frac{8}{3}, \quad a_0 = 1$$

$$\text{Max}\left\{1, |1| + \left|\frac{8}{3}\right| + \left|-\frac{2}{3}\right|\right\} = \text{Max}\left\{1, \frac{13}{3}\right\} = \frac{13}{3} \approx 4.333$$

$$1 + \text{Max}\left\{|1|, \left|\frac{8}{3}\right|, \left|-\frac{2}{3}\right|\right\} = 1 + \frac{8}{3} = \frac{11}{3} \approx 3.667$$

The smaller of the two numbers is 3.67. Thus, every zero of f lies

between –3.67 and 3.67.

Graphing using the bounds and ZOOM-FIT: (Second graph has a better window.)

Step 4: (a) From the graph it appears that there is an x-intercepts at $-\dfrac{1}{3}$.

(b) Using synthetic division:

$$-\frac{1}{2}\overline{\big)\,1 \quad -\frac{2}{3} \quad \frac{8}{2} \quad 1}$$

$$\phantom{-\frac{1}{2}\big)\,1}\; -\frac{1}{3} \quad \frac{1}{3} \quad -1$$

$$\phantom{-\frac{1}{2}\big)}\; 1 \quad -1 \quad 3 \quad 0$$

Since the remainder is 0, $x+\dfrac{1}{3}$ is a factor.

The other factor is the quotient: $x^2 - x + 3$.

(c) The real zero is $-\dfrac{1}{3}$. ($x^2 - x + 3 = 0$ has no real solutions.)

63. Using the TABLE feature to show that there is a zero in the interval:
$$f(x) = 8x^4 - 2x^2 + 5x - 1; \quad [0,1]$$

X	Y1
-1	0
0	-1
1	10
2	129
3	644
4	2035
5	4974

X=-1

$f(0) = -1 < 0$ and $f(1) = 10 > 0$
Since one is positive and one is negative, there is a zero in the interval.

Using the TABLE feature to approximate the zero to two decimal places:

X	Y1
.213	-.0093
.214	-.0048
.215	-4E-4
.216	.0041
.217	.00856
.218	.01302
.219	.01748

X=.219

The zero is approximately 0.22.

65. Using the TABLE feature to show that there is a zero in the interval:
$$f(x) = 2x^3 + 6x^2 - 8x + 2; \quad [-5, -4]$$

X	Y1
-8	-574
-7	-334
-6	-166
-5	-58
-4	2
-3	26
-2	26

Y1=2X^3+6X²-8X+2

$f(-5) = -58 < 0$ and $f(-4) = 2 > 0$
Since one is positive and one is negative, there is a zero in the interval.

Using the TABLE feature to approximate the zero to two decimal places:

X	Y1
-4.052	-.129
-4.051	-.0871
-4.05	-.0453
-4.049	-.0035
-4.048	.03831
-4.047	.08003
-4.046	.12172

Y1=2X^3+6X²-8X+2 The zero is approximately -4.05.

67.   Using the TABLE feature to show that there is a zero in the interval:
$$f(x) = x^5 - x^4 + 7x^3 - 7x^2 - 18x + 18; \quad [1.4, 1.5]$$

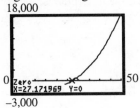

$f(1.4) = -0.1754 < 0$ and $f(1.5) = 1.4063 > 0$
Since one is positive and one is negative, there is a zero in the interval.

Using the TABLE feature to approximate the zero to two decimal places:

X	Y1
1.411	-.041
1.412	-.0283
1.413	-.0156
1.414	-.0028
1.415	.01016
1.416	.02315
1.417	.03621

Y1 ⊟ X^5−X^4+7X^3...   The zero is approximately 1.41.

69. $C(x) = 3000$
$$0.216x^3 - 2.347x^2 + 14.328x + 10.224 = 3000$$
$$0.216x^3 - 2.347x^2 + 14.328x - 2989.776 = 0$$
There are at most 3 solutions.
Graphing and solving:

18,000

Zero
X=27.171969 Y=0

50

−3,000   About 27 Cavaliers can be manufactured.

71. $x - 2$ is a factor of $f(x) = x^3 - kx^2 + kx + 2$ only if the remainder that results when $f(x)$ is divided by $x - 2$ is 0. Dividing, we have:

$$
\begin{array}{r|rrrr}
2 & 1 & -k & k & 2 \\
  &   & 2 & -2k+4 & -2k+8 \\
\hline
  & 1 & -k+2 & -k+4 & -2k+10
\end{array}
$$

Since we want the remainder to equal 0, set the remainder equal to zero and solve:
$$-2k + 10 = 0 \Rightarrow -2k = -10 \Rightarrow k = 5$$

73.   By the Remainder Theorem we know that the remainder from synthetic division by c is equal to $f(c)$. Thus the easiest way to find the remainder is to evaluate:
$$f(1) = 2(1)^{20} - 8(1)^{10} + 1 - 2 = 2 - 8 + 1 - 2 = -7$$
The remainder is −7.

75. $f(x) = 2x^6 - 5x^4 + x^3 - x + 1$

By the Rational Zero Theorem, the only possible rational zeros are: $\dfrac{p}{q} = \pm 1, \pm \dfrac{1}{2}$

Since $\dfrac{3}{5}$ is not in the list of possible rational zeros, it is not a zero of $f(x)$.

77. Let x be the length of a side of the original cube.
     After removing the 1 inch slice, one dimension will be $x-1$.
     The volume of the new solid will be:

$$(x-1) \cdot x \cdot x = 294 \Rightarrow x^3 - x^2 = 294 \Rightarrow x^3 - x^2 - 294 = 0$$

The possible rational zeros are:

$$p = \pm 1, \pm 2, \pm 3, \pm 6, \pm 7, \pm 14, \pm 21, \pm 42, \pm 49, \pm 98, \pm 147, \pm 294; \quad q = \pm 1$$

The rational zeros are the same as the values for p.
Using synthetic division:

$$\begin{array}{r|rrrr} 7 & 1 & -1 & 0 & -294 \\ & & 7 & 42 & 294 \\ \hline & 1 & 6 & 42 & 0 \end{array}$$

7 is a zero, so the length of the original edge of the cube was 7 inches.

The Zeros of a Polynomial Function

5.3 Complex Numbers; Quadratic Equations with a Negative Discriminant

1. $(2 - 3i) + (6 + 8i) = (2 + 6) + (-3 + 8)i = 8 + 5i$

3. $(-3 + 2i) - (4 - 4i) = (-3 - 4) + (2 - (-4))i = -7 + 6i$

5. $(2 - 5i) - (8 + 6i) = (2 - 8) + (-5 - 6)i = -6 - 11i$

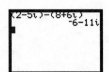

7. $3(2 - 6i) = 6 - 18i$

9. $2i(2 - 3i) = 4i - 6i^2$
$$= 4i - 6(-1) = 6 + 4i$$

11. $(3 - 4i)(2 + i) = 6 + 3i - 8i - 4i^2$
$$= 6 - 5i - 4(-1) = 10 - 5i$$

13. $(-6 + i)(-6 - i) = 36 + 6i - 6i - i^2$
$$= 36 - (-1) = 37$$

15. $\dfrac{10}{3 - 4i} = \dfrac{10}{3 - 4i} \cdot \dfrac{3 + 4i}{3 + 4i} = \dfrac{30 + 40i}{9 + 12i - 12i - 16i^2} = \dfrac{30 + 40i}{9 - 16(-1)} = \dfrac{30 + 40i}{25}$
$$= \dfrac{30}{25} + \dfrac{40}{25}i = \dfrac{6}{5} + \dfrac{8}{5}i$$

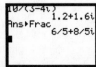

17. $\dfrac{2+i}{i} = \dfrac{2+i}{i} \cdot \dfrac{-i}{-i} = \dfrac{-2i-i^2}{-i^2}$

$= \dfrac{-2i-(-1)}{-(-1)} = \dfrac{1-2i}{1} = 1-2i$

19. $\dfrac{6-i}{1+i} = \dfrac{6-i}{1+i} \cdot \dfrac{1-i}{1-i} = \dfrac{6-6i-i+i^2}{1-i+i-i^2}$

$= \dfrac{6-7i+(-1)}{1-(-1)} = \dfrac{5-7i}{2} = \dfrac{5}{2} - \dfrac{7}{2}i$

21. $\left(\dfrac{1}{2} + \dfrac{\sqrt{3}}{2}i\right)^2 = \dfrac{1}{4} + 2\left(\dfrac{1}{2}\right)\left(\dfrac{\sqrt{3}}{2}i\right) + \dfrac{3}{4}i^2$

$= \dfrac{1}{4} + \dfrac{\sqrt{3}}{2}i + \dfrac{3}{4}(-1) = -\dfrac{1}{2} + \dfrac{\sqrt{3}}{2}i$

23. $(1+i)^2 = 1 + 2i + i^2$

$= 1 + 2i + (-1) = 2i$

25. $i^{23} = i^{22+1} = i^{22} \cdot i = \left(i^2\right)^{11} \cdot i = (-1)^{11}i = -i$

27. $i^{-15} = \dfrac{1}{i^{15}} = \dfrac{1}{i^{14+1}} = \dfrac{1}{i^{14} \cdot i} = \dfrac{1}{(i^2)^7 \cdot i} = \dfrac{1}{(-1)^7 i} = \dfrac{1}{-i} = \dfrac{1}{-i} \cdot \dfrac{i}{i} = \dfrac{i}{-i^2} = \dfrac{i}{-(-1)} = i$

29. $i^6 - 5 = \left(i^2\right)^3 - 5 = (-1)^3 - 5 = -1 - 5 = -6$

31. $6i^3 - 4i^5 = i^3(6 - 4i^2)$

$= i^2 \cdot i(6 - 4(-1)) = -1 \cdot i(10) = -10i$

33. $(1+i)^3 = (1+i)(1+i)(1+i) = (1+2i+i^2)(1+i) = (1+2i-1)(1+i) = 2i(1+i)$

$= 2i + 2i^2 = 2i + 2(-1) = -2 + 2i$

35. $i^7(1+i^2) = i^7(1+(-1)) = i^7(0) = 0$

37. $i^6 + i^4 + i^2 + 1 = (i^2)^3 + (i^2)^2 + i^2 + 1 = (-1)^3 + (-1)^2 + (-1) + 1 = -1 + 1 - 1 + 1 = 0$

39. $\sqrt{-4} = 2i$ 41. $\sqrt{-25} = 5i$

43. $\sqrt{(3+4i)(4i-3)} = \sqrt{12i - 9 + 16i^2 - 12i} = \sqrt{-9 + 16(-1)} = \sqrt{-25} = 5i$

45. $x^2 + 4 = 0$

$a = 1, b = 0, c = 4, \quad b^2 - 4ac = 0^2 - 4(1)(4) = -16$

$$x = \frac{-0 \pm \sqrt{-16}}{2(1)} = \frac{\pm 4i}{2} = \pm 2i$$

The solution set is $\{\pm 2i\}$.

47. $x^2 - 16 = 0$

$(x+4)(x-4) = 0 \Rightarrow x = -4, x = 4$

The solution set is $\{\pm 4\}$.

49. $x^2 - 6x + 13 = 0$

$a = 1, b = -6, c = 13,$

$b^2 - 4ac = (-6)^2 - 4(1)(13) = 36 - 52 = -16$

$$x = \frac{-(-6) \pm \sqrt{-16}}{2(1)} = \frac{6 \pm 4i}{2} = 3 \pm 2i$$

The solution set is $\{3 - 2i, 3 + 2i\}$.

51. $x^2 - 6x + 10 = 0$

$a = 1, b = -6, c = 10$

$b^2 - 4ac = (-6)^2 - 4(1)(10) = 36 - 40 = -4$

$$x = \frac{-(-6) \pm \sqrt{-4}}{2(1)} = \frac{6 \pm 2i}{2} = 3 \pm i$$

The solution set is $\{3 - i, 3 + i\}$.

53. $8x^2 - 4x + 1 = 0$
$a = 8, b = -4, c = 1$

$b^2 - 4ac = (-4)^2 - 4(8)(1) = 16 - 32 = -16$

$x = \dfrac{-(-4) \pm \sqrt{-16}}{2(8)} = \dfrac{4 \pm 4i}{16} = \dfrac{1}{4} \pm \dfrac{1}{4}i$

The solution set is $\left\{ \dfrac{1}{4} - \dfrac{1}{4}i, \ \dfrac{1}{4} + \dfrac{1}{4}i \right\}$.

55. $5x^2 + 1 = 2x \Rightarrow 5x^2 - 2x + 1 = 0$
$a = 5, b = -2, c = 1$

$b^2 - 4ac = (-2)^2 - 4(5)(1) = 4 - 20 = -16$

$x = \dfrac{-(-2) \pm \sqrt{-16}}{2(5)} = \dfrac{2 \pm 4i}{10} = \dfrac{1}{5} \pm \dfrac{2}{5}i$

The solution set is $\left\{ \dfrac{1}{5} - \dfrac{2}{5}i, \ \dfrac{1}{5} + \dfrac{2}{5}i \right\}$.

57. $x^2 + x + 1 = 0$
$a = 1, b = 1, c = 1, \quad b^2 - 4ac = 1^2 - 4(1)(1) = 1 - 4 = -3$

$x = \dfrac{-1 \pm \sqrt{-3}}{2(1)} = \dfrac{-1 \pm \sqrt{3}i}{2} = -\dfrac{1}{2} \pm \dfrac{\sqrt{3}}{2}i$

The solution set is $\left\{ -\dfrac{1}{2} - \dfrac{\sqrt{3}}{2}i, \ -\dfrac{1}{2} + \dfrac{\sqrt{3}}{2}i \right\}$.

59. $x^3 - 8 = 0$
$(x - 2)(x^2 + 2x + 4) = 0$

$\qquad\qquad x - 2 = 0 \Rightarrow x = 2$

$\qquad\quad x^2 + 2x + 4 = 0$
$a = 1, b = 2, c = 4$

$b^2 - 4ac = 2^2 - 4(1)(4) = 4 - 16 = -12$

$x = \dfrac{-2 \pm \sqrt{-12}}{2(1)} = \dfrac{-2 \pm 2\sqrt{3}i}{2} = -1 \pm \sqrt{3}i$

The solution set is $\left\{ 2, \ -1 - \sqrt{3}i, \ -1 + \sqrt{3}i \right\}$.

61. $x^4 = 16 \Rightarrow x^4 - 16 = 0$
$(x^2 - 4)(x^2 + 4) = 0 \Rightarrow (x - 2)(x + 2)(x^2 + 4) = 0$

$\qquad\quad x - 2 = 0 \Rightarrow x = 2; \ x + 2 = 0 \Rightarrow x = -2$

$\qquad\qquad x^2 + 4 = 0 \Rightarrow x = \pm 2i$

The solution set is $\{-2, \ 2, \ -2i, \ 2i\}$.

63. $x^4 + 13x^2 + 36 = 0$

$\left(x^2 + 9\right)\left(x^2 + 4\right) = 0$

$x^2 + 9 = 0 \Rightarrow x = \pm 3i$

$x^2 + 4 = 0 \Rightarrow x = \pm 2i$

The solution set is $\{-3i, \; 3i, \; -2i, \; 2i\}$.

65. $3x^2 - 3x + 4 = 0$

$a = 3, b = -3, c = 4$

$b^2 - 4ac = (-3)^2 - 4(3)(4) = 9 - 48 = -39$

The equation has two complex conjugate solutions.

67. $2x^2 + 3x - 4 = 0$

$a = 2, b = 3, c = -4$

$b^2 - 4ac = 3^2 - 4(2)(-4) = 9 + 32 = 41$

The equation has two unequal real solutions.

69. $9x^2 - 12x + 4 = 0$

$a = 9, b = -12, c = 4$

$b^2 - 4ac = (-12)^2 - 4(9)(4) = 144 - 144 = 0$

The equation has a repeated real solution.

71. The other solution is the conjugate of $2 + 3i$, namely, $2 - 3i$.

73. $z + \bar{z} = 3 - 4i + \overline{3 - 4i} = 3 - 4i + 3 + 4i = 6$

75. $z \cdot \bar{z} = (3 - 4i)(\overline{3 - 4i}) = (3 - 4i)(3 + 4i) = 9 + 12i - 12i - 16i^2 = 9 - 16(-1) = 25$

77. $z + \bar{z} = a + bi + \overline{a + bi} = a + bi + a - bi = 2a$

$z - \bar{z} = a + bi - (\overline{a + bi}) = a + bi - (a - bi) = a + bi - a + bi = 2bi$

79. $\overline{z + w} = \overline{(a + bi) + (c + di)} = \overline{(a + c) + (b + d)i} = (a + c) - (b + d)i$

$= (a - bi) + (c - di) = \overline{a + bi} + \overline{c + di} = \bar{z} + \bar{w}$

81. – 83.   Answers will vary.

Chapter 5

The Zeros of a Polynomial Function

5.4   Complex Zeros; Fundamental Theorem of Algebra

1.   Since complex zeros appear in conjugate pairs, $4+i$, the conjugate of $4-i$, is the remaining zero of f.

3.   Since complex zeros appear in conjugate pairs, $-i$, the conjugate of i, and $1-i$, the conjugate of $1+i$, are the remaining zeros of f.

5.   Since complex zeros appear in conjugate pairs, $-i$, the conjugate of i, and $-2i$, the conjugate of $2i$, are the remaining zeros of f.

7.   Since complex zeros appear in conjugate pairs, $-i$, the conjugate of i, is the remaining zero of f.

9.   Since complex zeros appear in conjugate pairs, $2-i$, the conjugate of $2+i$, and $-3+i$, the conjugate of $-3-i$, are the remaining zeros of f.

11. Since $3+2i$ is a zero, its conjugate $3-2i$ is also a zero of f. Finding the function:
$$f(x)=(x-4)(x-4)\big(x-(3+2i)\big)\big(x-(3-2i)\big)=\left(x^2-8x+16\right)\big((x-3)-2i\big)\big((x-3)+2i\big)$$
$$=\left(x^2-8x+16\right)\left(x^2-6x+9-4i^2\right)=\left(x^2-8x+16\right)\left(x^2-6x+13\right)$$
$$=x^4-6x^3+13x^2-8x^3+48x^2-104x+16x^2-96x+208$$
$$=x^4-14x^3+77x^2-200x+208$$

13. Since $-i$ is a zero, its conjugate i is also a zero, and since $1+i$ is a zero, its conjugate $1-i$ is also a zero of f. Finding the function:
$$f(x)=(x-2)(x+i)(x-i)\big(x-(1+i)\big)\big(x-(1-i)\big)=(x-2)\left(x^2-i^2\right)\big((x-1)-i\big)\big((x-1)+i\big)$$
$$=(x-2)\left(x^2+1\right)\left(x^2-2x+1-i^2\right)=\left(x^3-2x^2+x-2\right)\left(x^2-2x+2\right)$$
$$=x^5-2x^4+2x^3-2x^4+4x^3-4x^2+x^3-2x^2+2x-2x^2+4x-4$$
$$=x^5-4x^4+7x^3-8x^2+6x-4$$

15. Since $-i$ is a zero, its conjugate i is also a zero of f. Finding the function:
$$f(x)=(x-3)(x-3)(x+i)(x-i)=\left(x^2-6x+9\right)\left(x^2-i^2\right)$$
$$=\left(x^2-6x+9\right)\left(x^2+1\right)=x^4+x^2-6x^3-6x+9x^2+9$$
$$=x^4-6x^3+10x^2-6x+9$$

285

17.   Since $2i$ is a zero, its conjugate $-2i$ is also a zero of f. $x - 2i$ and $x + 2i$ are factors of f.
       Thus, $(x - 2i)(x + 2i) = x^2 + 4$ is a factor of f.
       Using division to find the other factor:

$$
\begin{array}{r}
x - 4 \\
x^2 + 4 \overline{\smash{)}\, x^3 - 4x^2 + 4x - 16} \\
\underline{x^3 \qquad\quad + 4x} \\
-4x^2 \qquad\ -16 \\
\underline{-4x^2 \qquad\ -16}
\end{array}
$$

       $x - 4$ is a factor and the remaining zero is 4. The zeros of f are $4, 2i, -2i$.

19.   Since $-2i$ is a zero, its conjugate $2i$ is also a zero of f. $x - 2i$ and $x + 2i$ are factors of f.
       Thus, $(x - 2i)(x + 2i) = x^2 + 4$ is a factor of f. Using division to find the other factor:

$$
\begin{array}{r}
2x^2 + 5x - 3 \\
x^2 + 4 \overline{\smash{)}\, 2x^4 + 5x^3 + 5x^2 + 20x - 12} \\
\underline{2x^4 \qquad\quad\ + 8x^2} \\
5x^3 - 3x^2 + 20x \\
\underline{5x^3 \qquad\quad + 20x} \\
-3x^2 \qquad\ -12 \\
\underline{-3x^2 \qquad\ -12}
\end{array}
$$

       $2x^2 + 5x - 3 = (2x - 1)(x + 3)$ are factors and the remaining zeros are $\dfrac{1}{2}$ and -3.

       The zeros of f are $2i, -2i, -3, \dfrac{1}{2}$.

21.   Since $3 - 2i$ is a zero, its conjugate $3 + 2i$ is also a zero of h. $x - (3 - 2i)$ and $x - (3 + 2i)$
       are factors of h. Thus,
       $(x - (3 - 2i))(x - (3 + 2i)) = ((x - 3) + 2i)((x - 3) - 2i) = x^2 - 6x + 9 - 4i^2 = x^2 - 6x + 13$ is
       a factor of h.

Using division to find the other factor:

$$\begin{array}{r}
x^2 - 3x - 10 \\
x^2 - 6x + 13 \overline{\smash{)}x^4 - 9x^3 + 21x^2 + 21x - 130} \\
\underline{x^4 - 6x^3 + 13x^2} \\
-3x^3 + 8x^2 + 21x \\
\underline{-3x^3 + 18x^2 - 39x} \\
-10x^2 + 60x - 130 \\
\underline{-10x^2 + 60x - 130}
\end{array}$$

$x^2 - 3x - 10 = (x + 2)(x - 5)$ are factors and the remaining zeros are -2 and 5.
The zeros of h are $3 - 2i, 3 + 2i, -2, 5$.

23.   Since $-4i$ is a zero, its conjugate $4i$ is also a zero of h. $x - 4i$ and $x + 4i$ are factors of h.
Thus, $(x - 4i)(x + 4i) = x^2 + 16$ is a factor of h. Using division to find the other factor:

$$\begin{array}{r}
3x^3 + 2x^2 - 33x - 22 \\
x^2 + 16 \overline{\smash{)}3x^5 + 2x^4 + 15x^3 + 10x^2 - 528x - 352} \\
\underline{3x^5 \qquad\quad + 48x^3} \\
2x^4 - 33x^3 + 10x^2 \\
\underline{2x^4 \qquad\quad + 32x^2} \\
-33x^3 - 22x^2 - 528x \\
\underline{-33x^3 \qquad\quad - 528x} \\
-22x^2 \qquad\quad - 352 \\
\underline{-22x^2 \qquad\quad - 352}
\end{array}$$

$3x^3 + 2x^2 - 33x - 22 = x^2(3x + 2) - 11(3x + 2) = (3x + 2)(x^2 - 11)$

$= (3x + 2)\left(x - \sqrt{11}\right)\left(x + \sqrt{11}\right)$ are factors and the remaining zeros are $-\dfrac{2}{3}, \sqrt{11},$ and $-\sqrt{11}$.

The zeros of h are $4i, -4i, -\sqrt{11}, \sqrt{11}, -\dfrac{2}{3}$.

25. $f(x) = x^3 - 1 = (x-1)(x^2 + x + 1)$ The zeros of $x^2 + x + 1 = 0$ are:

$$x = \frac{-1 \pm \sqrt{1^2 - 4(1)(1)}}{2(1)} = \frac{-1 \pm \sqrt{-3}}{2} = -\frac{1}{2} + \frac{\sqrt{3}}{2}i \text{ or } -\frac{1}{2} - \frac{\sqrt{3}}{2}i$$

The zeros are: $1, \ -\frac{1}{2} + \frac{\sqrt{3}}{2}i, \ -\frac{1}{2} - \frac{\sqrt{3}}{2}i$.

Evaluating f at each zero:

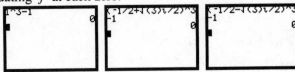

27. $f(x) = x^3 - 8x^2 + 25x - 26$

Step 1: $f(x)$ has 3 complex zeros.

Step 2:   Possible rational zeros: $p = \pm 1, \pm 2, \pm 13, \pm 26; \quad q = \pm 1; \quad \dfrac{p}{q} = \pm 1, \pm 2, \pm 13, \pm 26$

Step 3:   Using synthetic division:

```
2)1   -8    25   -26
        2   -12    26
   1   -6    13     0
```

Since the remainder is 0, $x - 2$ is a factor.

The other factor is the quotient: $x^2 - 6x + 13$.

Using the quadratic formula to find the zeros of $x^2 - 6x + 13 = 0$:

$$x = \frac{-(-6) \pm \sqrt{(-6)^2 - 4(1)(13)}}{2(1)} = \frac{6 \pm \sqrt{-16}}{2} = \frac{6 \pm 4i}{2} = 3 \pm 2i.$$

The complex zeros are $2, \ 3 - 2i, \ 3 + 2i$.

Evaluating f at each zero:

29. $f(x) = x^4 + 5x^2 + 4 = (x^2 + 4)(x^2 + 1) = (x + 2i)(x - 2i)(x + i)(x - i)$

The zeros are: $-2i, \ -i, \ i, \ 2i$.

Evaluating f at each zero:

31. $f(x) = x^4 + 2x^3 + 22x^2 + 50x - 75$

Step 1: $f(x)$ has 4 complex zeros.

Step 2:   Possible rational zeros: $p = \pm 1, \pm 3, \pm 5, \pm 15, \pm 25, \pm 75; \quad q = \pm 1;$

$$\frac{p}{q} = \pm 1, \pm 3, \pm 5, \pm 15, \pm 25, \pm 75$$

Step 3:   Using synthetic division:

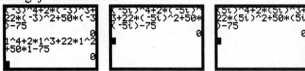

Since the remainder is 0, $x + 3$ is a factor. The other factor is the quotient:

$$x^3 - x^2 + 25x - 25 = x^2(x-1) + 25(x-1) = (x-1)(x^2 + 25)$$
$$= (x-1)(x+5i)(x-5i)$$

The complex zeros are -3, 1, $-5i$, $5i$.

Evaluating f at each zero:

33. $f(x) = 3x^4 - x^3 - 9x^2 + 159x - 52$

Step 1: $f(x)$ has 4 complex zeros.

Step 2:   Possible rational zeros: $p = \pm 1, \pm 2, \pm 4, \pm 13, \pm 26, \pm 52;$ $q = \pm 1, \pm 3;$

$$\frac{p}{q} = \pm 1, \pm 2, \pm 4, \pm 13, \pm 26, \pm 52, \pm \frac{1}{3}, \pm \frac{2}{3}, \pm \frac{4}{3}, \pm \frac{13}{3}, \pm \frac{26}{3}, \pm \frac{52}{3}$$

Step 3:   Using synthetic division:

$$
\begin{array}{r|rrrrr}
-4 & 3 & -1 & -9 & 159 & -52 \\
   &   & -12 & 52 & -172 & 52 \\
\hline
   & 3 & -13 & 43 & -13 & 0
\end{array}
\qquad
\begin{array}{r|rrrr}
\frac{1}{3} & 3 & -13 & 43 & -13 \\
   &   & 1 & -4 & 13 \\
\hline
   & 3 & -12 & 39 & 0
\end{array}
$$

Since the remainder is 0, $x + 4$ and $x - \dfrac{1}{3}$ are factors.

The other factor is the quotient: $3x^2 - 12x + 39 = 3(x^2 - 4x + 13)$.

Using the quadratic formula to find the zeros of $x^2 - 4x + 13 = 0$:

$$x = \frac{-(-4) \pm \sqrt{(-4)^2 - 4(1)(13)}}{2(1)} = \frac{4 \pm \sqrt{-36}}{2} = \frac{4 \pm 6i}{2} = 2 \pm 3i.$$

The complex zeros are -4, $\dfrac{1}{3}$, $2 - 3i$, $2 + 3i$.

Evaluating f at each zero:

35.   If the coefficients are real numbers and $2 + i$ is a zero, then $2 - i$ would also be a zero.
This would then require a polynomial of degree 4.

Chapter 5

The Zeros of a Polynomial Function

5.R   Chapter Review

1. Use synthetic division:

$$1\overline{)8 \;-3 \;\;1 \;\;4}$$
$$\quad\quad 8\;\;5\;\;6$$
$$\overline{\;8\;\;5\;\;6\;\;10}$$

Quotient: $8x^2 + 5x + 6$ Remainder: $10 \neq 0$

Therefore, g is not a factor of f.

3. Use synthetic division:

$$-2\overline{)1 \;-2 \;\;0 \;\;15 \;-2}$$
$$\quad\quad -2\;\;8\;-16\;\;2$$
$$\overline{\;1\;-4\;\;8\;-1\;\;0}$$

Quotient: $x^3 - 4x^2 + 8x - 1$ Remainder: 0

Therefore, g is a factor of f.

5. $f(x) = 2x^8 - x^7 + 8x^4 - 2x^3 + x + 3$
Step 1: $f(x)$ has at most 8 real zeros.
Step 2:   Possible rational zeros:
   p must be a factor of 3: $p = \pm 1, \pm 3$
   q must be a factor of 2: $q = \pm 1, \pm 2$

   The possible rational zeros are: $\dfrac{p}{q} = \pm 1, \pm \dfrac{1}{2}, \pm 3, \pm \dfrac{3}{2}$

7. $f(x) = x^3 - 3x^2 - 6x + 8$
Step 1: $f(x)$ has at most 3 real zeros.

Step 2:   Possible rational zeros: $p = \pm 1, \pm 2, \pm 4, \pm 8;\quad q = \pm 1;\quad \dfrac{p}{q} = \pm 1, \pm 2, \pm 4, \pm 8$

Step 3:   Using the Bounds on Zeros Theorem:
   $a_2 = -3,\;\; a_1 = -6,\;\; a_0 = 8$
   Max $\{1, |8| + |-6| + |-3|\}$ = Max $\{1, 17\}$ = 17
   $1 + $ Max $\{|8|, |-6|, |-3|\}$ = $1 + 8 = 9$
   The smaller of the two numbers is 9. Thus, every zero of f lies between -9 and 9.

Graphing using the bounds and ZOOM-FIT: (Second graph has a better window.)

Step 4: (a) From the graph it appears that there are x-intercepts at –2, 1, and 4.

(b) Using synthetic division:

$$-2{\overline{\smash{\big)}\,1 \quad -3 \quad -6 \quad 8}}$$
$$\;\; -2 \quad 10 \quad -8$$
$$\overline{\;\; 1 \quad -5 \quad 4 \quad 0}$$

Since the remainder is 0, $x - (-2) = x + 2$ is a factor.

The other factor is the quotient: $x^2 - 5x + 4$.

(c) Thus, $f(x) = (x + 2)(x^2 - 5x + 4) = (x + 2)(x - 1)(x - 4)$.

The zeros are –2, 1, and 4.

9. $f(x) = 4x^3 + 4x^2 - 7x + 2$

Step 1: $f(x)$ has at most 3 real zeros.

Step 2: Possible rational zeros: $p = \pm 1, \pm 2$; $q = \pm 1, \pm 2, \pm 4$; $\dfrac{p}{q} = \pm 1, \pm 2, \pm \dfrac{1}{2}, \pm \dfrac{1}{4}$

Step 3: Using the Bounds on Zeros Theorem:

$$f(x) = 4\left(x^3 + x^2 - 1.75x + 0.5\right)$$

$$a_2 = 1, \quad a_1 = -1.75, \quad a_0 = 0.5$$

$$\text{Max}\left\{1, |0.5| + |-1.75| + |1|\right\} = \text{Max}\left\{1, 3.25\right\} = 3.25$$

$$1 + \text{Max}\left\{|0.5|, |-1.75|, |1|\right\} = 1 + 1.75 = 2.75$$

The smaller of the two numbers is 2.75. Thus, every zero of f lies between –2.75 and 2.75.

Graphing using the bounds and ZOOM-FIT: (Second graph has a better window.)

Step 4: (a) From the graph it appears that there are x-intercepts at –2 and 0.5.

(b) Using synthetic division:

$$-2{\overline{\smash{\big)}\,4 \quad 4 \quad -7 \quad 2}}$$
$$\;\; -8 \quad 8 \quad -2$$
$$\overline{\;\; 4 \quad -4 \quad 1 \quad 0}$$

Since the remainder is 0, $x - (-2) = x + 2$ is a factor.

The other factor is the quotient: $4x^2 - 4x + 1$.

(c) Thus, $f(x) = (x + 2)(4x^2 - 4x + 1) = (x + 2)(2x - 1)(2x - 1)$.

The zeros are –2 and 0.5 (multiplicity 2).

11. $f(x) = x^4 - 4x^3 + 9x^2 - 20x + 20$

   Step 1: $f(x)$ has at most 4 real zeros.

   Step 2:   Possible rational zeros:

   $$p = \pm 1, \pm 2, \pm 4, \pm 5, \pm 10, \pm 20; \quad q = \pm 1;$$

   $$\frac{p}{q} = \pm 1, \pm 2, \pm 4, \pm 5, \pm 10, \pm 20$$

   Step 3:   Using the Bounds on Zeros Theorem:

   $$a_3 = -4, \ a_2 = 9, \ a_1 = -20, \ a_0 = 20$$

   $$\text{Max} \left\{ 1, |20| + |-20| + |9| + |-4| \right\} = \text{Max} \left\{ 1, 53 \right\} = 53$$

   $$1 + \text{Max} \left\{ |20|, |-20|, |9|, |-4| \right\} = 1 + 20 = 21$$

   The smaller of the two numbers is 21. Thus, every zero of f lies between –21 and 21.

   Graphing using the bounds and ZOOM-FIT: (Second graph has a better window.)

   Step 4:   (a)   From the graph it appears that there is an x-intercept at 2.
            (b)   Using synthetic division:

2)1	– 4	9	– 20	20		2)1	– 2	5	– 10
	2	– 4	10	– 20			2	0	10
1	– 2	5	– 10	0		1	0	5	0

   Since the remainder is 0, $x - 2$ is a factor twice.
   The other factor is the quotient: $x^2 + 5$.

            (c)   Thus, $f(x) = (x - 2)(x - 2)(x^2 + 5) = (x - 2)^2(x^2 + 5)$.

   The zero is 2 (multiplicity 2). ($x^2 + 5 = 0$ has no real solutions.)

13. $f(x) = 2x^3 - 11.84x^2 - 9.116x + 82.46$

   $f(x)$ has at most 3 real zeros.

   Solving by graphing (using ZERO):

             The zeros are approximately –2.5, 3.1, and 5.32.

15. $g(x) = 15x^4 - 21.5x^3 - 1718.3x^2 + 5308x + 3796.8$

   $g(x)$ has at most 4 real zeros.

   Solving by graphing (using ZERO):

             The zeros are approximately –11.3, –0.6, 4, and 9.33.

17. $2x^4 + 2x^3 - 11x^2 + x - 6 = 0$

The solutions of the equation are the zeros of $f(x) = 2x^4 + 2x^3 - 11x^2 + x - 6$.

Step 1: $f(x)$ has at most 4 real zeros.

Step 2: Possible rational zeros:

$$p = \pm 1, \pm 2, \pm 3, \pm 6; \quad q = \pm 1, \pm 2; \quad \frac{p}{q} = \pm 1, \pm 2, \pm 3, \pm 6, \pm \frac{1}{2}, \pm \frac{3}{2}$$

Step 3: Using the Bounds on Zeros Theorem:

$$f(x) = 2\left(x^4 + x^3 - 5.5x^2 + 0.5x - 3\right)$$

$$a_3 = 1, \ a_2 = -5.5, \ a_1 = 0.5, \ a_0 = -3$$

$$\text{Max}\left\{1, |-3| + |0.5| + |-5.5| + |1|\right\} = \text{Max}\left\{1, 10\right\} = 10$$

$$1 + \text{Max}\left\{|-3|, |0.5|, |-5.5|, |1|\right\} = 1 + 5.5 = 6.5$$

The smaller of the two numbers is 6.5. Thus, every zero of f lies between –6.5 and 6.5.

Graphing using the bounds and ZOOM-FIT: (Second graph has a better window.)

Step 4: (a)   From the graph it appears that there are x-intercepts at –3 and 2.

(b)   Using synthetic division:

$$-3\overline{)2 \quad\ 2 \quad -11 \quad\ 1 \quad -6}$$
$$\underline{\quad\quad -6 \quad\ 12 \quad -3 \quad\ 6}$$
$$\quad\ 2 \quad -4 \quad\quad 1 \quad -2 \quad\ 0$$

$$2\overline{)2 \quad -4 \quad\ 1 \quad -2}$$
$$\underline{\quad\quad\quad\ 4 \quad\ 0 \quad\ 2}$$
$$\quad\ 2 \quad\quad 0 \quad\ 1 \quad\ 0$$

Since the remainder is 0, $x + 3$ and $x - 2$ are factors.
The other factor is the quotient: $2x^2 + 1$.

(c)   The zeros are –3 and 2. ($2x^2 + 1 = 0$ has no real solutions.)

19. $2x^4 + 7x^3 + x^2 - 7x - 3 = 0$

The solutions of the equation are the zeros of $f(x) = 2x^4 + 7x^3 + x^2 - 7x - 3$.

Step 1: $f(x)$ has at most 4 real zeros.

Step 2: Possible rational zeros: $p = \pm 1, \pm 3; \quad q = \pm 1, \pm 2; \quad \frac{p}{q} = \pm 1, \pm 3, \pm \frac{1}{2}, \pm \frac{3}{2}$

Step 3: Using the Bounds on Zeros Theorem:

$$f(x) = 2\left(x^4 + 3.5x^3 + 0.5x^2 - 3.5x - 1.5\right)$$

$$a_3 = 3.5, \ a_2 = 0.5, \ a_1 = -3.5, \ a_0 = -1.5$$

$$\text{Max}\left\{1, |-1.5| + |-3.5| + |0.5| + |3.5|\right\} = \text{Max}\left\{1, 9\right\} = 9$$

$$1 + \text{Max}\left\{|-1.5|, |-3.5|, |0.5|, |3.5|\right\} = 1 + 3.5 = 4.5$$

The smaller of the two numbers is 4.5.
Thus, every zero of f lies between –4.5 and 4.5.

Graphing using the bounds and ZOOM-FIT: (Second graph has a better window.)

Step 4: (a) From the graph it appears that there are x-intercepts at $-3, -1, -0.5$, and 1.

(b) Using synthetic division:

$$-3\overline{)2 \quad 7 \quad 1 \quad -7 \quad -3}$$
$$\underline{\quad -6 \quad -3 \quad 6 \quad 3}$$
$$2 \quad 1 \quad -2 \quad -1 \quad 0$$

$$-1\overline{)2 \quad 1 \quad -2 \quad -1}$$
$$\underline{\quad -2 \quad 1 \quad 1}$$
$$2 \quad -1 \quad -1 \quad 0$$

Since the remainder is 0, $x+3$ and $x+1$ are factors.
The other factor is the quotient: $2x^2 - x - 1$.

(c) Thus, $f(x) = (x+3)(x+1)(2x^2 - x - 1) = (x+3)(x+1)(2x+1)(x-1)$.
The zeros are $-3, -1, -0.5$, and 1.

21. $f(x) = x^3 - x^2 - 4x + 2$

$a_2 = -1, \quad a_1 = -4, \quad a_0 = 2$

Max $\{1, |2| + |-4| + |-1|\}$ = Max $\{1, 7\} = 7$

$1 +$ Max $\{|2|, |-4|, |-1|\} = 1 + 4 = 5$

The smaller of the two numbers is 5. Thus, every zero of f lies between -5 and 5.

Graphing using the bounds and ZOOM-FIT: (Second graph has a better window.)

23. $f(x) = 2x^3 - 7x^2 - 10x + 35 = 2(x^3 - 3.5x^2 - 5x + 17.5)$

$a_2 = -3.5, \quad a_1 = -5, \quad a_0 = 17.5$

Max $\{1, |17.5| + |-5| + |-3.5|\}$ = Max $\{1, 26\} = 26$

$1 +$ Max $\{|17.5|, |-5|, |-3.5|\} = 1 + 17.5 = 18.5$

The smaller of the two numbers is 18.5. Thus, every zero of f lies between -18.5 and 18.5.

Graphing using the bounds and ZOOM-FIT: (Second graph has a better window.)

25. Using the TABLE feature to show that there is a zero in the interval:
$f(x) = 3x^3 - x - 1$; $[0, 1]$

$f(0) = -1 < 0$ and $f(1) = 1 > 0$

Since one is positive and one is negative, there is a zero in the interval.

Using the TABLE feature to approximate the zero to two decimal places:

The zero is approximately 0.85.

27. Using the TABLE feature to show that there is a zero in the interval:
$f(x) = 8x^4 - 4x^3 - 2x - 1$; $[0, 1]$

$f(0) = -1 < 0$ and $f(1) = 1 > 0$
Since one is positive and one is negative, there is a zero in the interval.

Using the TABLE feature to approximate the zero to two decimal places:

The zero is approximately 0.94.

29. $(6 + 3i) - (2 - 4i) = (6 - 2) + (3 - (-4))i = 4 + 7i$

31. $4(3 - i) + 3(-5 + 2i) = 12 - 4i - 15 + 6i = -3 + 2i$

33. $\dfrac{3}{3+i} = \dfrac{3}{3+i} \cdot \dfrac{3-i}{3-i} = \dfrac{9-3i}{9-3i+3i-i^2} = \dfrac{9-3i}{10} = \dfrac{9}{10} - \dfrac{3}{10}i$

35. $i^{50} = i^{48} \cdot i^2 = (i^4)^{12} \cdot i^2 = 1^{12}(-1) = -1$

37. $(2+3i)^3 = (2+3i)^2(2+3i) = \left(4+12i+9i^2\right)(2+3i) = (-5+12i)(2+3i)$
$$= -10 - 15i + 24i + 36i^2 = -46 + 9i$$

39. Since complex zeros appear in conjugate pairs, $4-i$, the conjugate of $4+i$, is the remaining zero of f.

$$f(x) = (x-6)(x-(4-i))(x-(4+i)) = (x-6)(x-4+i)(x-4-i)$$
$$= (x-6)\left((x-4)^2 - i^2\right) = (x-6)\left((x-4)^2 + 1\right)$$
$$= (x-6)(x^2-8x+16+1) = (x-6)(x^2-8x+17)$$
$$= x^3 - 8x^2 + 17x - 6x^2 + 48x - 102$$

$f(x) = x^3 - 14x^2 + 65x - 102$

41. Since complex zeros appear in conjugate pairs, $-i$, the conjugate of i, and $1-i$, the conjugate of $1+i$, are the remaining zeros of f.

$$f(x) = (x-i)(x+i)(x-(1-i))(x-(1+i)) = (x^2-i^2)(x-1+i)(x-1-i)$$
$$= (x^2+1)\left((x-1)^2 - i^2\right) = (x^2+1)\left((x-1)^2 + 1\right)$$
$$= (x^2+1)(x^2-2x+1+1) = (x^2+1)(x^2-2x+2)$$
$$= x^4 - 2x^3 + 2x^2 + x^2 - 2x + 2$$

$f(x) = x^3 - 2x^3 + 3x^2 - 2x + 2$

43. $x^2 + x + 1 = 0$

$a = 1, b = 1, c = 1, \quad b^2 - 4ac = 1^2 - 4(1)(1) = 1 - 4 = -3$

$$x = \frac{-1 \pm \sqrt{-3}}{2(1)} = \frac{-1 \pm \sqrt{3}\,i}{2} = -\frac{1}{2} \pm \frac{\sqrt{3}}{2}i$$

The solution set is $\left\{ -\dfrac{1}{2} - \dfrac{\sqrt{3}}{2}i, \; -\dfrac{1}{2} + \dfrac{\sqrt{3}}{2}i \right\}$.

45. $2x^2 + x - 2 = 0$

$a = 2, b = 1, c = -2, \quad b^2 - 4ac = 1^2 - 4(2)(-2) = 1 + 16 = 17$

$x = \dfrac{-1 \pm \sqrt{17}}{2(2)} = \dfrac{-1 \pm \sqrt{17}}{4}$

The solution set is $\left\{ \dfrac{-1 - \sqrt{17}}{4}, \ \dfrac{-1 + \sqrt{17}}{4} \right\}$.

47. $x^2 + 3 = x$

$x^2 - x + 3 = 0$

$a = 1, b = -1, c = 3, \quad b^2 - 4ac = (-1)^2 - 4(1)(3) = 1 - 12 = -11$

$x = \dfrac{-(-1) \pm \sqrt{-11}}{2(1)} = \dfrac{1 \pm \sqrt{11}\,i}{2} = \dfrac{1}{2} \pm \dfrac{\sqrt{11}}{2} i$

The solution set is $\left\{ \dfrac{1}{2} - \dfrac{\sqrt{11}}{2} i, \ \dfrac{1}{2} + \dfrac{\sqrt{11}}{2} i \right\}$.

49. $x(1 - x) = 6$

$-x^2 + x - 6 = 0$

$a = -1, b = 1, c = -6, \quad b^2 - 4ac = 1^2 - 4(-1)(-6) = 1 - 24 = -23$

$x = \dfrac{-1 \pm \sqrt{-23}}{2(-1)} = \dfrac{-1 \pm \sqrt{23}\,i}{-2} = \dfrac{1}{2} \pm \dfrac{\sqrt{23}}{2} i$

The solution set is $\left\{ \dfrac{1}{2} - \dfrac{\sqrt{23}}{2} i, \ \dfrac{1}{2} + \dfrac{\sqrt{23}}{2} i \right\}$.

51. $x^4 + 2x^2 - 8 = 0$

$\left(x^2 + 4 \right)\left(x^2 - 2 \right) = 0$

$x^2 + 4 = 0 \ \text{ or } \ x^2 - 2 = 0$

$x^2 = -4 \ \text{ or } \ x^2 = 2$

$x = \pm 2i \ \text{ or } \ x = \pm\sqrt{2}$

The solution set is $\left\{ -2i, \ 2i, \ -\sqrt{2}, \ \sqrt{2} \right\}$.

53. $x^3 - x^2 - 8x + 12 = 0$

The solutions of the equation are the zeros of the function $f(x) = x^3 - x^2 - 8x + 12$.

Step 1: $f(x)$ has 3 complex zeros.

Step 2: Possible rational zeros:

$p = \pm 1, \pm 2, \pm 3, \pm 4, \pm 6, \pm 12; \quad q = \pm 1; \quad \dfrac{p}{q} = \pm 1, \pm 2, \pm 3, \pm 4, \pm 6, \pm 12$

Step 3: Graphing the function:

From the graph it appears that there are x-intercepts at –3 and 2.

Step 4:   Using synthetic division:

$$2\overline{)1 \quad -1 \quad -8 \quad 12}$$
$$\underline{ \quad 2 \quad 2 \quad -12}$$
$$1 \quad 1 \quad -6 \quad 0$$

Since the remainder is 0, $x - 2$ is a factor.

The other factor is the quotient: $x^2 + x - 6 = (x + 3)(x - 2)$.

The complex zeros are -3, 2 (multiplicity 2).

55. $3x^4 - 4x^3 + 4x^2 - 4x + 1 = 0$

The solutions of the equation are the zeros of the function
$$f(x) = 3x^4 - 4x^3 + 4x^2 - 4x + 1$$

Step 1: $f(x)$ has 4 complex zeros.

Step 2:   Possible rational zeros: $p = \pm 1$; $q = \pm 1, \pm 3$; $\dfrac{p}{q} = \pm 1, \pm \dfrac{1}{3}$

Step 3:   Graphing the function:

From the graph it appears that there are x-intercepts at $\dfrac{1}{3}$ and 1.

Step 4:   Using synthetic division:

$$1\overline{)3 \quad -4 \quad 4 \quad -4 \quad 1}$$
$$\underline{ \quad 3 \quad -1 \quad 3 \quad -1}$$
$$3 \quad -1 \quad 3 \quad -1 \quad 0$$

$$\tfrac{1}{3}\overline{)3 \quad -1 \quad 3 \quad -1}$$
$$\underline{ \quad 1 \quad 0 \quad 1}$$
$$3 \quad 0 \quad 3 \quad 0$$

Since the remainder is 0, $x - 1$ and $x - \dfrac{1}{3}$ are factors.

The other factor is the quotient: $3x^2 + 3 = 3(x^2 + 1)$.

Solving $x^2 + 1 = 0$:
$$x^2 = -1 \Rightarrow x = \pm i$$

The complex zeros are 1, $\dfrac{1}{3}$, $-i$, i.

The Zeros of a Polynomial Function

5.CR Cumulative Review

1. (a) $4^2 = 16$ (b) $3^{-4} = \dfrac{1}{3^4} = \dfrac{1}{81}$

    (c) $1.2^3 \approx 1.728$ (d) $3^{3.2} \approx 33.635$

3. $f(x) = -2x + 5$

5. $f(x) = -2x^3 + 7x - 1$; Use ZERO (or ROOT) on the graph of $y_1 = -2x^3 + 7x - 1$.
Use MAXIMUM to determine that f has a local   Use MINIMUM to determine that f has a
maximum at the point $(1.08, 4.04)$.   local minimum at the point $(-1.08, -6.04)$.

f is increasing on the interval $(-1.08, 1.08)$
f is decreasing on the intervals $(-3, -1.08)$
and $(1.08, 3)$.

7.   Domain: $\{x \mid -5 \le x \le 4\}$; Range: $\{y \mid -3 \le y \le 6\}$
      x-intercepts: $(-4, 0), (-0.5, 0), (1.2, 0)$;   y-intercept: $(0, -0.9)$

9. $R(x) = \dfrac{2x^2 - 5x - 3}{x^2 + x - 6} = \dfrac{(2x+1)(x-3)}{(x+3)(x-2)}$ $p(x) = 2x^2 - 5x - 3;\ q(x) = x^2 + x - 6;\ n = 2;\ m = 2$

Step 1:   The domain of R is the set of x-values for which $q(x) = x^2 + x - 6 \neq 0$
          Domain: $\{x \mid x \neq -3, x \neq 2\}$

Step 2: $R(x) = \dfrac{2x^2 - 5x - 3}{x^2 + x - 6} = \dfrac{(2x+1)(x-3)}{(x+3)(x-2)}$ is in lowest terms.

Step 3:   The x-intercepts occur when $(2x+1)(x-3) = 0$, that is x $= -0.5$ and x $= 3$.

          The y-intercept is $R(0) = \dfrac{0 - 0 - 3}{0 + 0 - 6} = \dfrac{-3}{-6} = \dfrac{1}{2} = 0.5$

Step 4:   Test for symmetry.

$$R(-x) = \frac{2(-x)^2 - 5(-x) - 3}{(-x)^2 + (-x) - 6} = \frac{2x^2 + 5x - 3}{x^2 - x - 6} \neq R(x)$$

$$R(-x) = \frac{2x^2 + 5x - 3}{x^2 - x - 6} \neq -R(x)$$

Therefore, R is not symmetric with respect to the y-axis nor with respect to the origin.

Step 5:   The vertical asymptotes occur when $(x + 3)(x - 2) = 0$,
          that is when $x = -3$ and $x = 2$.

Step 6:   Since $n = m$, the line $y = 2$ is the horizontal asymptote.

$$R(x) = \frac{2x^2 - 5x - 3}{x^2 + x - 6} = 2 \Rightarrow 2x^2 - 5x - 3 = 2(x^2 + x - 6)$$

$$2x^2 - 5x - 3 = 2x^2 + 2x - 12$$

$$9 = 7x \Rightarrow x = \frac{9}{7}$$

The graph of R intersects the horizontal asymptote at $\left(\dfrac{9}{7}, 2\right)$.

Step 7:   graphing utility:

Step 8: Graphing by hand:

	-3	$-1/2$	2	3

Interval	$(-\infty, -3)$	$(-3, -1/2)$	$(-1/2, 2)$	$(2, 3)$	$(3, \infty)$
Number Chosen	-4	-1	0	2.5	4
Value of R	$R(-4) \approx 8.17$	$R(-1) \approx -0.67$	$R(0) = 0.5$	$R(2.5) \approx -1.09$	$R(4) \approx 0.64$
Location of Graph	Above x-axis	Below x-axis	Above x-axis	Below x-axis	Above x-axis
Point on Graph	$(-4, 8.17)$	$(-1, -0.67)$	$(0, 0.5)$	$(2.5, -1.09)$	$(4, 0.64)$

We can solve the inequality $R(x) = \dfrac{2x^2 - 5x - 3}{x^2 + x - 6} \geq 0$ by determining the intervals where the

graph of $R(x) = \dfrac{2x^2 - 5x - 3}{x^2 + x - 6}$ is above the x-axis and by identifying the x-intercepts for the

function $R(x) = \dfrac{2x^2 - 5x - 3}{x^2 + x - 6}$.

Our work shows that the solution set is $\left\{ x \mid -\infty < x < -3 \ \text{ or } \ -0.5 \leq x < 2 \ \text{ or } \ 3 \leq x < \infty \right\}$.

Chapter 6

Exponential and Logarithmic Functions

6.1 One-to-One Functions; Inverse Functions

1. (a) Domain   Range

       (b) Inverse is a function.

3. (a) Domain   Range

       (b) Inverse is not a function since $200
corresponds to two elements in the
range.

5. (a) $\{(6,2), (6,-3), (9,4), (10,1)\}$ (b) Inverse is not a function since 6
corresponds to 2 and -3.

7. (a) $\{(0,0), (1,1), (16,2), (81,3)\}$ (b) Inverse is a function.

9. Every horizontal line intersects the graph of f at exactly one point. One-to-One.

11. There are horizontal lines that intersect the graph of f at more than one point.
Not One-to-One.

13. Every horizontal line intersects the graph of f at exactly one point. One-to-One.

15. Graphing the inverse: 17.   Graphing the inverse:

19. Graphing the inverse:

21. $f(x) = 3x + 4,$ $g(x) = \dfrac{1}{3}(x-4)$

$f(g(x)) = f\left(\dfrac{1}{3}(x-4)\right) = 3\left(\dfrac{1}{3}(x-4)\right) + 4 = (x-4) + 4 = x$

$g(f(x)) = g(3x+4) = \dfrac{1}{3}\left((3x+4)-4\right) = \dfrac{1}{3}(3x) = x$

23. $f(x) = 4x - 8,$ $g(x) = \dfrac{x}{4} + 2$

$f(g(x)) = f\left(\dfrac{x}{4}+2\right) = 4\left(\dfrac{x}{4}+2\right) - 8 = (x+8) - 8 = x$

$g(f(x)) = g(4x-8) = \dfrac{4x-8}{4} + 2 = x - 2 + 2 = x$

25. $f(x) = x^3 - 8,$ $g(x) = \sqrt[3]{x+8}$

$f(g(x)) = f\left(\sqrt[3]{x+8}\right) = \left(\sqrt[3]{x+8}\right)^3 - 8 = (x+8) - 8 = x$

$g(f(x)) = g(x^3 - 8) = \sqrt[3]{(x^3 - 8) + 8} = \sqrt[3]{x^3} = x$

27. $f(x) = \dfrac{1}{x},$ $g(x) = \dfrac{1}{x}$

$f(g(x)) = f\left(\dfrac{1}{x}\right) = \dfrac{1}{\left(\dfrac{1}{x}\right)} = x$

$g(f(x)) = g\left(\dfrac{1}{x}\right) = \dfrac{1}{\left(\dfrac{1}{x}\right)} = x$

303

29. $f(x) = \dfrac{2x+3}{x+4}, \qquad g(x) = \dfrac{4x-3}{2-x}$

$$f(g(x)) = f\left(\dfrac{4x-3}{2-x}\right) = \dfrac{2\left(\dfrac{4x-3}{2-x}\right)+3}{\left(\dfrac{4x-3}{2-x}\right)+4} = \dfrac{\left(\dfrac{8x-6+6-3x}{2-x}\right)}{\left(\dfrac{4x-3+8-4x}{2-x}\right)} = \dfrac{\left(\dfrac{5x}{2-x}\right)}{\left(\dfrac{5}{2-x}\right)} = \dfrac{5x}{2-x} \cdot \dfrac{2-x}{5} = x$$

$$g(f(x)) = g\left(\dfrac{2x+3}{x+4}\right) = \dfrac{4\left(\dfrac{2x+3}{x+4}\right)-3}{2-\left(\dfrac{2x+3}{x+4}\right)} = \dfrac{\left(\dfrac{8x+12-3x-12}{x+4}\right)}{\left(\dfrac{2x+8-2x-3}{x+4}\right)} = \dfrac{\left(\dfrac{5x}{x+4}\right)}{\left(\dfrac{5}{x+4}\right)} = \dfrac{5x}{x+4} \cdot \dfrac{x+4}{5} = x$$

31. $f(x) = 3x$

$y = 3x$

$x = 3y$ Inverse

$y = \dfrac{x}{3} \Rightarrow f^{-1}(x) = \dfrac{x}{3}$

Verify: $f\left(f^{-1}(x)\right) = f\left(\dfrac{x}{3}\right) = 3\left(\dfrac{x}{3}\right) = x$

$f^{-1}\left(f(x)\right) = f^{-1}(3x) = \dfrac{3x}{3} = x$

Domain of f = range of f^{-1} = $(-\infty, \infty)$
Range of f = domain of f^{-1} = $(-\infty, \infty)$

33. $f(x) = 4x + 2$

$y = 4x + 2$

$x = 4y + 2$ Inverse

$4y = x - 2 \Rightarrow y = \dfrac{x-2}{4} \Rightarrow f^{-1}(x) = \dfrac{x-2}{4}$

Verify:

$$f\left(f^{-1}(x)\right) = f\left(\dfrac{x-2}{4}\right) = 4\left(\dfrac{x-2}{4}\right)+2$$

$$= x - 2 + 2 = x$$

$$f^{-1}\left(f(x)\right) = f^{-1}(4x+2) = \dfrac{(4x+2)-2}{4}$$

$$= \dfrac{4x}{4} = x$$

Domain of f = range of f^{-1} = $(-\infty, \infty)$
Range of f = domain of f^{-1} = $(-\infty, \infty)$

35. $f(x) = x^3 - 1$

$y = x^3 - 1$

$x = y^3 - 1$ Inverse

$y^3 = x + 1 \Rightarrow y = \sqrt[3]{x+1} \Rightarrow f^{-1}(x) = \sqrt[3]{x+1}$

Verify:

$f\left(f^{-1}(x)\right) = f\left(\sqrt[3]{x+1}\right) = \left(\sqrt[3]{x+1}\right)^3 - 1$

$= x + 1 - 1 = x$

$f^{-1}\left(f(x)\right) = f^{-1}\left(x^3 - 1\right) = \sqrt[3]{\left(x^3 - 1\right) + 1}$

$= \sqrt[3]{x^3} = x$

Domain of f = range of $f^{-1} = (-\infty, \infty)$

Range of f = domain of $f^{-1} = (-\infty, \infty)$

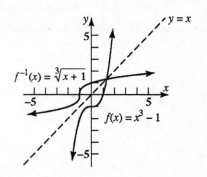

37. $f(x) = x^2 + 4, \ x \geq 0$

$y = x^2 + 4 \ \ x \geq 0$

$x = y^2 + 4 \ \ y \geq 0$ Inverse

$y^2 = x - 4 \ \ y \geq 0$

$y = \sqrt{x-4} \Rightarrow f^{-1}(x) = \sqrt{x-4}$

Verify:

$f\left(f^{-1}(x)\right) = f\left(\sqrt{x-4}\right) = \left(\sqrt{x-4}\right)^2 + 4$

$= x - 4 + 4 = x$

$f^{-1}\left(f(x)\right) = f^{-1}\left(x^2 + 4\right) = \sqrt{\left(x^2 + 4\right) - 4}$

$= \sqrt{x^2} = |x| = x, \ x \geq 0$

Domain of f = range of $f^{-1} = [0, \infty)$

Range of f = domain of $f^{-1} = [4, \infty)$

39. $f(x) = \dfrac{4}{x}$

$y = \dfrac{4}{x}$

$x = \dfrac{4}{y}$ Inverse

$xy = 4 \Rightarrow y = \dfrac{4}{x} \Rightarrow f^{-1}(x) = \dfrac{4}{x}$

Verify: $f\left(f^{-1}(x)\right) = f\left(\dfrac{4}{x}\right) = \dfrac{4}{\left(\dfrac{4}{x}\right)} = 4 \cdot \left(\dfrac{x}{4}\right) = x$

$f^{-1}\left(f(x)\right) = f^{-1}\left(\dfrac{4}{x}\right) = \dfrac{4}{\left(\dfrac{4}{x}\right)} = 4 \cdot \left(\dfrac{x}{4}\right) = x$

Domain of f = range of f^{-1}
= all real numbers except 0

Range of f = domain of f^{-1}
= all real numbers except 0

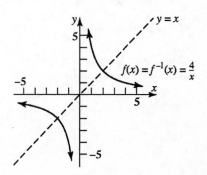

41. $f(x) = \dfrac{1}{x-2}$

$y = \dfrac{1}{x-2}$

$x = \dfrac{1}{y-2}$ Inverse

$x(y-2) = 1$

$xy - 2x = 1$

$xy = 2x + 1$

$y = \dfrac{2x+1}{x}$

$f^{-1}(x) = \dfrac{2x+1}{x}$

Domain of f = range of f^{-1}
= all real numbers except 2

Range of f = domain of f^{-1}
= all real numbers except 0

Verify: $f\left(f^{-1}(x)\right) = f\left(\dfrac{2x+1}{x}\right) = \dfrac{1}{\left(\dfrac{2x+1}{x} - 2\right)} = \dfrac{1}{\left(\dfrac{2x+1-2x}{x}\right)} = \dfrac{1}{\left(\dfrac{1}{x}\right)} = 1 \cdot \left(\dfrac{1}{x}\right) = x$

$f^{-1}\left(f(x)\right) = f^{-1}\left(\dfrac{1}{x-2}\right) = \dfrac{2\left(\dfrac{1}{x-2}\right)+1}{\left(\dfrac{1}{x-2}\right)} = \dfrac{\left(\dfrac{2+x-2}{x-2}\right)}{\left(\dfrac{1}{x-2}\right)} = \left(\dfrac{x}{x-2}\right)\cdot\left(\dfrac{x-2}{1}\right) = x$

43. $f(x) = \dfrac{2}{3+x}$

$y = \dfrac{2}{3+x}$

$x = \dfrac{2}{3+y}$ Inverse

$x(3+y) = 2$

$3x + xy = 2$

$xy = 2 - 3x$

$y = \dfrac{2-3x}{x}$

$f^{-1}(x) = \dfrac{2-3x}{x}$

Domain of f =
range of f^{-1} = all real numbers except -3

Range of f =
domain of f^{-1} = all real numbers except 0

Verify: $f\left(f^{-1}(x)\right) = f\left(\dfrac{2-3x}{x}\right) = \dfrac{2}{3+\left(\dfrac{2-3x}{x}\right)} = \dfrac{2}{\left(\dfrac{3x+2-3x}{x}\right)} = \dfrac{2}{\left(\dfrac{2}{x}\right)} = 2 \cdot \left(\dfrac{x}{2}\right) = x$

$f^{-1}\left(f(x)\right) = f^{-1}\left(\dfrac{2}{3+x}\right) = \dfrac{2 - 3\left(\dfrac{2}{3+x}\right)}{\left(\dfrac{2}{3+x}\right)} = \dfrac{\left(\dfrac{6+2x-6}{3+x}\right)}{\left(\dfrac{2}{3+x}\right)} = \left(\dfrac{2x}{3+x}\right)\cdot\left(\dfrac{3+x}{2}\right) = x$

45. $f(x) = (x+2)^2, \ x \geq -2$

      $y = (x+2)^2 \ \ x \geq -2$

      $x = (y+2)^2 \ \ y \geq -2$ Inverse

      $\sqrt{x} = y+2, \ \ \ x \geq 0$

      $y = \sqrt{x} - 2, \ \ x \geq 0$

    $f^{-1}(x) = \sqrt{x} - 2, \ \ x \geq 0$

Domain of f = range of $f^{-1} = [-2, \infty)$

Range of f = domain of $f^{-1} = [0, \infty)$

    Verify: $f\left(f^{-1}(x)\right) = f\left(\sqrt{x} - 2\right) = \left(\sqrt{x} - 2 + 2\right)^2 = \left(\sqrt{x}\right)^2 = x$

            $f^{-1}\left(f(x)\right) = f^{-1}\left((x+2)^2\right) = \sqrt{(x+2)^2} - 2 = x + 2 - 2 = x, \ \ x \geq -2$

47. $f(x) = \dfrac{2x}{x-1}$

     $y = \dfrac{2x}{x-1}$

     $x = \dfrac{2y}{y-1}$ Inverse

   $x(y-1) = 2y \Rightarrow xy - x = 2y$

   $xy - 2y = x \Rightarrow y(x-2) = x$

     $y = \dfrac{x}{x-2} \Rightarrow f^{-1}(x) = \dfrac{x}{x-2}$

Domain of f = range of f^{-1}

= all real numbers except 1

Range of f = domain of f^{-1}

= all real numbers except 2

    Verify: $f\left(f^{-1}(x)\right) = f\left(\dfrac{x}{x-2}\right) = \dfrac{2\left(\dfrac{x}{x-2}\right)}{\left(\dfrac{x}{x-2}\right)-1} = \dfrac{\left(\dfrac{2x}{x-2}\right)}{\left(\dfrac{x-x+2}{x-2}\right)} = \dfrac{\left(\dfrac{2x}{x-2}\right)}{\left(\dfrac{2}{x-2}\right)} = \left(\dfrac{2x}{x-2}\right)\cdot\left(\dfrac{x-2}{2}\right) = x$

           $f^{-1}\left(f(x)\right) = f^{-1}\left(\dfrac{2x}{x-1}\right) = \dfrac{\left(\dfrac{2x}{x-1}\right)}{\left(\dfrac{2x}{x-1}\right)-2} = \dfrac{\left(\dfrac{2x}{x-1}\right)}{\left(\dfrac{2x-2x+2}{x-1}\right)} = \left(\dfrac{2x}{x-1}\right)\cdot\left(\dfrac{x-1}{2}\right) = x$

49. $f(x) = \dfrac{3x+4}{2x-3}$

     $y = \dfrac{3x+4}{2x-3}$

     $x = \dfrac{3y+4}{2y-3}$ Inverse

   $x(2y-3) = 3y+4 \Rightarrow 2xy - 3x = 3y + 4$

   $2xy - 3y = 3x + 4 \Rightarrow y(2x-3) = 3x + 4$

     $y = \dfrac{3x+4}{2x-3} \Rightarrow f^{-1}(x) = \dfrac{3x+4}{2x-3}$

Domain of f = range of f^{-1}

= all real numbers except $\dfrac{3}{2}$

Range of f = domain of f^{-1}

= all real numbers except $\dfrac{3}{2}$

Verify:

$$f\left(f^{-1}(x)\right) = f\left(\frac{3x+4}{2x-3}\right) = \frac{3\left(\dfrac{3x+4}{2x-3}\right)+4}{2\left(\dfrac{3x+4}{2x-3}\right)-3} = \frac{\left(\dfrac{9x+12+8x-12}{2x-3}\right)}{\left(\dfrac{6x+8-6x+9}{2x-3}\right)} = \frac{\left(\dfrac{17x}{2x-3}\right)}{\left(\dfrac{17}{2x-3}\right)}$$

$$= \frac{17x}{2x-3} \cdot \frac{2x-3}{17} = x$$

$$f^{-1}\left(f(x)\right) = f^{-1}\left(\frac{3x+4}{2x-3}\right) = \frac{3\left(\dfrac{3x+4}{2x-3}\right)+4}{2\left(\dfrac{3x+4}{2x-3}\right)-3} = \frac{\left(\dfrac{9x+12+8x-12}{2x-3}\right)}{\left(\dfrac{6x+8-6x+9}{2x-3}\right)} = \frac{\left(\dfrac{17x}{2x-3}\right)}{\left(\dfrac{17}{2x-3}\right)}$$

$$= \frac{17x}{2x-3} \cdot \frac{2x-3}{17} = x$$

51. $f(x) = \dfrac{2x+3}{x+2}$

$\quad\quad y = \dfrac{2x+3}{x+2}$

$\quad\quad x = \dfrac{2y+3}{y+2}$ Inverse

$\quad\quad x(y+2) = 2y+3$

$\quad\quad xy + 2x = 2y + 3$

$\quad\quad xy - 2y = -2x + 3$

$\quad\quad y(x-2) = -2x+3$

$\quad\quad y = \dfrac{-2x+3}{x-2}$

$\quad f^{-1}(x) = \dfrac{-2x+3}{x-2}$

Domain of f =
range of f^{-1} = all real numbers except -2

Range of f =
domain of f^{-1} = all real numbers except 2

Verify:

$$f\left(f^{-1}(x)\right) = f\left(\frac{-2x+3}{x-2}\right) = \frac{2\left(\dfrac{-2x+3}{x-2}\right)+3}{\left(\dfrac{-2x+3}{x-2}\right)+2} = \frac{\left(\dfrac{-4x+6+3x-6}{x-2}\right)}{\left(\dfrac{-2x+3+2x-4}{x-2}\right)} = \frac{\left(\dfrac{-x}{x-2}\right)}{\left(\dfrac{-1}{x-2}\right)}$$

$$= \left(\frac{-x}{x-2}\right) \cdot \left(\frac{x-2}{-1}\right) = x$$

$$f^{-1}\left(f(x)\right) = f^{-1}\left(\frac{2x+3}{x+2}\right) = \frac{-2\left(\dfrac{2x+3}{x+2}\right)+3}{\left(\dfrac{2x+3}{x+2}\right)-2} = \frac{\left(\dfrac{-4x-6+3x+6}{x+2}\right)}{\left(\dfrac{2x+3-2x-4}{x+2}\right)} = \frac{\left(\dfrac{-x}{x+2}\right)}{\left(\dfrac{-1}{x+2}\right)}$$

$$= \left(\frac{-x}{x+2}\right) \cdot \left(\frac{x+2}{-1}\right) = x$$

53. $f(x) = 2\sqrt[3]{x}$

     $y = 2\sqrt[3]{x}$

     $x = 2\sqrt[3]{y}$ Inverse

     $x^3 = 8y$

     $y = \dfrac{x^3}{8}$

   $f^{-1}(x) = \dfrac{x^3}{8}$

Domain of f = range of $f^{-1} = (-\infty, \infty)$

Range of f = domain of $f^{-1} = (-\infty, \infty)$

Verify: $f\!\left(f^{-1}(x)\right) = f\!\left(\dfrac{x^3}{8}\right) = 2\!\left(\sqrt[3]{\dfrac{x^3}{8}}\right) = 2 \cdot \left(\dfrac{x}{2}\right) = x$

        $f^{-1}\!\left(f(x)\right) = f^{-1}\!\left(2\sqrt[3]{x}\right) = \dfrac{\left(2\sqrt[3]{x}\right)^3}{8} = \dfrac{8x}{8} = x$

55. $f(x) = mx + b, \quad m \neq 0$

     $y = mx + b$

     $x = my + b$ Inverse

  $x - b = my$

     $y = \dfrac{x-b}{m} \Rightarrow f^{-1}(x) = \dfrac{x-b}{m}, \quad m \neq 0$

57. f^{-1} lies in quadrant I. Whenever (a,b) is on f, then (b,a) is on f^{-1}. Since both coordinates of (a,b) are positive, both coordinates of (b,a) are positive and it is in quadrant I.

59. $f(x) = |x|, x \geq 0$ is one-to-one. Thus, $f(x) = x, x \geq 0$ and $f^{-1}(x) = x, x \geq 0$.

61. $f(x) = \dfrac{9}{5}x + 32 \qquad g(x) = \dfrac{5}{9}(x - 32)$

   $f(g(x)) = f\!\left(\dfrac{5}{9}(x - 32)\right) = \dfrac{9}{5}\!\left(\dfrac{5}{9}(x - 32)\right) + 32 = x - 32 + 32 = x$

   $g(f(x)) = g\!\left(\dfrac{9}{5}x + 32\right) = \dfrac{5}{9}\!\left(\dfrac{9}{5}x + 32 - 32\right) = \dfrac{5}{9}\!\left(\dfrac{9}{5}x\right) = x$

63. $T(l) = 2\pi\sqrt{\dfrac{l}{g}}, \quad g \approx 32.2$

   $T = 2\pi\sqrt{\dfrac{l}{g}} \quad \Rightarrow \quad \dfrac{T}{2\pi} = \sqrt{\dfrac{l}{g}}$

   $\Rightarrow \dfrac{T^2}{4\pi^2} = \dfrac{l}{g} \quad \Rightarrow \quad l = \dfrac{gT^2}{4\pi^2}$

 $l(T) = \dfrac{gT^2}{4\pi^2}$

65. Yes, consider the function $f(x) = \dfrac{1}{x}$. In general the graph of f must have symmetry across the line $y = x$.

67. $f(x) = \begin{cases} \dfrac{1}{x}, & \text{if } x < 0 \\ x, & \text{if } x \geq 0 \end{cases}$

Exponential and Logarithmic Functions

6.2 Exponential Functions

1. (a) $3^{2.2} \approx 11.212$ (b) $3^{2.23} \approx 11.587$ (c) $3^{2.236} \approx 11.664$ (d) $3^{\sqrt{5}} \approx 11.665$

3. (a) $2^{3.14} \approx 8.815$ (b) $2^{3.141} \approx 8.821$ (c) $2^{3.1415} \approx 8.824$ (d) $2^{\pi} \approx 8.825$

5. (a) $3.1^{2.7} \approx 21.217$ (b) $3.14^{2.71} \approx 22.217$
   (c) $3.141^{2.718} \approx 22.440$ (d) $\pi^{e} \approx 22.459$

7. $e^{1.2} \approx 3.320$ 9. $e^{-0.85} \approx 0.427$

11. B   13. D   15. A   17. E

19. $f(x) = 2^{x} + 1$
    Using the graph of $y = 2^{x}$, shift the graph
    up 1 unit.
    Domain: $(-\infty, \infty)$
    Range: $(1, \infty)$
    Horizontal Asymptote: $y = 1$

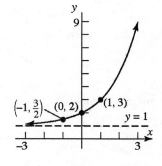

21. $f(x) = 3^{-x} - 2$
    Using the graph of $y = 3^{x}$, reflect the
    graph about the y-axis, and shift down 2
    units.
    Domain: $(-\infty, \infty)$
    Range: $(-2, \infty)$
    Horizontal Asymptote: $y = -2$

23. $f(x) = 3(4^x)$

Using the graph of $y = 4^x$, stretch the
graph vertically by a factor of 3.
Domain: $(-\infty, \infty)$
Range: $(0, \infty)$
Horizontal Asymptote: $y = 0$

25. $f(x) = 3^{x/2}$

Using the graph of $y = 3^x$, stretch the
graph horizontally by a factor of 2.
Domain: $(-\infty, \infty)$
Range: $(0, \infty)$
Horizontal Asymptote: $y = 0$

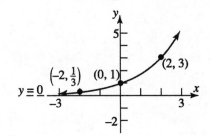

27. $f(x) = 5 - 2(3^{(x+1)}) = -2(3^{(x+1)}) + 5$

Using the graph of $y = 3^x$, shift the graph
one unit to the left, stretch vertically by a
factor of 2, reflect on the x-axis, and shift
up 5 units.
Domain: $(-\infty, \infty)$
Range: $(-\infty, 5)$
Horizontal Asymptote: $y = 5$

29. $f(x) = e^{-x}$

Using the graph of $y = e^x$, reflect the
graph about the y-axis.
Domain: $(-\infty, \infty)$
Range: $(0, \infty)$
Horizontal Asymptote: $y = 0$

31. $f(x) = e^{x+2}$
Using the graph of $y = e^x$, shift the graph
2 units to the left.
Domain: $(-\infty, \infty)$
Range: $(0, \infty)$
Horizontal Asymptote: $y = 0$

33. $f(x) = 5 + e^{-x} = e^{-x} + 5$
Using the graph of $y = e^x$, reflect the
graph about the y-axis and shift up 5
units.
Domain: $(-\infty, \infty)$
Range: $(5, \infty)$
Horizontal Asymptote: $y = 5$

35. $f(x) = 2 - e^{x/2} = -e^{x/2} + 2$
Using the graph of $y = e^x$, stretch
horizontally by a factor of 2, reflect about
the x-axis, and shift up 2 units.
Domain: $(-\infty, \infty)$
Range: $(-\infty, 2)$
Horizontal Asymptote: $y = 2$

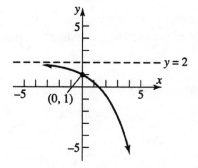

37. We need a function of the form $f(x) = k \cdot a^{p \cdot x}$, with $a > 0, a \neq 1$.

The graph contains the points $\left(-1, \dfrac{1}{3}\right), (0,1), (1,3)$ and $(2,9)$.

In other words, $f(-1) = \dfrac{1}{3}, f(0) = 1, f(1) = 3$ and $f(2) = 9$.

Therefore, $f(0) = k \cdot a^{p \cdot (0)} = k \cdot a^0 = k \cdot 1 = k \Rightarrow k = 1$.

and $f(1) = a^{p \cdot (1)} = a^p \Rightarrow a^p = 3$.

Let's choose $a = 3, p = 1$. Then $f(x) = 3^x$.

Now we need to verify that this function yields the other known points on the graph.

$$f(-1) = 3^{-1} = \frac{1}{3}; \qquad f(2) = 3^2 = 9$$

So we have the function $f(x) = 3^x$.

39.   We need a function of the form $f(x) = k \cdot a^{p \cdot x}$, with $a > 0, a \neq 1$.

The graph contains the points $\left(-1, \frac{1}{2}\right), (0,2), (1,8)$ and $(2,32)$.

In other words, $f(-1) = \frac{1}{2}, f(0) = 2, f(1) = 8$ and $f(2) = 32$.

Therefore, $f(0) = k \cdot a^{p \cdot (0)} = k \cdot a^0 = k \cdot 1 = k \Rightarrow k = 2$.

and $f(1) = 2a^{p \cdot (1)} = 2a^p \Rightarrow 2a^p = 8 \Rightarrow a^p = 4$.

Let's choose $a = 4, p = 1$. Then $f(x) = 2 \cdot 4^x$.

Now we need to verify that this function yields the other known points on the graph.

$$f(-1) = 2 \cdot 4^{-1} = 2 \cdot \frac{1}{4} = \frac{1}{2}; \quad f(2) = 2 \cdot 4^2 = 2 \cdot 16 = 32$$

So we have the function $f(x) = 2 \cdot 4^x$.

41.   We need a function of the form $f(x) = k \cdot a^{p \cdot x}$, with $a > 0, a \neq 1$.

The graph contains the points $\left(-1, -\frac{1}{6}\right), (0,-1), (1,-6)$ and $(2,-36)$.

In other words, $f(-1) = -\frac{1}{6}, f(0) = -1, f(1) = -6$ and $f(2) = -36$.

Therefore, $f(0) = k \cdot a^{p \cdot (0)} = k \cdot a^0 = k \cdot 1 = k \Rightarrow k = -1$.

and $f(1) = -a^{p \cdot (1)} = -a^p \Rightarrow -a^p = -6 \Rightarrow a^p = 6$.

Let's choose $a = 6, p = 1$. Then $f(x) = -6^x$.

Now we need to verify that this function yields the other known points on the graph.

$$f(-1) = -6^{-1} = -\frac{1}{6}; \quad f(2) = -6^2 = -36$$

So we have the function $f(x) = -6^x$.

43. $2^{2x+1} = 4$

$2^{2x+1} = 2^2$

$2x + 1 = 2 \Rightarrow 2x = 1 \Rightarrow x = \frac{1}{2}$

The solution set is $\left\{\frac{1}{2}\right\}$.

45. $3^{x^3} = 9^x$

$3^{x^3} = \left(3^2\right)^x \Rightarrow 3^{x^3} = 3^{2x}$

$x^3 = 2x \Rightarrow x^3 - 2x = 0 \Rightarrow x(x^2 - 2) = 0$

$x = 0$ or $x^2 = 2 \Rightarrow x = \pm\sqrt{2}$

The solution set is $\left\{-\sqrt{2}, \ 0, \ \sqrt{2}\right\}$.

47. $8^{x^2-2x} = \frac{1}{2}$

$\left(2^3\right)^{x^2-2x} = 2^{-1} \Rightarrow 2^{3x^2-6x} = 2^{-1}$

$3x^2 - 6x = -1 \Rightarrow 3x^2 - 6x + 1 = 0$

$x = \frac{-(-6) \pm \sqrt{(-6)^2 - 4(3)(1)}}{2(3)} = \frac{6 \pm \sqrt{24}}{6} = \frac{6 \pm 2\sqrt{6}}{6} = \frac{3 \pm \sqrt{6}}{3}$

The solution set is $\left\{\frac{3-\sqrt{6}}{3}, \ \frac{3+\sqrt{6}}{3}\right\}$.

49. $2^x \cdot 8^{-x} = 4^x$

$2^x \cdot \left(2^3\right)^{-x} = \left(2^2\right)^x$

$2^x \cdot 2^{-3x} = 2^{2x}$

$2^{-2x} = 2^{2x}$

$-2x = 2x \Rightarrow -4x = 0 \Rightarrow x = 0$

The solution set is $\{0\}$.

51. $\left(\dfrac{1}{5}\right)^{2-x} = 25$

$\left(5^{-1}\right)^{2-x} = 5^2$

$5^{x-2} = 5^2$

$x - 2 = 2 \Rightarrow x = 4$

The solution set is $\{4\}$.

53. $4^x = 8$

$\left(2^2\right)^x = 2^3$

$2^{2x} = 2^3 \Rightarrow 2x = 3 \Rightarrow x = \dfrac{3}{2}$

The solution set is $\left\{\dfrac{3}{2}\right\}$.

55. $e^{x^2} = e^{3x} \cdot \dfrac{1}{e^2}$

$e^{x^2} = e^{3x-2}$

$x^2 = 3x - 2$

$x^2 - 3x + 2 = 0$

$(x-1)(x-2) = 0 \Rightarrow x = 1 \text{ or } x = 2$

The solution set is $\{1, 2\}$.

57. $4^x = 7$

$\left(4^x\right)^{-2} = 7^{-2} \quad \Rightarrow \quad 4^{-2x} = \dfrac{1}{7^2} = \dfrac{1}{49}$

59. $3^{-x} = 2$

$(3^{-x})^{-2} = 2^{-2} \quad \Rightarrow \quad 3^{2x} = \dfrac{1}{2^2} = \dfrac{1}{4}$

61. $p = 100e^{-0.03n}$

(a) $p = 100e^{-0.03(10)} = 100e^{-0.3} \approx 100(0.741) = 74.1\%$ of light

(b) $p = 100e^{-0.03(25)} = 100e^{-0.75} \approx 100(0.472) = 47.2\%$ of light

63. $w(d) = 50e^{-0.004d}$

(a) $w(30) = 50e^{-0.004(30)} = 50e^{-0.12} \approx 50(0.887) = 44.35$ watts

(b) $w(365) = 50e^{-0.004(365)} = 50e^{-1.46} \approx 50(0.232) = 11.61$ watts

65. $D(h) = 5e^{-0.4h}$

$D(1) = 5e^{-0.4(1)} = 5e^{-0.4} \approx 5(0.670) = 3.35$ milligrams

$D(6) = 5e^{-0.4(6)} = 5e^{-2.4} \approx 5(0.091) = 0.45$ milligrams

67. $F(t) = 1 - e^{-0.1t}$

(a) $F(10) = 1 - e^{-0.1(10)} = 1 - e^{-1} \approx 1 - 0.368 = 0.632 = 63.2\%$

(b) $F(40) = 1 - e^{-0.1(40)} = 1 - e^{-4} \approx 1 - 0.018 = 0.982 = 98.2\%$

(c) as $t \to +\infty$, $F(t) = 1 - e^{-0.1t} \to 1 - 0 = 1$

(d) Graphing the function:

69. $P(x) = \dfrac{20^x e^{-20}}{x!}$

(a) $P(15) = \dfrac{20^{15} e^{-20}}{15!} \approx 0.0516 = 5.16\%$ The probability that 15 cars will arrive between

5:00 p.m. and 6:00 p.m. is 5.16%.

(b) $P(20) = \dfrac{20^{20} e^{-20}}{20!} \approx 0.0888 = 8.88\%$ The probability that 20 cars will arrive between

5:00 p.m. and 6:00 p.m. is 8.88%.

71. $R = 10^{\left(\frac{2345}{T} - \frac{2345}{D} + 2\right)}$

(a) $R = 10^{\left(\frac{2345}{283} - \frac{2345}{278} + 2\right)} \approx 10^{1.851} \approx 70.96\%$ (b) $R = 10^{\left(\frac{2345}{293} - \frac{2345}{288} + 2\right)} \approx 10^{1.861} \approx 72.61\%$

(c) $R = 10^{\left(\frac{2345}{x} - \frac{2345}{x} + 2\right)} = 10^2 = 100\%$

73. $I = \dfrac{E}{R}\left[1 - e^{-\left(\frac{R}{L}\right)t}\right]$

(a) $I = \dfrac{120}{10}\left[1 - e^{-\left(\frac{10}{5}\right)0.3}\right] = 12\left[1 - e^{-0.6}\right] \approx 5.414$ amperes after 0.3 second

$I = \dfrac{120}{10}\left[1 - e^{-\left(\frac{10}{5}\right)0.5}\right] = 12\left[1 - e^{-1}\right] \approx 7.585$ amperes after 0.5 second

$I = \dfrac{120}{10}\left[1 - e^{-\left(\frac{10}{5}\right)1}\right] = 12\left[1 - e^{-2}\right] \approx 10.376$ amperes after 1 second

(b) As $t \to \infty$, $e^{-\left(\frac{10}{5}\right)t} \to 0$. Therefore, the maximum current is 12 amperes.

(c), (f) Graphing the function:

(d) $I = \dfrac{120}{5}\left[1 - e^{-\left(\frac{5}{10}\right)0.3}\right] = 24\left[1 - e^{-0.15}\right] \approx 3.343$ amperes after 0.3 second

$I = \dfrac{120}{5}\left[1 - e^{-\left(\frac{5}{10}\right)0.5}\right] = 24\left[1 - e^{-0.25}\right] \approx 5.309$ amperes after 0.5 second

$$I = \frac{120}{5}\left|1 - e^{-\left(\frac{5}{10}\right)t}\right| = 24\left[1 - e^{-0.5}\right] \approx 9.443 \text{ amperes after 1 second}$$

(e)   As $t \to \infty$, $e^{-\left(\frac{5}{10}\right)t} \to 0$. Therefore, the maximum current is 24 amperes.

75. $2 + \dfrac{1}{2!} + \dfrac{1}{3!} + \dfrac{1}{4!} + \ldots + \dfrac{1}{n!}$

$n = 4;\quad 2 + \dfrac{1}{2!} + \dfrac{1}{3!} + \dfrac{1}{4!} = 2.7083$

$n = 6;\quad 2 + \dfrac{1}{2!} + \dfrac{1}{3!} + \dfrac{1}{4!} + \dfrac{1}{5!} + \dfrac{1}{6!} = 2.7181$

$n = 8;\quad 2 + \dfrac{1}{2!} + \dfrac{1}{3!} + \dfrac{1}{4!} + \dfrac{1}{5!} + \dfrac{1}{6!} + \dfrac{1}{7!} + \dfrac{1}{8!} = 2.7182788$

$n = 10;\quad 2 + \dfrac{1}{2!} + \dfrac{1}{3!} + \dfrac{1}{4!} + \dfrac{1}{5!} + \dfrac{1}{6!} + \dfrac{1}{7!} + \dfrac{1}{8!} + \dfrac{1}{9!} + \dfrac{1}{10!} = 2.7182818$

$e = 2.718281828$

77. $f(x) = a^x$

$$\frac{f(x+h) - f(x)}{h} = \frac{a^{x+h} - a^x}{h} = \frac{a^x a^h - a^x}{h} = \frac{a^x\left(a^h - 1\right)}{h} = a^x\left(\frac{a^h - 1}{h}\right)$$

79. $f(x) = a^x$

$$f(-x) = a^{-x} = \frac{1}{a^x} = \frac{1}{f(x)}$$

81. $\sinh x = \dfrac{1}{2}\left(e^x - e^{-x}\right)$

(a) $f(-x) = \sinh(-x) = \dfrac{1}{2}\left(e^{-x} - e^x\right) = -\dfrac{1}{2}\left(e^x - e^{-x}\right) = -\sinh x = -f(x)$

Therefore, $f(x) = \sinh x$ is an odd function.

(b)   Graphing:

317

83. $f(x) = 2^{\left(2^x\right)} + 1$

$f(1) = 2^{\left(2^1\right)} + 1 = 2^2 + 1 = 4 + 1 = 5$

$f(2) = 2^{\left(2^2\right)} + 1 = 2^4 + 1 = 16 + 1 = 17$

$f(3) = 2^{\left(2^3\right)} + 1 = 2^8 + 1 = 256 + 1 = 257$

$f(4) = 2^{\left(2^4\right)} + 1 = 2^{16} + 1 = 65536 + 1 = 65537$

$f(5) = 2^{\left(2^5\right)} + 1 = 2^{32} + 1 = 4,294,967,296 + 1 = 4,294,967,297$
      $4,294,967,297 = 641 \times 6,700,417$

85.   Answers will vary.

Exponential and Logarithmic Functions

6.3 Logarithmic Functions

1. $9 = 3^2$ is equivalent to $2 = \log_3 9$

3. $a^2 = 1.6$ is equivalent to $2 = \log_a 1.6$

5. $1.1^2 = M$ is equivalent to $2 = \log_{1.1} M$

7. $2^x = 7.2$ is equivalent to $x = \log_2 7.2$

9. $x^{\sqrt{2}} = \pi$ is equivalent to $\sqrt{2} = \log_x \pi$

11. $e^x = 8$ is equivalent to $x = \ln 8$

13. $\log_2 8 = 3$ is equivalent to $2^3 = 8$

15. $\log_a 3 = 6$ is equivalent to $a^6 = 3$

17. $\log_3 2 = x$ is equivalent to $3^x = 2$

19. $\log_2 M = 1.3$ is equivalent to $2^{1.3} = M$

21. $\log_{\sqrt{2}} \pi = x$ is equivalent to $\left(\sqrt{2}\right)^x = \pi$

23. $\ln 4 = x$ is equivalent to $e^x = 4$

25. $\log_2 1 = 0$ since $2^0 = 1$

27. $\log_5 25 = 2$ since $5^2 = 25$

29. $\log_{\frac{1}{2}} 16 = -4$ since $\left(\dfrac{1}{2}\right)^{-4} = 2^4 = 16$

31. $\log_{10} \sqrt{10} = \dfrac{1}{2}$ since $10^{1/2} = \sqrt{10}$

33. $\log_{\sqrt{2}} 4 = 4$ since $\left(\sqrt{2}\right)^4 = 4$

35. $\ln \sqrt{e} = \dfrac{1}{2}$ since $e^{1/2} = \sqrt{e}$

37. The domain of $f(x) = \ln(x-3)$ is:
$$x - 3 > 0 \Rightarrow x > 3$$
$$\{x \mid x > 3\}$$

39. The domain of $F(x) = \log_2 x^2$ is:
$$x^2 > 0$$
$$\{x \mid x \neq 0\}$$

41. The domain of $h(x) = \log_{\frac{1}{2}}\left(x^2 - 2x + 1\right)$ is:
$$x^2 - 2x + 1 > 0 \Rightarrow (x-1)^2 > 0$$
$$\{x \mid x \neq 1\}$$

43. The domain of $f(x) = \ln\left(\dfrac{1}{x+1}\right)$ is:
$$\dfrac{1}{x+1} > 0 \Rightarrow x + 1 > 0$$
$$x > -1$$
$$\{x \mid x > -1\}$$

45. The domain of $g(x) = \log_5\left(\dfrac{x+1}{x}\right)$ requires that $\dfrac{x+1}{x} > 0$.

The expression is zero or undefined when $x = -1$ or $x = 0$.

Interval	Test Number	$f(x) = \dfrac{x+1}{x}$	Positive/Negative
$-\infty < x < -1$	-2	0.5	Positive
$-1 < x < 0$	-0.5	-1	Negative
$0 < x < \infty$	1	2	Positive

The domain is $\{x \,|\, x < -1 \text{ or } x > 0\}$

47. $\ln\left(\dfrac{5}{3}\right) \approx 0.511$

49. $\dfrac{\ln(10/3)}{0.04} \approx 30.099$

51. For $f(x) = \log_a x$, find a so that $f(2) = \log_a 2 = 2$ or $a^2 = 2$ or $a = \sqrt{2}$.
    (The base a must be positive by definition.)

53. B   55. D   57. A   59. E

61. $f(x) = \ln(x+4)$
    Using the graph of $y = \ln x$, shift the
    graph 4 units to the left.
    Domain: $(-4, \infty)$
    Range: $(-\infty, \infty)$
    Vertical Asymptote: $x = -4$

63. $f(x) = 2 + \ln(x) = \ln(x) + 2$
    Using the graph of $y = \ln x$, shift up 2
    units.
    Domain: $(0, \infty)$
    Range: $(-\infty, \infty)$
    Vertical Asymptote: $x = 0$

65. $g(x) = \ln(2x)$

Using the graph of $y = \ln x$, compress the graph horizontally by a factor of $\frac{1}{2}$.

Domain: $(0, \infty)$
Range: $(-\infty, \infty)$
Vertical Asymptote: $x = 0$

67. $f(x) = 3\ln x$

Using the graph of $y = \ln x$, stretch the graph vertically by a factor of 3.
Domain: $(0, \infty)$
Range: $(-\infty, \infty)$
Vertical Asymptote: $x = 0$

69. $g(x) = \ln(3 - x) = \ln(-(x - 3))$

Using the graph of $y = \ln x$, reflect the graph about the y-axis, and shift 3 units to the right.
Domain: $(-\infty, 3)$
Range: $(-\infty, \infty)$
Vertical Asymptote: $x = 3$

71. $f(x) = -\ln(x - 1)$

Using the graph of $y = \ln x$, shift the graph 1 unit to the right, and reflect about the x-axis.
Domain: $(1, \infty)$
Range: $(-\infty, \infty)$
Vertical Asymptote: $x = 1$

321

73. $f(x) = \log(x - 4)$
      Using the graph of $y = \log x$, shift 4 units
      to the right.
      Domain: $(4, \infty)$
      Range: $(-\infty, \infty)$
      Vertical Asymptote: $x = 4$

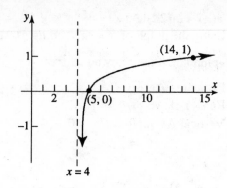

75. $h(x) = 4\log x$
      Using the graph of $y = \log x$, stretch the
      graph vertically by a factor of 4.
      Domain: $(0, \infty)$
      Range: $(-\infty, \infty)$
      Vertical Asymptote: $x = 0$

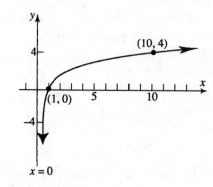

77. $f(x) = \log(2x)$
      Using the graph of $y = \log x$, compress

      the graph horizontally by a factor of $\dfrac{1}{2}$.

      Domain: $(0, \infty)$
      Range: $(-\infty, \infty)$
      Vertical Asymptote: $x = 0$

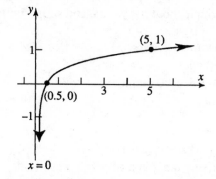

79. $f(x) = 2\log(x + 3)$
      Using the graph of $y = \log x$, shift 3 units
      to the left and stretch vertically by a
      factor of 2.
      Domain: $(-3, \infty)$
      Range: $(-\infty, \infty)$
      Vertical Asymptote: $x = -3$

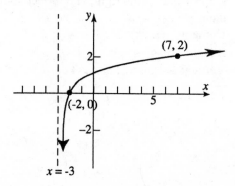

81. $f(x) = 3 + \log(x+2) = \log(x+2) + 3$
Using the graph of $y = \log x$, shift 2 units
to the left, and shift up 3 units.
Domain: $(-2, \infty)$
Range: $(-\infty, \infty)$
Vertical Asymptote: $x = -2$

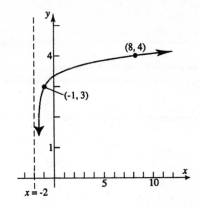

83. $f(x) = \log(2-x) = \log(-(x-2))$
Using the graph of $y = \log x$, reflect the
graph about the y-axis, and shift 2 units to
the right.
Domain: $(-\infty, 2)$
Range: $(-\infty, \infty)$
Vertical Asymptote: $x = 2$

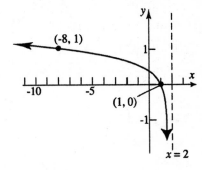

85. $\log_3 x = 2$
$$x = 3^2 \Rightarrow x = 9$$

87. $\log_2(2x+1) = 3$
$$2x+1 = 2^3 \Rightarrow 2x+1 = 8$$
$$2x = 7 \Rightarrow x = \frac{7}{2}$$

89. $\log_x 4 = 2$
$$x^2 = 4$$
$$x = 2 \quad (x \neq -2, \text{ base is positive})$$

91. $\ln e^x = 5$
$$e^x = e^5 \Rightarrow x = 5$$

93. $\log_4 64 = x$
$$4^x = 64 \Rightarrow 4^x = 4^3 \Rightarrow x = 3$$

95. $\log_3 243 = 2x+1$
$$3^{2x+1} = 243$$
$$3^{2x+1} = 3^5$$
$$2x+1 = 5 \Rightarrow 2x = 4 \Rightarrow x = 2$$

97. $e^{3x} = 10$
$$3x = \ln(10) \Rightarrow x = \frac{\ln(10)}{3}$$

99. $e^{2x+5} = 8$
$$2x+5 = \ln(8)$$
$$2x = -5 + \ln(8) \Rightarrow x = \frac{-5+\ln(8)}{2}$$

101. $\log_3\left(x^2+1\right)=2$

$x^2+1=3^2$

$x^2+1=9 \Rightarrow x^2=8$

$x=\pm\sqrt{8}=\pm2\sqrt{2}$

103. $\log_2 8^x = -3$

$8^x = 2^{-3}$

$8^x = \dfrac{1}{8} \Rightarrow 8^x = 8^{-1} \Rightarrow x = -1$

105. (a)   Graphing $f(x)=2^x$:

Domain: $(-\infty,\ \infty)$
Range: $(0,\ \infty)$
Horizontal asymptote: $y=0$

(b)   Finding the inverse:

$$f(x)=2^x$$
$$y=2^x$$
$$x=2^y \quad \text{Inverse}$$
$$y=\log_2 x$$
$$f^{-1}(x)=\log_2 x$$

(c)   Graphing the inverse:

Domain: $(0,\ \infty)$
Range: $(-\infty,\ \infty)$
Vertical asymptote: $x=0$

107. (a)   Graphing $f(x)=2^{x+3}$:

Domain: $(-\infty,\ \infty)$
Range: $(0,\ \infty)$
Horizontal asymptote: $y=0$

(b)   Finding the inverse:

$$f(x)=2^{x+3}$$
$$y=2^{x+3}$$
$$x=2^{y+3} \quad \text{Inverse}$$
$$y+3=\log_2 x$$
$$y=-3+\log_2 x$$
$$f^{-1}(x)=-3+\log_2 x$$

(c)   Graphing the inverse:

Domain: $(0, \infty)$

Range: $(-\infty, \infty)$

Vertical asymptote: $x = 0$

109. $P = 100e^{-0.1n}$

(a) $50 = 100e^{-0.1n}$

$0.5 = e^{-0.1n}$

$\ln(0.5) = -0.1n$

$n = \dfrac{\ln(0.5)}{-0.1} \Rightarrow n \approx 6.93$

7 panes of glass are needed.

(b) $25 = 100e^{-0.1n}$

$0.25 = e^{-0.1n}$

$\ln(0.25) = -0.1n$

$n = \dfrac{\ln(0.25)}{-0.1} \Rightarrow n \approx 13.86$

14 panes of glass are needed.

111. $w = 50e^{-0.004d}$

(a) $30 = 50e^{-0.004d}$

$0.6 = e^{-0.004d}$

$\ln(0.6) = -0.004d$

$d = \dfrac{\ln(0.6)}{-0.004} \approx 127.7$

Approximately 128 days.

(b) $5 = 50e^{-0.004d}$

$0.1 = e^{-0.004d}$

$\ln(0.1) = -0.004d$

$d = \dfrac{\ln(0.1)}{-0.004} \approx 575.6$

Approximately 576 days.

113. $F(t) = 1 - e^{-0.1t}$

(a) $0.5 = 1 - e^{-0.1t}$

$-0.5 = -e^{-0.1t}$

$0.5 = e^{-0.1t} \Rightarrow \ln(0.5) = -0.1t$

$t = \dfrac{\ln(0.5)}{-0.1} \approx 6.93$

Approximately 7 minutes.

(b) $0.8 = 1 - e^{-0.1t}$

$-0.2 = -e^{-0.1t}$

$0.2 = e^{-0.1t} \Rightarrow \ln(0.2) = -0.1t$

$t = \dfrac{\ln(0.2)}{-0.1} \approx 16.09$

Approximately 16 minutes.

(c)   It is impossible for the probability to reach 100% because $e^{-0.1t}$ will never equal zero.

115. $D = 5e^{-0.4h}$

$\qquad 2 = 5e^{-0.4h}$

$\qquad 0.4 = e^{-0.4h}$

$\quad \ln(0.4) = -0.4h$

$\qquad h = \dfrac{\ln(0.4)}{-0.4} \approx 2.29$ hours

117. $I = \dfrac{E}{R}\left[1 - e^{-\left(\frac{R}{L}\right)t}\right]$

0.5 ampere:

$0.5 = \dfrac{12}{10}\left[1 - e^{-\left(\frac{10}{5}\right)t}\right]$

$0.4167 = 1 - e^{-2t}$

$e^{-2t} = 0.5833$

$-2t = \ln(0.5833)$

$t = \dfrac{\ln(0.5833)}{-2} \approx 0.2695$ seconds

1.0 ampere:

$1.0 = \dfrac{12}{10}\left[1 - e^{-\left(\frac{10}{5}\right)t}\right]$

$0.8333 = 1 - e^{-2t}$

$e^{-2t} = 0.1667$

$-2t = \ln(0.1667)$

$t = \dfrac{\ln(0.1667)}{-2} \approx 0.8958$ seconds

119. $L(10^{-7}) = 10 \log\left(\dfrac{10^{-7}}{10^{-12}}\right) = 10 \log\left(10^{5}\right) = 10 \cdot 5 = 50$ decibels

121. $L(10^{-1}) = 10 \log\left(\dfrac{10^{-1}}{10^{-12}}\right) = 10 \log\left(10^{11}\right) = 10 \cdot 11 = 110$ decibels

123. $M(125,892) = \log\left(\dfrac{125,892}{10^{-3}}\right) = 8.1$

125. $R = 3e^{kx}$

(a)
$$10 = 3e^{k(0.06)}$$
$$3.3333 = e^{0.06k}$$
$$\ln(3.3333) = 0.06k$$
$$k = \frac{\ln(3.3333)}{0.06}$$
$$k \approx 20.066$$

(b)
$$R = 3e^{20.066(0.17)}$$
$$R = 3e^{3.41122}$$
$$R = 90.9\%$$

(c)
$$100 = 3e^{20.066x}$$
$$33.3333 = e^{20.066x}$$
$$\ln(33.3333) = 20.066x$$
$$x = \frac{\ln(33.3333)}{20.066}$$
$$x \approx 0.175$$

(d)
$$15 = 3e^{20.066x}$$
$$5 = e^{20.066x}$$
$$\ln(5) = 20.066x$$
$$x = \frac{\ln(5)}{20.066}$$
$$x \approx 0.08$$

Exponential and Logarithmic Functions

6.4 Properties of Logarithms

1. $\log_3 3^{71} = 71$ 3. $\ln e^{-4} = -4$ 5. $2^{\log_2 7} = 7$

7. $\log_8 2 + \log_8 4 = \log_8(4 \cdot 2) = \log_8(8) = 1$

9. $\log_6 18 - \log_6 3 = \log_6\left(\dfrac{18}{3}\right) = \log_6(6) = 1$

11. $\log_2 6 \cdot \log_6 4$

$$= \log_6\left(4^{\log_2 6}\right) = \log_6\left(\left(2^2\right)^{\log_2 6}\right) = \log_6\left((2)^{2\log_2 6}\right) = \log_6\left((2)^{\log_2 6^2}\right) = \log_6\left(6^2\right) = 2$$

13. $3^{\log_3 5 - \log_3 4} = 3^{\log_3\left(\frac{5}{4}\right)} = \dfrac{5}{4}$

15. $e^{\log_{e^2} 16}$
    Simplify the exponent:
    $$\text{Let} \qquad a = \log_{e^2} 16$$
    $$\left(e^2\right)^a = 16$$
    $$e^{2a} = 16 = 4^2$$
    $$e^a = 4 \Rightarrow a = \ln 4$$
    Thus, $e^{\log_{e^2} 16} = e^{\ln 4} = 4$

17. $\ln 6 = \ln(3 \cdot 2) = \ln 3 + \ln 2 = b + a$ 19. $\ln(1.5) = \ln\left(\dfrac{3}{2}\right) = \ln 3 - \ln 2 = b - a$

21. $\ln 8 = \ln 2^3 = 3 \cdot \ln 2 = 3a$

23. $\ln\left(\sqrt[5]{6}\right) = \ln\left(6^{1/5}\right) = \dfrac{1}{5} \cdot \ln 6 = \dfrac{1}{5} \cdot \ln(2 \cdot 3) = \dfrac{1}{5} \cdot (\ln 2 + \ln 3) = \dfrac{1}{5} \cdot (a + b)$

25. $\log_5(25x) = \log_5(25) + \log_5(x) = 2 + \log_5(x)$

27. $\log_2(z^3) = 3\log_2(z)$

29. $\ln(ex) = \ln e + \ln x = 1 + \ln x$

31. $\ln(xe^x) = \ln x + \ln e^x = \ln x + x$

33. $\log_a(u^2 v^3) = \log_a u^2 + \log_a v^3 = 2\log_a u + 3\log_a v$

35. $\ln(x^2\sqrt{1-x}) = \ln x^2 + \ln\sqrt{1-x} = \ln x^2 + \ln(1-x)^{1/2} = 2\ln x + \dfrac{1}{2}\ln(1-x)$

37. $\log_2\left(\dfrac{x^3}{x-3}\right) = \log_2 x^3 - \log_2(x-3) = 3\log_2 x - \log_2(x-3)$

39. $\log\left[\dfrac{x(x+2)}{(x+3)^2}\right] = \log(x(x+2)) - \log(x+3)^2 = \log x + \log(x+2) - 2\log(x+3)$

41. $\ln\left[\dfrac{x^2 - x - 2}{(x+4)^2}\right]^{1/3} = \dfrac{1}{3}\ln\left[\dfrac{(x-2)(x+1)}{(x+4)^2}\right] = \dfrac{1}{3}\left[\ln(x-2)(x+1) - \ln(x+4)^2\right]$

$$= \dfrac{1}{3}[\ln(x-2) + \ln(x+1) - 2\ln(x+4)] = \dfrac{1}{3}\ln(x-2) + \dfrac{1}{3}\ln(x+1) - \dfrac{2}{3}\ln(x+4)$$

43. $\ln\left(\dfrac{5x\sqrt{1-3x}}{(x-4)^3}\right) = \ln(5x\sqrt{1-3x}) - \ln(x-4)^3 = \ln 5 + \ln x + \ln\sqrt{1-3x} - 3\ln(x-4)$

$$= \ln 5 + \ln x + \ln(1-3x)^{1/2} - 3\ln(x-4) = \ln 5 + \ln x + \dfrac{1}{2}\ln(1-3x) - 3\ln(x-4)$$

45. $3\log_5 u + 4\log_5 v = \log_5 u^3 + \log_5 v^4 = \log_5(u^3 v^4)$

47. $\log_3\sqrt{x} - \log_3 x^3 = \log_3\left(\dfrac{\sqrt{x}}{x^3}\right) = \log_3\left(\dfrac{x^{1/2}}{x^3}\right) = \log_3\left(x^{-5/2}\right) = -\dfrac{5}{2}\log_3 x$

49. $\log_4(x^2 - 1) - 5\log_4(x+1) = \log_4(x^2 - 1) - \log_4(x+1)^5 = \log_4\left(\dfrac{x^2 - 1}{(x+1)^5}\right)$

$$= \log_4\left(\dfrac{(x+1)(x-1)}{(x+1)^5}\right) = \log_4\left(\dfrac{x-1}{(x+1)^4}\right)$$

51. $\ln\left(\dfrac{x}{x-1}\right) + \ln\left(\dfrac{x+1}{x}\right) - \ln(x^2 - 1) = \ln\left[\dfrac{x}{x-1}\cdot\dfrac{x+1}{x}\right] - \ln(x^2 - 1) = \ln\left[\dfrac{x+1}{x-1} \div (x^2 - 1)\right]$

$$= \ln\left[\dfrac{x+1}{(x-1)(x-1)(x+1)}\right] = \ln\left(\dfrac{1}{(x-1)^2}\right) = \ln(x-1)^{-2} = -2\ln(x-1)$$

53. $8\log_2\sqrt{3x-2}-\log_2\left(\dfrac{4}{x}\right)+\log_2 4 = \log_2\left(\sqrt{3x-2}\right)^8 -\left(\log_2 4 - \log_2 x\right)+\log_2 4$

$$= \log_2(3x-2)^4 - \log_2 4 + \log_2 x + \log_2 4 = \log_2\left[x(3x-2)^4\right]$$

55. $2\log_a\left(5x^3\right)-\dfrac{1}{2}\log_a(2x+3) = \log_a\left(5x^3\right)^2 - \log_a(2x-3)^{1/2} = \log_a\left[\dfrac{25x^6}{(2x-3)^{1/2}}\right]$

57. $2\log_2(x+1)-\log_2(x+3)-\log_2(x-1) = \log_2(x+1)^2 - \log_2(x+3) - \log_2(x-1)$

$$= \log_2\left(\dfrac{(x+1)^2}{(x+3)}\right)-\log_2(x-1) = \log_2\left(\dfrac{\dfrac{(x+1)^2}{(x+3)}}{(x-1)}\right) = \log_2\left(\dfrac{(x+1)^2}{(x+3)(x-1)}\right)$$

59. $y = ab^x$

$\log(y) = \log\left(ab^x\right) = \log(a)+\log\left(b^x\right) = \log(a)+x\log(b)$

61. $\log_3 21 = \dfrac{\log 21}{\log 3} \approx \dfrac{1.32222}{0.47712} \approx 2.771$

63. $\log_{\frac{1}{3}} 71 = \dfrac{\log 71}{\log\left(\dfrac{1}{3}\right)} = \dfrac{\log 71}{-\log 3} \approx \dfrac{1.85126}{-0.47712} \approx -3.880$

65. $\log_{\sqrt{2}} 7 = \dfrac{\log 7}{\log\sqrt{2}} = \dfrac{\log 7}{\log 2^{1/2}} = \dfrac{\log 7}{\left(\dfrac{1}{2}\log 2\right)} \approx \dfrac{0.84510}{0.5(0.30103)} \approx 5.615$

67. $\log_\pi e = \dfrac{\ln e}{\ln \pi} \approx \dfrac{1}{1.14473} \approx 0.874$

69. $y = \log_4 x = \dfrac{\ln x}{\ln 4}$ or $y = \dfrac{\log x}{\log 4}$

71. $y = \log_2(x+2) = \dfrac{\ln(x+2)}{\ln 2}$

or $y = \dfrac{\log(x+2)}{\log 2}$

73. $y = \log_{x-1}(x+1) = \dfrac{\ln(x+1)}{\ln(x-1)}$

or $y = \dfrac{\log(x+1)}{\log(x-1)}$

75. $\ln y = \ln x + \ln C$
$\ln y = \ln(xC)$
$y = Cx$

77. $\ln y = \ln x + \ln(x+1) + \ln C$
$\ln y = \ln\big(x(x+1)C\big)$
$y = Cx(x+1)$

79. $\ln y = 3x + \ln C$
$\ln y = \ln e^{3x} + \ln C$
$\ln y = \ln(Ce^{3x})$
$y = Ce^{3x}$

81. $\ln(y-3) = -4x + \ln C$
$\ln(y-3) = \ln e^{-4x} + \ln C$
$\ln(y-3) = \ln\big(Ce^{-4x}\big)$
$y - 3 = Ce^{-4x} \Rightarrow y = Ce^{-4x} + 3$

83. $3\ln y = \dfrac{1}{2}\ln(2x+1) - \dfrac{1}{3}\ln(x+4) + \ln C$

$\ln y^3 = \ln(2x+1)^{1/2} - \ln(x+4)^{1/3} + \ln C$

$\ln y^3 = \ln\left[\dfrac{C(2x+1)^{1/2}}{(x+4)^{1/3}}\right] \Rightarrow y^3 = \dfrac{C(2x+1)^{1/2}}{(x+4)^{1/3}}$

$y = \left[\dfrac{C(2x+1)^{1/2}}{(x+4)^{\frac{1}{3}}}\right]^{1/3} \Rightarrow y = \dfrac{\sqrt[3]{C}(2x+1)^{1/6}}{(x+4)^{1/9}}$

85. $\log_2 3 \cdot \log_3 4 \cdot \log_4 5 \cdot \log_5 6 \cdot \log_6 7 \cdot \log_7 8$

$= \dfrac{\log 3}{\log 2} \cdot \dfrac{\log 4}{\log 3} \cdot \dfrac{\log 5}{\log 4} \cdot \dfrac{\log 6}{\log 5} \cdot \dfrac{\log 7}{\log 6} \cdot \dfrac{\log 8}{\log 7} = \dfrac{\log 8}{\log 2} = \dfrac{\log 2^3}{\log 2} = \dfrac{3\log 2}{\log 2} = 3$

87. $\log_2 3 \cdot \log_3 4 \cdot \ldots \cdot \log_n(n+1) \cdot \log_{n+1} 2$

$= \dfrac{\log 3}{\log 2} \cdot \dfrac{\log 4}{\log 3} \cdot \ldots \cdot \dfrac{\log(n+1)}{\log n} \cdot \dfrac{\log 2}{\log(n+1)} = \dfrac{\log 2}{\log 2} = 1$

89. Verifying:

$\log_a\left(x + \sqrt{x^2-1}\right) + \log_a\left(x - \sqrt{x^2-1}\right) = \log_a\left[\left(x + \sqrt{x^2-1}\right)\left(x - \sqrt{x^2-1}\right)\right]$

$= \log_a\left[x^2 - \left(x^2-1\right)\right] = \log_a\left[x^2 - x^2 + 1\right] = \log_a 1 = 0$

91. Verifying:

$2x + \ln\left(1 + e^{-2x}\right) = \ln e^{2x} + \ln\left(1 + e^{-2x}\right) = \ln\left(e^{2x}\left(1 + e^{-2x}\right)\right) = \ln\left(e^{2x} + e^{0}\right) = \ln\left(e^{2x} + 1\right)$

93. $f(x) = \log_a x$

$$x = a^{f(x)} \;\Rightarrow\; x^{-1} = a^{-f(x)} = \left(a^{-1}\right)^{f(x)} = \left(\frac{1}{a}\right)^{f(x)}$$

$$\log_{\frac{1}{a}} x^{-1} = f(x) \;\Rightarrow\; -\log_{\frac{1}{a}} x = f(x) \;\Rightarrow\; -f(x) = \log_{\frac{1}{a}} x$$

95. $f(x) = \log_a x$

$$a^{f(x)} = x \;\Rightarrow\; \frac{1}{a^{f(x)}} = \frac{1}{x} \;\Rightarrow\; a^{-f(x)} = \frac{1}{x} \;\Rightarrow\; -f(x) = \log_a \frac{1}{x} = f\left(\frac{1}{x}\right)$$

97. If $A = \log_a M$ and $B = \log_a N$, then $a^A = M$ and $a^B = N$.

$$\log_a\left(\frac{M}{N}\right) = \log_a\left(\frac{a^A}{a^B}\right) = \log_a a^{A-B} = A - B = \log_a M - \log_a N$$

Exponential and Logarithmic Functions

6.5 Logarithmic and Exponential Equations

1. $\log_4(x+2) = \log_4 8$
   $x+2 = 8 \Rightarrow x = 6$

3. $\dfrac{1}{2}\log_3 x = 2\log_3 2$
   $\log_3 x^{1/2} = \log_3 2^2$
   $x^{1/2} = 4 \Rightarrow x = 16$

5. $2\log_5 x = 3\log_5 4$
   $\log_5 x^2 = \log_5 4^3$
   $x^2 = 64$
   $x = \pm 8$
   Since $\log_5(-8)$ is undefined, the
   only solution is $x = 8$.

7. $3\log_2(x-1) + \log_2 4 = 5$
   $\log_2(x-1)^3 + \log_2 4 = 5$
   $\log_2\big(4(x-1)^3\big) = 5$
   $4(x-1)^3 = 2^5$
   $(x-1)^3 = \dfrac{32}{4}$
   $(x-1)^3 = 8$
   $x-1 = 2$
   $x = 3$

9. $\log x + \log(x+15) = 2$
   $\log\big(x(x+15)\big) = 2$
   $x(x+15) = 10^2$
   $x^2 + 15x - 100 = 0 \Rightarrow (x+20)(x-5) = 0$
   $x = -20 \text{ or } x = 5$
   Since $\log(-20)$ is undefined, the
   only solution is $x = 5$.

11. $\ln x + \ln(x+2) = 4$
    $\ln\big(x(x+2)\big) = 4$
    $x(x+2) = e^4 \Rightarrow x^2 + 2x - e^4 = 0$
    $x = \dfrac{-2 \pm \sqrt{2^2 - 4(1)(-e^4)}}{2(1)} = \dfrac{-2 \pm \sqrt{4 + 4e^4}}{2} = \dfrac{-2 \pm 2\sqrt{1+e^4}}{2} = -1 \pm \sqrt{1+e^4}$
    Since $\ln\left(-1 - \sqrt{1+e^4}\right)$ is undefined, the only solution is $x = -1 + \sqrt{1+e^4} \approx 6.456$.

13. $2^{2x} + 2^x - 12 = 0$

$$\left(2^x\right)^2 + 2^x - 12 = 0 \Rightarrow \left(2^x - 3\right)\left(2^x + 4\right) = 0$$

$$2^x - 3 = 0 \qquad \text{or} \ \ 2^x + 4 = 0$$

$$2^x = 3 \qquad \text{or} \qquad 2^x = -4$$

$$x = \log_2 3 \qquad \qquad \text{No solution}$$

$$x \approx 1.585$$

The only solution is $x = \log_2 3 \approx 1.585$.

15. $3^{2x} + 3^{x+1} - 4 = 0$

$$\left(3^x\right)^2 + 3 \cdot 3^x - 4 = 0 \Rightarrow \left(3^x - 1\right)\left(3^x + 4\right) = 0$$

$$3^x - 1 = 0 \quad \text{or} \qquad 3^x + 4 = 0$$

$$3^x = 1 \quad \text{or} \qquad 3^x = -4$$

$$x = 0 \qquad \qquad \text{No solution}$$

The only solution is $x = 0$.

17. $2^x = 10$

$$\log\left(2^x\right) = \log 10$$

$$x \log 2 = 1$$

$$x = \frac{1}{\log 2} \approx 3.322$$

19. $8^{-x} = 1.2$

$$\log\left(8^{-x}\right) = \log(1.2)$$

$$-x \log 8 = \log(1.2)$$

$$x = \frac{\log(1.2)}{-\log 8} \approx -0.088$$

21. $3^{1-2x} = 4^x$

$$\log\left(3^{1-2x}\right) = \log\left(4^x\right)$$

$$(1 - 2x)\log 3 = x \log 4$$

$$\log 3 - 2x \log 3 = x \log 4 \Rightarrow \log 3 = x \log 4 + 2x \log 3 \Rightarrow \log 3 = x(\log 4 + 2 \log 3)$$

$$x = \frac{\log 3}{\log 4 + 2 \log 3} \approx 0.307$$

23. $\left(\dfrac{3}{5}\right)^x = 7^{1-x}$

$$\log\left(\left(\frac{3}{5}\right)^x\right) = \log\left(7^{1-x}\right)$$

$$x \log\frac{3}{5} = (1 - x)\log 7 \Rightarrow x(\log 3 - \log 5) = \log 7 - x \log 7$$

$$x \log 3 - x \log 5 + x \log 7 = \log 7 \Rightarrow x(\log 3 - \log 5 + \log 7) = \log 7$$

$$x = \frac{\log 7}{\log 3 - \log 5 + \log 7} \approx 1.356$$

334

25. $1.2^x = (0.5)^{-x}$

$$\log 1.2^x = \log(0.5)^{-x}$$
$$x \log(1.2) = -x \log(0.5)$$
$$x \log(1.2) + x \log(0.5) = 0$$
$$x(\log(1.2) + \log(0.5)) = 0$$
$$x = 0$$

27. $\pi^{1-x} = e^x$

$$\ln \pi^{1-x} = \ln e^x$$
$$(1-x)\ln \pi = x$$
$$\ln \pi - x \ln \pi = x$$
$$\ln \pi = x + x \ln \pi$$
$$\ln \pi = x(1 + \ln \pi)$$
$$x = \frac{\ln \pi}{1 + \ln \pi} \approx 0.534$$

29. $5\left(2^{3x}\right) = 8$

$$2^{3x} = \frac{8}{5}$$
$$\log 2^{3x} = \log\left(\frac{8}{5}\right)$$
$$3x \log 2 = \log 8 - \log 5$$
$$x = \frac{\log 8 - \log 5}{3 \log 2} \approx 0.226$$

31. $\log_a(x-1) - \log_a(x+6) = \log_a(x-2) - \log_a(x+3)$

$$\log_a\left(\frac{x-1}{x+6}\right) = \log_a\left(\frac{x-2}{x+3}\right) \Rightarrow a^{\left(\log_a\left(\frac{x-1}{x+6}\right)\right)} = a^{\left(\log_a\left(\frac{x-2}{x+3}\right)\right)}$$

so

$$\frac{x-1}{x+6} = \frac{x-2}{x+3} \Rightarrow (x-1)(x+3) = (x-2)(x+6)$$

$$x^2 + 2x - 3 = x^2 + 4x - 12 \Rightarrow 2x - 3 = 4x - 12 \Rightarrow 9 = 2x \Rightarrow x = \frac{9}{2}$$

Since each of the original logarithms is defined for $x = \frac{9}{2}$, the solution is $x = \frac{9}{2}$.

33. $\log_{\frac{1}{3}}(x^2 + x) - \log_{\frac{1}{3}}(x^2 - x) = -1$

$$\log_{\frac{1}{3}}\left(\frac{x^2 + x}{x^2 - x}\right) = -1$$

$$\frac{x^2 + x}{x^2 - x} = \left(\frac{1}{3}\right)^{-1}$$

$$\frac{x(x+1)}{x(x-1)} = 3 \Rightarrow x + 1 = 3(x-1)$$

$$x + 1 = 3x - 3 \Rightarrow -2x = -4 \Rightarrow x = 2$$

Since each of the original logarithms is defined for $x = 2$, the solution is $x = 2$.

35. $\log_2(x+1) - \log_4 x = 1$

$$\log_2(x+1) - \frac{\log_2 x}{\log_2 4} = 1$$

$$\log_2(x+1) - \frac{\log_2 x}{2} = 1$$

$$2\log_2(x+1) - \log_2 x = 2$$

$$\log_2(x+1)^2 - \log_2 x = 2$$

$$\log_2\left(\frac{(x+1)^2}{x}\right) = 2$$

$$\frac{(x+1)^2}{x} = 2^2$$

$$x^2 + 2x + 1 = 4x$$

$$x^2 - 2x + 1 = 0$$

$$(x-1)^2 = 0$$

$$x - 1 = 0$$

$$x = 1$$

Since each of the original logarithms is defined for $x=1$, the solution is $x=1$.

37. $\log_{16} x + \log_4 x + \log_2 x = 7$

$$\frac{\log_2 x}{\log_2 16} + \frac{\log_2 x}{\log_2 4} + \log_2 x = 7$$

$$\frac{\log_2 x}{4} + \frac{\log_2 x}{2} + \log_2 x = 7$$

$$\log_2 x + 2\log_2 x + 4\log_2 x = 28$$

$$7\log_2 x = 28$$

$$\log_2 x = 4$$

$$x = 2^4 = 16$$

Since each of the original logarithms is defined for $x=16$, the solution is $x=16$.

39. $\left(\sqrt[3]{2}\right)^{2-x} = 2^{x^2}$

$$\left(2^{1/3}\right)^{2-x} = 2^{x^2}$$

$$2^{\frac{1}{3}(2-x)} = 2^{x^2}$$

$$\frac{1}{3}(2-x) = x^2 \Rightarrow 2 - x = 3x^2$$

$$3x^2 + x - 2 = 0 \Rightarrow (3x-2)(x+1) = 0$$

$$x = \frac{2}{3} \text{ or } x = -1$$

41. $\dfrac{e^x + e^{-x}}{2} = 1$

$$e^x + e^{-x} = 2$$

$$e^x\left(e^x + e^{-x}\right) = 2e^x$$

$$e^{2x} + 1 = 2e^x$$

$$(e^x)^2 - 2e^x + 1 = 0$$

$$\left(e^x - 1\right)^2 = 0$$

$$e^x - 1 = 0$$

$$e^x = 1$$

$$x = 0$$

43. $\dfrac{e^x - e^{-x}}{2} = 2$

$$e^x - e^{-x} = 4 \Rightarrow e^x\left(e^x - e^{-x}\right) = 4e^x \Rightarrow e^{2x} - 1 = 4e^x \Rightarrow (e^x)^2 - 4e^x - 1 = 0$$

$$e^x = \frac{-(-4) \pm \sqrt{(-4)^2 - 4(1)(-1)}}{2(1)} = \frac{4 \pm \sqrt{20}}{2} = \frac{4 \pm 2\sqrt{5}}{2} = 2 \pm \sqrt{5}$$

$$x = \ln\left(2 + \sqrt{5}\right)$$

Since $\ln\left(2 - \sqrt{5}\right)$ is undefined; it is not a solution.

45. Using INTERSECT to solve:
$y_1 = \ln(x)/\ln(5) + \ln(x)/\ln(3)$
$y_2 = 1$

The solution is 1.92.

47. Using INTERSECT to solve:
$y_1 = \ln(x+1)/\ln(5) - \ln(x-2)/\ln(4)$
$y_2 = 1$

The solution is 2.79.

49. Using INTERSECT to solve:
$y_1 = e^x; \ y_2 = -x$

The solution is −0.57.

51. Using INTERSECT to solve:
$y_1 = e^x; \ y_2 = x^2$

The solution is −0.70.

53. Using INTERSECT to solve:
$y_1 = \ln x; \ y_2 = -x$

The solution is 0.57.

55. Using INTERSECT to solve:
$y_1 = \ln x; \ y_2 = x^3 - 1$

The solutions are 0.39, 1.00.

57. Using INTERSECT to solve:
$y_1 = e^x + \ln x; \ y_2 = 4$

The solution is 1.32.

59. Using INTERSECT to solve:
$y_1 = e^{-x}; \ y_2 = \ln x$

The solution is 1.31.

Exponential and Logarithmic Functions

6.6 Compound Interest

1. $P = \$100$, $r = 0.04$, $n = 4$, $t = 2$

$$A = P\left(1 + \frac{r}{n}\right)^{nt} = 100\left(1 + \frac{0.04}{4}\right)^{(4)(2)} \approx \$108.29$$

3. $P = \$500$, $r = 0.08$, $n = 4$, $t = 2.5$

$$A = P\left(1 + \frac{r}{n}\right)^{nt} = 500\left(1 + \frac{0.08}{4}\right)^{(4)(2.5)} \approx \$609.50$$

5. $P = \$600$, $r = 0.05$, $n = 365$, $t = 3$

$$A = P\left(1 + \frac{r}{n}\right)^{nt} = 600\left(1 + \frac{0.05}{365}\right)^{(365)(3)} \approx \$697.09$$

7. $P = \$10$, $r = 0.11$, $t = 2$

$$A = Pe^{rt} = 10e^{(0.11)(2)} \approx \$12.46$$

9. $P = \$100$, $r = 0.10$, $t = 2.25$

$$A = Pe^{rt} = 100e^{(0.10)(2.25)} \approx \$125.23$$

11. $A = \$100$, $r = 0.06$, $n = 12$, $t = 2$

$$P = A\left(1 + \frac{r}{n}\right)^{-nt} = 100\left(1 + \frac{0.06}{12}\right)^{(-12)(2)} \approx \$88.72$$

13. $A = \$1000$, $r = 0.06$, $n = 365$, $t = 2.5$

$$P = A\left(1 + \frac{r}{n}\right)^{-nt} = 1000\left(1 + \frac{0.06}{365}\right)^{(-365)(2.5)} \approx \$860.72$$

15. $A = \$600$, $r = 0.04$, $n = 4$, $t = 2$

$$P = A\left(1 + \frac{r}{n}\right)^{-nt} = 600\left(1 + \frac{0.04}{4}\right)^{(-4)(2)} \approx \$554.09$$

17. $A = \$80$, $r = 0.09$, $t = 3.25$

$$P = Ae^{-rt} = 80e^{(-0.09)(3.25)} \approx \$59.71$$

19. $A = \$400$, $r = 0.10$, $t = 1$

$$P = Ae^{-rt} = 400e^{(-0.10)(1)} \approx \$361.93$$

21. $r_e = \left(1 + \dfrac{r}{n}\right)^n - 1 = \left(1 + \dfrac{0.0525}{4}\right)^4 - 1 \approx 1.0535 - 1 = 0.0535 = 5.35\%$

23. $2P = P(1+r)^3$

    $2 = (1+r)^3$

    $\sqrt[3]{2} = 1 + r$

    $r = \sqrt[3]{2} - 1 \approx 1.26 - 1 = 0.26 = 26\%$

25. 6% compounded quarterly:

    $A = 10{,}000\left(1 + \dfrac{0.06}{4}\right)^{(4)(1)} \approx \$10{,}613.64$

    $6\frac{1}{4}\%$ compounded annually:

    $A = 10{,}000(1 + 0.0625)^1 \approx \$10{,}625$

    $6\frac{1}{4}\%$ compounded annually yields the larger amount.

27. 9% compounded monthly:

    $A = 10{,}000\left(1 + \dfrac{0.09}{12}\right)^{(12)(1)} \approx \$10{,}938.07$

    8.8% compounded daily:

    $A = 10{,}000\left(1 + \dfrac{0.088}{365}\right)^{365} \approx \$10{,}919.77$

    9% compounded monthly yields the larger amount.

29. Compounded monthly:

    $2P = P\left(1 + \dfrac{0.08}{12}\right)^{12t}$

    $2 \approx (1.00667)^{12t}$

    $\ln 2 \approx 12t \ln(1.00667)$

    $t \approx \dfrac{\ln 2}{12 \ln(1.00667)} \approx 8.69$ years

Compounded continuously:

    $2P = Pe^{0.08t}$

    $2 = e^{0.08t}$

    $\ln 2 = 0.08t$

    $t = \dfrac{\ln 2}{0.08} \approx 8.66$ years

31. Compounded monthly:

    $150 = 100\left(1 + \dfrac{0.08}{12}\right)^{12t}$

    $1.5 \approx (1.00667)^{12t}$

    $\ln(1.5) \approx 12t \ln(1.00667)$

    $t \approx \dfrac{\ln(1.5)}{12 \ln(1.00667)} \approx 5.083$ years

Compounded continuously:

    $150 = 100e^{0.08t}$

    $1.5 = e^{0.08t}$

    $\ln(1.5) = 0.08t$

    $t = \dfrac{\ln(1.5)}{0.08} \approx 5.068$ years

33. $25{,}000 = 10{,}000e^{0.06\,t}$

$2.5 = e^{0.06\,t}$

$\ln(2.5) = 0.06\,t$

$t = \dfrac{\ln(2.5)}{0.06} \approx 15.27$ years

35. $A = 90{,}000(1 + 0.03)^5 \approx \$104{,}335$

37. $P = 15{,}000e^{(-0.05)(3)} \approx \$12{,}910.62$

39. $A = 1500(1 + 0.15)^5$
$= 1500(1.15)^5 \approx \$3017$

41. $850{,}000 = 650{,}000(1 + r)^3$

$\dfrac{85}{65} = (1 + r)^3 \Rightarrow \sqrt[3]{\dfrac{85}{65}} = 1 + r \Rightarrow r \approx \sqrt[3]{1.3077} - 1 \approx 0.0935 = 9.35\%$

43. 5.6% compounded continuously:
$A = 1000e^{(0.056)(1)} \approx \$1057.60$
Jim does not have enough money to buy the computer.
5.9% compounded monthly:
$A = 1000\left(1 + \dfrac{0.059}{12}\right)^{12} \approx \$1060.62$
The second bank offers the better deal.

45. Will - 9% compounded semiannually:
$A = 2000\left(1 + \dfrac{0.09}{2}\right)^{(2)(20)} \approx \$11{,}632.73$

Henry - 8.5% compounded continuously:
$A = 2000e^{(0.085)(20)} \approx \$10{,}947.89$
Will has more money after 20 years.

47. $P = 50{,}000;\ t = 5$
(a) Simple interest at 12% per annum:
$A = 50{,}000 + 50{,}000(0.12)(5) = \$80{,}000$
(b) 11.5% compounded monthly:
$A = 50{,}000\left(1 + \dfrac{0.115}{12}\right)^{(12)(5)} \approx \$88{,}613.59$
(c) 11.25% compounded continuously:
$A = 50{,}000e^{(0.1125)(5)} \approx \$87{,}752.73$
Subtract $50,000 from each to get the amount of interest:
(a) $30,000 (b) $38,613.59   (c) $37.752.73
Option (a) results in the least interest.

49. (a) $A = \$10{,}000,\ r = 0.10,\ n = 12,\ t = 20$ (compounded monthly)
$P = 10{,}000\left(1 + \dfrac{0.10}{12}\right)^{(-12)(20)} \approx \$1364.62$
(b) $A = \$10{,}000,\ r = 0.10,\ t = 20$ (compounded continuously)
$P = 10{,}000e^{(-0.10)(20)} \approx \$1353.35$

51. $A = \$10,000$, $r = 0.08$, $n = 1$, $t = 10$ (compounded annually)

$$P = 10,000\left(1 + \frac{0.08}{1}\right)^{(-1)(10)} \approx \$4631.93$$

53.   Answers will vary.

55.   (a) $y = \dfrac{\ln 2}{1 \cdot \ln\left(1 + \dfrac{0.12}{1}\right)} = \dfrac{\ln 2}{\ln(1.12)} \approx 6.12$ years

(b) $y = \dfrac{\ln 3}{4 \cdot \ln\left(1 + \dfrac{0.06}{4}\right)} = \dfrac{\ln 3}{4\ln(1.015)} \approx 18.45$ years

(c) $mP = P\left(1 + \dfrac{r}{n}\right)^{nt}$

$$m = \left(1 + \frac{r}{n}\right)^{nt} \Rightarrow \ln m = nt \cdot \ln\left(1 + \frac{r}{n}\right) \Rightarrow t = \frac{\ln m}{n \cdot \ln\left(1 + \dfrac{r}{n}\right)}$$

57.   Answers will vary.

Chapter 6

Exponential and Logarithmic Functions

6.7   Growth and Decay

1. $P(t) = 500e^{0.02t}$

   (a) $P(0) = 500e^{(0.02) \cdot (0)} = 500$ flies

   (b)   growth rate = 2 %

   (c)   graphing:

   (d) $P(10) = 500e^{(0.02) \cdot (10)} \approx 611$ flies

   (e)   Find t when $P = 800$:

$$800 = 500e^{0.02t}$$

$$1.6 = e^{0.02t}$$

$$\ln(1.6) = 0.02t$$

$$t = \frac{\ln(1.6)}{0.02} \approx 23.5 \text{ days}$$

   (f)   Find t when $P = 1000$:

$$1000 = 500e^{0.02t}$$

$$2 = e^{0.02t}$$

$$\ln(2) = 0.02t$$

$$t = \frac{\ln(2)}{0.02} \approx 34.7 \text{ days}$$

3. $A(t) = A_0 e^{-0.0244t} = 500e^{-0.0244t}$

   (a)   decay rate = 2.44 %

   (b)   graphing

   (c) $A(10) = 500e^{(-0.0244)(10)}$

$$\approx 391.74 \text{ grams}$$

   (d)   Find t when $A = 400$:

$$400 = 500e^{-0.0244t}$$

$$0.8 = e^{-0.0244t}$$

$$\ln(0.8) = -0.0244t$$

$$t = \frac{\ln(0.8)}{-0.0244} \approx 9.15 \text{ years}$$

   (e)   Find t when $A = 250$:

$$250 = 500e^{-0.0244t}$$

$$0.5 = e^{-0.0244t}$$

$$\ln(0.5) = -0.0244t$$

$$t = \frac{\ln(0.5)}{-0.0244} \approx 28.4 \text{ years}$$

5. Use $N(t) = N_0 e^{kt}$ and solve for k:
$$1800 = 1000 e^{k(1)} \Rightarrow 1.8 = e^k$$
$$k = \ln(1.8) \approx 0.5878$$
When $t = 3$:
$$N(3) = 1000 e^{0.5878\,(3)} = 5832 \text{ mosquitos}$$
Find t when $N(t) = 10{,}000$:
$$10{,}000 = 1000 e^{0.5878\,t} \Rightarrow 10 = e^{0.5878\,t}$$
$$\ln 10 = 0.5878\,t \Rightarrow t = \frac{\ln 10}{0.5878} \approx 3.9 \text{ days}$$

7. Use $P(t) = P_0 e^{kt}$ and solve for k:
$$2P_0 = P_0 e^{k(1.5)} \Rightarrow 2 = e^{1.5k}$$
$$\ln 2 = 1.5k \Rightarrow k = \frac{\ln 2}{1.5} \approx 0.4621$$
When $t = 2$:
$$P(2) = 10{,}000 e^{0.4621\,(2)} = 25{,}199 \text{ is the population 2 years from now.}$$

9. Use $A = A_0 e^{kt}$ and solve for k:
$$0.5 A_0 = A_0 e^{k(1690)} \Rightarrow 0.5 = e^{1690k}$$
$$\ln(0.5) = 1690k \Rightarrow k = \frac{\ln(0.5)}{1690} \approx -0.00041$$
When $A_0 = 10$ and $t = 50$: $A = 10 e^{-0.00041\,(50)} \approx 9.797 \text{ grams}$

11. Use $A = A_0 e^{kt}$ and solve for k:
    half-life $= 5600$ years
    $$\Rightarrow 0.5 A_0 = A_0 e^{k(5600)}$$
    $$0.5 = e^{5600\,k}$$
    $$\ln(0.5) = 5600k \Rightarrow k = \frac{\ln(0.5)}{5600} \approx -0.000124$$
    (a) Solve for t when $A = 0.3 A_0$:
    $$0.3 A_0 = A_0 e^{(-0.000124)t}$$
    $$0.3 = e^{(-0.000124)t}$$
    $$\ln(0.3) = -0.000124\,t$$
    $$t = \frac{\ln(0.3)}{-0.000124}$$
    $$\approx 9709 \text{ years ago}$$

(b) graphing $y_1 = e^{(-0.000124)x}$

(c) Using INTERSECT with $y_1 = e^{(-0.000124)x}$ and
$y_2 = 0.5$

(d) Using INTERSECT with
$y_1 = e^{(-0.000124)x}$ and $y_2 = 0.3$

$t \approx 5589.90$ years

$x \approx 9708.46$ years

13. (a) Using $u = T + (u_0 - T)e^{kt}$ where $t = 5$,

$T = 70, \ u_0 = 450, \ u = 300$:

$$300 = 70 + (450 - 70)e^{k(5)}$$

$$230 = 380e^{5k}$$

$$0.6053 = e^{5k}$$

$$5k = \ln(0.6053)$$

$$k = \frac{\ln(0.6053)}{5} \approx -0.1004$$

$T = 70, \ u_0 = 450, \ u = 135$:

$$135 = 70 + (450 - 70)e^{-0.1004\,t}$$

$$65 = 380e^{-0.1004\,t}$$

$$0.17105 = e^{-0.1004\,t}$$

$$-0.1004\,t = \ln(0.17105)$$

$$t = \frac{\ln(0.17105)}{-0.1004} \approx 17.6 \text{ minutes}$$

The pizza will be cool enough to eat at 5:18 p.m.

(b) graphing: $y_1 = 70 + 380e^{(-0.1004)x}$

(c) Using INTERSECT with $y_1 = 70 + 380e^{(-0.1004)x}$ and $y_2 = 160$

   The pizza will be 160°F after about 14.35 minutes.

(d) Use TRACE with $y_1 = 70 + 380e^{(-0.1004)x}$

As time passes the temperature gets closer to 70°F.

15. (a)   Using $u = T + (u_0 - T)e^{kt}$ where $t = 3$,
$T = 35$, $u_0 = 8$, $u = 15$:

$$15 = 35 + (8 - 35)e^{k(3)} \Rightarrow -20 = -27e^{3k} \Rightarrow 0.74074 = e^{3k}$$

$$3k = \ln(0.74074) \Rightarrow k = \frac{\ln(0.74074)}{3} \approx -0.100035$$

At $t = 5$:
$$u = 35 + (8 - 35)e^{-0.100035\,(5)} = 18.63°C$$
At $t = 10$:
$$u = 35 + (8 - 35)e^{-0.100035\,(10)} = 25.1°C$$

(b)   graphing $y_1 = 35 - 27e^{(-0.100035)x}$

Use TRACE on the graph of $y_1 = 35 - 27e^{(-0.100035)x}$:

17.   Use $A = A_0 e^{kt}$ and solve for k:
$$15 = 25e^{k(10)}$$

$$0.6 = e^{10k} \Rightarrow \ln(0.6) = 10k \Rightarrow k = \frac{\ln(0.6)}{10} \approx -0.0511$$

When $A_0 = 25$ and $t = 24$:
$$A = 25e^{-0.0511(24)} \approx 7.33 \text{ kilograms}$$
Find t when $A = 0.5A_0$:
$$0.5 = 25e^{-0.0511\,t}$$

$$0.02 = e^{-0.0511\,t} \Rightarrow \ln(0.02) = -0.0511t \Rightarrow t = \frac{\ln(0.02)}{-0.0511} \approx 76.6 \text{ hours}$$

19.   Use $A = A_0 e^{kt}$ and solve for k:

$$0.5A_0 = A_0 e^{k(8)}$$

$$0.5 = e^{8k} \Rightarrow \ln(0.5) = 8k$$

$$k = \frac{\ln(0.5)}{8} \approx -0.0866$$

Find t when $A = 0.1A_0$:

$$0.1A_0 = A_0 e^{-0.0866\,t}$$

$$0.1 = e^{-0.0866\,t} \Rightarrow \ln(0.1) = -0.0866t$$

$$t = \frac{\ln(0.1)}{-0.0866} \approx 26.6 \text{ days}$$

The farmers need to wait about 27 days before using the hay.

21. (a) The maximum proportion is the carrying capacity, 0.9 = 90%.

(b) $P(0) = \dfrac{0.9}{1 + 6e^{-0.32(0)}} = \dfrac{0.9}{1 + 6 \cdot 1} = \dfrac{0.9}{7} = 0.1286$

(c) graphing:

(d) $P(15) = \dfrac{0.9}{1 + 6e^{-0.32(15)}} \approx 0.8577$, so 85.77% owned a VCR in 1999.

(e) $0.8 = \dfrac{0.9}{1 + 6e^{-0.32t}}$

$0.8\left(1 + 6e^{-0.32t}\right) = 0.9 \Rightarrow 1 + 6e^{-0.32t} = 1.125 \Rightarrow 6e^{-0.32t} = 0.125$

$e^{-0.32t} = 0.020833 \Rightarrow -0.32t = \ln(0.020833)$

$t = \dfrac{\ln(0.020833)}{-0.32} \approx 12.1$

80% of households will own VCR's in 1996 (t = 12).

(f) $0.45 = \dfrac{0.9}{1 + 6e^{-0.32t}}$

$0.45\left(1 + 6e^{-0.32t}\right) = 0.9 \Rightarrow 1 + 6e^{-0.32t} = 2 \Rightarrow 6e^{-0.32t} = 1$

$e^{-0.32t} = \dfrac{1}{6} \Rightarrow -0.32t = \ln\left(\dfrac{1}{6}\right)$

$t = \dfrac{\ln\left(\dfrac{1}{6}\right)}{-0.32} \approx 5.60$ years

80% of households will own VCR's in 1996 (t = 12).

23. (a) As $t \to \infty$, $e^{-0.439t} \to 0$. Thus, $P(t) \to 1000$. The carrying capacity is 1000g.
Growth rate = 43.9%.

(b) $P(0) = \dfrac{1000}{1 + 32.33e^{-0.439(0)}} = \dfrac{1000}{33.33} = 30$ g

(c) graphing:

(d) $P(9) = \dfrac{1000}{1 + 32.33e^{-0.439(9)}} \approx 616.6$ g

(e) $700 = \dfrac{1000}{1 + 32.33e^{-0.439t}}$

$$700\left(1 + 32.33e^{-0.439t}\right) = 1000 \Rightarrow 1 + 32.33e^{-0.439t} = \dfrac{1000}{700} = \dfrac{10}{7}$$

$$32.33e^{-0.439t} = \dfrac{3}{7} \Rightarrow e^{-0.439t} = \dfrac{\left(\dfrac{3}{7}\right)}{32.33}$$

$$-0.439t = \ln\left(\dfrac{\left(\dfrac{3}{7}\right)}{32.33}\right) \Rightarrow t = \dfrac{\ln\left(\dfrac{\left(\dfrac{3}{7}\right)}{32.33}\right)}{-0.439} \approx 9.85 \text{ hours}$$

(f)   To reach half-carrying capacity, we need

$$500 = \dfrac{1000}{1 + 32.33e^{-0.439t}}$$

$$500\left(1 + 32.33e^{-0.439t}\right) = 1000 \Rightarrow 1 + 32.33e^{-0.439t} = 2$$

$$32.33e^{-0.439t} = 1 \Rightarrow e^{-0.439t} = \dfrac{1}{32.33}$$

$$-0.439t = \ln\left(\dfrac{1}{32.33}\right) \Rightarrow t = \dfrac{\ln\left(\dfrac{1}{32.33}\right)}{-0.439} \approx 7.92 \text{ hours}$$

25. (a) $y = \dfrac{6}{1 + e^{-(5.085 - 0.1156(100))}} \approx 0.0092 \text{ O-rings}$

(b) $y = \dfrac{6}{1 + e^{-(5.085 - 0.1156(60))}} \approx 0.8145 \text{ O-rings}$

(c) $y = \dfrac{6}{1 + e^{-(5.085 - 0.1156(30))}} \approx 5.0063 \text{ O-rings}$

(d)   Graphing:

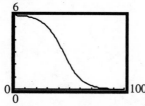

At 58°F, there would be 1 leaky O-ring.
At 44°F, there would be 3 leaky O-rings.
At 30°F, there would be 5 leaky O-rings.

Exponential and Logarithmic Functions

6.8   Exponential, Logarithmic and Logistic Models

1.   (a)   scatter diagram

(b)   Using EXPonential REGression on the data yields: $y = (0.0903)(1.3384)^x$

(c) $y = (0.0903)(1.3384)^x = (0.0903)\left(e^{\ln(1.3384)}\right)^x = (0.0903)\left(e^{\ln(1.3384)x}\right)$

$\qquad N(t) = (0.0903)\left(e^{\ln(1.3384)t}\right) = (0.0903)\left(e^{0.2915t}\right)$

(d)   graphing: $y_1 = (0.0903)\left(e^{0.2915x}\right)$

(e) $N(7) = (0.0903)\left(e^{(0.2915)\cdot 7}\right) \approx 0.695$ bacteria

(f)   Find t when $N(t) = 0.75$

$$(0.0903)\left(e^{(0.2915)\cdot t}\right) = 0.75$$

$$\left(e^{(0.2915)\cdot t}\right) = \frac{0.75}{0.0903} \approx 8.306$$

$$(0.2915)\cdot t = \ln(8.306)$$

$$t \approx \frac{\ln(8.306)}{0.2915} \approx 7.26 \text{ hours}$$

3.   (a)   scatter diagram

(b)   Using EXPonential REGression on the data yields: $y = (100.3262)(0.8769)^x$

(c) $y = (100.3262)(0.8769)^x = (100.3262)\left(e^{\ln(0.8769)}\right)^x = (100.3262)\left(e^{\ln(0.8769)x}\right)$

$A(t) = (100.3262)\left(e^{(-0.1314)t}\right)$

(d)   graphing: $y_1 = (100.3262)\left(e^{(-0.1314)x}\right)$

(e)   Find t when $A(t) = 0.5 \cdot A_0$

$(100.3262)\left(e^{(-0.1314)t}\right) = (0.5)(100.3262)$

$\left(e^{(-0.1314)t}\right) = 0.5$

$(-0.1314)t = \ln(0.5)$

$t = \dfrac{\ln(0.5)}{-0.1314} \approx 5.28$ weeks

(f) $A(50) = (100.3262)\left(e^{(-0.1314)\cdot 50}\right) \approx 0.141$ grams

(g)   Find t when $A(t) = 20$

$(100.3262)\left(e^{(-0.1314)t}\right) = 20$

$\left(e^{(-0.1314)t}\right) = \dfrac{20}{100.3262} \approx 0.1993$

$(-0.1314)t = \ln(0.1993)$

$t = \dfrac{\ln(0.1993)}{-0.1314} \approx 12.28$ weeks

5.   (a)   Let $x = 1$ correspond to 1991, $x = 2$ correspond to 1992, etc.

(b)   Using EXPonential REGression on the data yields: $y = (9478.4453)(1.0566)^x$

(c)   The average annual rate of return over the past 10 years is given by $0.0566 = 5.66\%$.

(d)   In the year 2021, $x = 21$, so $y = (9478.4453)(1.0566)^{21} \approx \$30{,}120.34$.

(e)   Find x when $y = 80000$

$$(9478.4453)(1.0566)^x = 80000$$

$$(1.0566)^x = \frac{80000}{9478.4453} \approx 8.84402$$

$$x \ln(1.0566) = \ln(8.84402) \Rightarrow x = \frac{\ln(8.84402)}{\ln(1.0566)} \approx 38.74 \text{ years}$$

7.   (a)   scatter diagram

(b)   Using LnREGression on the data yields: $y = 32741.02369 - 6070.956754 \ln(x)$

(c)   graphing $y_1 = 32741.02369 - 6070.956754 \ln(x)$

(d)   find x when $y = 1650$:

$$1650 = 32741.02369 - 6070.956754 \ln(x)$$

$$-31091.02369 = -6070.956754 \ln(x)$$

$$\frac{-31091.02369}{-6070.956754} = \ln(x)$$

$$5.1213 \approx \ln(x) \Rightarrow e^{5.1213} \approx x \Rightarrow x \approx 168 \text{ computers}$$

9.   (a)   Let $x = 0$ correspond to 1900, $x = 1$ correspond to 1910, etc.

(b)   Using LOGISTIC REGression on the data yields:

$$y = \frac{799475916.5}{1 + 9.1968e^{-0.1603x}}$$

(c)   graphing $y_1 = \dfrac{799475916.5}{1 + 9.1968e^{-0.1603x}}$:

(d)   as $x \to \infty$, $y = \dfrac{799475916.5}{1 + 9.1968e^{-0.1603x}} \to \dfrac{799475916.5}{1 + 0} = 799475916.5$

Therefore, the carrying capacity of the United States is approximately 799,475,916 people.

(e)   in the year 2001, $x = 10.1$, so $y = \dfrac{799475916.5}{1 + 9.1968e^{-0.1603(10.1)}} \approx 283,321,149$ people

(f)   Find x when $y = 300,000,000$

$$\frac{799475916.5}{1 + 9.1968e^{-0.1603x}} = 300000000$$

$$799475916.5 = 300000000\left(1 + 9.1968e^{-0.1603x}\right)$$

$$\frac{799475916.5}{300000000} = 1 + 9.1968e^{-0.1603x}$$

$$\frac{799475916.5}{300000000} - 1 = 9.1968e^{-0.1603x}$$

$$1.6649 \approx 9.1968e^{-0.1603x}$$

$$\frac{1.6649}{9.1968} = e^{-0.1603x}$$

$$0.1810 \approx e^{-0.1603x}$$

$$\ln(0.1810) \approx -0.1603x$$

$$\frac{\ln(0.1810)}{-0.1603} = x \Rightarrow x \approx 10.7$$

Therefore, the United States population will be 300,000,000 in the year 2007.

11.   (a)   Let $x = 0$ correspond to 1900, $x = 1$ correspond to 1910, etc.

(b)   Using LOGISTIC REGression on the data yields:

$$y = \frac{14471245.24}{1 + 2.01534e^{-0.2458x}}$$

(c)   graphing $y_1 = \dfrac{14471245.24}{1+2.01534e^{-0.2458x}}$:

(d)   as $x \to \infty$, $y = \dfrac{14471245.24}{1+2.01534e^{-0.2458x}} \to \dfrac{14471245.24}{1+0} = 14471245.24$

Therefore, the carrying capacity of Illinois is approximately 14,471,245 people.

(e)   in the year 2010, $x = 11$, so $y = \dfrac{14471245.24}{1+2.01534e^{-0.2458(11)}} \approx 12,750,802$ people

Exponential and Logarithmic Functions

6.R   Chapter Review

1.   inverse $\{(2,1),(5,3),(8,5),(10,6)\}$ is a function

3.

5. $f(x) = \dfrac{2x+3}{5x-2}$

$y = \dfrac{2x+3}{5x-2}$

$x = \dfrac{2y+3}{5y-2}$ Inverse

$x(5y-2) = 2y+3$

$5xy - 2x = 2y+3$

$5xy - 2y = 2x+3$

$y(5x-2) = 2x+3$

$y = \dfrac{2x+3}{5x-2}$

$f^{-1}(x) = \dfrac{2x+3}{5x-2}$

Domain of $f =$

range of $f^{-1} =$ all real numbers except $\dfrac{2}{5}$.

Range of $f =$

domain of $f^{-1} =$ all real numbers except $\dfrac{2}{5}$.

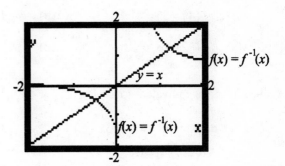

7. $f(x) = \dfrac{1}{x-1}$

$y = \dfrac{1}{x-1}$

$x = \dfrac{1}{y-1}$ Inverse

$x(y-1) = 1$

$xy - x = 1$

$xy = x + 1$

$y = \dfrac{x+1}{x}$

$f^{-1}(x) = \dfrac{x+1}{x}$

Domain of f =
range of f^{-1} = all real numbers except 1
Range of f =
domain of f^{-1} = all real numbers except 0

9. $f(x) = \dfrac{3}{x^{1/3}}$

$y = \dfrac{3}{x^{1/3}}$

$x = \dfrac{3}{y^{1/3}}$ Inverse

$xy^{1/3} = 3$

$y^{1/3} = \dfrac{3}{x}$

$y = \dfrac{27}{x^3}$

$f^{-1}(x) = \dfrac{27}{x^3}$

Domain of f =
range of f^{-1} = all real numbers except 0
Range of f =
domain of f^{-1} = all real numbers except 0

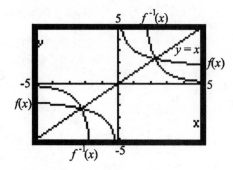

11.   (a) $f(4) = 3^4 = 81$ (b) $g(9) = \log_3(9) = \log_3(3^2) = 2$

(c) $f(-2) = 3^{-2} = \dfrac{1}{9}$ (d) $g\left(\dfrac{1}{27}\right) = \log_3\left(\dfrac{1}{27}\right) = \log_3(3^{-3}) = -3$

13. $5^2 = z$ is equivalent to $2 = \log_5 z$ 15. $\log_5 u = 13$ is equivalent to $5^{13} = u$

17.   The domain of $y = \log(3x-2)$ is:

$3x - 2 > 0 \Rightarrow x > \dfrac{2}{3}$

$\left\{ x \,\middle|\, x > \dfrac{2}{3} \right\}$

19.   The domain of $y = \log_2(x^2 - 3x + 2)$ is:

$x^2 - 3x + 2 > 0$

$(x-2)(x-1) > 0$

$x > 2$ or $x < 1$
$\{ x \mid x < 1 \text{ or } x > 2 \}$

21. $\log_2\left(\dfrac{1}{8}\right) = \log_2 2^{-3} = -3\log_2 2 = -3$

23. $\ln e^{\sqrt{2}} = \sqrt{2}$

25. $2^{\log_2 0.4} = 0.4$

27. $\log_3\left(\dfrac{uv^2}{w}\right) = \log_3 uv^2 - \log_3 w = \log_3 u + \log_3 v^2 - \log_3 w = \log_3 u + 2\log_3 v - \log_3 w$

29. $\log\left(x^2\sqrt{x^3+1}\right) = \log x^2 + \log\left(x^3+1\right)^{1/2} = 2\log x + \frac{1}{2}\log\left(x^3+1\right)$

31. $\ln\left(\dfrac{x\sqrt[3]{x^2+1}}{x-3}\right) = \ln\left(x\sqrt[3]{x^2+1}\right) - \ln(x-3) = \ln x + \ln\left(x^2+1\right)^{1/3} - \ln(x-3)$

$$= \ln x + \frac{1}{3}\ln\left(x^2+1\right) - \ln(x-3)$$

33. $3\log_4 x^2 + \dfrac{1}{2}\log_4\sqrt{x} = \log_4\left(x^2\right)^3 + \log_4\left(x^{1/2}\right)^{1/2} = \log_4 x^6 + \log_4 x^{1/4} = \log_4 x^6 \cdot x^{1/4}$

$$= \log_4 x^{25/4} = \frac{25}{4}\log_4 x$$

35. $\ln\left(\dfrac{x-1}{x}\right) + \ln\left(\dfrac{x}{x+1}\right) - \ln\left(x^2-1\right) = \ln\left(\dfrac{x-1}{x}\cdot\dfrac{x}{x+1}\right) - \ln\left(x^2-1\right) = \ln\left[\dfrac{\left|\dfrac{x-1}{x+1}\right|}{x^2-1}\right]$

$$= \ln\left(\dfrac{x-1}{x+1}\cdot\dfrac{1}{(x-1)(x+1)}\right) = \ln\dfrac{1}{(x+1)^2} = \ln(x+1)^{-2} = -2\ln(x+1)$$

37. $2\log 2 + 3\log x - \dfrac{1}{2}\left[\log(x+3) + \log(x-2)\right] = \log 2^2 + \log x^3 - \dfrac{1}{2}\log\left[(x+3)(x-2)\right]$

$$= \log 4x^3 - \log\left((x+3)(x-2)\right)^{1/2} = \log\left[\dfrac{4x^3}{\left((x+3)(x-2)\right)^{1/2}}\right]$$

39. $\log_4 19 = \dfrac{\log 19}{\log 4} \approx 2.124$

41. $y = \log_3(x) = \dfrac{\ln(x)}{\ln(3)}$

355

43. $f(x) = 2^{x-3}$
Using the graph of $y = 2^x$, shift the
graph 3 units to the right.
Domain: $(-\infty, \infty)$
Range: $(0, \infty)$
Horizontal Asymptote: $y = 0$

45. $f(x) = \dfrac{1}{2} \cdot 3^{-x}$
Using the graph of $y = 3^x$, reflect the
graph about the y-axis, and shrink
vertically by a factor of $\dfrac{1}{2}$.
Domain: $(-\infty, \infty)$
Range: $(0, \infty)$
Horizontal Asymptote: $y = 0$

47. $f(x) = 1 - e^x$
Using the graph of $y = e^x$, reflect about
the x-axis, and shift up 1 unit.
Domain: $(-\infty, \infty)$
Range: $(-\infty, 1)$
Horizontal Asymptote: $y = 1$

49. $f(x) = 3e^x$
Using the graph of $y = e^x$, stretch
vertically by a factor of 3.
Domain: $(-\infty, \infty)$
Range: $(0, \infty)$
Horizontal Asymptote: $y = 0$

51. $f(x) = 3 - e^{-x}$
Using the graph of $y = e^x$, reflect the
graph about the y-axis, reflect about the
x-axis, and shift up 3 units.
Domain: $(-\infty, \infty)$
Range: $(-\infty, 3)$
Horizontal Asymptote: $y = 3$

53. $4^{1-2x} = 2$

$\left(2^2\right)^{1-2x} = 2$

$2^{2-4x} = 2^1$

$2 - 4x = 1 \Rightarrow -4x = -1 \Rightarrow x = \dfrac{1}{4}$

55. $3^{x^2+x} = \sqrt{3}$

$3^{x^2+x} = 3^{1/2}$

$x^2 + x = \dfrac{1}{2} \Rightarrow 2x^2 + 2x - 1 = 0 \Rightarrow x = \dfrac{-2 \pm \sqrt{4 - 4(2)(-1)}}{2(2)} = \dfrac{-2 \pm \sqrt{12}}{4} = \dfrac{-2 \pm 2\sqrt{3}}{4} = \dfrac{-1 \pm \sqrt{3}}{2}$

$x = \dfrac{-1 - \sqrt{3}}{2}$ or $x = \dfrac{-1 + \sqrt{3}}{2}$

57. $\log_x 64 = -3$

$x^{-3} = 64$

$\left(x^{-3}\right)^{-1/3} = 64^{-1/3} \Rightarrow x = \dfrac{1}{\sqrt[3]{64}} = \dfrac{1}{4}$

59. $5^x = 3^{x+2}$

$\log\left(5^x\right) = \log\left(3^{x+2}\right)$

$x \log 5 = (x + 2)\log 3$

$x \log 5 = x \log 3 + 2 \log 3$

$x \log 5 - x \log 3 = 2 \log 3$

$x(\log 5 - \log 3) = 2 \log 3$

$x = \dfrac{2 \log 3}{\log 5 - \log 3}$

$x \approx 4.301$

61. $9^{2x} = 27^{3x-4}$

$\left(3^2\right)^{2x} = \left(3^3\right)^{3x-4}$

$3^{4x} = 3^{9x-12}$

$4x = 9x - 12 \Rightarrow -5x = -12$

$x = \dfrac{12}{5}$

63. $\log_3 \sqrt{x-2} = 2$

$\sqrt{x-2} = 3^2$

$x - 2 = 9^2 \Rightarrow x - 2 = 81 \Rightarrow x = 83$

65. $8 = 4^{x^2} \cdot 2^{5x}$

$2^3 = \left(2^2\right)^{x^2} \cdot 2^{5x}$

$2^3 = 2^{2x^2 + 5x}$

$3 = 2x^2 + 5x \Rightarrow 0 = 2x^2 + 5x - 3$

$0 = (2x - 1)(x + 3) \Rightarrow x = \dfrac{1}{2}$ or $x = -3$

67. $\log_6(x + 3) + \log_6(x + 4) = 1$

$\log_6(x + 3)(x + 4) = 1$

$(x + 3)(x + 4) = 6^1$

$x^2 + 7x + 12 = 6$

$x^2 + 7x + 6 = 0$

$(x + 6)(x + 1) = 0$

$x = -6$ or $x = -1$

The logarithms are undefined when
$x = -6$, so $x = -1$ is the only solution.

69. $e^{1-x} = 5$

$1 - x = \ln 5$

$-x = -1 + \ln 5$

$x = 1 - \ln 5 \approx -0.609$

71. $2^{3x} = 3^{2x+1}$

$\ln 2^{3x} = \ln 3^{2x+1}$

$3x \ln 2 = (2x + 1)\ln 3$

$3x \ln 2 = 2x \ln 3 + \ln 3$

$3x \ln 2 - 2x \ln 3 = \ln 3$

$x(3 \ln 2 - 2 \ln 3) = \ln 3$

$x = \dfrac{\ln 3}{3 \ln 2 - 2 \ln 3}$

$x \approx -9.327$

73. $h(300) = (30(0) + 8000)\log\left(\dfrac{760}{300}\right) \approx 8000\log(2.53333) \approx 3229.5$ meters

75. $P = 25e^{0.1d}$

     (a) $P = 25e^{0.1(4)}$

            $= 25e^{0.4} \approx 37.3$ watts

     (b) $50 = 25e^{0.1d}$

            $2 = e^{0.1d}$

            $\ln(2) = (0.1)d \Rightarrow d = \dfrac{\ln(2)}{0.1} \approx 6.9$ decibels

77.   (a) $n = \dfrac{\log(10000) - \log(90000)}{\log(1 - 0.20)} \approx 9.85$ years

     (b) $n = \dfrac{\log(0.5i) - \log(i)}{\log(1 - 0.15)} = \dfrac{\log\left(\dfrac{0.5i}{i}\right)}{\log(0.85)} = \dfrac{\log(0.5)}{\log(0.85)} \approx 4.27$ years

79. $P = A\left(1 + \dfrac{r}{n}\right)^{-nt} = 85000\left(1 + \dfrac{0.04}{2}\right)^{-2(18)} = \$41,668.97$

81. $A = A_0 e^{kt}$

         $0.5A_0 = A_0 e^{k(5600)}$

            $0.5 = e^{5600k} \Rightarrow \ln(0.5) = 5600k$

            $k = \dfrac{\ln(0.5)}{5600} \approx -0.000124$

$$0.05A_0 = A_0 e^{-0.000124\,t}$$

$$0.05 = e^{-0.000124\,t} \Rightarrow \ln(0.05) = -0.000124\,t \Rightarrow t = \frac{\ln(0.05)}{-0.000124} \approx 24{,}159 \text{ years ago}$$

83. $P = P_0 e^{kt} = 5{,}840{,}445{,}216 e^{0.0133\,(3)} \approx 6{,}078{,}190{,}457$

85.   (a) $P(0) = \dfrac{0.8}{1 + 1.67 e^{-0.16\,(0)}} = \dfrac{0.8}{1 + 1.67} = 0.2996$

       (b)   0.8

       (c)   Graphing:

       (d)   Using INTERSECT we have:

75% use Windows 98 in 2018.

87.   (a)   scatter diagram

       (b)   Using LnREGression on the data yields: $y = 44.1978 - 20.3314\ln(x)$

       (c)   graphing $y_1 = 44.1978 - 20.3314\ln(x)$

       (d)   if $x = 23,\ y = 44.1978 - 20.3314\ln(23) \approx -19.55^\circ F$.

Chapter 6

Exponential and Logarithmic Functions

6.CR   Cumulative Review

1. The graph represents a function since it passes the Vertical Line Test. The function is not a one-to-one function since the graph fails the Horizontal Line Test.

3. $x^2 + y^2 = 1$

   (a) $\left(\dfrac{1}{2}\right)^2 + \left(\dfrac{1}{2}\right)^2 = \dfrac{1}{4} + \dfrac{1}{4} = \dfrac{1}{2} \neq 1; \left(\dfrac{1}{2}, \dfrac{1}{2}\right)$ is not on the graph.

   (b) $\left(\dfrac{1}{2}\right)^2 + \left(\dfrac{\sqrt{3}}{2}\right)^2 = \dfrac{1}{4} + \dfrac{3}{4} = 1; \left(\dfrac{1}{2}, \dfrac{\sqrt{3}}{2}\right)$ is on the graph.

5. $2x - 4y = 16$

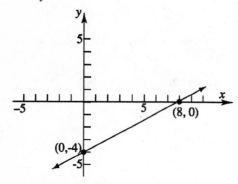

7. Given that the graph of $f(x) = ax^2 + bx + c$ has vertex $(4, -8)$ and passes through the point $(0, 24)$, we can conclude

$$\dfrac{-b}{2a} = 4, \qquad f(4) = -8, \quad \text{and} \qquad f(0) = 24$$

   Notice that $f(0) = 24 \Rightarrow a(0)^2 + b(0) + c = 24 \Rightarrow c = 24$

   Therefore $f(x) = ax^2 + bx + c = ax^2 + bx + 24$.

   Furthermore, $\dfrac{-b}{2a} = 4 \Rightarrow b = -8a$

   and $f(4) = -8 \Rightarrow a(4)^2 + b(4) + 24 = -8 \Rightarrow 16a + 4b + 24 = -8 \Rightarrow 16a + 4b = -32$

$$\Rightarrow 4a + b = -8$$

   Replacing b with $-8a$ in this equation yields

   $4a - 8a = -8 \Rightarrow -4a = -8 \Rightarrow a = 2$.

   So $b = -8a = -8(2) = -16$.

   Therefore, we have the function $f(x) = 2x^2 - 16x + 24$.

9. $f(x) = x^2 + 2$ $g(x) = \dfrac{2}{x-3}$

$$(f \circ g)(x) = f(g(x)) = f\left(\dfrac{2}{x-3}\right) = \left(\dfrac{2}{x-3}\right)^2 + 2 = \dfrac{4}{(x-3)^2} + 2$$

The domain of g is $\{x \mid x \neq 3\}$. The domain of f is {Real Numbers}

So the domain of $f \circ g$ is $\{x \mid x \neq 3\}$.

11.   (a) $g(x) = 3^x + 2$

Using the graph of $y = 3^x$, shift vertically
3 units up.
Domain: $(-\infty, \infty)$
Range: $(2, \infty)$
Horizontal Asymptote: $y = 2$

(b) $g(x) = 3^x + 2$

$y = 3^x + 2$

$x = 3^y + 2$ Inverse

$x - 2 = 3^y$

$\ln(x - 2) = \ln(3^y)$

$\ln(x - 2) = y \cdot \ln(3)$

$\dfrac{\ln(x - 2)}{\ln(3)} = y$

$g^{-1}(x) = \dfrac{\ln(x - 2)}{\ln(3)} = \log_3(x - 2)$

Domain: $(2, \infty)$
Range: $(-\infty, \infty)$
Vertical Asymptote: $x = 2$

(c)

13. $\log_3(x + 1) + \log_3(2x - 3) = 1$

$\log_3(x + 1)(2x - 3) = 1$

$(x + 1)(2x - 3) = 3^1$

$2x^2 - x - 3 = 3$

$2x^2 - x - 6 = 0$

$(2x + 3)(x - 2) = 0 \Rightarrow x = -\dfrac{3}{2}$ or $x = 2$

The logarithms are undefined when
$x = -\dfrac{3}{2}$, so $x = 2$ is the only solution.

Chapter 7

Systems of Equations and Inequalities

7.1 Systems of Linear Equations: Two Equations Containing Two Variables

1. Substituting the values of the variables:
$$\begin{cases} 2x - y = 5 \\ 5x + 2y = 8 \end{cases} \rightarrow \begin{array}{l} 2(2) - (-1) = 4 + 1 = 5 \\ 5(2) + 2(-1) = 10 - 2 = 8 \end{array}$$
Each equation is satisfied, so $x = 2$, $y = -1$ is a solution to the system of equations.

3. Substituting the values of the variables:
$$\begin{cases} 3x - 4y = 4 \quad \rightarrow \quad 3(2) - 4\left(\dfrac{1}{2}\right) = 6 - 2 = 4 \\ \dfrac{1}{2}x - 3y = -\dfrac{1}{2} \quad \rightarrow \quad \dfrac{1}{2}(2) - 3\left(\dfrac{1}{2}\right) = 1 - \dfrac{3}{2} = -\dfrac{1}{2} \end{cases}$$
Each equation is satisfied, so $x = 2$, $y = \dfrac{1}{2}$ is a solution to the system of equations.

5. Substituting the values of the variables:
$$\begin{cases} x - y = 3 \quad \rightarrow \quad 4 - 1 = 3 \\ \dfrac{1}{2}x + y = 3 \quad \rightarrow \quad \dfrac{1}{2}(4) + 1 = 2 + 1 = 3 \end{cases}$$
Each equation is satisfied, so $x = 4$, $y = 1$ is a solution to the system of equations.

7. Substituting the values of the variables:
$$\begin{cases} 3x + 3y + 2z = \quad 4 \rightarrow 3(1) + 3(-1) + 2(2) = 3 - 3 + 4 = 4 \\ x - y - \quad z = \quad 0 \rightarrow 1 - (-1) - 2 = 1 + 1 - 2 = 0 \\ 2y - 3z = -8 \rightarrow 2(-1) - 3(2) = -2 - 6 = -8 \end{cases}$$
Each equation is satisfied, so $x = 1$, $y = -1, z = 2$ is a solution to the system.

9. Solve the first equation for y, substitute into the second equation and solve:
$$\begin{cases} x + y = 8 \quad \rightarrow \quad y = 8 - x \\ x - y = 4 \end{cases}$$
$$x - (8 - x) = 4 \rightarrow x - 8 + x = 4$$
$$2x = 12 \rightarrow x = 6$$
Since $x = 6$, $y = 8 - 6 = 2$
The solution of the system is $x = 6$, $y = 2$.

11. Multiply each side of the first equation by 3 and add the equations:

$$\begin{cases} 5x - y = 13 \\ 2x + 3y = 12 \end{cases} \xrightarrow{\ 3\ } \begin{aligned} 15x - 3y &= 39 \\ 2x + 3y &= 12 \end{aligned}$$

$$\begin{aligned} 17x &= 51 \\ x &= 3 \end{aligned}$$

Substitute and solve for y:

$$5(3) - y = 13 \rightarrow 15 - y = 13 \rightarrow -y = -2 \rightarrow y = 2$$

The solution of the system is $x = 3, \ y = 2$.

13. Solve the first equation for x and substitute into the second equation:

$$\begin{cases} 3x = 24 \quad \rightarrow \quad x = 8 \\ x + 2y = 0 \end{cases}$$

$$8 + 2y = 0 \rightarrow 2y = -8 \rightarrow y = -4$$

The solution of the system is $x = 8, \ y = -4$.

15. Multiply each side of the first equation by 2 and each side of the second equation by 3 to eliminate y:

$$\begin{cases} 3x - 6y = 2 \\ 5x + 4y = 1 \end{cases} \begin{aligned} \xrightarrow{\ 2\ } \quad 6x - 12y &= 4 \\ \xrightarrow{\ 3\ } \quad 15x + 12y &= 3 \end{aligned}$$

$$21x = 7 \Rightarrow x = \frac{1}{3}$$

Substitute and solve for y:

$$3\left(\frac{1}{3}\right) - 6y = 2 \rightarrow 1 - 6y = 2 \rightarrow -6y = 1 \rightarrow y = -\frac{1}{6}$$

The solution of the system is $x = \frac{1}{3}, \ y = -\frac{1}{6}$.

17. Solve the first equation for y, substitute into the second equation and solve:

$$\begin{cases} 2x + y = 1 \quad \rightarrow \quad y = 1 - 2x \\ 4x + 2y = 3 \end{cases}$$

$$4x + 2(1 - 2x) = 3 \rightarrow 4x + 2 - 4x = 3 \rightarrow 0x = 1$$

This has no solution, so the system is inconsistent.

19. Solve the first equation for y, substitute into the second equation and solve:

$$\begin{cases} 2x - y = 0 \quad \rightarrow \quad 2x = y \\ 3x + 2y = 7 \end{cases}$$

$$3x + 2(2x) = 7 \rightarrow 3x + 4x = 7 \rightarrow 7x = 7 \rightarrow x = 1$$

Since $x = 1, \ y = 2(1) = 2$ The solution of the system is $x = 1, \ y = 2$.

21.   Solve the first equation for x, substitute into the second equation and solve:
$$\begin{cases} x + 2y = 4 \quad \rightarrow \quad x = 4 - 2y \\ 2x + 4y = 8 \end{cases}$$

$$2(4 - 2y) + 4y = 8 \rightarrow 8 - 4y + 4y = 8 \rightarrow 0y = 0$$
These equations are dependent. Any real number is a solution for y.
The solution of the system is $x = 4 - 2y$, where y is any real number.

23.   Multiply each side of the first equation by –5, and add the equations to eliminate x:
$$\begin{cases} 2x - 3y = -1 \quad \xrightarrow{-5} \quad -10x + 15y = 5 \\ 10x + y = 11 \quad \longrightarrow \quad \underline{10x + y = 11} \end{cases}$$
$$16y = 16$$
$$y = 1$$

Substitute and solve for x:

$$2x - 3(1) = -1 \rightarrow 2x - 3 = -1 \rightarrow 2x = 2 \rightarrow x = 1$$
The solution of the system is $x = 1$, $y = 1$.

25.   Solve the second equation for x, substitute into the first equation and solve:
$$\begin{cases} 2x + 3y = 6 \\ x - y = \dfrac{1}{2} \quad \rightarrow \quad x = y + \dfrac{1}{2} \end{cases}$$

$$2\left(y + \frac{1}{2}\right) + 3y = 6 \rightarrow 2y + 1 + 3y = 6 \rightarrow 5y = 5 \rightarrow y = 1$$
Since $y = 1$, $x = 1 + \dfrac{1}{2} = \dfrac{3}{2}$, the solution of the system is $x = \dfrac{3}{2}$, $y = 1$.

27.   Multiply each side of the first equation by –6 and each side of the second equation by 12 to eliminate x:
$$\begin{cases} \dfrac{1}{2}x + \dfrac{1}{3}y = 3 \quad \xrightarrow{-6} \quad -3x - 2y = -18 \\ \dfrac{1}{4}x - \dfrac{2}{3}y = -1 \quad \xrightarrow{12} \quad \underline{3x - 8y = -12} \end{cases}$$
$$-10y = -30$$
$$y = 3$$

Substitute and solve for x:
$$\frac{1}{2}x + \frac{1}{3}(3) = 3 \rightarrow \frac{1}{2}x + 1 = 3 \rightarrow \frac{1}{2}x = 2 \rightarrow x = 4$$
The solution of the system is $x = 4$, $y = 3$.

29. Add the equations to eliminate y and solve for x:

$$\begin{cases} 3x - 5y = 3 \\ 15x + 5y = 21 \end{cases}$$

$$\overline{18x \qquad = 24} \Rightarrow x = \frac{4}{3}$$

Substitute and solve for y: $3\left(\dfrac{4}{3}\right) - 5y = 3 \rightarrow 4 - 5y = 3 \rightarrow -5y = -1 \rightarrow y = \dfrac{1}{5}$

The solution of the system is $x = \dfrac{4}{3},\ y = \dfrac{1}{5}$.

31. Rewrite letting $a = \dfrac{1}{x},\ b = \dfrac{1}{y}$:

$$\begin{cases} \dfrac{1}{x} + \dfrac{1}{y} = 8 \\ \dfrac{3}{x} - \dfrac{5}{y} = 0 \end{cases} \longrightarrow \begin{array}{l} a + b = 8 \\ 3a - 5b = 0 \end{array}$$

Solve the first equation for a, substitute into the second equation and solve:

$$\begin{cases} a + b = 8 \quad \rightarrow \quad a = 8 - b \\ 3a - 5b = 0 \end{cases}$$

$$3(8 - b) - 5b = 0 \rightarrow 24 - 3b - 5b = 0 \rightarrow -8b = -24 \rightarrow b = 3$$

Since $b = 3,\ a = 8 - 3 = 5$

Thus, $x = \dfrac{1}{a} = \dfrac{1}{5},\ y = \dfrac{1}{b} = \dfrac{1}{3}$. The solution of the system is $x = \dfrac{1}{5},\ y = \dfrac{1}{3}$.

33. Graph the two equations as y_1 and y_2, and use INTERSECT to solve:

$$\begin{cases} y_1 = \sqrt{2}x - 20\sqrt{7} \\ y_2 = -0.1x + 20 \end{cases}$$

The solution of the system is $x = 48.15,\ y = 15.18$.

35. Solve for y in each equation, graph the two equations as y_1 and y_2, and use INTERSECT to solve:

$$\begin{cases} \sqrt{2}x + \sqrt{3}y + \sqrt{6} = 0 \\ \sqrt{3}x - \sqrt{2}y + 60 = 0 \end{cases}$$

$$\begin{cases} y_1 = \dfrac{-\sqrt{2}x - \sqrt{6}}{\sqrt{3}} \\ y_2 = \dfrac{\sqrt{3}x + 60}{\sqrt{2}} \end{cases}$$

The solution of the system is $x = -21.48,\ y = 16.12$.

37. Solve for y in each equation, graph the two equations as y_1 and y_2, and use INTERSECT to solve:

$$\begin{cases} \sqrt{3}x + \sqrt{2}y = \sqrt{0.3} \\ 100x - 95y = 20 \end{cases}$$

$$\begin{cases} y_1 = \dfrac{-\sqrt{3}x + \sqrt{0.3}}{\sqrt{2}} \\ y_2 = \dfrac{100x - 20}{95} \end{cases}$$

The solution of the system is $x = 0.26$, $y = 0.07$.

39. Solve the system by substitution:

$$Q_s = Q_d$$

$$-200 + 50p = 1000 - 25p \rightarrow 75p = 1200 \rightarrow p = 16$$

Therefore, $Q_s = -200 + 50(16) = -200 + 800 = 600$

The equilibrium price is \$16 and the equilibrium quantity is 600 T-shirts.

41. Let l be the length of the rectangle and w be the width of the rectangle. Then:

$$2l + 2w = 90$$

$$l = 2w$$

Solve by substitution:

$$2(2w) + 2w = 90 \Rightarrow 4w + 2w = 90 \Rightarrow 6w = 90 \Rightarrow w = 15 \text{ feet}$$

$$l = 2(15) = 30 \text{ feet}$$

The dimensions of the floor are 15 feet by 30 feet.

43. Let x = the cost of one cheeseburger and y = the cost of one shake. Then:

$$4x + 2y = 790$$

$$2y = x + 15$$

Solve by substitution:

$$4x + x + 15 = 790 \rightarrow 5x = 775 \rightarrow x = 155$$

$$2y = 155 + 15 \rightarrow 2y = 170 \rightarrow y = 85$$

A cheeseburger cost \$1.55 and a shake costs \$0.85.

45. Let x = the number of pounds of cashews.
Then $x + 30$ is the number of pounds in the mixture.
The value of the cashews is $5x$.
The value of the peanuts is $1.50(30) = 45$.
The value of the mixture is $3(x + 30)$.
Setting up a value equation:

$$5x + 45 = 3(x + 30)$$

$$5x + 45 = 3x + 90$$

$$2x = 45$$

$$x = 22.5$$

22.5 pounds of cashews should be used in the mixture.

47. Let x = the plane's air speed and y = the wind speed.

	Rate	Time	Distance
With Wind	$x + y$	3	600
Against	$x - y$	4	600

$(x + y)(3) = 600 \quad \rightarrow \quad x + y = 200$

$(x - y)(4) = 600 \quad \rightarrow \quad x - y = 150$

Solving by elimination:

$2x = 350$

$x = 175$

$y = 200 - x = 200 - 175 = 25$

The airspeed of the plane is 175 mph, and the wind speed is 25 mph.

49. Let x = the number of one design.

Let y = the number of the second design.

Then $x + y$ = the total number of sets of dishes.

$25x + 45y$ = the cost of the dishes.

Setting up the equations and solving by substitution:

$$\begin{cases} x + y = 200 \quad \rightarrow \quad y = 200 - x \\ 25x + 45y = 7400 \end{cases}$$

$25x + 45(200 - x) = 7400$

$25x + 9000 - 45x = 7400$

$-20x = -1600 \Rightarrow x = 80$

$y = 200 - 80 = 120$

80 sets of the $25 dishes and 120 sets of the $45 dishes should be ordered.

51. Let x = the cost per package of bacon.

Let y = the cost of a carton of eggs.

Set up a system of equations for the problem:

$$\begin{cases} 3x + 2y = 7.45 \\ 2x + 3y = 6.45 \end{cases}$$

Multiply each side of the first equation by 3 and each side of the second equation by –2 and solve by elimination:

$$\begin{cases} 3x + 2y = 7.45 \quad \xrightarrow{3} \quad 9x + 6y = 22.35 \\ 2x + 3y = 6.45 \quad \xrightarrow{-2} \quad -4x - 6y = -12.90 \end{cases}$$

$5x \qquad = \quad 9.45 \Rightarrow x = 1.89$

Substitute and solve for y:

$3(1.89) + 2y = 7.45$

$5.67 + 2y = 7.45 \Rightarrow 2y = 1.78 \Rightarrow y = 0.89$

A package of bacon costs $1.89 and a carton of eggs cost $0.89.

The refund for 2 packages of bacon and 2 cartons of eggs will be $5.56.

53.   Let x = the # of mg of liquid 1.
      Let y = the # of mg of liquid 2.
      Setting up the equations and solving by substitution:
$$\begin{cases} 0.2x + 0.4y = 40 & \text{vitamin C} \\ 0.3x + 0.2y = 30 & \text{vitamin D} \end{cases}$$
      multiplying each equation by 10 yields
$$\begin{cases} 2x + 4y = 400 \quad \longrightarrow \quad 2x + 4y = 400 \\ 3x + 2y = 300 \quad \xrightarrow{\;2\;} \quad 6x + 4y = 600 \end{cases}$$
      subtracting the bottom equation from the top equation yields
$$2x + 4y - (6x + 4y) = -200$$

$$2x - 6x = -200 \Rightarrow -4x = -200 \Rightarrow x = 50$$
$$\Rightarrow 2(50) + 4y = 400 \Rightarrow 100 + 4y = 400$$

$$\Rightarrow 4y = 300 \Rightarrow y = \frac{300}{4} = 75$$

So 50 mg of liquid 1 should be mixed with 75 mg of liquid 2.

55.   Solve the system by substitution:
$$R = C$$

$$8x = 4.5x + 17500 \rightarrow 3.5x = 17500 \rightarrow x = 5000$$
5000 units must be produced and sold for the firm to break-even.

57.   Answers will vary.

Systems of Equations and Inequalities

7.2 Systems of Linear Equations: Three Equations Containing Three Variables

1. Substituting the values of the variables:

$$\begin{cases} 3x + 3y + 2z = 4 & \longrightarrow \quad 3(1) + 3(-1) + 2(2) = 3 - 3 + 4 = 4 \\ x - y - z = 0 & \longrightarrow \quad 1 - (-1) - 2 = 1 + 1 - 2 = 0 \\ 2y - 3z = -8 & \longrightarrow \quad 2(-1) - 3(2) = -2 - 6 = -8 \end{cases}$$

Each equation is satisfied, so $x = 1$, $y = -1$, $z = 2$ is a solution to the system of equations.

3. Multiply each side of the first equation by –2 and add to the second equation to eliminate x:

$$\begin{cases} x - y = 6 & \xrightarrow{\ -2\ } \quad -2x + 2y \qquad\ \ = -12 \\ 2x - 3z = 16 & \longrightarrow \qquad 2x \qquad -3z = \ \ 16 \\ 2y + z = 4 \end{cases} \qquad \overline{\qquad\quad 2y - 3z = \quad 4}$$

Multiply each side of the result by –1 and add to the original third equation to eliminate y:

$$2y - 3z = 4 \quad \xrightarrow{\ -1\ } \quad -2y + 3z = -4$$
$$2y + z = 4 \quad \longrightarrow \quad \underline{\quad 2y + z = \ \ 4}$$
$$4z = \ \ 0$$
$$z = 0$$

Substituting and solving for the other variables:

$$\begin{array}{ll} 2y + 0 = 4 & 2x - 3(0) = 16 \\ 2y = 4 & 2x = 16 \\ y = 2 & x = 8 \end{array}$$

The solution is $x = 8$, $y = 2$, $z = 0$.

5. Multiply each side of the first equation by –2 and add to the second equation to eliminate x; and multiply each side of the first equation by 3 and add to the third equation to eliminate x:

$$\begin{cases} x - 2y + 3z = \ \ 7 & \xrightarrow{\ -2\ } \quad -2x + 4y - 6z = -14 \\ 2x + y + z = \ \ 4 & \longrightarrow \qquad \underline{2x + y + z = \quad 4} \\ -3x + 2y - 2z = -10 & \qquad\qquad\qquad 5y - 5z = -10 \quad \xrightarrow{\ 1/5\ } \quad y - z = -2 \\ & \xrightarrow{\ 3\ } \qquad 3x - 6y + 9z = \ \ 21 \\ & \longrightarrow \qquad \underline{-3x + 2y - 2z = -10} \\ & \qquad\qquad\quad -4y + 7z = \ \ 11 \end{cases}$$

Multiply each side of the first result by 4 and add to the second result to eliminate y:

$$y - z = -2 \xrightarrow{\ \ 4\ \ } 4y - 4z = -8$$

$$-4y + 7z = 11 \longrightarrow \ \underline{-4y + 7z = \ 11}$$

$$3z = \ \ 3 \rightarrow z = 1$$

Substituting and solving for the other variables:

$$y - 1 = -2$$
$$y = -1 \qquad\qquad x - 2(-1) + 3(1) = 7$$
$$x + 2 + 3 = 7 \rightarrow x = 2$$

The solution is $x = 2$, $y = -1$, $z = 1$.

7. Add the first and second equations to eliminate z:

$$\begin{cases} x - \ y - z = 1 \\ 2x + 3y + z = 2 \\ 3x + 2y \quad\ = 0 \end{cases} \begin{array}{l} \longrightarrow \\ \longrightarrow \end{array} \begin{array}{l} x - \ y - z = 1 \\ \underline{2x + 3y + z = 2} \\ 3x + 2y \quad\ = 3 \end{array}$$

Multiply each side of the result by –1 and add to the original third equation to eliminate y:

$$3x + 2y = 3 \xrightarrow{\ \ -1\ \ } -3x - 2y = -3$$
$$3x + 2y = 0 \longrightarrow \ \underline{3x + 2y = \ 0}$$
$$0 = -3$$

This result has no solution, so the system is inconsistent.

9. Add the first and second equations to eliminate x; and multiply the first equation by –3 and add to the third equation to eliminate x:

$$\begin{cases} x - \ y - \ z = \ 1 \\ -x + 2y - 3z = -4 \\ 3x - 2y - 7z = \ 0 \end{cases} \begin{array}{l} \longrightarrow \\ \longrightarrow \end{array} \begin{array}{l} x - \ y - \ z = \ 1 \\ \underline{-x + 2y - 3z = -4} \\ y - 4z = -3 \end{array}$$

$$\xrightarrow{\ \ -3\ \ } -3x + 3y + 3z = -3$$
$$\longrightarrow \ \underline{3x - 2y - 7z = \ 0}$$
$$y - 4z = -3$$

Multiply each side of the first result by –1 and add to the second result to eliminate y:

$$y - 4z = -3 \xrightarrow{\ \ -1\ \ } -y + 4z = \ 3$$
$$y - 4z = -3 \longrightarrow \ \underline{y - 4z = -3}$$
$$0 = 0$$

The system is dependent. If z is any real number, then $y = 4z - 3$.

Solving for x in terms of z in the first equation:

$$x - (4z - 3) - z = 1$$
$$x - 4z + 3 - z = 1$$
$$x - 5z + 3 = 1$$
$$x = 5z - 2$$

The solution is $x = 5z - 2$, $y = 4z - 3$, z is any real number.

11. Multiply the first equation by –2 and add to the second equation to eliminate x; and add the first and third equations to eliminate x:

$$\begin{cases} 2x - 2y + 3z = 6 \\ 4x - 3y + 2z = 0 \\ -2x + 3y - 7z = 1 \end{cases}$$

$$\xrightarrow{-2} \quad -4x + 4y - 6z = -12$$
$$\xrightarrow{} \quad \underline{4x - 3y + 2z = 0}$$
$$y - 4z = -12$$

$$\xrightarrow{} \quad 2x - 2y + 3z = 6$$
$$\xrightarrow{} \quad \underline{-2x + 3y - 7z = 1}$$
$$y - 4z = 7$$

Multiply each side of the first result by –1 and add to the second result to eliminate y:

$$y - 4z = -12 \quad \xrightarrow{-1} \quad -y + 4z = 12$$
$$y - 4z = 7 \quad \xrightarrow{} \quad \underline{y - 4z = 7}$$
$$0 = 19$$

This result has no solution, so the system is inconsistent.

13. Add the first and second equations to eliminate z; and multiply the second equation by 2 and add to the third equation to eliminate z:

$$\begin{cases} x + y - z = 6 \\ 3x - 2y + z = -5 \\ x + 3y - 2z = 14 \end{cases}$$

$$\xrightarrow{} \quad x + y - z = 6$$
$$\xrightarrow{} \quad \underline{3x - 2y + z = -5}$$
$$4x - y = 1$$

$$\xrightarrow{2} \quad 6x - 4y + 2z = -10$$
$$\xrightarrow{} \quad \underline{x + 3y - 2z = 14}$$
$$7x - y = 4$$

Multiply each side of the first result by –1 and add to the second result to eliminate y:

$$4x - y = 1 \quad \xrightarrow{-1} \quad -4x + y = -1$$
$$7x - y = 4 \quad \xrightarrow{} \quad \underline{7x - y = 4}$$
$$3x = 3$$
$$x = 1$$

Substituting and solving for the other variables:

$$\begin{array}{ll} 4(1) - y = 1 & 3(1) - 2(3) + z = -5 \\ -y = -3 & 3 - 6 + z = -5 \\ y = 3 & z = -2 \end{array}$$

The solution is $x = 1, \ y = 3, \ z = -2$.

15. Add the first and second equations to eliminate z; and multiply the second equation by 3 and add to the third equation to eliminate z:

$$\begin{cases} x + 2y - z = -3 \\ 2x - 4y + z = -7 \\ -2x + 2y - 3z = 4 \end{cases}$$

$$\xrightarrow{} \quad x + 2y - z = -3$$
$$\xrightarrow{} \quad \underline{2x - 4y + z = -7}$$
$$3x - 2y = -10$$

$$\xrightarrow{3} \quad 6x - 12y + 3z = -21$$
$$\longrightarrow \quad -2x + 2y - 3z = \quad 4$$
$$4x - 10y \quad\quad = -17$$

Multiply each side of the first result by –5 and add to the second result to eliminate y:

$$3x - 2y = -10 \quad \xrightarrow{-5} \quad -15x + 10y = \quad 50$$
$$4x - 10y = -17 \quad \longrightarrow \quad 4x - 10y = -17$$
$$-11x \quad\quad = \quad 33$$
$$x \quad\quad = \quad -3$$

Substituting and solving for the other variables:

$$3(-3) - 2y = -10 \qquad\qquad -3 + 2\left(\frac{1}{2}\right) - z = -3$$
$$-9 - 2y = -10 \qquad\qquad -3 + 1 - z = -3$$
$$-2y = -1 \qquad\qquad -z = -1$$
$$y = \frac{1}{2} \qquad\qquad z = 1$$

The solution is $x = -3$, $y = \dfrac{1}{2}$, $z = 1$.

17. $y = ax^2 + bx + c$

At (–1, 4) the equation becomes:
$$4 = a(-1)^2 + b(-1) + c$$
$$4 = a - b + c$$
$$a - b + c = 4$$

At (2, 3) the equation becomes:
$$3 = a(2)^2 + b(2) + c$$
$$3 = 4a + 2b + c$$
$$4a + 2b + c = 3$$

At (0, 1) the equation becomes:
$$1 = a(0)^2 + b(0) + c$$
$$c = 1$$

The system of equations is:
$$\begin{cases} a - b + c = 4 \\ 4a + 2b + c = 3 \\ c = 1 \end{cases}$$

Substitute $c = 1$ into the first and second equations and simplify:
$$\begin{cases} a - b + 1 = 4 \quad \rightarrow \quad a - b = 3 \quad \rightarrow \quad a = b + 3 \\ 4a + 2b + 1 = 3 \quad \rightarrow \quad 4a + 2b = 2 \end{cases}$$

Solve the first equation for a, substitute into the second equation and solve:

$4(b+3)+2b=2$

$4b+12+2b=2$

$$6b=-10 \rightarrow b=-\frac{5}{3}$$

$$a=-\frac{5}{3}+3=\frac{4}{3}$$

The solution is $a=\frac{4}{3}$, $b=-\frac{5}{3}$, $c=1$. So the equation is $y=\frac{4}{3}x^2-\frac{5}{3}x+1$.

19. Substitute the expression for I_2 into the second and third equations and simplify:

$$\begin{cases} I_2 = I_1 + I_3 \\ 5-3I_1-5I_2=0 \\ 10-5I_2-7I_3=0 \end{cases} \quad \begin{array}{l} \\ \rightarrow \quad 5-3I_1-5(I_1+I_3)=0 \quad \rightarrow \quad -8I_1-5I_3=-5 \\ \rightarrow \quad 10-5(I_1+I_3)-7I_3=0 \quad \rightarrow \quad -5I_1-12I_3=-10 \end{array}$$

Multiply both sides of the second equation by 5 and multiply both sides of the third equation by –8 to eliminate I_1:

$$\begin{array}{rl} -8I_1 - 5I_3 = -5 & \xrightarrow{5} \quad -40I_1-25I_3=-25 \\ -5I_1-12I_3=-10 & \xrightarrow{-8} \quad \underline{40I_1+96I_3=80} \\ & 71I_3 = 55 \\ & I_3 = \frac{55}{71} \end{array}$$

Substituting and solving for the other variables:

$$-8I_1-5\left(\frac{55}{71}\right)=-5 \qquad\qquad I_2=\frac{10}{71}+\frac{55}{71}$$

$$-8I_1-\frac{275}{71}=-5 \qquad\qquad\quad I_2=\frac{65}{71}$$

$$-8I_1=-\frac{80}{71}$$

$$I_1=\frac{10}{71}$$

The solution is $I_1=\frac{10}{71}$, $I_2=\frac{65}{71}$, $I_3=\frac{55}{71}$.

21. Let $x =$ the number of orchestra seats.
Let $y =$ the number of main seats.
Let $z =$ the number of balcony seats.
Since the total number of seats is 500, $x+y+z=500$.
Since the total revenue is $17,100 if all seats are sold, $50x+35y+25z=17,100$.
If only half of the orchestra seats are sold, the revenue is $14,600. So,

$$50\left(\frac{1}{2}x\right)+35y+25z=14,600 \, .$$

Multiply each side of the first equation by –25 and add to the second equation to eliminate z; and multiply each side of the third equation by –1 and add to the second equation to eliminate z:

$$\begin{cases} x + y + z = 500 \\ 50x + 35y + 25z = 17100 \\ 25x + 35y + 25z = 14600 \end{cases} \xrightarrow{-25} \begin{array}{r} -25x - 25y - 25z = -12500 \\ 50x + 35y + 25z = 17100 \\ \hline 25x + 10y \qquad = 4600 \end{array}$$

$$\xrightarrow{} \begin{array}{r} 50x + 35y + 25z = 17100 \\ \xrightarrow{-1} \quad -25x - 35y - 25z = -14600 \\ \hline 25x \qquad\qquad = 2500 \\ x = 100 \end{array}$$

Substituting and solving for the other variables:

$$\begin{array}{ll} 25(100) + 10y = 4600 & 100 + 210 + z = 500 \\ 2500 + 10y = 4600 & 310 + z = 500 \\ 10y = 2100 & z = 190 \\ y = 210 & \end{array}$$

There are 100 orchestra seats, 210 main seats, and 190 balcony seats.

23. Let x = the number of servings of chicken.
Let y = the number of servings of corn.
Let z = the number of servings of 2% milk.
Protein equation: $30x + 3y + 9z = 66$
Carbohydrate equation: $35x + 16y + 13z = 94.5$
Calcium equation: $200x + 10y + 300z = 910$
Multiply each side of the first equation by –16 and multiply each side of the second equation by 3 and add them to eliminate y; and multiply each side of the second equation by –5 and multiply each side of the third equation by 8 and add to eliminate y:

$$\begin{cases} 30x + 3y + 9z = 66 \\ 35x + 16y + 13z = 94.5 \\ 200x + 10y + 300z = 910 \end{cases} \begin{array}{r} \xrightarrow{-16} \quad -480x - 48y - 144z = -1056 \\ \xrightarrow{3} \quad 105x + 48y + 39z = 283.5 \\ \hline -375x \qquad -105z = -772.5 \end{array}$$

$$\begin{array}{r} \xrightarrow{-5} \quad -175x - 80y - 65z = -472.5 \\ \xrightarrow{8} \quad 1600x + 80y + 2400z = 7280 \\ \hline 1425x \qquad + 2335z = 6807.5 \end{array}$$

Multiply each side of the first result by 19 and multiply each side of the second result by 5 to eliminate x:

$$\begin{array}{r} -375x - 105z = -772.5 \quad \xrightarrow{19} \quad -7125x - 1995z = -14677.5 \\ 1425x + 2335z = 6807.5 \quad \xrightarrow{5} \quad 7125x + 11675z = 34037.5 \\ \hline 9680z = 19360 \\ z = 2 \end{array}$$

Substituting and solving for the other variables:

$$\begin{array}{ll} -375x - 105(2) = -772.5 & 30(1.5) + 3y + 9(2) = 66 \\ -375x - 210 = -772.5 & 45 + 3y + 18 = 66 \\ -375x = -562.5 & 3y = 3 \\ x = 1.5 & y = 1 \end{array}$$

The dietitian should serve 1.5 servings of chicken, 1 serving of corn, and 2 servings of 2% milk.

25. Let x = the price of 1 hamburger.
Let y = the price of 1 order of fries.
Let z = the price of 1 drink.
We can construct the system

$$\begin{cases} 8x + 6y + 6z = 26.10 \\ 10x + 6y + 8z = 31.60 \end{cases}$$

A system involving only 2 equations that contain 3 or more unknowns cannot be solved uniquely. In other words, we can create as many solutions as we want by choosing a specific value for one of the variables and then solving the resulting 2 x 2 system.

For example, suppose we know that

$$\$1.75 < \text{hamburger price} < \$2.25$$

$$\$0.75 < \text{fries price} < \$1.00$$

$$\$0.60 < \text{fries price} < \$0.90$$

Pick a specific value for x, y or z	2x2 system	Solution
$x = \$2.00$	$\begin{cases} 8(2) + 6y + 6z = 26.10 \\ 10(2) + 6y + 8z = 31.60 \end{cases}$	$x = \$2.00$
	$\Downarrow$	$y = \$0.93$
	$\begin{cases} 16 + 6y + 6z = 26.10 \\ 20 + 6y + 8z = 31.60 \end{cases}$	$z = \$0.75$
	$\Downarrow$	
	$\begin{cases} 6y + 6z = 10.10 \\ 6y + 8z = 11.60 \end{cases}$	
$y = \$0.90$	$\begin{cases} 8x + 6(0.9) + 6z = 26.10 \\ 10x + 6(0.9) + 8z = 31.60 \end{cases}$	$x = \$2.00$
	$\Downarrow$	$y = \$0.90$
	$\begin{cases} 8x + 5.4 + 6z = 26.10 \\ 10x + 5.4 + 8z = 31.60 \end{cases}$	$z = \$0.65$
	$\Downarrow$	
	$\begin{cases} 8x + 6z = 20.7 \\ 10x + 8z = 26.2 \end{cases}$	

$z = \$0.80$

$$\begin{cases} 8x + 6y + 6(.8) = 26.10 \\ 10x + 6y + 8(.8) = 31.60 \end{cases}$$

$x = \$1.95$

$\Downarrow$

$y = \$0.95$

$$\begin{cases} 8x + 6y + 4.8 = 26.10 \\ 10x + 6y + 6.4 = 31.60 \end{cases}$$

$z = \$0.80$

$\Downarrow$

$$\begin{cases} 8x + 6y = 21.3 \\ 10x + 6y = 25.2 \end{cases}$$

27. Let x = Beth's time working alone.
Let y = Bill's time working alone.
Let z = Edie's time working alone.
We can use the following tables to organize our work:

	Beth	Bill	Edie	Together
Hours to do job	x	y	z	10
Part of job done in 1 hour	$\dfrac{1}{x}$	$\dfrac{1}{y}$	$\dfrac{1}{z}$	$\dfrac{1}{10}$

Equation: $\dfrac{1}{x} + \dfrac{1}{y} + \dfrac{1}{z} = \dfrac{1}{10}$

	Bill	Edie	Together
Hours to do job	y	z	15
Part of job done in 1 hour	$\dfrac{1}{y}$	$\dfrac{1}{z}$	$\dfrac{1}{15}$

Equation: $\dfrac{1}{y} + \dfrac{1}{z} = \dfrac{1}{15}$

	Beth	Bill	Edie	All three	Beth and Bill
Hours to do job	x	y	z	4	8
Part of job done in 1 hour	$\dfrac{1}{x}$	$\dfrac{1}{y}$	$\dfrac{1}{z}$	$\dfrac{1}{4}$	$\dfrac{1}{8}$

Equation: $4\left(\dfrac{1}{x} + \dfrac{1}{y} + \dfrac{1}{z}\right) + 8\left(\dfrac{1}{x} + \dfrac{1}{y}\right) = 1 \rightarrow \dfrac{12}{x} + \dfrac{12}{y} + \dfrac{4}{z} = 1$

We can construct the system

$$\begin{cases} \dfrac{1}{x}+\dfrac{1}{y}+\dfrac{1}{z}=\dfrac{1}{10} \\[2mm] \dfrac{1}{y}+\dfrac{1}{z}=\dfrac{1}{15} \\[2mm] \dfrac{12}{x}+\dfrac{12}{y}+\dfrac{4}{z}=1 \end{cases} \longrightarrow$$

subtracting the second equation from
the first equation yields

$$\dfrac{1}{x}+\dfrac{1}{y}+\dfrac{1}{z}=\dfrac{1}{10}$$

$$\dfrac{1}{y}+\dfrac{1}{z}=\dfrac{1}{15}$$

$$\dfrac{1}{x}=\dfrac{1}{10}-\dfrac{1}{15} \qquad \rightarrow \dfrac{1}{x}=\dfrac{1}{30} \rightarrow x=30$$

Plugging $x = 30$ into the original system yields

$$\dfrac{1}{30}+\dfrac{1}{y}+\dfrac{1}{z}=\dfrac{1}{10} \longrightarrow \dfrac{1}{y}+\dfrac{1}{z}=\dfrac{1}{10}-\dfrac{1}{30} \longrightarrow \dfrac{1}{y}+\dfrac{1}{z}=\dfrac{1}{15}$$

$$\begin{cases} \dfrac{1}{y}+\dfrac{1}{z}=\dfrac{1}{15} \\[2mm] \dfrac{12}{30}+\dfrac{12}{y}+\dfrac{4}{z}=1 \longrightarrow \dfrac{12}{y}+\dfrac{4}{z}=1-\dfrac{12}{30} \longrightarrow \dfrac{12}{y}+\dfrac{4}{z}=\dfrac{3}{5} \end{cases}$$

Now consider the system

$$\begin{cases} \dfrac{1}{y}+\dfrac{1}{z}=\dfrac{1}{15} \xrightarrow{-12} \dfrac{-12}{y}+\dfrac{-12}{z}=\dfrac{-12}{15} \\[2mm] \dfrac{12}{y}+\dfrac{4}{z}=\dfrac{3}{5} \longrightarrow \dfrac{12}{y}+\dfrac{4}{z}=\dfrac{3}{5} \end{cases}$$

adding these 2 equations yields

$$\dfrac{-12}{y}+\dfrac{-12}{z}=\dfrac{-12}{15}$$

$$\dfrac{12}{y}+\dfrac{4}{z}=\dfrac{3}{5}$$

$$\overline{\dfrac{-12}{z}+\dfrac{4}{z}=\dfrac{-12}{15}+\dfrac{3}{5}} \qquad \rightarrow \dfrac{-8}{z}=\dfrac{-3}{15} \rightarrow \dfrac{8}{z}=\dfrac{1}{5} \rightarrow z=40$$

plugging $z = 40$ into the equation

$$\dfrac{12}{y}+\dfrac{4}{z}=\dfrac{3}{5} \Rightarrow \dfrac{12}{y}+\dfrac{4}{40}=\dfrac{3}{5}$$

$$\dfrac{12}{y}+\dfrac{1}{10}=\dfrac{3}{5} \Rightarrow \dfrac{12}{y}=\dfrac{3}{5}-\dfrac{1}{10} \Rightarrow \dfrac{12}{y}=\dfrac{1}{2} \Rightarrow y=24$$

So, working alone, it would take Beth 30 hours, Bill 24 hours and Edie 40 hours to finish
the job.

Chapter 7

Systems of Equations and Inequalities

7.3 Systems of Linear Equations: Matrices

1. Writing the augmented matrix for the system of equations:
$$\begin{cases} x - 5y = 5 \\ 4x + 3y = 6 \end{cases} \rightarrow \begin{bmatrix} 1 & -5 & | & 5 \\ 4 & 3 & | & 6 \end{bmatrix}$$

3. Writing the augmented matrix for the system of equations:
$$\begin{cases} 2x + 3y - 6 = 0 \\ 4x - 6y + 2 = 0 \end{cases} \rightarrow \begin{cases} 2x + 3y = 6 \\ 4x - 6y = -2 \end{cases} \rightarrow \begin{bmatrix} 2 & 3 & | & 6 \\ 4 & -6 & | & -2 \end{bmatrix}$$

5. Writing the augmented matrix for the system of equations:
$$\begin{cases} 0.01x - 0.03y = 0.06 \\ 0.13x + 0.10y = 0.20 \end{cases} \rightarrow \begin{bmatrix} 0.01 & -0.03 & | & 0.06 \\ 0.13 & 0.10 & | & 0.20 \end{bmatrix}$$

7. Writing the augmented matrix for the system of equations:
$$\begin{cases} x - y + z = 10 \\ 3x + 3y = 5 \\ x + y + 2z = 2 \end{cases} \rightarrow \begin{bmatrix} 1 & -1 & 1 & | & 10 \\ 3 & 3 & 0 & | & 5 \\ 1 & 1 & 2 & | & 2 \end{bmatrix}$$

9. Writing the augmented matrix for the system of equations:
$$\begin{cases} x + y - z = 2 \\ 3x - 2y = 2 \\ 5x + 3y - z = 1 \end{cases} \rightarrow \begin{bmatrix} 1 & 1 & -1 & | & 2 \\ 3 & -2 & 0 & | & 2 \\ 5 & 3 & -1 & | & 1 \end{bmatrix}$$

11. Writing the augmented matrix for the system of equations:
$$\begin{cases} x - y - z = 10 \\ 2x + y + 2z = -1 \\ -3x + 4y = 5 \\ 4x - 5y + z = 0 \end{cases} \rightarrow \begin{bmatrix} 1 & -1 & -1 & | & 10 \\ 2 & 1 & 2 & | & -1 \\ -3 & 4 & 0 & | & 5 \\ 4 & -5 & 1 & | & 0 \end{bmatrix}$$

13. $\begin{bmatrix} 1 & -3 & | & -2 \\ 2 & -5 & | & 5 \end{bmatrix} \rightarrow \begin{bmatrix} 1 & -3 & | & -2 \\ 0 & 1 & | & 9 \end{bmatrix}$

$$R_2 = -2r_1 + r_2$$

15. $\begin{vmatrix} 1 & -3 & 4 & 3 \\ 2 & -5 & 6 & 6 \\ -3 & 3 & 4 & 6 \end{vmatrix} \rightarrow \begin{vmatrix} 1 & -3 & 4 & 3 \\ 0 & 1 & -2 & 0 \\ -3 & 3 & 4 & 6 \end{vmatrix} \rightarrow \begin{vmatrix} 1 & -3 & 4 & 3 \\ 0 & 1 & -2 & 0 \\ 0 & -6 & 16 & 15 \end{vmatrix}$

   (a) $R_2 = -2r_1 + r_2$ (b) $R_3 = 3r_1 + r_3$

17. $\begin{vmatrix} 1 & -3 & 2 & -6 \\ 2 & -5 & 3 & -4 \\ -3 & -6 & 4 & 6 \end{vmatrix} \rightarrow \begin{vmatrix} 1 & -3 & 2 & -6 \\ 0 & 1 & -1 & 8 \\ -3 & -6 & 4 & 6 \end{vmatrix} \rightarrow \begin{vmatrix} 1 & -3 & 2 & -6 \\ 0 & 1 & -1 & 8 \\ 0 & -15 & 10 & -12 \end{vmatrix}$

   (a) $R_2 = -2r_1 + r_2$ (b) $R_3 = 3r_1 + r_3$

19. $\begin{vmatrix} 1 & -3 & 1 & -2 \\ 2 & -5 & 6 & -2 \\ -3 & 1 & 4 & 6 \end{vmatrix} \rightarrow \begin{vmatrix} 1 & -3 & 1 & -2 \\ 0 & 1 & 4 & 2 \\ -3 & 1 & 4 & 6 \end{vmatrix} \rightarrow \begin{vmatrix} 1 & -3 & 1 & -2 \\ 0 & 1 & 4 & 2 \\ 0 & -8 & 7 & 0 \end{vmatrix}$

   (a) $R_2 = -2r_1 + r_2$ (b) $R_3 = 3r_1 + r_3$

21. $\begin{cases} x = 5 \\ y = -1 \end{cases}$ consistent $x = 5$, $y = -1$

23. $\begin{cases} x = 1 \\ y = 2 \\ 0 = 3 \end{cases}$ inconsistent

25. $\begin{cases} x + 2z = -1 \\ y - 4z = -2 \\ \quad\ 0 = 0 \end{cases}$ consistent $x = -1 - 2z$, $y = -2 + 4z$, z is any real number

27.

   $\begin{cases} \quad\ x_1 = 1 \\ x_2 + x_4 = 2 \\ x_3 + 2x_4 = 3 \end{cases}$ consistent $x_1 = 1, x_2 = 2 - x_4, x_3 = 3 - 2x_4, x_4$ is any real number

29.

   $\begin{cases} \quad\ x_1 + 4x_4 = 2 \\ x_2 + + x_3 + 3x_4 = 3 \\ \quad\quad\ 0 = 0 \end{cases}$ consistent $x_1 = 2 - 4x_4, x_2 = 3 - x_3 - 3x_4,$
   x_3, x_4 are any real numbers

31.

$$\begin{cases} x_1 + x_4 = -2 \\ x_2 + 2x_4 = 2 \\ x_3 - x_4 = 0 \\ \quad\quad 0 = 0 \end{cases}$$

consistent $x_1 = -2 - x_4, x_2 = 2 - 2x_4, x_3 = x_4,$

x_4 is any real number

33. $\begin{cases} x + y = 8 \\ x - y = 4 \end{cases}$ can be written as: $\begin{bmatrix} 1 & 1 & | & 8 \\ 1 & -1 & | & 4 \end{bmatrix}$

$\rightarrow \begin{bmatrix} 1 & 1 & | & 8 \\ 0 & -2 & | & -4 \end{bmatrix} \rightarrow \begin{bmatrix} 1 & 1 & | & 8 \\ 0 & 1 & | & 2 \end{bmatrix} \rightarrow \begin{bmatrix} 1 & 0 & | & 6 \\ 0 & 1 & | & 2 \end{bmatrix}$

$R_2 = -r_1 + r_2 \quad R_2 = -\tfrac{1}{2}r_2 \quad R_1 = -r_2 + r_1$

The solution is $x = 6, y = 2$.

35. $\begin{cases} 2x - 4y = -2 \\ 3x + 2y = 3 \end{cases}$ can be written as: $\begin{bmatrix} 2 & -4 & | & -2 \\ 3 & 2 & | & 3 \end{bmatrix}$

$\rightarrow \begin{bmatrix} 1 & -2 & | & -1 \\ 3 & 2 & | & 3 \end{bmatrix} \rightarrow \begin{bmatrix} 1 & -2 & | & -1 \\ 0 & 8 & | & 6 \end{bmatrix} \rightarrow \begin{bmatrix} 1 & -2 & | & -1 \\ 0 & 1 & | & \tfrac{3}{4} \end{bmatrix} \rightarrow \begin{bmatrix} 1 & 0 & | & \tfrac{1}{2} \\ 0 & 1 & | & \tfrac{3}{4} \end{bmatrix}$

$R_1 = \tfrac{1}{2}r_1 \quad R_2 = -3r_1 + r_2 \quad R_2 = \tfrac{1}{8}r_2 \quad R_1 = 2r_2 + r_1$

The solution is $x = \dfrac{1}{2}, y = \dfrac{3}{4}$.

37. $\begin{cases} x + 2y = 4 \\ 2x + 4y = 8 \end{cases}$ can be written as: $\begin{bmatrix} 1 & 2 & | & 4 \\ 2 & 4 & | & 8 \end{bmatrix}$

$\rightarrow \begin{bmatrix} 1 & 2 & | & 4 \\ 0 & 0 & | & 0 \end{bmatrix}$

$R_2 = -2r_1 + r_2$

This is a dependent system and the solution is $x = -2y + 4$, y is any real number.

39. $\begin{cases} 2x + 3y = 6 \\ x - y = \dfrac{1}{2} \end{cases}$ can be written as: $\begin{bmatrix} 2 & 3 & | & 6 \\ 1 & -1 & | & \tfrac{1}{2} \end{bmatrix}$

$\rightarrow \begin{bmatrix} 1 & \tfrac{3}{2} & | & 3 \\ 1 & -1 & | & \tfrac{1}{2} \end{bmatrix} \rightarrow \begin{bmatrix} 1 & \tfrac{3}{2} & | & 3 \\ 0 & -\tfrac{5}{2} & | & -\tfrac{5}{2} \end{bmatrix} \rightarrow \begin{bmatrix} 1 & \tfrac{3}{2} & | & 3 \\ 0 & 1 & | & 1 \end{bmatrix} \rightarrow \begin{bmatrix} 1 & 0 & | & \tfrac{3}{2} \\ 0 & 1 & | & 1 \end{bmatrix}$

$R_1 = \tfrac{1}{2}r_1 \quad R_2 = -r_1 + r_2 \quad R_2 = -\tfrac{2}{5}r_2 \quad R_1 = -\tfrac{3}{2}r_2 + r_1$

The solution is $x = \dfrac{3}{2}, y = 1$.

41. $\begin{cases} 3x - 5y = 3 \\ 15x + 5y = 21 \end{cases}$ can be written as: $\begin{bmatrix} 3 & -5 & | & 3 \\ 15 & 5 & | & 21 \end{bmatrix}$

$$\rightarrow \begin{bmatrix} 1 & -\frac{5}{3} & | & 1 \\ 15 & 5 & | & 21 \end{bmatrix} \rightarrow \begin{bmatrix} 1 & -\frac{5}{3} & | & 1 \\ 0 & 30 & | & 6 \end{bmatrix} \rightarrow \begin{bmatrix} 1 & -\frac{5}{3} & | & 1 \\ 0 & 1 & | & \frac{1}{5} \end{bmatrix} \rightarrow \begin{bmatrix} 1 & 0 & | & \frac{4}{3} \\ 0 & 1 & | & \frac{1}{5} \end{bmatrix}$$

$R_1 = \frac{1}{3} r_1$ $R_2 = -15 r_1 + r_2$ $R_2 = \frac{1}{30} r_2$ $R_1 = \frac{5}{3} r_2 + r_1$

The solution is $x = \dfrac{4}{3}, y = \dfrac{1}{5}$.

43. $\begin{cases} x - y = 6 \\ 2x - 3z = 16 \\ 2y + z = 4 \end{cases}$ can be written as: $\begin{bmatrix} 1 & -1 & 0 & | & 6 \\ 2 & 0 & -3 & | & 16 \\ 0 & 2 & 1 & | & 4 \end{bmatrix}$

$$\rightarrow \begin{bmatrix} 1 & -1 & 0 & | & 6 \\ 0 & 2 & -3 & | & 4 \\ 0 & 2 & 1 & | & 4 \end{bmatrix} \rightarrow \begin{bmatrix} 1 & -1 & 0 & | & 6 \\ 0 & 1 & -\frac{3}{2} & | & 2 \\ 0 & 2 & 1 & | & 4 \end{bmatrix} \rightarrow \begin{bmatrix} 1 & 0 & -\frac{3}{2} & | & 8 \\ 0 & 1 & -\frac{3}{2} & | & 2 \\ 0 & 0 & 4 & | & 0 \end{bmatrix} \rightarrow \begin{bmatrix} 1 & 0 & -\frac{3}{2} & | & 8 \\ 0 & 1 & -\frac{3}{2} & | & 2 \\ 0 & 0 & 1 & | & 0 \end{bmatrix}$$

$R_2 = -2 r_1 + r_2$ $R_2 = \frac{1}{2} r_2$ $R_1 = r_2 + r_1$ $R_3 = \frac{1}{4} r_3$

$R_3 = -2 r_2 + r_3$

$$\rightarrow \begin{vmatrix} 1 & 0 & 0 & | & 8 \\ 0 & 1 & 0 & | & 2 \\ 0 & 0 & 1 & | & 0 \end{vmatrix}$$

$R_1 = \frac{3}{2} r_3 + r_1$

$R_2 = \frac{3}{2} r_3 + r_2$

The solution is $x = 8, y = 2, z = 0$.

45. $\begin{cases} x - 2y + 3z = 7 \\ 2x + y + z = 4 \\ -3x + 2y - 2z = -10 \end{cases}$ can be written as: $\begin{bmatrix} 1 & -2 & 3 & | & 7 \\ 2 & 1 & 1 & | & 4 \\ -3 & 2 & -2 & | & -10 \end{bmatrix}$

$$\rightarrow \begin{bmatrix} 1 & -2 & 3 & | & 7 \\ 0 & 5 & -5 & | & -10 \\ 0 & -4 & 7 & | & 11 \end{bmatrix} \rightarrow \begin{bmatrix} 1 & -2 & 3 & | & 7 \\ 0 & 1 & -1 & | & -2 \\ 0 & -4 & 7 & | & 11 \end{bmatrix} \rightarrow \begin{bmatrix} 1 & 0 & 1 & | & 3 \\ 0 & 1 & -1 & | & -2 \\ 0 & 0 & 3 & | & 3 \end{bmatrix}$$

$R_2 = -2 r_1 + r_2$ $R_2 = \frac{1}{5} r_2$ $R_1 = 2 r_2 + r_1$

$R_3 = 3 r_1 + r_3$ $R_3 = 4 r_2 + r_3$

$$\rightarrow \begin{bmatrix} 1 & 0 & 1 & | & 3 \\ 0 & 1 & -1 & | & -2 \\ 0 & 0 & 1 & | & 1 \end{bmatrix} \rightarrow \begin{bmatrix} 1 & 0 & 0 & | & 2 \\ 0 & 1 & 0 & | & -1 \\ 0 & 0 & 1 & | & 1 \end{bmatrix}$$

$R_3 = \frac{1}{3} r_3$ $R_1 = -r_3 + r_1$

$R_2 = r_3 + r_2$

The solution is $x = 2, y = -1, z = 1$.

47. $\begin{cases} 2x - 2y - 2z = 2 \\ 2x + 3y + z = 2 \\ 3x + 2y = 0 \end{cases}$ can be written as: $\begin{bmatrix} 2 & -2 & -2 & | & 2 \\ 2 & 3 & 1 & | & 2 \\ 3 & 2 & 0 & | & 0 \end{bmatrix}$

$\rightarrow \begin{bmatrix} 1 & -1 & -1 & | & 1 \\ 2 & 3 & 1 & | & 2 \\ 3 & 2 & 0 & | & 0 \end{bmatrix} \rightarrow \begin{bmatrix} 1 & -1 & -1 & | & 1 \\ 0 & 5 & 3 & | & 0 \\ 0 & 5 & 3 & | & -3 \end{bmatrix} \rightarrow \begin{bmatrix} 1 & -1 & -1 & | & 1 \\ 0 & 5 & 3 & | & 0 \\ 0 & 0 & 0 & | & -3 \end{bmatrix}$

$R_1 = \frac{1}{2} r_1$ $R_2 = -2r_1 + r_2$ $R_3 = -r_2 + r_3$

                         $R_3 = -3r_1 + r_3$

There is no solution. The system is inconsistent.

49. $\begin{cases} -x + y + z = -1 \\ -x + 2y - 3z = -4 \\ 3x - 2y - 7z = 0 \end{cases}$ can be written as: $\begin{bmatrix} -1 & 1 & 1 & | & -1 \\ -1 & 2 & -3 & | & -4 \\ 3 & -2 & -7 & | & 0 \end{bmatrix}$

$\rightarrow \begin{bmatrix} 1 & -1 & -1 & | & 1 \\ -1 & 2 & -3 & | & -4 \\ 3 & -2 & -7 & | & 0 \end{bmatrix} \rightarrow \begin{bmatrix} 1 & -1 & -1 & | & 1 \\ 0 & 1 & -4 & | & -3 \\ 0 & 1 & -4 & | & -3 \end{bmatrix} \rightarrow \begin{bmatrix} 1 & 0 & -5 & | & -2 \\ 0 & 1 & -4 & | & -3 \\ 0 & 0 & 0 & | & 0 \end{bmatrix} \rightarrow \begin{array}{l} x - 5z = -2 \\ y - 4z = -3 \end{array}$

$R_1 = -r_1$ $R_2 = r_1 + r_2$ $R_1 = r_2 + r_1$

                     $R_3 = -3r_1 + r_3$ $R_3 = -r_2 + r_3$

The solution is $x = 5z - 2$, $y = 4z - 3$, z is any real number.

51. $\begin{cases} 2x - 2y + 3z = 6 \\ 4x - 3y + 2z = 0 \\ -2x + 3y - 7z = 1 \end{cases}$ can be written as: $\begin{bmatrix} 2 & -2 & 3 & | & 6 \\ 4 & -3 & 2 & | & 0 \\ -2 & 3 & -7 & | & 1 \end{bmatrix}$

$\rightarrow \begin{bmatrix} 1 & -1 & \frac{3}{2} & | & 3 \\ 4 & -3 & 2 & | & 0 \\ -2 & 3 & -7 & | & 1 \end{bmatrix} \rightarrow \begin{bmatrix} 1 & -1 & \frac{3}{2} & | & 3 \\ 0 & 1 & -4 & | & -12 \\ 0 & 1 & -4 & | & 7 \end{bmatrix} \rightarrow \begin{bmatrix} 1 & 0 & -\frac{5}{2} & | & -9 \\ 0 & 1 & -4 & | & -12 \\ 0 & 0 & 0 & | & 19 \end{bmatrix}$

$R_1 = \frac{1}{2} r_1$ $R_2 = -4r_1 + r_2$ $R_1 = r_2 + r_1$

                   $R_3 = 2r_1 + r_3$ $R_3 = -r_2 + r_3$

There is no solution. The system is inconsistent.

53. $\begin{cases} x + y - z = 6 \\ 3x - 2y + z = -5 \\ x + 3y - 2z = 14 \end{cases}$ can be written as: $\begin{bmatrix} 1 & 1 & -1 & | & 6 \\ 3 & -2 & 1 & | & -5 \\ 1 & 3 & -2 & | & 14 \end{bmatrix}$

$\rightarrow \begin{bmatrix} 1 & 1 & -1 & | & 6 \\ 0 & -5 & 4 & | & -23 \\ 0 & 2 & -1 & | & 8 \end{bmatrix} \rightarrow \begin{bmatrix} 1 & 1 & -1 & | & 6 \\ 0 & 1 & -\frac{4}{5} & | & \frac{23}{5} \\ 0 & 2 & -1 & | & 8 \end{bmatrix} \rightarrow \begin{bmatrix} 1 & 0 & -\frac{1}{5} & | & \frac{7}{5} \\ 0 & 1 & -\frac{4}{5} & | & \frac{23}{5} \\ 0 & 0 & \frac{3}{5} & | & -\frac{6}{5} \end{bmatrix}$

$R_2 = -3r_1 + r_2$ $R_2 = -\frac{1}{5} r_2$ $R_1 = -r_2 + r_1$

$R_3 = -r_1 + r_3$ $R_3 = -2r_2 + r_3$

$$\rightarrow \begin{vmatrix} 1 & 0 & -\frac{1}{5} & \frac{7}{5} \\ 0 & 1 & -\frac{4}{5} & \frac{23}{5} \\ 0 & 0 & 1 & -2 \end{vmatrix} \rightarrow \begin{bmatrix} 1 & 0 & 0 & 1 \\ 0 & 1 & 0 & 3 \\ 0 & 0 & 1 & -2 \end{bmatrix}$$

$$R_3 = \tfrac{5}{3}r_3 \qquad\qquad R_1 = \tfrac{1}{5}r_3 + r_1$$
$$R_2 = \tfrac{4}{5}r_3 + r_2$$

The solution is $x = 1,\ y = 3,\ z = -2$.

55. $\begin{cases} x + 2y - z = -3 \\ 2x - 4y + z = -7 \\ -2x + 2y - 3z = 4 \end{cases}$ can be written as: $\begin{bmatrix} 1 & 2 & -1 & -3 \\ 2 & -4 & 1 & -7 \\ -2 & 2 & -3 & 4 \end{bmatrix}$

$$\rightarrow \begin{bmatrix} 1 & 2 & -1 & -3 \\ 0 & -8 & 3 & -1 \\ 0 & 6 & -5 & -2 \end{bmatrix} \rightarrow \begin{bmatrix} 1 & 2 & -1 & -3 \\ 0 & 1 & -\frac{3}{8} & \frac{1}{8} \\ 0 & 6 & -5 & -2 \end{bmatrix} \rightarrow \begin{bmatrix} 1 & 0 & -\frac{1}{4} & -\frac{13}{4} \\ 0 & 1 & -\frac{3}{8} & \frac{1}{8} \\ 0 & 0 & -\frac{11}{4} & -\frac{11}{4} \end{bmatrix}$$

$$R_2 = -2r_1 + r_2 \qquad R_2 = -\tfrac{1}{8}r_2 \qquad R_1 = -2r_2 + r_1$$
$$R_3 = 2r_1 + r_3 \qquad\qquad\qquad R_3 = -6r_2 + r_3$$

$$\rightarrow \begin{bmatrix} 1 & 0 & -\frac{1}{4} & -\frac{13}{4} \\ 0 & 1 & -\frac{3}{8} & \frac{1}{8} \\ 0 & 0 & 1 & 1 \end{bmatrix} \rightarrow \begin{bmatrix} 1 & 0 & 0 & -3 \\ 0 & 1 & 0 & \frac{1}{2} \\ 0 & 0 & 1 & 1 \end{bmatrix}$$

$$R_3 = -\tfrac{4}{11}r_3 \qquad\qquad R_1 = \tfrac{1}{4}r_3 + r_1$$
$$R_2 = \tfrac{3}{8}r_3 + r_2$$

The solution is $x = -3,\ y = \dfrac{1}{2},\ z = 1$.

57. $\begin{cases} 3x + y - z = \dfrac{2}{3} \\ 2x - y + z = 1 \\ 4x + 2y = \dfrac{8}{3} \end{cases}$ can be written as: $\begin{bmatrix} 3 & 1 & -1 & \frac{2}{3} \\ 2 & -1 & 1 & 1 \\ 4 & 2 & 0 & \frac{8}{3} \end{bmatrix}$

$$\rightarrow \begin{bmatrix} 1 & \frac{1}{3} & -\frac{1}{3} & \frac{2}{9} \\ 2 & -1 & 1 & 1 \\ 4 & 2 & 0 & \frac{8}{3} \end{bmatrix} \rightarrow \begin{bmatrix} 1 & \frac{1}{3} & -\frac{1}{3} & \frac{2}{9} \\ 0 & -\frac{5}{3} & \frac{5}{3} & \frac{5}{9} \\ 0 & \frac{2}{3} & \frac{4}{3} & \frac{16}{9} \end{bmatrix} \rightarrow \begin{bmatrix} 1 & \frac{1}{3} & -\frac{1}{3} & \frac{2}{9} \\ 0 & 1 & -1 & -\frac{1}{3} \\ 0 & \frac{2}{3} & \frac{4}{3} & \frac{16}{9} \end{bmatrix} \rightarrow \begin{bmatrix} 1 & 0 & 0 & \frac{1}{3} \\ 0 & 1 & -1 & -\frac{1}{3} \\ 0 & 0 & 2 & 2 \end{bmatrix}$$

$$R_1 = \tfrac{1}{3}r_1 \qquad R_2 = -2r_1 + r_2 \qquad R_2 = -\tfrac{3}{5}r_2 \qquad R_1 = -\tfrac{1}{3}r_2 + r_1$$
$$\qquad\qquad R_3 = -4r_1 + r_3 \qquad\qquad\qquad R_3 = -\tfrac{2}{3}r_2 + r_3$$

383

$$\rightarrow \begin{bmatrix} 1 & 0 & 0 & | & \frac{1}{3} \\ 0 & 1 & -1 & | & -\frac{1}{3} \\ 0 & 0 & 1 & | & 1 \end{bmatrix} \rightarrow \begin{bmatrix} 1 & 0 & 0 & | & \frac{1}{3} \\ 0 & 1 & 0 & | & \frac{2}{3} \\ 0 & 0 & 1 & | & 1 \end{bmatrix}$$

$$R_3 = \tfrac{1}{2}r_3 \qquad\qquad R_2 = r_3 + r_2$$

The solution is $x = \dfrac{1}{3}, y = \dfrac{2}{3}, z = 1.$

59. $\begin{cases} x + y + z + w = 4 \\ 2x - y + z = 0 \\ 3x + 2y + z - w = 6 \\ x - 2y - 2z + 2w = -1 \end{cases}$ can be written as: $\begin{bmatrix} 1 & 1 & 1 & 1 & | & 4 \\ 2 & -1 & 1 & 0 & | & 0 \\ 3 & 2 & 1 & -1 & | & 6 \\ 1 & -2 & -2 & 2 & | & -1 \end{bmatrix}$

$$\rightarrow \begin{bmatrix} 1 & 1 & 1 & 1 & | & 4 \\ 0 & -3 & -1 & -2 & | & -8 \\ 0 & -1 & -2 & -4 & | & -6 \\ 0 & -3 & -3 & 1 & | & -5 \end{bmatrix} \rightarrow \begin{bmatrix} 1 & 1 & 1 & 1 & | & 4 \\ 0 & -1 & -2 & -4 & | & -6 \\ 0 & -3 & -1 & -2 & | & -8 \\ 0 & -3 & -3 & 1 & | & -5 \end{bmatrix} \rightarrow \begin{bmatrix} 1 & 1 & 1 & 1 & | & 4 \\ 0 & 1 & 2 & 4 & | & 6 \\ 0 & -3 & -1 & -2 & | & -8 \\ 0 & -3 & -3 & 1 & | & -5 \end{bmatrix}$$

$$\begin{aligned} R_2 &= -2r_1 + r_2 \\ R_3 &= -3r_1 + r_3 \\ R_4 &= -r_1 + r_4 \end{aligned} \qquad \text{Interchange } r_2 \text{ and } r_3 \qquad R_2 = -r_2$$

$$\rightarrow \begin{bmatrix} 1 & 0 & -1 & -3 & | & -2 \\ 0 & 1 & 2 & 4 & | & 6 \\ 0 & 0 & 5 & 10 & | & 10 \\ 0 & 0 & 3 & 13 & | & 13 \end{bmatrix} \rightarrow \begin{bmatrix} 1 & 0 & -1 & -3 & | & -2 \\ 0 & 1 & 2 & 4 & | & 6 \\ 0 & 0 & 1 & 2 & | & 2 \\ 0 & 0 & 3 & 13 & | & 13 \end{bmatrix} \rightarrow \begin{bmatrix} 1 & 0 & 0 & -1 & | & 0 \\ 0 & 1 & 0 & 0 & | & 2 \\ 0 & 0 & 1 & 2 & | & 2 \\ 0 & 0 & 0 & 7 & | & 7 \end{bmatrix}$$

$$\begin{aligned} R_1 &= -r_2 + r_1 \\ R_3 &= 3r_2 + r_3 \\ R_4 &= 3r_2 + r_4 \end{aligned} \qquad R_3 = \tfrac{1}{5}r_3 \qquad \begin{aligned} R_1 &= r_3 + r_1 \\ R_2 &= -2r_3 + r_2 \\ R_4 &= -3r_3 + r_4 \end{aligned}$$

$$\rightarrow \begin{bmatrix} 1 & 0 & 0 & -1 & | & 0 \\ 0 & 1 & 0 & 0 & | & 2 \\ 0 & 0 & 1 & 2 & | & 2 \\ 0 & 0 & 0 & 1 & | & 1 \end{bmatrix} \rightarrow \begin{bmatrix} 1 & 0 & 0 & 0 & | & 1 \\ 0 & 1 & 0 & 0 & | & 2 \\ 0 & 0 & 1 & 0 & | & 0 \\ 0 & 0 & 0 & 1 & | & 1 \end{bmatrix}$$

$$R_4 = \tfrac{1}{7}r_4 \qquad \begin{aligned} R_1 &= r_4 + r_1 \\ R_3 &= -2r_4 + r_3 \end{aligned}$$

The solution is $x = 1, y = 2, z = 0, w = 1.$

61. $\begin{cases} x + 2y + z = 1 \\ 2x - y + 2z = 2 \\ 3x + y + 3z = 3 \end{cases}$ can be written as: $\begin{bmatrix} 1 & 2 & 1 & | & 1 \\ 2 & -1 & 2 & | & 2 \\ 3 & 1 & 3 & | & 3 \end{bmatrix}$

$$\rightarrow \begin{bmatrix} 1 & 2 & 1 & | & 1 \\ 0 & -5 & 0 & | & 0 \\ 0 & -5 & 0 & | & 0 \end{bmatrix} \rightarrow \begin{bmatrix} 1 & 2 & 1 & | & 1 \\ 0 & -5 & 0 & | & 0 \\ 0 & 0 & 0 & | & 0 \end{bmatrix} \rightarrow \begin{array}{l} x+2y+z = 1 \\ -5y = 0 \end{array}$$

$$R_2 = -2r_1 + r_2 \qquad R_3 = -r_2 + r_3$$
$$R_3 = -3r_1 + r_3$$

Substitute and solve:
$$y = 0$$
$$x + 2(0) + z = 1$$
$$x + z = 1$$
$$x = 1 - z$$

The solution is $y = 0$, $x = 1 - z$, z is any real number.

63. $\begin{cases} x - y + z = 5 \\ 3x + 2y - 2z = 0 \end{cases}$ can be written as: $\begin{bmatrix} 1 & -1 & 1 & | & 5 \\ 3 & 2 & -2 & | & 0 \end{bmatrix}$

$$\rightarrow \begin{bmatrix} 1 & -1 & 1 & | & 5 \\ 0 & 5 & -5 & | & -15 \end{bmatrix} \rightarrow \begin{bmatrix} 1 & -1 & 1 & | & 5 \\ 0 & 1 & -1 & | & -3 \end{bmatrix} \rightarrow \begin{bmatrix} 1 & 0 & 0 & | & 2 \\ 0 & 1 & -1 & | & -3 \end{bmatrix}$$

$$R_2 = -3r_1 + r_2 \qquad R_2 = \tfrac{1}{5}r_2 \qquad R_1 = r_2 + r_1$$

The matrix in the third step represents the system $\begin{cases} x = 2 \\ y - z = -3 \end{cases}$

Therefore the solution is $x = 2; y = -3 + z;$ z is any real number

or

$$x = 2; z = y + 3;\ \ y \text{ is any real number}$$

65. $\begin{cases} 2x + 3y - z = 3 \\ x - y - z = 0 \\ -x + y + z = 0 \\ x + y + 3z = 5 \end{cases}$ can be written as: $\begin{bmatrix} 2 & 3 & -1 & | & 3 \\ 1 & -1 & -1 & | & 0 \\ -1 & 1 & 1 & | & 0 \\ 1 & 1 & 3 & | & 5 \end{bmatrix}$

$$\rightarrow \begin{bmatrix} 1 & -1 & -1 & | & 0 \\ 2 & 3 & -1 & | & 3 \\ -1 & 1 & 1 & | & 0 \\ 1 & 1 & 3 & | & 5 \end{bmatrix} \longrightarrow \begin{bmatrix} 1 & -1 & -1 & | & 0 \\ 0 & 5 & 1 & | & 3 \\ 0 & 0 & 0 & | & 0 \\ 0 & 2 & 4 & | & 5 \end{bmatrix} \rightarrow \begin{bmatrix} 1 & -1 & -1 & | & 0 \\ 0 & 5 & 1 & | & 3 \\ 0 & 2 & 4 & | & 5 \\ 0 & 0 & 0 & | & 0 \end{bmatrix}$$

$$\text{interchange } r_1 \text{ and } r_2 \qquad R_2 = -2r_1 + r_2 \qquad \text{interchange } r_3 \text{ and } r_4$$
$$R_3 = r_1 + r_3$$
$$R_4 = -r_1 + r_4$$

$$\rightarrow \begin{vmatrix} 1 & -1 & -1 & 0 \\ 0 & 1 & -7 & -7 \\ 0 & 2 & 4 & 5 \\ 0 & 0 & 0 & 0 \end{vmatrix} \longrightarrow \begin{vmatrix} 1 & 0 & -8 & -7 \\ 0 & 1 & -7 & -7 \\ 0 & 1 & 18 & 19 \\ 0 & 0 & 0 & 0 \end{vmatrix} \rightarrow \begin{vmatrix} 1 & 0 & -8 & -7 \\ 0 & 1 & -7 & -7 \\ 0 & 0 & 1 & \frac{19}{18} \\ 0 & 0 & 0 & 0 \end{vmatrix}$$

$$R_2 = -2r_3 + r_2 \qquad\qquad R_1 = r_2 + r_1 \qquad\qquad R_3 = \tfrac{1}{18}r_3$$
$$R_3 = -2r_2 + r_3$$

The matrix in the last step represents the system $\begin{cases} x - 8z = -7 \\ y - 7z = -7 \\ \quad z = \dfrac{19}{18} \end{cases}$

Therefore the solution is

$$z = \frac{19}{18}$$

$$x = -7 + 8z = -7 + 8\left(\frac{19}{18}\right) = \frac{13}{9}; \quad y = -7 + 7z = -7 + 7\left(\frac{19}{18}\right) = \frac{7}{18}$$

67. $\begin{cases} 4x + y + z - w = 4 \\ x - y + 2z + 3w = 3 \end{cases}$ can be written as: $\begin{vmatrix} 4 & 1 & 1 & -1 & 4 \\ 1 & -1 & 2 & 3 & 3 \end{vmatrix}$

$$\rightarrow \begin{vmatrix} 1 & -1 & 2 & 3 & 3 \\ 4 & 1 & 1 & -1 & 4 \end{vmatrix} \longrightarrow \begin{vmatrix} 1 & -1 & 2 & 3 & 3 \\ 0 & 5 & -7 & -13 & -8 \end{vmatrix}$$

interchange r_1 and r_2 $R_2 = -4r_1 + r_2$

The matrix in the last step represents the system $\begin{cases} x - y + 2z + 3w = 3 \\ 5y - 7z - 13w = -8 \end{cases}$

The second equation yields

$$5y - 7z - 13w = -8 \rightarrow 5y = -8 + 7z + 13w \rightarrow y = -\frac{8}{5} + \frac{7}{5}z + \frac{13}{5}w$$

The first equation yields

$$x - y + 2z + 3w = 3 \rightarrow x = 3 + y - 2z - 3w$$

substituting for y

$$x = 3 + \left(-\frac{8}{5} + \frac{7}{5}z + \frac{13}{5}w \right) - 2z - 3w$$

$$x = -\frac{3}{5}z - \frac{2}{5}w + \frac{7}{5}$$

Therefore the solution is

$$x = -\frac{3}{5}z - \frac{2}{5}w + \frac{7}{5}; \quad y = -\frac{8}{5} + \frac{7}{5}z + \frac{13}{5}w$$

z and w are any real numbers

69. Each of the points must satisfy the equation $y = ax^2 + bx + c$.

$(1,2)$:　　　$2 = a + b + c$
$(-2,-7)$:　　$-7 = 4a - 2b + c$
$(2,-3)$:　　$-3 = 4a + 2b + c$

Set up a matrix and solve:

$$\begin{bmatrix} 1 & 1 & 1 & | & 2 \\ 4 & -2 & 1 & | & -7 \\ 4 & 2 & 1 & | & -3 \end{bmatrix} \rightarrow \begin{bmatrix} 1 & 1 & 1 & | & 2 \\ 0 & -6 & -3 & | & -15 \\ 0 & -2 & -3 & | & -11 \end{bmatrix} \rightarrow \begin{bmatrix} 1 & 1 & 1 & | & 2 \\ 0 & 1 & \frac{1}{2} & | & \frac{5}{2} \\ 0 & -2 & -3 & | & -11 \end{bmatrix} \rightarrow \begin{bmatrix} 1 & 0 & \frac{1}{2} & | & -\frac{1}{2} \\ 0 & 1 & \frac{1}{2} & | & \frac{5}{2} \\ 0 & 0 & -2 & | & -6 \end{bmatrix}$$

$$\begin{array}{c} R_2 = -4r_1 + r_2 \\ R_3 = -4r_1 + r_3 \end{array} \qquad R_2 = -\tfrac{1}{6}r_2 \qquad \begin{array}{c} R_1 = -r_2 + r_1 \\ R_3 = 2r_2 + r_3 \end{array}$$

$$\rightarrow \begin{bmatrix} 1 & 0 & \frac{1}{2} & | & -\frac{1}{2} \\ 0 & 1 & \frac{1}{2} & | & \frac{5}{2} \\ 0 & 0 & 1 & | & 3 \end{bmatrix} \rightarrow \begin{bmatrix} 1 & 0 & 0 & | & -2 \\ 0 & 1 & 0 & | & 1 \\ 0 & 0 & 1 & | & 3 \end{bmatrix}$$

$$R_3 = -\tfrac{1}{2}r_3 \qquad \begin{array}{c} R_1 = -\tfrac{1}{2}r_3 + r_1 \\ R_2 = -\tfrac{1}{2}r_3 + r_2 \end{array}$$

The solution is $a = -2$, $b = 1$, $c = 3$; so the equation is $y = -2x^2 + x + 3$.

71. Each of the points must satisfy the equation $f(x) = ax^3 + bx^2 + cx + d$.

$f(-3) = -112$:　　$-27a + 9b - 3c + d = -112$
$f(-1) = -2$:　　$-a + b - c + d = -2$
$f(1) = 4$:　　　$a + b + c + d = 4$
$f(2) = 13$:　　$8a + 4b + 2c + d = 13$

Set up a matrix and solve:

$$\begin{bmatrix} -27 & 9 & -3 & 1 & | & -112 \\ -1 & 1 & -1 & 1 & | & -2 \\ 1 & 1 & 1 & 1 & | & 4 \\ 8 & 4 & 2 & 1 & | & 13 \end{bmatrix} \rightarrow \begin{bmatrix} 1 & 1 & 1 & 1 & | & 4 \\ -1 & 1 & -1 & 1 & | & -2 \\ -27 & 9 & -3 & 1 & | & -112 \\ 8 & 4 & 2 & 1 & | & 13 \end{bmatrix} \rightarrow \begin{bmatrix} 1 & 1 & 1 & 1 & | & 4 \\ 0 & 2 & 0 & 2 & | & 2 \\ 0 & 36 & 24 & 28 & | & -4 \\ 0 & -4 & -6 & -7 & | & -19 \end{bmatrix}$$

$$\text{Interchange } r_3 \text{ and } r_1 \qquad \begin{array}{c} R_2 = r_1 + r_2 \\ R_3 = 27r_1 + r_3 \\ R_4 = -8r_1 + r_4 \end{array}$$

$$\rightarrow \begin{bmatrix} 1 & 1 & 1 & 1 & | & 4 \\ 0 & 1 & 0 & 1 & | & 1 \\ 0 & 36 & 24 & 28 & | & -4 \\ 0 & -4 & -6 & -7 & | & -19 \end{bmatrix} \rightarrow \begin{bmatrix} 1 & 0 & 1 & 0 & | & 3 \\ 0 & 1 & 0 & 1 & | & 1 \\ 0 & 0 & 24 & -8 & | & -40 \\ 0 & 0 & -6 & -3 & | & -15 \end{bmatrix} \rightarrow \begin{bmatrix} 1 & 0 & 1 & 0 & | & 3 \\ 0 & 1 & 0 & 1 & | & 1 \\ 0 & 0 & 1 & -\frac{1}{3} & | & -\frac{5}{3} \\ 0 & 0 & -6 & -3 & | & -15 \end{bmatrix}$$

$$R_2 = \tfrac{1}{2}r_2 \qquad \begin{array}{c} R_1 = -r_2 + r_1 \\ R_3 = -36r_2 + r_3 \\ R_4 = 4r_2 + r_4 \end{array} \qquad R_3 = \tfrac{1}{24}r_3$$

$$\rightarrow \begin{bmatrix} 1 & 0 & 0 & \frac{1}{3} & \frac{14}{3} \\ 0 & 1 & 0 & 1 & 1 \\ 0 & 0 & 1 & -\frac{1}{3} & -\frac{5}{3} \\ 0 & 0 & 0 & -5 & -25 \end{bmatrix} \rightarrow \begin{bmatrix} 1 & 0 & 0 & \frac{1}{3} & \frac{14}{3} \\ 0 & 1 & 0 & 1 & 1 \\ 0 & 0 & 1 & -\frac{1}{3} & -\frac{5}{3} \\ 0 & 0 & 0 & 1 & 5 \end{bmatrix} \rightarrow \begin{bmatrix} 1 & 0 & 0 & 0 & 3 \\ 0 & 1 & 0 & 0 & -4 \\ 0 & 0 & 1 & 0 & 0 \\ 0 & 0 & 0 & 1 & 5 \end{bmatrix}$$

$$\begin{array}{lll} R_1 = -r_3 + r_1 & R_4 = -\frac{1}{5}r_4 & R_1 = -\frac{1}{3}r_4 + r_1 \\ R_4 = 6r_3 + r_4 & & R_2 = -r_4 + r_2 \\ & & R_3 = \frac{1}{3}r_4 + r_3 \end{array}$$

The solution is $a = 3$, $b = -4$, $c = 0$, $d = 5$; so the equation is $f(x) = 3x^3 - 4x^2 + 5$.

73. Let x = the number of servings of salmon steak.
Let y = the number of servings of baked eggs.
Let z = the number of servings of acorn squash.
Protein equation: $30x + 15y + 3z = 78$
Carbohydrate equation: $20x + 2y + 25z = 59$
Vitamin A equation: $2x + 20y + 32z = 75$
Set up a matrix and solve:

$$\begin{bmatrix} 30 & 15 & 3 & 78 \\ 20 & 2 & 25 & 59 \\ 2 & 20 & 32 & 75 \end{bmatrix} \rightarrow \begin{bmatrix} 2 & 20 & 32 & 75 \\ 20 & 2 & 25 & 59 \\ 30 & 15 & 3 & 78 \end{bmatrix} \rightarrow \begin{bmatrix} 1 & 10 & 16 & 37.5 \\ 20 & 2 & 25 & 59 \\ 30 & 15 & 3 & 78 \end{bmatrix}$$

Interchange r_3 and r_1 $R_1 = \frac{1}{2}r_1$

$$\rightarrow \begin{bmatrix} 1 & 10 & 16 & 37.5 \\ 0 & -198 & -295 & -691 \\ 0 & -285 & -477 & -1047 \end{bmatrix} \rightarrow \begin{bmatrix} 1 & 10 & 16 & 37.5 \\ 0 & -198 & -295 & -691 \\ 0 & 0 & -\frac{3457}{66} & -\frac{3457}{66} \end{bmatrix}$$

$$\begin{array}{ll} R_2 = -20r_1 + r_2 & R_3 = -\frac{95}{66}r_2 + r_3 \\ R_3 = -30r_1 + r_3 & \end{array}$$

$$\rightarrow \begin{bmatrix} 1 & 10 & 16 & 37.5 \\ 0 & -198 & -295 & -691 \\ 0 & 0 & 1 & 1 \end{bmatrix}$$

$$R_3 = -\frac{66}{3457}r_3$$

Substitute $z = 1$ and solve:

$$\begin{array}{ll} -198y - 295(1) = -691 & x + 10(2) + 16(1) = 37.5 \\ -198y = -396 & x + 36 = 37.5 \\ y = 2 & x = 1.5 \end{array}$$

The dietitian should serve 1.5 servings of salmon steak, 2 servings of baked eggs, and 1 serving of acorn squash.

75. Let x = the amount invested in Treasury bills.
Let y = the amount invested in Treasury bonds.
Let z = the amount invested in corporate bonds.
Total investment equation: $x + y + z = 10000$
Annual income equation: $0.06x + 0.07y + 0.08z = 680$
Condition on investment equation: $z = 0.5x$

Set up a matrix and solve:

$$\begin{vmatrix} 1 & 1 & 1 & 10000 \\ 0.06 & 0.07 & 0.08 & 680 \\ 1 & 0 & -2 & 0 \end{vmatrix} \rightarrow \begin{vmatrix} 1 & 1 & 1 & 10000 \\ 0 & 0.01 & 0.02 & 80 \\ 0 & -1 & -3 & -10000 \end{vmatrix} \rightarrow \begin{vmatrix} 1 & 1 & 1 & 10000 \\ 0 & 1 & 2 & 8000 \\ 0 & -1 & -3 & -10000 \end{vmatrix}$$

$$R_2 = -0.06\, r_1 + r_2 \qquad\qquad R_2 = 100\, r_2$$
$$R_3 = -r_1 + r_3$$

$$\rightarrow \begin{vmatrix} 1 & 0 & -1 & 2000 \\ 0 & 1 & 2 & 8000 \\ 0 & 0 & -1 & -2000 \end{vmatrix} \rightarrow \begin{vmatrix} 1 & 0 & -1 & 2000 \\ 0 & 1 & 2 & 8000 \\ 0 & 0 & 1 & 2000 \end{vmatrix} \rightarrow \begin{vmatrix} 1 & 0 & 0 & 4000 \\ 0 & 1 & 0 & 4000 \\ 0 & 0 & 1 & 2000 \end{vmatrix}$$

$$R_1 = -r_2 + r_1 \qquad R_3 = -r_3 \qquad R_1 = r_3 + r_1$$
$$R_3 = r_2 + r_3 \qquad\qquad\qquad R_2 = -2r_3 + r_2$$

Carletta should invest \$4000 in Treasury bills, \$4000 in Treasury bonds, and \$2000 in corporate bonds.

77. Let x = the number of Deltas produced.
Let y = the number of Betas produced.
Let z = the number of Sigmas produced.
Painting equation: $10x + 16y + 8z = 240$
Drying equation: $3x + 5y + 2z = 69$
Polishing equation: $2x + 3y + z = 41$
Set up a matrix and solve:

$$\begin{bmatrix} 10 & 16 & 8 & 240 \\ 3 & 5 & 2 & 69 \\ 2 & 3 & 1 & 41 \end{bmatrix} \rightarrow \begin{bmatrix} 1 & 1 & 2 & 33 \\ 3 & 5 & 2 & 69 \\ 2 & 3 & 1 & 41 \end{bmatrix} \rightarrow \begin{bmatrix} 1 & 1 & 2 & 33 \\ 0 & 2 & -4 & -30 \\ 0 & 1 & -3 & -25 \end{bmatrix} \rightarrow \begin{bmatrix} 1 & 1 & 2 & 33 \\ 0 & 1 & -2 & -15 \\ 0 & 1 & -3 & -25 \end{bmatrix}$$

$$R_1 = -3r_2 + r_1 \qquad R_2 = -3r_1 + r_2 \qquad R_2 = \tfrac{1}{2}r_2$$
$$R_3 = -2r_1 + r_3$$

$$\rightarrow \begin{bmatrix} 1 & 0 & 4 & 48 \\ 0 & 1 & -2 & -15 \\ 0 & 0 & -1 & -10 \end{bmatrix} \rightarrow \begin{bmatrix} 1 & 0 & 4 & 48 \\ 0 & 1 & -2 & -15 \\ 0 & 0 & 1 & 10 \end{bmatrix} \rightarrow \begin{bmatrix} 1 & 0 & 0 & 8 \\ 0 & 1 & 0 & 5 \\ 0 & 0 & 1 & 10 \end{bmatrix}$$

$$R_1 = -r_2 + r_1 \qquad R_3 = -r_3 \qquad R_1 = -4r_3 + r_1$$
$$R_3 = -r_2 + r_3 \qquad\qquad\qquad R_2 = 2r_3 + r_2$$

The company should produce 8 Deltas, 5 Betas, and 10 Sigmas.

79. Rewrite the system as set up and solve the matrix:

$$\begin{cases} -4 + 8 - 2I_2 = 0 \\ 8 = 5I_4 + I_1 \\ 4 = 3I_3 + I_1 \\ I_3 + I_4 = I_1 \end{cases} \rightarrow \begin{cases} 2I_2 = 4 \\ I_1 + 5I_4 = 8 \\ I_1 + 3I_3 = 4 \\ I_1 - I_3 - I_4 = 0 \end{cases}$$

$$\begin{vmatrix} 0 & 2 & 0 & 0 & 4 \\ 1 & 0 & 0 & 5 & 8 \\ 1 & 0 & 3 & 0 & 4 \\ 1 & 0 & -1 & -1 & 0 \end{vmatrix} \rightarrow \begin{vmatrix} 1 & 0 & 0 & 5 & 8 \\ 0 & 2 & 0 & 0 & 4 \\ 1 & 0 & 3 & 0 & 4 \\ 1 & 0 & -1 & -1 & 0 \end{vmatrix} \rightarrow \begin{vmatrix} 1 & 0 & 0 & 5 & 8 \\ 0 & 1 & 0 & 0 & 2 \\ 0 & 0 & 3 & -5 & -4 \\ 0 & 0 & -1 & -6 & -8 \end{vmatrix}$$

Interchange r_2 and r_1 $R_2 = \frac{1}{2}r_2$

$$R_3 = -r_1 + r_3$$

$$R_4 = -r_1 + r_4$$

$$\rightarrow \begin{vmatrix} 1 & 0 & 0 & 5 & 8 \\ 0 & 1 & 0 & 0 & 2 \\ 0 & 0 & -1 & -6 & -8 \\ 0 & 0 & 3 & -5 & -4 \end{vmatrix} \rightarrow \begin{vmatrix} 1 & 0 & 0 & 5 & 8 \\ 0 & 1 & 0 & 0 & 2 \\ 0 & 0 & 1 & 6 & 8 \\ 0 & 0 & 0 & -23 & -28 \end{vmatrix} \rightarrow \begin{vmatrix} 1 & 0 & 0 & 5 & 8 \\ 0 & 1 & 0 & 0 & 2 \\ 0 & 0 & 1 & 6 & 8 \\ 0 & 0 & 0 & 1 & \frac{28}{23} \end{vmatrix}$$

Interchange r_3 and r_4 $R_3 = -r_3$ $R_4 = -\frac{1}{23}r_4$

$$R_4 = -3r_3 + r_4$$

$$\rightarrow \begin{bmatrix} 1 & 0 & 0 & 0 & \frac{44}{23} \\ 0 & 1 & 0 & 0 & 2 \\ 0 & 0 & 1 & 0 & \frac{16}{23} \\ 0 & 0 & 0 & 1 & \frac{28}{23} \end{bmatrix}$$

$$R_1 = -5r_4 + r_1$$

$$R_3 = -6r_4 + r_3$$

The solution is $I_1 = \dfrac{44}{23}$, $I_2 = 2$, $I_3 = \dfrac{16}{23}$, $I_4 = \dfrac{28}{23}$.

81. Let x = the amount invested in Treasury bills.
    Let y = the amount invested in Treasury bonds.
    Let z = the amount invested in corporate bonds.

    (a) Total investment equation: $x + y + z = 20000$
         Annual income equation: $0.07x + 0.09y + 0.11z = 2000$
    Set up a matrix and solve:

$$\begin{vmatrix} 1 & 1 & 1 & 20000 \\ .07 & .09 & .11 & 2000 \end{vmatrix} \rightarrow \begin{vmatrix} 1 & 1 & 1 & 20000 \\ 7 & 9 & 11 & 200000 \end{vmatrix} \rightarrow \begin{vmatrix} 1 & 1 & 1 & 20000 \\ 0 & 2 & 4 & 60000 \end{vmatrix}$$

$$R_2 = 100r_2 \qquad\qquad R_2 = r_2 - 7r_1$$

$$\rightarrow \begin{bmatrix} 1 & 1 & 1 & 20000 \\ 0 & 1 & 2 & 30000 \end{bmatrix} \rightarrow \begin{bmatrix} 1 & 0 & -1 & -10000 \\ 0 & 1 & 2 & 30000 \end{bmatrix}$$

$$R_2 = \frac{1}{2}r_2 \qquad\qquad R_1 = r_1 - r_2$$

The matrix in the last step represents the system $\begin{cases} x - z = -10000 \\ y + 2z = 30000 \end{cases}$

Therefore the solution is

$$x = -10000 + z; \quad y = 30000 - 2z; \quad z \text{ is any real number}$$

Possible investment strategies:

Amount invested at

7%	9%	11%
0	10000	10000
1000	8000	11000
2000	6000	12000
3000	4000	13000
4000	2000	14000
5000	0	15000

(b) Total investment equation: $\quad x + y + z = 25000$

Annual income equation: $\quad\quad 0.07x + 0.09y + 0.11z = 2000$

Set up a matrix and solve:

$$\begin{bmatrix} 1 & 1 & 1 & | & 25000 \\ .07 & .09 & .11 & | & 2000 \end{bmatrix} \rightarrow \begin{bmatrix} 1 & 1 & 1 & | & 25000 \\ 7 & 9 & 11 & | & 200000 \end{bmatrix} \rightarrow \begin{bmatrix} 1 & 1 & 1 & | & 25000 \\ 0 & 2 & 4 & | & 25000 \end{bmatrix}$$

$$R_2 = 100r_2 \quad\quad\quad R_2 = r_2 - 7r_1$$

$$\rightarrow \begin{bmatrix} 1 & 1 & 1 & | & 25000 \\ 0 & 1 & 2 & | & 12500 \end{bmatrix} \rightarrow \begin{bmatrix} 1 & 0 & -1 & | & 12500 \\ 0 & 1 & 2 & | & 12500 \end{bmatrix}$$

$$R_2 = \tfrac{1}{2}r_2 \quad\quad\quad R_1 = r_1 - r_2$$

The matrix in the last step represents the system $\quad \begin{cases} x - z = 12500 \\ y + 2z = 12500 \end{cases}$

Therefore the solution is

$$x = 12500 + z; \quad y = 12500 - 2z; \quad z \text{ is any real number}$$

Possible investment strategies:

Amount invested at

7%	9%	11%
12500	12500	0
14500	8500	2000
16500	4500	4000
18750	0	6250

(c) Total investment equation: $\quad x + y + z = 30000$

Annual income equation: $\quad\quad 0.07x + 0.09y + 0.11z = 2000$

Set up a matrix and solve:

$$\begin{bmatrix} 1 & 1 & 1 & | & 30000 \\ .07 & .09 & .11 & | & 2000 \end{bmatrix} \rightarrow \begin{bmatrix} 1 & 1 & 1 & | & 30000 \\ 7 & 9 & 11 & | & 200000 \end{bmatrix} \rightarrow \begin{bmatrix} 1 & 1 & 1 & | & 30000 \\ 0 & 2 & 4 & | & -10000 \end{bmatrix}$$

$$R_2 = 100r_2 \quad\quad\quad R_1 = r_2 - 7r_1$$

$$\rightarrow \begin{bmatrix} 1 & 1 & 1 & | & 30000 \\ 0 & 1 & 2 & | & -5000 \end{bmatrix} \rightarrow \begin{bmatrix} 1 & 0 & -1 & | & 35000 \\ 0 & 1 & 2 & | & -5000 \end{bmatrix}$$

$$R_2 = \tfrac{1}{2}r_2 \quad\quad\quad R_1 = r_1 - r_2$$

The matrix in the last step represents the system $\begin{cases} x - z = 35000 \\ y + 2z = -5000 \end{cases}$

Therefore the solution is

$$x = 35000 + z; \quad y = -5000 - 2z; \quad z \text{ is any real number}$$

One possible investment strategy

Amount invested at

7%	9%	11%
30000	0	0

This will yield ($30000)(.07) = $2100, which is more than the required income.

83. Let x = the amount of liquid 1.
Let y = the amount of liquid 2.
Let z = the amount of liquid 3.

$.20x + .40y + .30z = 40$ Vitamin C
$.30x + .20y + .50z = 30$ Vitamin D

multiplying each equation by 10 yields

$2x + 4y + 3z = 400$
$3x + 2y + 5z = 300$

Set up a matrix and solve: $\begin{vmatrix} 2 & 4 & 3 & 400 \\ 3 & 2 & 5 & 300 \end{vmatrix} \rightarrow \begin{vmatrix} 1 & 2 & \frac{3}{2} & 200 \\ 3 & 2 & 5 & 300 \end{vmatrix} \rightarrow \begin{vmatrix} 1 & 2 & \frac{3}{2} & 200 \\ 0 & -4 & \frac{1}{2} & -300 \end{vmatrix}$

$R_1 = \frac{1}{2} r_1 \qquad\qquad R_2 = r_2 - 3r_1$

$\rightarrow \begin{vmatrix} 1 & 2 & \frac{3}{2} & 200 \\ 0 & 1 & -\frac{1}{8} & 75 \end{vmatrix} \rightarrow \begin{vmatrix} 1 & 0 & \frac{7}{4} & 50 \\ 0 & 1 & -\frac{1}{8} & 75 \end{vmatrix}$

$R_2 = -\frac{1}{4} r_2 \qquad R_1 = r_1 - 2r_2$

The matrix in the last step represents the system $\begin{cases} x + \frac{7}{4} z = 50 \\ y - \frac{1}{8} z = 75 \end{cases}$

Therefore the solution is $x = 50 - \dfrac{7}{4} z; \quad y = 75 + \dfrac{1}{8} z; \quad z$ is any real number

Possible combinations:

Liquid 1	Liquid 2	Liquid 3
50mg	75mg	0mg
36mg	76mg	8mg
22mg	77mg	16mg
8mg	78mg	24mg

85 – 87. Answers will vary.

Systems of Equations and Inequalities

7.4 Systems of Linear Equations: Determinants

1. (a) Evaluating the determinant: $\begin{vmatrix} 3 & 1 \\ 4 & 2 \end{vmatrix} = 3(2) - 4(1) = 6 - 4 = 2$

    (b) Use MATRIX EDIT to create the matrix   Then compute det([A]):

    $A = \begin{bmatrix} 3 & 1 \\ 4 & 2 \end{bmatrix}$

3. (a) Evaluating the determinant: $\begin{vmatrix} 6 & 4 \\ -1 & 3 \end{vmatrix} = 6(3) - (-1)(4) = 18 + 4 = 22$

    (b) Use MATRIX EDIT to create the matrix   Then compute det([A]):

    $A = \begin{bmatrix} 6 & 4 \\ -1 & 3 \end{bmatrix}$

5. (a) Evaluating the determinant: $\begin{vmatrix} -3 & -1 \\ 4 & 2 \end{vmatrix} = -3(2) - 4(-1) = -6 + 4 = -2$

    (b) Use MATRIX EDIT to create the matrix   Then compute det([A]):

    $A = \begin{bmatrix} -3 & -1 \\ 4 & 2 \end{bmatrix}$

7.   (a) Evaluating the determinant:

$$\begin{vmatrix} 3 & 4 & 2 \\ 1 & -1 & 5 \\ 1 & 2 & -2 \end{vmatrix} = 3\begin{vmatrix} -1 & 5 \\ 2 & -2 \end{vmatrix} - 4\begin{vmatrix} 1 & 5 \\ 1 & -2 \end{vmatrix} + 2\begin{vmatrix} 1 & -1 \\ 1 & 2 \end{vmatrix}$$

$$= 3\big[(-1)(-2) - 2(5)\big] - 4\big[1(-2) - 1(5)\big] + 2\big[1(2) - 1(-1)\big]$$

$$= 3(2-10) - 4(-2-5) + 2(2+1) = 3(-8) - 4(-7) + 2(3) = -24 + 28 + 6 = 10$$

(b) Use MATRIX EDIT to create the matrix

$$A = \begin{bmatrix} 3 & 4 & 2 \\ 1 & -1 & 5 \\ 1 & 2 & -2 \end{bmatrix}$$

Then compute det([A]):

9.   (a)   Evaluating the determinant:

$$\begin{vmatrix} 4 & -1 & 2 \\ 6 & -1 & 0 \\ 1 & -3 & 4 \end{vmatrix} = 4\begin{vmatrix} -1 & 0 \\ -3 & 4 \end{vmatrix} - (-1)\begin{vmatrix} 6 & 0 \\ 1 & 4 \end{vmatrix} + 2\begin{vmatrix} 6 & -1 \\ 1 & -3 \end{vmatrix}$$

$$= 4\big[-1(4) - 0(-3)\big] + 1\big[6(4) - 1(0)\big] + 2\big[6(-3) - 1(-1)\big]$$

$$= 4(-4) + 1(24) + 2(-17) = -16 + 24 - 34 = -26$$

(b) Use MATRIX EDIT to create the matrix

$$A = \begin{bmatrix} 4 & -1 & 2 \\ 6 & -1 & 0 \\ 1 & -3 & 4 \end{bmatrix}$$

Then compute det([A]):

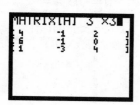

11. (a) Set up and evaluate the determinants to use Cramer's Rule:

$$\begin{cases} x + y = 8 \\ x - y = 4 \end{cases}$$

$$D = \begin{vmatrix} 1 & 1 \\ 1 & -1 \end{vmatrix} = -1 - 1 = -2$$

$$D_x = \begin{vmatrix} 8 & 1 \\ 4 & -1 \end{vmatrix} = -8 - 4 = -12; \quad D_y = \begin{vmatrix} 1 & 8 \\ 1 & 4 \end{vmatrix} = 4 - 8 = -4$$

Find the solutions by Cramer's Rule:

$$x = \frac{D_x}{D} = \frac{-12}{-2} = 6 \qquad y = \frac{D_y}{D} = \frac{-4}{-2} = 2$$

(b) Use MATRIX EDIT to create the matrices   Then compute

$$A = \begin{vmatrix} 1 & 1 \\ 1 & -1 \end{vmatrix}; \quad B = \begin{vmatrix} 8 & 1 \\ 4 & -1 \end{vmatrix}; \quad C = \begin{vmatrix} 1 & 8 \\ 1 & 4 \end{vmatrix}$$

$$x = \det([B]) / \det([A]);$$

$$y = \det([C]) / \det([A])$$

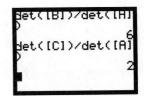

13. (a) Set up and evaluate the determinants to use Cramer's Rule:

$$\begin{cases} 5x - y = 13 \\ 2x + 3y = 12 \end{cases}$$

$$D = \begin{vmatrix} 5 & -1 \\ 2 & 3 \end{vmatrix} = 15 + 2 = 17$$

$$D_x = \begin{vmatrix} 13 & -1 \\ 12 & 3 \end{vmatrix} = 39 + 12 = 51; \quad D_y = \begin{vmatrix} 5 & 13 \\ 2 & 12 \end{vmatrix} = 60 - 26 = 34$$

Find the solutions by Cramer's Rule:

$$x = \frac{D_x}{D} = \frac{51}{17} = 3 \qquad y = \frac{D_y}{D} = \frac{34}{17} = 2$$

(b) Use MATRIX EDIT to create the matrices   Then compute

$$A = \begin{vmatrix} 5 & -1 \\ 2 & 3 \end{vmatrix}; \quad B = \begin{vmatrix} 13 & -1 \\ 12 & 3 \end{vmatrix}; \quad C = \begin{vmatrix} 5 & 13 \\ 2 & 12 \end{vmatrix}$$

$$x = \det([B]) / \det([A]);$$

$$y = \det([C]) / \det([A])$$

15. (a) Set up and evaluate the determinants to use Cramer's Rule:

$$\begin{cases} 3x \quad\;\; = 24 \\ x + 2y = \;\; 0 \end{cases}$$

$$D = \begin{vmatrix} 3 & 0 \\ 1 & 2 \end{vmatrix} = 6 - 0 = 6$$

$$D_x = \begin{vmatrix} 24 & 0 \\ 0 & 2 \end{vmatrix} = 48 - 0 = 48; \quad D_y = \begin{vmatrix} 3 & 24 \\ 1 & 0 \end{vmatrix} = 0 - 24 = -24$$

Find the solutions by Cramer's Rule:

$$x = \frac{D_x}{D} = \frac{48}{6} = 8 \qquad y = \frac{D_y}{D} = \frac{-24}{6} = -4$$

(b) Use MATRIX EDIT to create the matrices

$$A = \begin{vmatrix} 3 & 0 \\ 1 & 2 \end{vmatrix}; \quad B = \begin{vmatrix} 24 & 0 \\ 0 & 2 \end{vmatrix}; \quad C = \begin{vmatrix} 3 & 24 \\ 1 & 0 \end{vmatrix}$$

Then compute

$$x = \det([B])/\det([A]);$$

$$y = \det([C])/\det([A])$$

17. (a) Set up and evaluate the determinants to use Cramer's Rule:

$$\begin{cases} 3x - 6y = 24 \\ 5x + 4y = 12 \end{cases}$$

$$D = \begin{vmatrix} 3 & -6 \\ 5 & 4 \end{vmatrix} = 12 - (-30) = 42$$

$$D_x = \begin{vmatrix} 24 & -6 \\ 12 & 4 \end{vmatrix} = 96 - (-72) = 168; \quad D_y = \begin{vmatrix} 3 & 24 \\ 5 & 12 \end{vmatrix} = 36 - 120 = -84$$

Find the solutions by Cramer's Rule:

$$x = \frac{D_x}{D} = \frac{168}{42} = 4 \qquad y = \frac{D_y}{D} = \frac{-84}{42} = -2$$

(b) Use MATRIX EDIT to create the matrices   Then compute

$$A = \begin{vmatrix} 3 & -6 \\ 5 & 4 \end{vmatrix}; \quad B = \begin{vmatrix} 24 & -6 \\ 12 & 4 \end{vmatrix}; \quad C = \begin{vmatrix} 3 & 24 \\ 5 & 12 \end{vmatrix}$$

$$x = \det([B]) / \det([A]);$$

$$y = \det([C]) / \det([A])$$

19. (a) Set up and evaluate the determinants to use Cramer's Rule:

$$\begin{cases} 3x - 2y = 4 \\ 6x - 4y = 0 \end{cases}$$

$$D = \begin{vmatrix} 3 & -2 \\ 6 & -4 \end{vmatrix} = -12 - (-12) = 0$$

Since $D = 0$, Cramer's Rule does not apply.

(b) Use MATRIX EDIT to create the matrix   Then compute det([A]):

$$A = \begin{vmatrix} 3 & -2 \\ 6 & -4 \end{vmatrix}$$

Cramer's Rule does not apply.

21.   Set up and evaluate the determinants to use Cramer's Rule:

$$\begin{cases} 2x - 4y = -2 \\ 3x + 2y = 3 \end{cases}$$

$$D = \begin{vmatrix} 2 & -4 \\ 3 & 2 \end{vmatrix} = 4 - (-12) = 16$$

$$D_x = \begin{vmatrix} -2 & -4 \\ 3 & 2 \end{vmatrix} = -4 - (-12) = 8; \quad D_y = \begin{vmatrix} 2 & -2 \\ 3 & 3 \end{vmatrix} = 6 - (-6) = 12$$

Find the solutions by Cramer's Rule:

$$x = \frac{D_x}{D} = \frac{8}{16} = \frac{1}{2} \qquad y = \frac{D_y}{D} = \frac{12}{16} = \frac{3}{4}$$

(b) Use MATRIX EDIT to create the matrices

$$A = \begin{vmatrix} 2 & -4 \\ 3 & 2 \end{vmatrix}; \quad B = \begin{vmatrix} -2 & -4 \\ 3 & 2 \end{vmatrix}; \quad C = \begin{vmatrix} 2 & -2 \\ 3 & 3 \end{vmatrix}$$

Then compute

$$x = \det([B])/\det([A]);$$

$$y = \det([C])/\det([A])$$

23.   (a) Set up and evaluate the determinants to use Cramer's Rule:

$$\begin{cases} 2x - 3y = -1 \\ 10x + 10y = 5 \end{cases}$$

$$D = \begin{vmatrix} 2 & -3 \\ 10 & 10 \end{vmatrix} = 20 - (-30) = 50$$

$$D_x = \begin{vmatrix} -1 & -3 \\ 5 & 10 \end{vmatrix} = -10 - (-15) = 5; \quad D_y = \begin{vmatrix} 2 & -1 \\ 10 & 5 \end{vmatrix} = 10 - (-10) = 20$$

Find the solutions by Cramer's Rule:

$$x = \frac{D_x}{D} = \frac{5}{50} = \frac{1}{10} \qquad y = \frac{D_y}{D} = \frac{20}{50} = \frac{2}{5}$$

(b) Use MATRIX EDIT to create the matrices

$$A = \begin{vmatrix} 2 & -3 \\ 10 & 10 \end{vmatrix}; \quad B = \begin{vmatrix} -1 & -3 \\ 5 & 10 \end{vmatrix}; \quad C = \begin{vmatrix} 2 & -1 \\ 10 & 5 \end{vmatrix}$$

Then compute

$$x = \det([B])/\det([A]);$$

$y = \det([C])/\det([A])$

25.   (a) Set up and evaluate the determinants to use Cramer's Rule:

$$\begin{cases} 2x + 3y = 6 \\ x - y = \dfrac{1}{2} \end{cases}$$

$$D = \begin{vmatrix} 2 & 3 \\ 1 & -1 \end{vmatrix} = -2 - 3 = -5$$

$$D_x = \begin{vmatrix} 6 & 3 \\ \frac{1}{2} & -1 \end{vmatrix} = -6 - \frac{3}{2} = -\frac{15}{2}; \quad D_y = \begin{vmatrix} 2 & 6 \\ 1 & \frac{1}{2} \end{vmatrix} = 1 - 6 = -5$$

Find the solutions by Cramer's Rule:

$$x = \frac{D_x}{D} = \frac{\left(-\dfrac{15}{2}\right)}{-5} = \frac{3}{2} \qquad y = \frac{D_y}{D} = \frac{-5}{-5} = 1$$

(b) Use MATRIX EDIT to create the matrices   Then compute

$$A = \begin{vmatrix} 2 & 3 \\ 1 & -1 \end{vmatrix}; \quad B = \begin{vmatrix} 6 & 3 \\ \frac{1}{2} & -1 \end{vmatrix}; \quad C = \begin{vmatrix} 2 & 6 \\ 1 & \frac{1}{2} \end{vmatrix}$$

$x = \det([B])/\det([A]);$

$y = \det([C])/\det([A])$

27. Set up and evaluate the determinants to use Cramer's Rule:

$$\begin{cases} 3x - 5y = 3 \\ 15x + 5y = 21 \end{cases}$$

$$D = \begin{vmatrix} 3 & -5 \\ 15 & 5 \end{vmatrix} = 15 - (-75) = 90$$

$$D_x = \begin{vmatrix} 3 & -5 \\ 21 & 5 \end{vmatrix} = 15 - (-105) = 120; \quad D_y = \begin{vmatrix} 3 & 3 \\ 15 & 21 \end{vmatrix} = 63 - 45 = 18$$

Find the solutions by Cramer's Rule:

$$x = \frac{D_x}{D} = \frac{120}{90} = \frac{4}{3} \qquad y = \frac{D_y}{D} = \frac{18}{90} = \frac{1}{5}$$

(b) Use MATRIX EDIT to create the matrices   Then compute

$$A = \begin{bmatrix} 3 & -5 \\ 15 & 5 \end{bmatrix}; \quad B = \begin{bmatrix} 3 & -5 \\ 21 & 5 \end{bmatrix}; \quad C = \begin{bmatrix} 3 & 3 \\ 15 & 21 \end{bmatrix}$$

$$x = \det([B])/\det([A]);$$

$$y = \det([C])/\det([A])$$

29. Set up and evaluate the determinants to use Cramer's Rule:

$$\begin{cases} x + y - z = 6 \\ 3x - 2y + z = -5 \\ x + 3y - 2z = 14 \end{cases}$$

$$D = \begin{vmatrix} 1 & 1 & -1 \\ 3 & -2 & 1 \\ 1 & 3 & -2 \end{vmatrix} = 1 \begin{vmatrix} -2 & 1 \\ 3 & -2 \end{vmatrix} - 1 \begin{vmatrix} 3 & 1 \\ 1 & -2 \end{vmatrix} + (-1) \begin{vmatrix} 3 & -2 \\ 1 & 3 \end{vmatrix}$$

$$= 1(4 - 3) - 1(-6 - 1) - 1(9 + 2) = 1 + 7 - 11 = -3$$

$$D_x = \begin{vmatrix} 6 & 1 & -1 \\ -5 & -2 & 1 \\ 14 & 3 & -2 \end{vmatrix} = 6 \begin{vmatrix} -2 & 1 \\ 3 & -2 \end{vmatrix} - 1 \begin{vmatrix} -5 & 1 \\ 14 & -2 \end{vmatrix} + (-1) \begin{vmatrix} -5 & -2 \\ 14 & 3 \end{vmatrix}$$

$$= 6(4 - 3) - 1(10 - 14) - 1(-15 + 28) = 6 + 4 - 13 = -3$$

$$D_y = \begin{vmatrix} 1 & 6 & -1 \\ 3 & -5 & 1 \\ 1 & 14 & -2 \end{vmatrix} = 1\begin{vmatrix} -5 & 1 \\ 14 & -2 \end{vmatrix} - 6\begin{vmatrix} 3 & 1 \\ 1 & -2 \end{vmatrix} + (-1)\begin{vmatrix} 3 & -5 \\ 1 & 14 \end{vmatrix}$$

$$= 1(10 - 14) - 6(-6 - 1) - 1(42 + 5) = -4 + 42 - 47 = -9$$

$$\bullet \, D_z = \begin{vmatrix} 1 & 1 & 6 \\ 3 & -2 & -5 \\ 1 & 3 & 14 \end{vmatrix} = 1\begin{vmatrix} -2 & -5 \\ 3 & 14 \end{vmatrix} - 1\begin{vmatrix} 3 & -5 \\ 1 & 14 \end{vmatrix} + 6\begin{vmatrix} 3 & -2 \\ 1 & 3 \end{vmatrix}$$

$$= 1(-28 + 15) - 1(42 + 5) + 6(9 + 2) = -13 - 47 + 66 = 6$$

Find the solutions by Cramer's Rule:

$$x = \frac{D_x}{D} = \frac{-3}{-3} = 1 \qquad y = \frac{D_y}{D} = \frac{-9}{-3} = 3 \qquad z = \frac{D_z}{D} = \frac{6}{-3} = -2$$

(b) Use MATRIX EDIT to create the matrices

$$A = \begin{bmatrix} 1 & 1 & -1 \\ 3 & -2 & 1 \\ 1 & 3 & -2 \end{bmatrix}; \quad B = \begin{bmatrix} 6 & 1 & -1 \\ -5 & -2 & 1 \\ 14 & 3 & -2 \end{bmatrix};$$

$$C = \begin{vmatrix} 1 & 6 & -1 \\ 3 & -5 & 1 \\ 1 & 14 & -2 \end{vmatrix}; \quad D = \begin{bmatrix} 1 & 1 & 6 \\ 3 & -2 & -5 \\ 1 & 3 & 14 \end{bmatrix}$$

Then compute
$x = \det([B])/\det([A]);$
$y = \det([C])/\det([A]);$
$z = \det([D])/\det([A])$

31. (a) Set up and evaluate the determinants to use Cramer's Rule:

$$\begin{cases} x + 2y - z = -3 \\ 2x - 4y + z = -7 \\ -2x + 2y - 3z = 4 \end{cases}$$

$$D = \begin{vmatrix} 1 & 2 & -1 \\ 2 & -4 & 1 \\ -2 & 2 & -3 \end{vmatrix} = 1\begin{vmatrix} -4 & 1 \\ 2 & -3 \end{vmatrix} - 2\begin{vmatrix} 2 & 1 \\ -2 & -3 \end{vmatrix} + (-1)\begin{vmatrix} 2 & -4 \\ -2 & 2 \end{vmatrix}$$

$$= 1(12 - 2) - 2(-6 + 2) - 1(4 - 8) = 10 + 8 + 4 = 22$$

$$D_x = \begin{vmatrix} -3 & 2 & -1 \\ -7 & -4 & 1 \\ 4 & 2 & -3 \end{vmatrix} = -3\begin{vmatrix} -4 & 1 \\ 2 & -3 \end{vmatrix} - 2\begin{vmatrix} -7 & 1 \\ 4 & -3 \end{vmatrix} + (-1)\begin{vmatrix} -7 & -4 \\ 4 & 2 \end{vmatrix}$$

$$= -3(12 - 2) - 2(21 - 4) - 1(-14 + 16) = -30 - 34 - 2 = -66$$

$$D_y = \begin{vmatrix} 1 & -3 & -1 \\ 2 & -7 & 1 \\ -2 & 4 & -3 \end{vmatrix} = 1\begin{vmatrix} -7 & 1 \\ 4 & -3 \end{vmatrix} - (-3)\begin{vmatrix} 2 & 1 \\ -2 & -3 \end{vmatrix} + (-1)\begin{vmatrix} 2 & -7 \\ -2 & 4 \end{vmatrix}$$

$$= 1(21-4) + 3(-6+2) - 1(8-14) = 17 - 12 + 6 = 11$$

$$D_z = \begin{vmatrix} 1 & 2 & -3 \\ 2 & -4 & -7 \\ -2 & 2 & 4 \end{vmatrix} = 1\begin{vmatrix} -4 & -7 \\ 2 & 4 \end{vmatrix} - 2\begin{vmatrix} 2 & -7 \\ -2 & 4 \end{vmatrix} + (-3)\begin{vmatrix} 2 & -4 \\ -2 & 2 \end{vmatrix}$$

$$= 1(-16+14) - 2(8-14) - 3(4-8) = -2 + 12 + 12 = 22$$

Find the solutions by Cramer's Rule:

$$x = \frac{D_x}{D} = \frac{-66}{22} = -3 \qquad y = \frac{D_y}{D} = \frac{11}{22} = \frac{1}{2} \qquad z = \frac{D_z}{D} = \frac{22}{22} = 1$$

(b) Use MATRIX EDIT to create the matrices

$$A = \begin{bmatrix} 1 & 2 & -1 \\ 2 & -4 & 1 \\ -2 & 2 & -3 \end{bmatrix}; \quad B = \begin{bmatrix} -3 & 2 & -1 \\ -7 & -4 & 1 \\ 4 & 2 & -3 \end{bmatrix};$$

$$C = \begin{bmatrix} 1 & -3 & -1 \\ 2 & -7 & 1 \\ -2 & 4 & -3 \end{bmatrix}; \quad D = \begin{bmatrix} 1 & 2 & -3 \\ 2 & -4 & -7 \\ -2 & 2 & 4 \end{bmatrix}$$

Then compute
$$x = \det([B])/\det([A]);$$
$$y = \det([C])/\det([A]);$$
$$z = \det([D])/\det([A])$$

33. (a) Set up and evaluate the determinants to use Cramer's Rule:

$$\begin{cases} x - 2y + 3z = 1 \\ 3x + y - 2z = 0 \\ 2x - 4y + 6z = 2 \end{cases}$$

$$D = \begin{vmatrix} 1 & -2 & 3 \\ 3 & 1 & -2 \\ 2 & -4 & 6 \end{vmatrix} = 1\begin{vmatrix} 1 & -2 \\ -4 & 6 \end{vmatrix} - (-2)\begin{vmatrix} 3 & -2 \\ 2 & 6 \end{vmatrix} + 3\begin{vmatrix} 3 & 1 \\ 2 & -4 \end{vmatrix}$$

$$= 1(6-8) + 2(18+4) + 3(-12-2) = -2 + 44 - 42 = 0$$

Since $D = 0$, Cramer's Rule does not apply.

(b) Use MATRIX EDIT to create the matrices

$$A = \begin{vmatrix} 1 & -2 & 3 \\ 3 & 1 & -2 \\ 2 & -4 & 6 \end{vmatrix}$$

Then compute det([A]):

Cramer's Rule does not apply.

35. (a) Set up and evaluate the determinants to use Cramer's Rule:

$$\begin{cases} x + 2y - \ z = 0 \\ 2x - 4y + \ z = 0 \\ -2x + 2y - 3z = 0 \end{cases}$$

$$D = \begin{vmatrix} 1 & 2 & -1 \\ 2 & -4 & 1 \\ -2 & 2 & -3 \end{vmatrix} = 1\begin{vmatrix} -4 & 1 \\ 2 & -3 \end{vmatrix} - 2\begin{vmatrix} 2 & 1 \\ -2 & -3 \end{vmatrix} + (-1)\begin{vmatrix} 2 & -4 \\ -2 & 2 \end{vmatrix}$$

$$= 1(12 - 2) - 2(-6 + 2) - 1(4 - 8) = 10 + 8 + 4 = 22$$

$$D_x = \begin{vmatrix} 0 & 2 & -1 \\ 0 & -4 & 1 \\ 0 & 2 & -3 \end{vmatrix} = 0 \quad \text{(By Theorem 12)}$$

$$D_y = \begin{vmatrix} 1 & 0 & -1 \\ 2 & 0 & 1 \\ -2 & 0 & -3 \end{vmatrix} = 0 \quad \text{(By Theorem 12)}; \quad D_z = \begin{vmatrix} 1 & 2 & 0 \\ 2 & -4 & 0 \\ -2 & 2 & 0 \end{vmatrix} = 0 \quad \text{(By Theorem 12)}$$

Find the solutions by Cramer's Rule:

$$x = \frac{D_x}{D} = \frac{0}{22} = 0 \qquad y = \frac{D_y}{D} = \frac{0}{22} = 0 \qquad z = \frac{D_z}{D} = \frac{0}{22} = 0$$

(b) Use MATRIX EDIT to create the matrices

$$A = \begin{vmatrix} 1 & 2 & -1 \\ 2 & -4 & 1 \\ -2 & 2 & -3 \end{vmatrix}; \quad B = \begin{vmatrix} 0 & 2 & -1 \\ 0 & -4 & 1 \\ 0 & 2 & -3 \end{vmatrix};$$

$$C = \begin{vmatrix} 1 & 0 & -1 \\ 2 & 0 & 1 \\ -2 & 0 & -3 \end{vmatrix}; \quad D = \begin{vmatrix} 1 & 2 & 0 \\ 2 & -4 & 0 \\ -2 & 2 & 0 \end{vmatrix}$$

Then compute
$$x = \det([B])/\det([A]);$$
$$y = \det([C])/\det([A]);$$
$$z = \det([D])/\det([A])$$

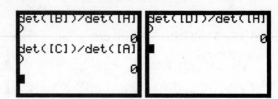

37. (a) Set up and evaluate the determinants to use Cramer's Rule:

$$\begin{cases} x - 2y + 3z = 0 \\ 3x + y - 2z = 0 \\ 2x - 4y + 6z = 0 \end{cases}$$

$$D = \begin{vmatrix} 1 & -2 & 3 \\ 3 & 1 & -2 \\ 2 & -4 & 6 \end{vmatrix} = 1\begin{vmatrix} 1 & -2 \\ -4 & 6 \end{vmatrix} - (-2)\begin{vmatrix} 3 & -2 \\ 2 & 6 \end{vmatrix} + 3\begin{vmatrix} 3 & 1 \\ 2 & -4 \end{vmatrix}$$

$$= 1(6-8) + 2(18+4) + 3(-12-2) = -2 + 44 - 42 = 0$$

Since $D = 0$, Cramer's Rule does not apply.

(b) Use MATRIX EDIT to create the matrices

$$A = \begin{vmatrix} 1 & -2 & 3 \\ 3 & 1 & -2 \\ 2 & -4 & 6 \end{vmatrix}$$

Then compute det([A]):

Cramer's Rule does not apply.

39. (a) Rewrite the system letting $u = \dfrac{1}{x}$ and $v = \dfrac{1}{y}$:

$$\begin{cases} \dfrac{1}{x} + \dfrac{1}{y} = 8 \\ \dfrac{3}{x} - \dfrac{5}{y} = 0 \end{cases} \rightarrow \begin{cases} u + v = 8 \\ 3u - 5v = 0 \end{cases}$$

Set up and evaluate the determinants to use Cramer's Rule:

$$D = \begin{vmatrix} 1 & 1 \\ 3 & -5 \end{vmatrix} = -5 - 3 = -8; \quad D_u = \begin{vmatrix} 8 & 1 \\ 0 & -5 \end{vmatrix} = -40 - 0 = -40; \quad D_v = \begin{vmatrix} 1 & 8 \\ 3 & 0 \end{vmatrix} = 0 - 24 = -24$$

Find the solutions by Cramer's Rule:

$$u = \frac{D_u}{D} = \frac{-40}{-8} = 5 \Rightarrow \frac{1}{x} = 5 \Rightarrow x = \frac{1}{5}$$

$$v = \frac{D_v}{D} = \frac{-24}{-8} = 3 \Rightarrow \frac{1}{y} = 3 \Rightarrow y = \frac{1}{3}$$

The solutions are $x = \dfrac{1}{5}$, $y = \dfrac{1}{3}$.

(b) Use MATRIX EDIT to create the matrices

$$A = \begin{vmatrix} 1 & 1 \\ 3 & -5 \end{vmatrix}; \quad B = \begin{vmatrix} 8 & 1 \\ 0 & -5 \end{vmatrix}; \quad C = \begin{vmatrix} 1 & 8 \\ 3 & 0 \end{vmatrix}$$

Then compute

$u = \det([B])/\det([A]);$
$v = \det([C])/\det([A])$

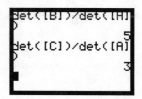

41. Solve for x:

$$\begin{vmatrix} x & x \\ 4 & 3 \end{vmatrix} = 3x - 4x = -x \Rightarrow -x = 5 \Rightarrow x = -5$$

43. Solve for x:

$$\begin{vmatrix} x & 1 & 1 \\ 4 & 3 & 2 \\ -1 & 2 & 5 \end{vmatrix} = x \begin{vmatrix} 3 & 2 \\ 2 & 5 \end{vmatrix} - 1 \begin{vmatrix} 4 & 2 \\ -1 & 5 \end{vmatrix} + 1 \begin{vmatrix} 4 & 3 \\ -1 & 2 \end{vmatrix}$$

$$= x(15 - 4) - (20 + 2) + (8 + 3) = 11x - 22 + 11 = 11x - 11$$

So, $11x - 11 = 2 \Rightarrow 11x = 13 \Rightarrow x = \dfrac{13}{11}$

45. Solve for x:

$$\begin{vmatrix} x & 2 & 3 \\ 1 & x & 0 \\ 6 & 1 & -2 \end{vmatrix} = x \begin{vmatrix} x & 0 \\ 1 & -2 \end{vmatrix} - 2 \begin{vmatrix} 1 & 0 \\ 6 & -2 \end{vmatrix} + 3 \begin{vmatrix} 1 & x \\ 6 & 1 \end{vmatrix}$$

$$= x(-2x - 0) - 2(-2 - 0) + 3(1 - 6x)$$

$$= -2x^2 + 4 + 3 - 18x = -2x^2 - 18x + 7$$

So, $-2x^2 - 18x + 7 = 7 \Rightarrow -2x^2 - 18x = 0 \Rightarrow -2x(x + 9) = 0 \Rightarrow x = 0$ or $x = -9$

47. Let $\begin{vmatrix} x & y & z \\ u & v & w \\ 1 & 2 & 3 \end{vmatrix} = 4$

Then $\begin{vmatrix} 1 & 2 & 3 \\ u & v & w \\ x & y & z \end{vmatrix} = -4$ by Theorem 11

The value of the determinant changes sign when two rows are interchanged.

Problems 49 – 53 use the Laws for Determinants in reverse order.

49. Let $\begin{vmatrix} x & y & z \\ u & v & w \\ 1 & 2 & 3 \end{vmatrix} = 4$

$$\begin{vmatrix} x & y & z \\ -3 & -6 & -9 \\ u & v & w \end{vmatrix} = -3 \begin{vmatrix} x & y & z \\ 1 & 2 & 3 \\ u & v & w \end{vmatrix} = -3(-1) \begin{vmatrix} x & y & z \\ u & v & w \\ 1 & 2 & 3 \end{vmatrix} = 3(4) = 12$$

$\qquad\qquad$ Theorem 14 $\qquad\qquad$ Theorem 11

51. Let $\begin{vmatrix} x & y & z \\ u & v & w \\ 1 & 2 & 3 \end{vmatrix} = 4$

$$\begin{vmatrix} 1 & 2 & 3 \\ x-3 & y-6 & z-9 \\ 2u & 2v & 2w \end{vmatrix} = 2 \begin{vmatrix} 1 & 2 & 3 \\ x-3 & y-6 & z-9 \\ u & v & w \end{vmatrix} = 2(-1) \begin{vmatrix} x-3 & y-6 & z-9 \\ 1 & 2 & 3 \\ u & v & w \end{vmatrix}$$

$\qquad\qquad\qquad$ Theorem 14 $\qquad\qquad\qquad$ Theorem 11

$$= 2(-1)(-1) \begin{vmatrix} x-3 & y-6 & z-9 \\ u & v & w \\ 1 & 2 & 3 \end{vmatrix} = 2(-1)(-1) \begin{vmatrix} x & y & z \\ u & v & w \\ 1 & 2 & 3 \end{vmatrix} = 2(-1)(-1)(4) = 8$$

$\qquad$ Theorem 11 $\qquad\qquad\qquad$ Theorem 15 $\;(R_1 = -3r_3 + r_1)$

53. Let $\begin{vmatrix} x & y & z \\ u & v & w \\ 1 & 2 & 3 \end{vmatrix} = 4$

$$\begin{vmatrix} 1 & 2 & 3 \\ 2x & 2y & 2z \\ u-1 & v-2 & w-3 \end{vmatrix} = 2 \begin{vmatrix} 1 & 2 & 3 \\ x & y & z \\ u-1 & v-2 & w-3 \end{vmatrix} = 2(-1) \begin{vmatrix} x & y & z \\ 1 & 2 & 3 \\ u-1 & v-2 & w-3 \end{vmatrix}$$

$\qquad\qquad\qquad$ Theorem 14 $\qquad\qquad\qquad$ Theorem 11

$$= 2(-1)(-1) \begin{vmatrix} x & y & z \\ u-1 & v-2 & w-3 \\ 1 & 2 & 3 \end{vmatrix} = 2(-1)(-1) \begin{vmatrix} x & y & z \\ u & v & w \\ 1 & 2 & 3 \end{vmatrix} = 2(-1)(-1)(4) = 8$$

$\qquad$ Theorem 11 $\qquad\qquad\qquad$ Theorem 15 $\;(R_2 = -r_3 + r_2)$

55. Expanding the determinant:

$$\begin{vmatrix} x & y & 1 \\ x_1 & y_1 & 1 \\ x_2 & y_2 & 1 \end{vmatrix} = x \begin{vmatrix} y_1 & 1 \\ y_2 & 1 \end{vmatrix} - y \begin{vmatrix} x_1 & 1 \\ x_2 & 1 \end{vmatrix} + 1 \begin{vmatrix} x_1 & y_1 \\ x_2 & y_2 \end{vmatrix}$$

$$= x(y_1 - y_2) - y(x_1 - x_2) + (x_1 y_2 - x_2 y_1) = 0$$

$$x(y_1 - y_2) + y(x_2 - x_1) = x_2 y_1 - x_1 y_2$$

$$y(x_2 - x_1) = x_2 y_1 - x_1 y_2 + x(y_2 - y_1)$$

$$y(x_2 - x_1) - y_1(x_2 - x_1) = x_2 y_1 - x_1 y_2 + x(y_2 - y_1) - y_1(x_2 - x_1)$$

$$(x_2 - x_1)(y - y_1) = x(y_2 - y_1) + x_2 y_1 - x_1 y_2 - y_1 x_2 + y_1 x_1$$

$$(x_2 - x_1)(y - y_1) = (y_2 - y_1)x - (y_2 - y_1)x_1$$

$$(x_2 - x_1)(y - y_1) = (y_2 - y_1)(x - x_1) \Rightarrow (y - y_1) = \frac{(y_2 - y_1)}{(x_2 - x_1)}(x - x_1)$$

57. Expanding the determinant:

$$\begin{vmatrix} x^2 & x & 1 \\ y^2 & y & 1 \\ z^2 & z & 1 \end{vmatrix} = x^2 \begin{vmatrix} y & 1 \\ z & 1 \end{vmatrix} - x \begin{vmatrix} y^2 & 1 \\ z^2 & 1 \end{vmatrix} + 1 \begin{vmatrix} y^2 & y \\ z^2 & z \end{vmatrix}$$

$$= x^2(y - z) - x(y^2 - z^2) + 1(y^2 z - z^2 y)$$

$$= x^2(y - z) - x(y - z)(y + z) + yz(y - z)$$

$$= (y - z)\left[x^2 - xy - xz + yz\right]$$

$$= (y - z)\left[x(x - y) - z(x - y)\right] = (y - z)(x - y)(x - z)$$

59. Evaluating the determinant to show the relationship:

$$\begin{vmatrix} a_{13} & a_{12} & a_{11} \\ a_{23} & a_{22} & a_{21} \\ a_{33} & a_{32} & a_{31} \end{vmatrix} = a_{13} \begin{vmatrix} a_{22} & a_{21} \\ a_{32} & a_{31} \end{vmatrix} - a_{12} \begin{vmatrix} a_{23} & a_{21} \\ a_{33} & a_{31} \end{vmatrix} + a_{11} \begin{vmatrix} a_{23} & a_{22} \\ a_{33} & a_{32} \end{vmatrix}$$

$$= a_{13}(a_{22}a_{31} - a_{21}a_{32}) - a_{12}(a_{23}a_{31} - a_{21}a_{33}) + a_{11}(a_{23}a_{32} - a_{22}a_{33})$$

$$= a_{13}a_{22}a_{31} - a_{13}a_{21}a_{32} - a_{12}a_{23}a_{31} + a_{12}a_{21}a_{33} + a_{11}a_{23}a_{32} - a_{11}a_{22}a_{33}$$

$$= -a_{11}a_{22}a_{33} + a_{11}a_{23}a_{32} + a_{12}a_{21}a_{33} - a_{12}a_{23}a_{31} - a_{13}a_{21}a_{32} + a_{13}a_{22}a_{31}$$

$$= -a_{11}(a_{22}a_{33} - a_{23}a_{32}) + a_{12}(a_{21}a_{33} - a_{23}a_{31}) - a_{13}(a_{21}a_{32} - a_{22}a_{31})$$

$$= -a_{11} \begin{vmatrix} a_{22} & a_{23} \\ a_{32} & a_{33} \end{vmatrix} + a_{12} \begin{vmatrix} a_{21} & a_{23} \\ a_{31} & a_{33} \end{vmatrix} - a_{13} \begin{vmatrix} a_{21} & a_{22} \\ a_{31} & a_{32} \end{vmatrix}$$

$$= -\left[a_{11} \begin{vmatrix} a_{22} & a_{23} \\ a_{32} & a_{33} \end{vmatrix} - a_{12} \begin{vmatrix} a_{21} & a_{23} \\ a_{31} & a_{33} \end{vmatrix} + a_{13} \begin{vmatrix} a_{21} & a_{22} \\ a_{31} & a_{32} \end{vmatrix} \right] = - \begin{vmatrix} a_{11} & a_{12} & a_{13} \\ a_{21} & a_{22} & a_{23} \\ a_{31} & a_{32} & a_{33} \end{vmatrix}$$

61. Set up a 3 by 3 determinant in which the first column and third column are the same and evaluate:

$$\begin{vmatrix} a & b & a \\ c & d & c \\ e & f & e \end{vmatrix} = -b \begin{vmatrix} c & c \\ e & e \end{vmatrix} + d \begin{vmatrix} a & a \\ e & e \end{vmatrix} - f \begin{vmatrix} a & a \\ c & c \end{vmatrix}$$

$$= -b(ce - ce) + d(ae - ae) - f(ac - ac)$$

$$= -b(0) + d(0) - f(0) = 0$$

Systems of Equations and Inequalities

7.5 Matrix Algebra

1. (a) $A + B = \begin{vmatrix} 0 & 3 & -5 \\ 1 & 2 & 6 \end{vmatrix} + \begin{vmatrix} 4 & 1 & 0 \\ -2 & 3 & -2 \end{vmatrix} = \begin{vmatrix} 0+4 & 3+1 & -5+0 \\ 1+(-2) & 2+3 & 6+(-2) \end{vmatrix} = \begin{vmatrix} 4 & 4 & -5 \\ -1 & 5 & 4 \end{vmatrix}$

    (b) Use MATRIX EDIT to create the matrices $\qquad$ Then compute $[A]+[B]$:

    $A = \begin{bmatrix} 0 & 3 & -5 \\ 1 & 2 & 6 \end{bmatrix}; \quad B = \begin{bmatrix} 4 & 1 & 0 \\ -2 & 3 & -2 \end{bmatrix}$

3. (a) $4A = 4 \begin{bmatrix} 0 & 3 & -5 \\ 1 & 2 & 6 \end{bmatrix} = \begin{bmatrix} 4\cdot0 & 4\cdot3 & 4(-5) \\ 4\cdot1 & 4\cdot2 & 4\cdot6 \end{bmatrix} = \begin{bmatrix} 0 & 12 & -20 \\ 4 & 8 & 24 \end{bmatrix}$

    (b) Use MATRIX EDIT to create the matrix $\qquad$ Then compute $4*[A]$:

    $A = \begin{bmatrix} 0 & 3 & -5 \\ 1 & 2 & 6 \end{bmatrix}$

5. (a) $3A - 2B = 3 \begin{bmatrix} 0 & 3 & -5 \\ 1 & 2 & 6 \end{bmatrix} - 2 \begin{bmatrix} 4 & 1 & 0 \\ -2 & 3 & -2 \end{bmatrix}$

    $= \begin{bmatrix} 0 & 9 & -15 \\ 3 & 6 & 18 \end{bmatrix} - \begin{bmatrix} 8 & 2 & 0 \\ -4 & 6 & -4 \end{bmatrix} = \begin{bmatrix} -8 & 7 & -15 \\ 7 & 0 & 22 \end{bmatrix}$

    (b) Use MATRIX EDIT to create the matrices $\qquad$ Then compute $3*[A]-2*[B]$:

    $A = \begin{bmatrix} 0 & 3 & -5 \\ 1 & 2 & 6 \end{bmatrix}; \quad B = \begin{bmatrix} 4 & 1 & 0 \\ -2 & 3 & -2 \end{bmatrix}$

7.   (a) $AC = \begin{bmatrix} 0 & 3 & -5 \\ 1 & 2 & 6 \end{bmatrix} \cdot \begin{bmatrix} 4 & 1 \\ 6 & 2 \\ -2 & 3 \end{bmatrix}$

$= \begin{bmatrix} 0(4)+3(6)+(-5)(-2) & 0(1)+3(2)+(-5)(3) \\ 1(4)+2(6)+6(-2) & 1(1)+2(2)+6(3) \end{bmatrix} = \begin{bmatrix} 28 & -9 \\ 4 & 23 \end{bmatrix}$

(b) Use MATRIX EDIT to create the matrices   Then compute $[A]*[C]$:

$A = \begin{bmatrix} 0 & 3 & -5 \\ 1 & 2 & 6 \end{bmatrix}; \quad C = \begin{bmatrix} 4 & 1 \\ 6 & 2 \\ -2 & 3 \end{bmatrix}$

9.   (a) $CA = \begin{bmatrix} 4 & 1 \\ 6 & 2 \\ -2 & 3 \end{bmatrix} \cdot \begin{bmatrix} 0 & 3 & -5 \\ 1 & 2 & 6 \end{bmatrix}$

$= \begin{bmatrix} 4(0)+1(1) & 4(3)+1(2) & 4(-5)+1(6) \\ 6(0)+2(1) & 6(3)+2(2) & 6(-5)+2(6) \\ -2(0)+3(1) & -2(3)+3(2) & -2(-5)+3(6) \end{bmatrix} = \begin{bmatrix} 1 & 14 & -14 \\ 2 & 22 & -18 \\ 3 & 0 & 28 \end{bmatrix}$

(b) Use MATRIX EDIT to create the matrices   Then compute $[C]*[A]$:

$A = \begin{bmatrix} 0 & 3 & -5 \\ 1 & 2 & 6 \end{bmatrix}; \quad C = \begin{bmatrix} 4 & 1 \\ 6 & 2 \\ -2 & 3 \end{bmatrix}$

11.   (a) $C(A+B) = \begin{bmatrix} 4 & 1 \\ 6 & 2 \\ -2 & 3 \end{bmatrix} \left(\begin{bmatrix} 0 & 3 & -5 \\ 1 & 2 & 6 \end{bmatrix} + \begin{bmatrix} 4 & 1 & 0 \\ -2 & 3 & -2 \end{bmatrix} \right)$

$= \begin{bmatrix} 4 & 1 \\ 6 & 2 \\ -2 & 3 \end{bmatrix} \cdot \begin{bmatrix} 4 & 4 & -5 \\ -1 & 5 & 4 \end{bmatrix} = \begin{bmatrix} 15 & 21 & -16 \\ 22 & 34 & -22 \\ -11 & 7 & 22 \end{bmatrix}$

(b) Use MATRIX EDIT to create the matrices   Then compute $[C]*([A]+[B])$:

$A = \begin{bmatrix} 0 & 3 & -5 \\ 1 & 2 & 6 \end{bmatrix}; \quad B = \begin{bmatrix} 4 & 1 & 0 \\ -2 & 3 & -2 \end{bmatrix}; \quad C = \begin{bmatrix} 4 & 1 \\ 6 & 2 \\ -2 & 3 \end{bmatrix}$

13. (a) $AC - 3I_2 = \begin{bmatrix} 0 & 3 & -5 \\ 1 & 2 & 6 \end{bmatrix} \cdot \begin{bmatrix} 4 & 1 \\ 6 & 2 \\ -2 & 3 \end{bmatrix} - 3 \begin{bmatrix} 1 & 0 \\ 0 & 1 \end{bmatrix} = \begin{bmatrix} 28 & -9 \\ 4 & 23 \end{bmatrix} - \begin{bmatrix} 3 & 0 \\ 0 & 3 \end{bmatrix} = \begin{bmatrix} 25 & -9 \\ 4 & 20 \end{bmatrix}$

(b) Use MATRIX EDIT to create the matrices   Then compute
$[A]*[C]-3*\text{identity}(2)$:

$A = \begin{bmatrix} 0 & 3 & -5 \\ 1 & 2 & 6 \end{bmatrix}$; $C = \begin{bmatrix} 4 & 1 \\ 6 & 2 \\ -2 & 3 \end{bmatrix}$

15. (a) $CA - CB = \begin{bmatrix} 4 & 1 \\ 6 & 2 \\ -2 & 3 \end{bmatrix} \cdot \begin{bmatrix} 0 & 3 & -5 \\ 1 & 2 & 6 \end{bmatrix} - \begin{bmatrix} 4 & 1 \\ 6 & 2 \\ -2 & 3 \end{bmatrix} \cdot \begin{bmatrix} 4 & 1 & 0 \\ -2 & 3 & -2 \end{bmatrix}$

$= \begin{bmatrix} 1 & 14 & -14 \\ 2 & 22 & -18 \\ 3 & 0 & 28 \end{bmatrix} - \begin{bmatrix} 14 & 7 & -2 \\ 20 & 12 & -4 \\ -14 & 7 & -6 \end{bmatrix} = \begin{bmatrix} -13 & 7 & -12 \\ -18 & 10 & -14 \\ 17 & -7 & 34 \end{bmatrix}$

(b) Use MATRIX EDIT to create the matrices   Then compute $[C]*[A]-[C]*[B]$:

$A = \begin{bmatrix} 0 & 3 & -5 \\ 1 & 2 & 6 \end{bmatrix}$; $B = \begin{bmatrix} 4 & 1 & 0 \\ -2 & 3 & -2 \end{bmatrix}$; $C = \begin{bmatrix} 4 & 1 \\ 6 & 2 \\ -2 & 3 \end{bmatrix}$

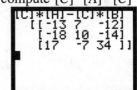

410

17. (a) $\begin{vmatrix} 2 & -2 \\ 1 & 0 \end{vmatrix}\begin{vmatrix} 2 & 1 & 4 & 6 \\ 3 & -1 & 3 & 2 \end{vmatrix}$

$$= \begin{bmatrix} 2(2)+(-2)(3) & 2(1)+(-2)(-1) & 2(4)+(-2)(3) & 2(6)+(-2)(2) \\ 1(2)+0(3) & 1(1)+0(-1) & 1(4)+0(3) & 1(6)+0(2) \end{bmatrix}$$

$$= \begin{bmatrix} -2 & 4 & 2 & 8 \\ 2 & 1 & 4 & 6 \end{bmatrix}$$

(b) Use MATRIX EDIT to create the matrices   Then compute $[A]*[B]$:

$A = \begin{vmatrix} 2 & -2 \\ 1 & 0 \end{vmatrix}; \ B = \begin{vmatrix} 2 & 1 & 4 & 6 \\ 3 & -1 & 3 & 2 \end{vmatrix}$

19. (a) $\begin{vmatrix} 1 & 0 & 1 \\ 2 & 4 & 1 \\ 3 & 6 & 1 \end{vmatrix}\begin{vmatrix} 1 & 3 \\ 6 & 2 \\ 8 & -1 \end{vmatrix} = \begin{vmatrix} 1(1)+0(6)+1(8) & 1(3)+0(2)+1(-1) \\ 2(1)+4(6)+1(8) & 2(3)+4(2)+1(-1) \\ 3(1)+6(6)+1(8) & 3(3)+6(2)+1(-1) \end{vmatrix} = \begin{vmatrix} 9 & 2 \\ 34 & 13 \\ 47 & 20 \end{vmatrix}$

(b) Use MATRIX EDIT to create the matrices   Then compute $[A]*[B]$:

$A = \begin{vmatrix} 1 & 0 & 1 \\ 2 & 4 & 1 \\ 3 & 6 & 1 \end{vmatrix}; \ B = \begin{vmatrix} 1 & 3 \\ 6 & 2 \\ 8 & -1 \end{vmatrix}$

21. Augment the matrix with the identity and use row operations to find the inverse:

$$A = \begin{bmatrix} 2 & 1 \\ 1 & 1 \end{bmatrix} \ \rightarrow \ \begin{bmatrix} 2 & 1 & | & 1 & 0 \\ 1 & 1 & | & 0 & 1 \end{bmatrix}$$

$$\rightarrow \begin{bmatrix} 1 & 1 & | & 0 & 1 \\ 2 & 1 & | & 1 & 0 \end{bmatrix} \rightarrow \begin{bmatrix} 1 & 1 & | & 0 & 1 \\ 0 & -1 & | & 1 & -2 \end{bmatrix} \rightarrow \begin{bmatrix} 1 & 1 & | & 0 & 1 \\ 0 & 1 & | & -1 & 2 \end{bmatrix} \rightarrow \begin{bmatrix} 1 & 0 & | & 1 & -1 \\ 0 & 1 & | & -1 & 2 \end{bmatrix}$$

Interchange $R_2 = -2r_1 + r_2$ $R_2 = -r_2$ $R_1 = -r_2 + r_1$

r_1 and r_2

$$A^{-1} = \begin{bmatrix} 1 & -1 \\ -1 & 2 \end{bmatrix}$$

23. Augment the matrix with the identity and use row operations to find the inverse:

$$A = \begin{bmatrix} 6 & 5 \\ 2 & 2 \end{bmatrix} \ \rightarrow \ \begin{bmatrix} 6 & 5 & | & 1 & 0 \\ 2 & 2 & | & 0 & 1 \end{bmatrix}$$

$$\rightarrow \begin{bmatrix} 2 & 2 & | & 0 & 1 \\ 6 & 5 & | & 1 & 0 \end{bmatrix} \rightarrow \begin{bmatrix} 2 & 2 & | & 0 & 1 \\ 0 & -1 & | & 1 & -3 \end{bmatrix} \rightarrow \begin{bmatrix} 1 & 1 & | & 0 & \frac{1}{2} \\ 0 & 1 & | & -1 & 3 \end{bmatrix} \rightarrow \begin{bmatrix} 1 & 0 & | & 1 & -\frac{5}{2} \\ 0 & 1 & | & -1 & 3 \end{bmatrix}$$

Interchange $\quad R_2 = -3r_1 + r_2 \quad R_1 = \frac{1}{2}r_1 \quad\quad R_1 = -r_2 + r_1$

r_1 and r_2 $\quad\quad\quad\quad\quad\quad\quad\quad\quad\quad R_2 = -r_2$

$$A^{-1} = \begin{bmatrix} 1 & -\frac{5}{2} \\ -1 & 3 \end{bmatrix}$$

25. Augment the matrix with the identity and use row operations to find the inverse:

$$A = \begin{bmatrix} 2 & 1 \\ a & a \end{bmatrix} \rightarrow \begin{bmatrix} 2 & 1 & | & 1 & 0 \\ a & a & | & 0 & 1 \end{bmatrix} \text{ where } a \neq 0.$$

$$\rightarrow \begin{bmatrix} 1 & \frac{1}{2} & | & \frac{1}{2} & 0 \\ a & a & | & 0 & 1 \end{bmatrix} \rightarrow \begin{bmatrix} 1 & \frac{1}{2} & | & \frac{1}{2} & 0 \\ 0 & \frac{1}{2}a & | & -\frac{1}{2}a & 1 \end{bmatrix} \rightarrow \begin{bmatrix} 1 & \frac{1}{2} & | & \frac{1}{2} & 0 \\ 0 & 1 & | & -1 & \frac{2}{a} \end{bmatrix} \rightarrow \begin{bmatrix} 1 & 0 & | & 1 & -\frac{1}{a} \\ 0 & 1 & | & -1 & \frac{2}{a} \end{bmatrix}$$

$R_1 = \frac{1}{2}r_1 \quad\quad\quad R_2 = -ar_1 + r_2 \quad R_2 = \left(\frac{2}{a}\right)r_2 \quad R_1 = -\frac{1}{2}r_2 + r_1$

$$A^{-1} = \begin{bmatrix} 1 & -\frac{1}{a} \\ -1 & \frac{2}{a} \end{bmatrix}$$

27. Augment the matrix with the identity and use row operations to find the inverse:

$$A = \begin{bmatrix} 1 & -1 & 1 \\ 0 & -2 & 1 \\ -2 & -3 & 0 \end{bmatrix} \rightarrow \begin{bmatrix} 1 & -1 & 1 & | & 1 & 0 & 0 \\ 0 & -2 & 1 & | & 0 & 1 & 0 \\ -2 & -3 & 0 & | & 0 & 0 & 1 \end{bmatrix}$$

$$\rightarrow \begin{bmatrix} 1 & -1 & 1 & | & 1 & 0 & 0 \\ 0 & -2 & 1 & | & 0 & 1 & 0 \\ 0 & -5 & 2 & | & 2 & 0 & 1 \end{bmatrix} \rightarrow \begin{bmatrix} 1 & -1 & 1 & | & 1 & 0 & 0 \\ 0 & 1 & -\frac{1}{2} & | & 0 & -\frac{1}{2} & 0 \\ 0 & -5 & 2 & | & 2 & 0 & 1 \end{bmatrix} \rightarrow \begin{bmatrix} 1 & 0 & \frac{1}{2} & | & 1 & -\frac{1}{2} & 0 \\ 0 & 1 & -\frac{1}{2} & | & 0 & -\frac{1}{2} & 0 \\ 0 & 0 & -\frac{1}{2} & | & 2 & -\frac{5}{2} & 1 \end{bmatrix}$$

$R_3 = 2r_1 + r_3 \quad\quad\quad R_2 = -\frac{1}{2}r_2 \quad\quad\quad\quad R_1 = r_2 + r_1$

$\quad\quad\quad\quad\quad\quad\quad\quad\quad\quad\quad\quad\quad\quad\quad\quad\quad\quad\quad R_3 = 5r_2 + r_3$

$$\rightarrow \begin{bmatrix} 1 & 0 & \frac{1}{2} & | & 1 & -\frac{1}{2} & 0 \\ 0 & 1 & -\frac{1}{2} & | & 0 & -\frac{1}{2} & 0 \\ 0 & 0 & 1 & | & -4 & 5 & -2 \end{bmatrix} \rightarrow \begin{bmatrix} 1 & 0 & 0 & | & 3 & -3 & 1 \\ 0 & 1 & 0 & | & -2 & 2 & -1 \\ 0 & 0 & 1 & | & -4 & 5 & -2 \end{bmatrix}$$

$R_3 = -2r_3 \quad\quad\quad\quad\quad R_1 = -\frac{1}{2}r_3 + r_1$

$\quad\quad\quad\quad\quad\quad\quad\quad\quad R_2 = \frac{1}{2}r_3 + r_2$

$$A^{-1} = \begin{bmatrix} 3 & -3 & 1 \\ -2 & 2 & -1 \\ -4 & 5 & -2 \end{bmatrix}$$

29. Augment the matrix with the identity and use row operations to find the inverse:

$$A = \begin{bmatrix} 1 & 1 & 1 \\ 3 & 2 & -1 \\ 3 & 1 & 2 \end{bmatrix} \rightarrow \begin{bmatrix} 1 & 1 & 1 & | & 1 & 0 & 0 \\ 3 & 2 & -1 & | & 0 & 1 & 0 \\ 3 & 1 & 2 & | & 0 & 0 & 1 \end{bmatrix}$$

$$\rightarrow \begin{bmatrix} 1 & 1 & 1 & | & 1 & 0 & 0 \\ 0 & -1 & -4 & | & -3 & 1 & 0 \\ 0 & -2 & -1 & | & -3 & 0 & 1 \end{bmatrix} \rightarrow \begin{bmatrix} 1 & 1 & 1 & | & 1 & 0 & 0 \\ 0 & 1 & 4 & | & 3 & -1 & 0 \\ 0 & -2 & -1 & | & -3 & 0 & 1 \end{bmatrix} \rightarrow \begin{bmatrix} 1 & 0 & -3 & | & -2 & 1 & 0 \\ 0 & 1 & 4 & | & 3 & -1 & 0 \\ 0 & 0 & 7 & | & 3 & -2 & 1 \end{bmatrix}$$

$R_2 = -3r_1 + r_2 \quad\quad R_2 = -r_2 \quad\quad\quad\quad R_1 = -r_2 + r_1$

$R_3 = -3r_1 + r_3 \quad\quad\quad\quad\quad\quad\quad\quad\quad\quad\quad R_3 = 2r_2 + r_3$

$$\to \begin{vmatrix} 1 & 0 & -3 \\ 0 & 1 & 4 \\ 0 & 0 & 1 \end{vmatrix}\begin{matrix} -2 & 1 & 0 \\ 3 & -1 & 0 \\ \frac{3}{7} & -\frac{2}{7} & \frac{1}{7} \end{matrix} \to \begin{vmatrix} 1 & 0 & 0 \\ 0 & 1 & 0 \\ 0 & 0 & 1 \end{vmatrix}\begin{matrix} -\frac{5}{7} & \frac{1}{7} & \frac{3}{7} \\ \frac{9}{7} & \frac{1}{7} & -\frac{4}{7} \\ \frac{3}{7} & -\frac{2}{7} & \frac{1}{7} \end{matrix}$$

$$R_3 = \tfrac{1}{7}r_3 \qquad\qquad R_1 = 3r_3 + r_1$$
$$R_2 = -4r_3 + r_2$$

$$A^{-1} = \begin{bmatrix} -\frac{5}{7} & \frac{1}{7} & \frac{3}{7} \\ \frac{9}{7} & \frac{1}{7} & -\frac{4}{7} \\ \frac{3}{7} & -\frac{2}{7} & \frac{1}{7} \end{bmatrix}$$

31. Rewrite the system of equations in matrix form:
$$\begin{cases} 2x + y = 8 \\ x + y = 5 \end{cases} \qquad A = \begin{bmatrix} 2 & 1 \\ 1 & 1 \end{bmatrix}, \quad X = \begin{bmatrix} x \\ y \end{bmatrix}, \quad B = \begin{bmatrix} 8 \\ 5 \end{bmatrix}$$
Find the inverse of A and solve $X = A^{-1}B$:

From Problem 21, $A^{-1} = \begin{bmatrix} 1 & -1 \\ -1 & 2 \end{bmatrix}$ and $X = A^{-1}B = \begin{bmatrix} 1 & -1 \\ -1 & 2 \end{bmatrix}\begin{bmatrix} 8 \\ 5 \end{bmatrix} = \begin{bmatrix} 3 \\ 2 \end{bmatrix}.$

The solution is $x = 3, y = 2$.

33. Rewrite the system of equations in matrix form:
$$\begin{cases} 2x + y = 0 \\ x + y = 5 \end{cases} \qquad A = \begin{bmatrix} 2 & 1 \\ 1 & 1 \end{bmatrix}, \quad X = \begin{bmatrix} x \\ y \end{bmatrix}, \quad B = \begin{bmatrix} 0 \\ 5 \end{bmatrix}$$
Find the inverse of A and solve $X = A^{-1}B$:

From Problem 21, $A^{-1} = \begin{bmatrix} 1 & -1 \\ -1 & 2 \end{bmatrix}$ and $X = A^{-1}B = \begin{bmatrix} 1 & -1 \\ -1 & 2 \end{bmatrix}\begin{bmatrix} 0 \\ 5 \end{bmatrix} = \begin{bmatrix} -5 \\ 10 \end{bmatrix}.$

The solution is $x = -5, y = 10$.

35. Rewrite the system of equations in matrix form:
$$\begin{cases} 6x + 5y = 7 \\ 2x + 2y = 2 \end{cases} \qquad A = \begin{bmatrix} 6 & 5 \\ 2 & 2 \end{bmatrix}, \quad X = \begin{bmatrix} x \\ y \end{bmatrix}, \quad B = \begin{bmatrix} 7 \\ 2 \end{bmatrix}$$
Find the inverse of A and solve $X = A^{-1}B$:

From Problem 23, $A^{-1} = \begin{bmatrix} 1 & -\frac{5}{2} \\ -1 & 3 \end{bmatrix}$ and $X = A^{-1}B = \begin{bmatrix} 1 & -\frac{5}{2} \\ -1 & 3 \end{bmatrix}\begin{bmatrix} 7 \\ 2 \end{bmatrix} = \begin{bmatrix} 2 \\ -1 \end{bmatrix}.$

The solution is $x = 2, y = -1$.

37. Rewrite the system of equations in matrix form:
$$\begin{cases} 6x + 5y = 13 \\ 2x + 2y = 5 \end{cases} \qquad A = \begin{bmatrix} 6 & 5 \\ 2 & 2 \end{bmatrix}, \quad X = \begin{bmatrix} x \\ y \end{bmatrix}, \quad B = \begin{bmatrix} 13 \\ 5 \end{bmatrix}$$
Find the inverse of A and solve $X = A^{-1}B$:

From Problem 23, $A^{-1} = \begin{bmatrix} 1 & -\frac{5}{2} \\ -1 & 3 \end{bmatrix}$ and $X = A^{-1}B = \begin{bmatrix} 1 & -\frac{5}{2} \\ -1 & 3 \end{bmatrix}\begin{bmatrix} 13 \\ 5 \end{bmatrix} = \begin{bmatrix} \frac{1}{2} \\ 2 \end{bmatrix}.$

The solution is $x = \dfrac{1}{2}, y = 2$.

39.   Rewrite the system of equations in matrix form:

$$\begin{cases} 2x + y = -3 \\ ax + ay = -a \end{cases} \quad a \neq 0 \qquad A = \begin{bmatrix} 2 & 1 \\ a & a \end{bmatrix}, \quad X = \begin{bmatrix} x \\ y \end{bmatrix}, \quad B = \begin{bmatrix} -3 \\ -a \end{bmatrix}$$

Find the inverse of A and solve $X = A^{-1}B$:

From Problem 25, $A^{-1} = \begin{bmatrix} 1 & -\frac{1}{a} \\ -1 & \frac{2}{a} \end{bmatrix}$ and $X = A^{-1}B = \begin{bmatrix} 1 & -\frac{1}{a} \\ -1 & \frac{2}{a} \end{bmatrix}\begin{bmatrix} -3 \\ -a \end{bmatrix} = \begin{bmatrix} -2 \\ 1 \end{bmatrix}.$

The solution is $x = -2, y = 1.$

41.   Rewrite the system of equations in matrix form:

$$\begin{cases} 2x + y = \dfrac{7}{a} \\ ax + ay = 5 \end{cases} \quad a \neq 0 \qquad A = \begin{bmatrix} 2 & 1 \\ a & a \end{bmatrix}, \quad X = \begin{bmatrix} x \\ y \end{bmatrix}, \quad B = \begin{bmatrix} \frac{7}{a} \\ 5 \end{bmatrix}$$

Find the inverse of A and solve $X = A^{-1}B$:

From Problem 25, $A^{-1} = \begin{bmatrix} 1 & -\frac{1}{a} \\ -1 & \frac{2}{a} \end{bmatrix}$ and $X = A^{-1}B = \begin{bmatrix} 1 & -\frac{1}{a} \\ -1 & \frac{2}{a} \end{bmatrix}\begin{bmatrix} \frac{7}{a} \\ 5 \end{bmatrix} = \begin{bmatrix} \frac{2}{a} \\ \frac{3}{a} \end{bmatrix}.$

The solution is $x = \dfrac{2}{a}, y = \dfrac{3}{a}.$

43.   Rewrite the system of equations in matrix form:

$$\begin{cases} x - y + z = 0 \\ -2y + z = -1 \\ -2x - 3y = -5 \end{cases} \qquad A = \begin{bmatrix} 1 & -1 & 1 \\ 0 & -2 & 1 \\ -2 & -3 & 0 \end{bmatrix}, \quad X = \begin{bmatrix} x \\ y \\ z \end{bmatrix}, \quad B = \begin{bmatrix} 0 \\ -1 \\ -5 \end{bmatrix}$$

Find the inverse of A and solve $X = A^{-1}B$:

From Problem 27,

$$A^{-1} = \begin{bmatrix} 3 & -3 & 1 \\ -2 & 2 & -1 \\ -4 & 5 & -2 \end{bmatrix} \text{ and } X = A^{-1}B = \begin{bmatrix} 3 & -3 & 1 \\ -2 & 2 & -1 \\ -4 & 5 & -2 \end{bmatrix}\begin{bmatrix} 0 \\ -1 \\ -5 \end{bmatrix} = \begin{bmatrix} -2 \\ 3 \\ 5 \end{bmatrix}.$$

The solution is $x = -2, y = 3, z = 5.$

45.   Rewrite the system of equations in matrix form:

$$\begin{cases} x - y + z = 2 \\ -2y + z = 2 \\ -2x - 3y = \dfrac{1}{2} \end{cases} \qquad A = \begin{bmatrix} 1 & -1 & 1 \\ 0 & -2 & 1 \\ -2 & -3 & 0 \end{bmatrix}, \quad X = \begin{bmatrix} x \\ y \\ z \end{bmatrix}, \quad B = \begin{bmatrix} 2 \\ 2 \\ \frac{1}{2} \end{bmatrix}$$

Find the inverse of A and solve $X = A^{-1}B$:

From Problem 27,

$$A^{-1} = \begin{bmatrix} 3 & -3 & 1 \\ -2 & 2 & -1 \\ -4 & 5 & -2 \end{bmatrix} \text{ and } X = A^{-1}B = \begin{bmatrix} 3 & -3 & 1 \\ -2 & 2 & -1 \\ -4 & 5 & -2 \end{bmatrix}\begin{bmatrix} 2 \\ 2 \\ \frac{1}{2} \end{bmatrix} = \begin{bmatrix} \frac{1}{2} \\ -\frac{1}{2} \\ 1 \end{bmatrix}.$$

The solution is $x = \dfrac{1}{2}, y = -\dfrac{1}{2}, z = 1.$

47. Rewrite the system of equations in matrix form:

$$\begin{cases} x+ y+ z = 9 \\ 3x+2y- z = 8 \\ 3x+ y+2z = 1 \end{cases} \quad A = \begin{bmatrix} 1 & 1 & 1 \\ 3 & 2 & -1 \\ 3 & 1 & 2 \end{bmatrix}, \quad X = \begin{bmatrix} x \\ y \\ z \end{bmatrix}, \quad B = \begin{bmatrix} 9 \\ 8 \\ 1 \end{bmatrix}$$

Find the inverse of A and solve $X = A^{-1}B$:

From Problem 29,

$$A^{-1} = \begin{bmatrix} -\frac{5}{7} & \frac{1}{7} & \frac{3}{7} \\ \frac{9}{7} & \frac{1}{7} & -\frac{4}{7} \\ \frac{3}{7} & -\frac{2}{7} & \frac{1}{7} \end{bmatrix} \text{ and } X = A^{-1}B = \begin{bmatrix} -\frac{5}{7} & \frac{1}{7} & \frac{3}{7} \\ \frac{9}{7} & \frac{1}{7} & -\frac{4}{7} \\ \frac{3}{7} & -\frac{2}{7} & \frac{1}{7} \end{bmatrix}\begin{bmatrix} 9 \\ 8 \\ 1 \end{bmatrix} = \begin{bmatrix} -\frac{34}{7} \\ \frac{85}{7} \\ \frac{12}{7} \end{bmatrix}.$$

The solution is $x = -\dfrac{34}{7}, y = \dfrac{85}{7}, z = \dfrac{12}{7}$.

49. Rewrite the system of equations in matrix form:

$$\begin{cases} x+ y+ z = 2 \\ 3x+2y- z = \dfrac{7}{3} \\ 3x+ y+2z = \dfrac{10}{3} \end{cases} \quad A = \begin{bmatrix} 1 & 1 & 1 \\ 3 & 2 & -1 \\ 3 & 1 & 2 \end{bmatrix}, \quad X = \begin{bmatrix} x \\ y \\ z \end{bmatrix}, \quad B = \begin{bmatrix} 2 \\ \frac{7}{3} \\ \frac{10}{3} \end{bmatrix}$$

Find the inverse of A and solve $X = A^{-1}B$:

From Problem 29,

$$A^{-1} = \begin{bmatrix} -\frac{5}{7} & \frac{1}{7} & \frac{3}{7} \\ \frac{9}{7} & \frac{1}{7} & -\frac{4}{7} \\ \frac{3}{7} & -\frac{2}{7} & \frac{1}{7} \end{bmatrix} \text{ and } X = A^{-1}B = \begin{bmatrix} -\frac{5}{7} & \frac{1}{7} & \frac{3}{7} \\ \frac{9}{7} & \frac{1}{7} & -\frac{4}{7} \\ \frac{3}{7} & -\frac{2}{7} & \frac{1}{7} \end{bmatrix}\begin{bmatrix} 2 \\ \frac{7}{3} \\ \frac{10}{3} \end{bmatrix} = \begin{bmatrix} \frac{1}{3} \\ 1 \\ \frac{2}{3} \end{bmatrix}.$$

The solution is $x = \dfrac{1}{3}, y = 1, z = \dfrac{2}{3}$.

51. Augment the matrix with the identity and use row operations to find the inverse:

$$A = \begin{bmatrix} 4 & 2 \\ 2 & 1 \end{bmatrix} \rightarrow \begin{bmatrix} 4 & 2 & | & 1 & 0 \\ 2 & 1 & | & 0 & 1 \end{bmatrix}$$

$$\rightarrow \begin{bmatrix} 4 & 2 & | & 1 & 0 \\ 0 & 0 & | & -\frac{1}{2} & 1 \end{bmatrix} \rightarrow \begin{bmatrix} 1 & \frac{1}{2} & | & \frac{1}{4} & 0 \\ 0 & 0 & | & -\frac{1}{2} & 1 \end{bmatrix}$$

$$R_2 = -\tfrac{1}{2}r_1 + r_2 \qquad R_1 = \tfrac{1}{4}r_1$$

There is no way to obtain the identity matrix on the left; thus, there is no inverse.

53. Augment the matrix with the identity and use row operations to find the inverse:

$$A = \begin{bmatrix} 15 & 3 \\ 10 & 2 \end{bmatrix} \rightarrow \begin{bmatrix} 15 & 3 & | & 1 & 0 \\ 10 & 2 & | & 0 & 1 \end{bmatrix} \rightarrow \begin{bmatrix} 15 & 3 & | & 1 & 0 \\ 0 & 0 & | & -\frac{2}{3} & 1 \end{bmatrix} \rightarrow \begin{bmatrix} 1 & \frac{1}{5} & | & \frac{1}{15} & 0 \\ 0 & 0 & | & -\frac{2}{3} & 1 \end{bmatrix}$$

$$R_2 = -\tfrac{2}{3}r_1 + r_2 \qquad R_1 = \tfrac{1}{15}r_1$$

There is no way to obtain the identity matrix on the left; thus, there is no inverse.

55. Augment the matrix with the identity and use row operations to find the inverse:

$$A = \begin{bmatrix} -3 & 1 & -1 \\ 1 & -4 & -7 \\ 1 & 2 & 5 \end{bmatrix} \rightarrow \left[\begin{array}{ccc|ccc} -3 & 1 & -1 & 1 & 0 & 0 \\ 1 & -4 & -7 & 0 & 1 & 0 \\ 1 & 2 & 5 & 0 & 0 & 1 \end{array} \right]$$

$$\rightarrow \left[\begin{array}{ccc|ccc} 1 & 2 & 5 & 0 & 0 & 1 \\ 1 & -4 & -7 & 0 & 1 & 0 \\ -3 & 1 & -1 & 1 & 0 & 0 \end{array} \right] \rightarrow \left[\begin{array}{ccc|ccc} 1 & 2 & 5 & 0 & 0 & 1 \\ 0 & -6 & -12 & 0 & 1 & -1 \\ 0 & 7 & 14 & 1 & 0 & 3 \end{array} \right] \rightarrow \left[\begin{array}{ccc|ccc} 1 & 2 & 5 & 0 & 0 & 1 \\ 0 & 1 & 2 & 0 & -\frac{1}{6} & \frac{1}{6} \\ 0 & 7 & 14 & 1 & 0 & 3 \end{array} \right]$$

$$\text{Interchange } r_1 \text{ and } r_3 \qquad R_2 = -r_1 + r_2 \qquad\qquad R_2 = -\tfrac{1}{6} r_2$$
$$R_3 = 3r_1 + r_3$$

$$\rightarrow \left[\begin{array}{ccc|ccc} 1 & 0 & 1 & 0 & \frac{1}{3} & \frac{2}{3} \\ 0 & 1 & 2 & 0 & -\frac{1}{6} & \frac{1}{6} \\ 0 & 0 & 0 & 1 & \frac{7}{6} & \frac{11}{6} \end{array} \right]$$

$$R_1 = -2r_2 + r_1$$
$$R_3 = -7r_2 + r_3$$

There is no way to obtain the identity matrix on the left; thus, there is no inverse.

57. Use MATRIX EDIT to create the matrix

$$A = \begin{bmatrix} 25 & 61 & -12 \\ 18 & -2 & 4 \\ 8 & 35 & 21 \end{bmatrix}$$

Then compute $[A]^\wedge(-1)$:

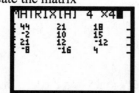

$$A^{-1} = \begin{bmatrix} 0.01 & 0.05 & -0.01 \\ 0.01 & -0.02 & 0.01 \\ -0.02 & 0.01 & 0.03 \end{bmatrix}$$

59. Use MATRIX EDIT to create the matrix

$$A = \begin{bmatrix} 44 & 21 & 18 & 6 \\ -2 & 10 & 15 & 5 \\ 21 & 12 & -12 & 4 \\ -8 & -16 & 4 & 9 \end{bmatrix}$$

Then compute $[A]^\wedge(-1)$:

$$A^{-1} = \begin{bmatrix} 0.02 & -0.04 & -0.01 & 0.01 \\ -0.02 & 0.05 & 0.03 & -0.03 \\ 0.02 & 0.01 & -0.04 & 0.00 \\ -0.02 & 0.06 & 0.07 & 0.06 \end{bmatrix}$$

61. Use MATRIX EDIT to create the matrices

$$A = \begin{vmatrix} 25 & 61 & -12 \\ 18 & -12 & 7 \\ 3 & 4 & -1 \end{vmatrix}; \quad B = \begin{vmatrix} 10 \\ -9 \\ 12 \end{vmatrix}$$

Then compute $([A]^\wedge(-1)) * [B]$:

$x = 4.57, \; y = -6.44, \; z = -24.07$

63. Use MATRIX EDIT to create the matrices

$$A = \begin{vmatrix} 25 & 61 & -12 \\ 18 & -12 & 7 \\ 3 & 4 & -1 \end{vmatrix}; \quad B = \begin{vmatrix} 21 \\ 7 \\ -2 \end{vmatrix}$$

Then compute $([A]^\wedge(-1)) * [B]$:

$x = -1.19, \; y = 2.46, \; z = 8.27$

65. (a) The rows of the 2 by 3 matrix represent stainless steel and aluminum. The columns represent 10-gallon, 5-gallon, and 1-gallon.

The 2 by 3 matrix is: The 3 by 2 matrix is:

$$\begin{bmatrix} 500 & 350 & 400 \\ 700 & 500 & 850 \end{bmatrix} \qquad \begin{bmatrix} 500 & 700 \\ 350 & 500 \\ 400 & 850 \end{bmatrix}$$

(b) The 3 by 1 matrix representing the amount of material is:

$$\begin{bmatrix} 15 \\ 8 \\ 3 \end{bmatrix}$$

(c) The days usage of materials is:

$$\begin{bmatrix} 500 & 350 & 400 \\ 700 & 500 & 850 \end{bmatrix} \cdot \begin{bmatrix} 15 \\ 8 \\ 3 \end{bmatrix} = \begin{bmatrix} 11{,}500 \\ 17{,}050 \end{bmatrix}$$

11,500 pounds of stainless steel and 17,050 pounds of aluminum are used each day.

(d) The 1 by 2 matrix representing cost is:

$$\begin{bmatrix} 0.10 & 0.05 \end{bmatrix}$$

(e) The total cost of the days production was:

$$\begin{bmatrix} 0.10 & 0.05 \end{bmatrix} \cdot \begin{bmatrix} 11{,}500 \\ 17{,}050 \end{bmatrix} = \begin{bmatrix} 2002.50 \end{bmatrix}$$

The total cost of the days production was $2,002.50.

67. Answers will vary.

417

Chapter 7

Systems of Equations and Inequalities

7.6 Systems of Linear Inequalities: Linear Programming

1. $x \geq 0$
(a) Graph the line $x = 0$. Use a solid line since the inequality uses $\geq$.
Choose a test point not on the line, such as $(2, 0)$.
Since $2 \geq 0$ is true, shade the side of the line containing $(2, 0)$.

(b) Use the VERTICAL function and the SHADE function in the calculator's DRAW menu:

Vertical 0

Shade$(-5,5,0,2)$

3. $x \geq 4$
(a) Graph the line $x = 4$. Use a solid line since the inequality uses $\geq$.
Choose a test point not on the line, such as $(5, 0)$.
Since $5 \geq 0$ is true, shade the side of the line containing $(5, 0)$.

(b) Use the VERTICAL function and the SHADE function in the calculator's DRAW menu:
Vertical 4

Shade$(-5,5,4,8)$.

5. $x + y > 1$

(a) Graph the line $x + y = 1$. Use a dotted line since the
inequality uses $>$.
Choose a test point not on the line, such as $(0, 0)$.
Since $0 + 0 > 1$ is false, shade the opposite side of the
line from $(0, 0)$.

(b) Use the SHADE function in the calculator's DRAW
menu: Shade$(-x + 1, 5)$.

7. $2x + y \geq 6$

(a) Graph the line $2x + y = 6$. Use a solid line since the
inequality uses $\geq$.
Choose a test point not on the line, such as $(0, 0)$.
Since $2(0) + 0 \geq 6$ is false, shade the opposite side of
the line from $(0, 0)$.

(b) Use the SHADE function in the calculator's DRAW
menu: Shade$(-2x + 6, 6)$.

9. $\begin{cases} x + y \le 2 \\ 2x + y \ge 4 \end{cases}$

(a) Graph the line $x + y = 2$. Use a solid line since the inequality uses $\le$.
Choose a test point not on the line, such as $(0, 0)$. Since $0 + 0 \le 2$ is true, shade the side of the line containing $(0, 0)$.

(b) Graph the line $2x + y = 4$. Use a solid line since the inequality uses $\ge$.
Choose a test point not on the line, such as $(0, 0)$. Since $2(0) + 0 \ge 4$ is false, shade the opposite side of the line from $(0, 0)$.

(c) The overlapping region is the solution.

11. $\begin{cases} 2x - y \le 4 \\ 3x + 2y \ge -6 \end{cases}$

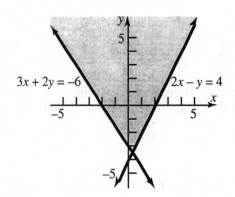

(a) Graph the line $2x - y = 4$. Use a solid line since the inequality uses $\le$.
Choose a test point not on the line, such as $(0, 0)$. Since $2(0) - 0 \le 4$ is true, shade the side of the line containing $(0, 0)$.

(b) Graph the line $3x + 2y = -6$. Use a solid line since the inequality uses $\ge$.
Choose a test point not on the line, such as $(0, 0)$. Since $3(0) + 2(0) \ge -6$ is true, shade the side of the line containing $(0, 0)$.

(c) The overlapping region is the solution.

13. $\begin{cases} 2x - 3y \le 0 \\ 3x + 2y \le 6 \end{cases}$

(a) Graph the line $2x - 3y = 0$. Use a solid line since the inequality uses $\le$.
     Choose a test point not on the line, such as (0, 3). Since $2(0) - 3(3) \le 0$ is true,
     shade the side of the line containing (0, 3).
(b) Graph the line $3x + 2y = 6$. Use a solid line since the inequality uses $\le$.
     Choose a test point not on the line, such as (0, 0). Since $3(0) + 2(0) \le 6$ is true,
     shade the side of the line containing (0, 0).
(c) The overlapping region is the solution.

15. $\begin{cases} x - 2y \le 6 \\ 2x - 4y \ge 0 \end{cases}$

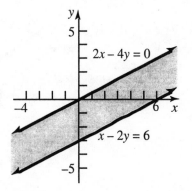

(a) Graph the line $x - 2y = 6$. Use a solid line since the inequality uses $\le$.
     Choose a test point not on the line, such as (0, 0). Since $0 - 2(0) \le 6$ is true, shade
     the side of the line containing (0, 0).
(b) Graph the line $2x - 4y = 0$. Use a solid line since the inequality uses $\ge$.
     Choose a test point not on the line, such as (0, 2). Since $2(0) - 4(2) \ge 0$ is false,
     shade the opposite side of the line from (0, 2).
(c) The overlapping region is the solution.

17. $\begin{cases} 2x + y \geq -2 \\ 2x + y \geq 2 \end{cases}$

(a)　Graph the line $2x + y = -2$. Use a solid line since the inequality uses $\geq$.
　　　Choose a test point not on the line, such as $(0, 0)$. Since $2(0) + 0 \geq -2$ is true, shade the side of the line containing $(0, 0)$.

(b)　Graph the line $2x + y = 2$. Use a solid line since the inequality uses $\geq$.
　　　Choose a test point not on the line, such as $(0, 0)$. Since $2(0) + 0 \geq 2$ is false, shade the opposite side of the line from $(0, 0)$.

(c)　The overlapping region is the solution.

19. $\begin{cases} 2x + 3y \geq 6 \\ 2x + 3y \leq 0 \end{cases}$

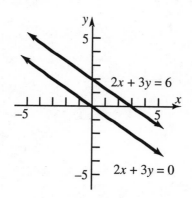

(a)　Graph the line $2x + 3y = 6$. Use a solid line since the inequality uses $\geq$.
　　　Choose a test point not on the line, such as $(0, 0)$. Since $2(0) + 3(0) \geq 6$ is false, shade the opposite side of the line from $(0, 0)$.

(b)　Graph the line $2x + 3y = 0$. Use a solid line since the inequality uses $\leq$.
　　　Choose a test point not on the line, such as $(0, 2)$. Since $2(0) + 3(2) \leq 0$ is false, shade the opposite side of the line from $(0, 2)$.

(c)　Since the regions do not overlap, the solution is an empty set.

21.   Graph the system of linear inequalities:

$$\begin{cases} x \geq 0 \\ y \geq 0 \\ 2x + y \leq 6 \\ x + 2y \leq 6 \end{cases}$$

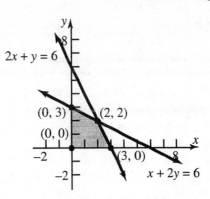

(a)   Graph $x \geq 0$; $y \geq 0$. Shaded region is the first quadrant.
(b)   Graph the line $2x + y = 6$. Use a solid line since the inequality uses $\leq$.
Choose a test point not on the line, such as $(0, 0)$. Since $2(0) + 0 \leq 6$ is true, shade the side of the line containing $(0, 0)$.
(c)   Graph the line $x + 2y = 6$. Use a solid line since the inequality uses $\leq$.
Choose a test point not on the line, such as $(0, 0)$. Since $0 + 2(0) \leq 6$ is true, shade the side of the line containing $(0, 0)$.
(d)   The overlapping region is the solution.
(e)   The graph is bounded.
(f)   Find the vertices:
The x-axis and y-axis intersect at $(0, 0)$.
The intersection of $x + 2y = 6$ and the y-axis is $(0, 3)$.
The intersection of $2x + y = 6$ and the x-axis is $(3, 0)$.
To find the intersection of $x + 2y = 6$ and $2x + y = 6$, solve the system:
$$\begin{cases} x + 2y = 6 \quad \rightarrow \quad x = 6 - 2y \\ 2x + y = 6 \end{cases}$$
Substitute and solve:
$$2(6 - 2y) + y = 6 \rightarrow 12 - 4y + y = 6 \rightarrow -3y = -6 \rightarrow y = 2$$
$$x = 6 - 2(2) = 6 - 4 = 2$$
The point of intersection is $(2, 2)$.
The four corner points are $(0, 0)$, $(0, 3)$, $(3, 0)$, and $(2, 2)$.

23.   Graph the system of linear inequalities:

$$\begin{cases} x \geq 0 \\ y \geq 0 \\ x + y \geq 2 \\ 2x + y \geq 4 \end{cases}$$

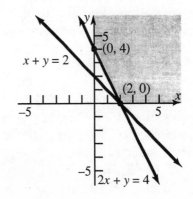

    (a)   Graph $x \geq 0$; $y \geq 0$. Shaded region is the first quadrant.

    (b)   Graph the line $x + y = 2$. Use a solid line since the inequality uses $\geq$.

        Choose a test point not on the line, such as (0, 0). Since $0 + 0 \geq 2$ is false, shade the opposite side of the line from (0, 0).

    (c)   Graph the line $2x + y = 4$. Use a solid line since the inequality uses $\geq$.

        Choose a test point not on the line, such as (0, 0). Since $2(0) + 0 \geq 4$ is false, shade the opposite side of the line from (0, 0).

    (d)   The overlapping region is the solution.

    (e)   The graph is unbounded.

    (f)   Find the vertices:

        The intersection of $x + y = 2$ and the x-axis is (2, 0).

        The intersection of $2x + y = 4$ and the y-axis is (0, 4).

        The two corner points are (2, 0), and (0, 4).

25.   Graph the system of linear inequalities:

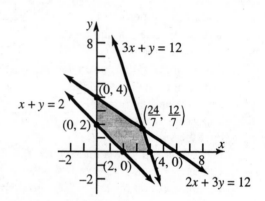

    (a)   Graph $x \geq 0$; $y \geq 0$. Shaded region is the first quadrant.

    (b)   Graph the line $x + y = 2$. Use a solid line since the inequality uses $\geq$.

        Choose a test point not on the line, such as (0, 0). Since $0 + 0 \geq 2$ is false, shade the opposite side of the line from (0, 0).

    (c)   Graph the line $2x + 3y = 12$. Use a solid line since the inequality uses $\leq$.

        Choose a test point not on the line, such as (0, 0). Since $2(0) + 3(0) \leq 12$ is true, shade the side of the line containing (0, 0).

    (d)   Graph the line $3x + y = 12$. Use a solid line since the inequality uses $\leq$.

        Choose a test point not on the line, such as (0, 0). Since $3(0) + 0 \leq 12$ is true, shade the side of the line containing (0, 0).

    (e)   The overlapping region is the solution.

    (f)   The graph is bounded.

    (g)   Find the vertices:

        The intersection of $x + y = 2$ and the y-axis is (0, 2).

        The intersection of $x + y = 2$ and the x-axis is (2, 0).

        The intersection of $2x + 3y = 12$ and the y-axis is (0, 4).

        The intersection of $3x + y = 12$ and the x-axis is (4, 0).

        To find the intersection of $2x + 3y = 12$ and $3x + y = 12$, solve the system:

$$\begin{cases} 2x + 3y = 12 \\ 3x + y = 12 \end{cases} \rightarrow \quad y = 12 - 3x$$

Substitute and solve:
$$2x + 3(12 - 3x) = 12 \rightarrow 2x + 36 - 9x = 12$$

$$-7x = -24 \rightarrow x = \frac{24}{7}$$

$$y = 12 - 3\left(\frac{24}{7}\right) = 12 - \frac{72}{2} = \frac{12}{7}$$

The point of intersection is $\left(\frac{24}{7}, \frac{12}{7}\right)$.

The five corner points are (0, 2), (0, 4), (2, 0), (4, 0), and $\left(\frac{24}{7}, \frac{12}{7}\right)$.

27.   Graph the system of linear inequalities:

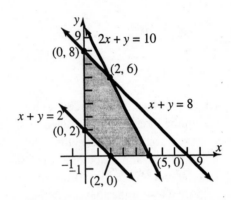

(a)   Graph $x \geq 0$; $y \geq 0$. Shaded region is the first quadrant.

(b)   Graph the line $x + y = 2$. Use a solid line since the inequality uses $\geq$.
Choose a test point not on the line, such as (0, 0). Since $0 + 0 \geq 2$ is false, shade the opposite side of the line from (0, 0).

(c)   Graph the line $x + y = 8$. Use a solid line since the inequality uses $\leq$.
Choose a test point not on the line, such as (0, 0). Since $0 + 0 \leq 8$ is true, shade the side of the line containing (0, 0).

(d)   Graph the line $2x + y = 10$. Use a solid line since the inequality uses $\leq$.
Choose a test point not on the line, such as (0, 0). Since $2(0) + 0 \leq 10$ is true, shade the side of the line containing (0, 0).

(e)   The overlapping region is the solution.

(f)   The graph is bounded.

(g)   Find the vertices:
The intersection of $x + y = 2$ and the y-axis is (0, 2).
The intersection of $x + y = 2$ and the x-axis is (2, 0).
The intersection of $x + y = 8$ and the y-axis is (0, 8).
The intersection of $2x + y = 10$ and the x-axis is (5, 0).
To find the intersection of $x + y = 8$ and $2x + y = 10$, solve the system:
$$\begin{cases} x + y = 8 \\ 2x + y = 10 \end{cases} \rightarrow \quad y = 8 - x$$

Substitute and solve:
$$2x + 8 - x = 10 \rightarrow x = 2$$
$$y = 8 - 2 = 6$$
The point of intersection is (2, 6).
The five corner points are (0, 2), (0, 8), (2, 0), (5, 0), and (2, 6).

29. Graph the system of linear inequalities:

$$\begin{cases} x \geq 0 \\ y \geq 0 \\ x + 2y \geq 1 \\ x + 2y \leq 10 \end{cases}$$

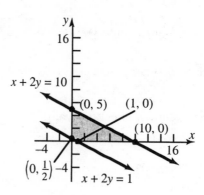

(a) Graph $x \geq 0$; $y \geq 0$. Shaded region is the first quadrant.
(b) Graph the line $x + 2y = 1$. Use a solid line since the inequality uses $\geq$.
     Choose a test point not on the line, such as (0, 0). Since $0 + 2(0) \geq 1$ is false, shade
     the opposite side of the line from (0, 0).
(c) Graph the line $x + 2y = 10$. Use a solid line since the inequality uses $\leq$.
     Choose a test point not on the line, such as (0, 0). Since $0 + 2(0) \leq 10$ is true,
     shade the side of the line containing (0, 0).
(d) The overlapping region is the solution.
(e) The graph is bounded.
(f) Find the vertices:
     The intersection of $x + 2y = 1$ and the y-axis is (0, 0.5).
     The intersection of $x + 2y = 1$ and the x-axis is (1, 0).
     The intersection of $x + 2y = 10$ and the y-axis is (0, 5).
     The intersection of $x + 2y = 10$ and the x-axis is (10, 0).
     The four corner points are (0, 0.5), (0, 5), (1, 0), and (10, 0).

31. The system of linear inequalities is:

$$\begin{cases} x \geq 0 \\ y \geq 0 \\ x \leq 4 \\ x + y \leq 6 \end{cases}$$

33. The system of linear inequalities is:

$$\begin{cases} x \geq 0 \\ y \geq 15 \\ x \leq 20 \\ x + y \leq 50 \\ x - y \leq 0 \end{cases}$$

35. $z = x + y$

Vertex	Value of $z = x + y$
(0, 3)	$z = 0 + 3 = 3$
(0, 6)	$z = 0 + 6 = 6$
(5, 6)	$z = 5 + 6 = 11$
(5, 2)	$z = 5 + 2 = 7$
(4, 0)	$z = 4 + 0 = 4$

The maximum value is 11 at (5, 6), and the minimum value is 3 at (0, 3).

37. $z = x + 10y$

Vertex	Value of $z = x + 10y$
(0, 3)	$z = 0 + 10(3) = 30$
(0, 6)	$z = 0 + 10(6) = 60$
(5, 6)	$z = 5 + 10(6) = 65$
(5, 2)	$z = 5 + 10(2) = 25$
(4, 0)	$z = 4 + 10(0) = 4$

The maximum value is 65 at (5, 6), and the minimum value is 4 at (4, 0).

39. $z = 5x + 7y$

Vertex	Value of $z = 5x + 7y$
(0, 3)	$z = 5(0) + 7(3) = 21$
(0, 6)	$z = 5(0) + 7(6) = 42$
(5, 6)	$z = 5(5) + 7(6) = 67$
(5, 2)	$z = 5(5) + 7(2) = 39$
(4, 0)	$z = 5(4) + 7(0) = 20$

The maximum value is 67 at (5, 6), and the minimum value is 20 at (4, 0).

41. Maximize $z = 2x + y$
Subject to $x \geq 0$, $y \geq 0$, $x + y \leq 6$, $x + y \geq 1$
Graph the constraints.

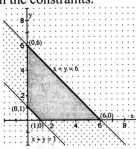

The corner points are (0, 1), (1, 0), (0, 6), (6, 0).
Evaluate the objective function:

Vertex	Value of $z = 2x + y$
(0, 1)	$z = 2(0) + 1 = 1$
(0, 6)	$z = 2(0) + 6 = 6$
(1, 0)	$z = 2(1) + 0 = 2$
(6, 0)	$z = 2(6) + 0 = 12$

The maximum value is 12 at (6, 0).

43. Minimize $z = 2x + 5y$

Subject to $x \geq 0,\ y \geq 0,\ x + y \geq 2,\ x \leq 5,\ y \leq 3$

Graph the constraints.

The corner points are (0, 2), (2, 0), (0, 3), (5, 0), (5, 3).

Evaluate the objective function:

Vertex	Value of $z = 2x + 5y$
(0, 2)	$z = 2(0) + 5(2) = 10$
(0, 3)	$z = 2(0) + 5(3) = 15$
(2, 0)	$z = 2(2) + 5(0) = 4$
(5, 0)	$z = 2(5) + 5(0) = 10$
(5, 3)	$z = 2(5) + 5(3) = 25$

The minimum value is 4 at (2, 0).

45. Maximize $z = 3x + 5y$

Subject to $x \geq 0,\ y \geq 0,\ x + y \geq 2,\ 2x + 3y \leq 12,\ 3x + 2y \leq 12$

Graph the constraints.

To find the intersection of $2x + 3y = 12$ and $3x + 2y = 12$, solve the system:

$$\begin{cases} 2x + 3y = 12 \\ 3x + 2y = 12 \end{cases} \rightarrow y = 6 - \frac{3}{2}x$$

Substitute and solve:

$$2x + 3\left(6 - \frac{3}{2}x\right) = 12 \rightarrow 2x + 18 - \frac{9}{2}x = 12 \rightarrow -\frac{5}{2}x = -6$$

$$x = \frac{12}{5} \qquad y = 6 - \frac{3}{2}\left(\frac{12}{5}\right) = 6 - \frac{18}{5} = \frac{12}{5}$$

The point of intersection is $(2.4, 2.4)$.

The corner points are $(0, 2)$, $(2, 0)$, $(0, 4)$, $(4, 0)$, $(2.4, 2.4)$.
Evaluate the objective function:

Vertex	Value of $z = 3x + 5y$
$(0, 2)$	$z = 3(0) + 5(2) = 10$
$(0, 4)$	$z = 3(0) + 5(4) = 20$
$(2, 0)$	$z = 3(2) + 5(0) = 6$
$(4, 0)$	$z = 3(4) + 5(0) = 12$
$(2.4, 2.4)$	$z = 3(2.4) + 5(2.4) = 19.2$

The maximum value is 20 at $(0, 4)$.

47. Minimize $z = 5x + 4y$
Subject to $x \geq 0$, $y \geq 0$, $x + y \geq 2$, $2x + 3y \leq 12$, $3x + y \leq 12$
Graph the constraints.

To find the intersection of $2x + 3y = 12$ and $3x + y = 12$, solve the system:
$$\begin{cases} 2x + 3y = 12 \\ 3x + y = 12 \end{cases} \rightarrow \quad y = 12 - 3x$$

Substitute and solve:
$$2x + 3(12 - 3x) = 12 \rightarrow 2x + 36 - 9x = 12 \rightarrow -7x = -24 \rightarrow x = \frac{24}{7}$$

$$y = 12 - 3\left(\frac{24}{7}\right) = 12 - \frac{72}{7} = \frac{12}{7}$$

The point of intersection is $\left(\frac{24}{7}, \frac{12}{7}\right)$.

The corner points are $(0, 2)$, $(2, 0)$, $(0, 4)$, $(4, 0)$, $\left(\frac{24}{7}, \frac{12}{7}\right)$.

Evaluate the objective function:

Vertex	Value of $z = 5x + 4y$
$(0, 2)$	$z = 5(0) + 4(2) = 8$
$(0, 4)$	$z = 5(0) + 4(4) = 16$
$(2, 0)$	$z = 5(2) + 4(0) = 10$
$(4, 0)$	$z = 5(4) + 4(0) = 20$
$\left(\dfrac{24}{7}, \dfrac{12}{7}\right)$	$z = 5\left(\dfrac{24}{7}\right) + 4\left(\dfrac{12}{7}\right) = \dfrac{120}{7} + \dfrac{48}{7} = \dfrac{168}{7} = 24$

The minimum value is 8 at $(0, 2)$.

49.   Maximize $z = 5x + 2y$
      Subject to $x \geq 0, \quad y \geq 0, \quad x + y \leq 10, \quad 2x + y \geq 10, \quad x + 2y \geq 10$
      Graph the constraints.

To find the intersection of $2x + y = 10$ and $x + 2y = 10$, solve the system:
$$\begin{cases} 2x + y = 10 & \rightarrow \quad y = 10 - 2x \\ x + 2y = 10 \end{cases}$$

Substitute and solve:
$$x + 2(10 - 2x) = 10 \rightarrow x + 20 - 4x = 10 \rightarrow -3x = -10 \rightarrow x = \frac{10}{3}$$

$$y = 10 - 2\left(\frac{10}{3}\right) = 10 - \frac{20}{3} = \frac{10}{3}$$

The point of intersection is $\left(\dfrac{10}{3}, \dfrac{10}{3}\right)$.

The corner points are $(0, 10)$, $(10, 0)$, $\left(\dfrac{10}{3}, \dfrac{10}{3}\right)$.

Evaluate the objective function:

Vertex	Value of $z = 5x + 2y$
$(0, 10)$	$z = 5(0) + 2(10) = 20$
$(10, 0)$	$z = 5(10) + 2(0) = 50$
$\left(\dfrac{10}{3}, \dfrac{10}{3}\right)$	$z = 5\left(\dfrac{10}{3}\right) + 2\left(\dfrac{10}{3}\right) = \dfrac{50}{3} + \dfrac{20}{3} = \dfrac{70}{3} = 23\frac{1}{3}$

The maximum value is 50 at $(10, 0)$.

51.   Let x = the number of downhill skis produced.
      Let y = the number of cross-country skis produced.
      The total profit is: $P = 70x + 50y$. Profit is to be maximized; thus, this is the objective
      function.
      The constraints are:
      $x \geq 0, \quad y \geq 0$ A positive number of skis must be produced.
      $2x + y \leq 40$ Only 40 hours of manufacturing time is available.
      $x + y \leq 32$ Only 32 hours of finishing time is available.

Graph the constraints.

To find the intersection of $x + y = 32$ and $2x + y = 40$, solve the system:

$$\begin{cases} x + y = 32 & \rightarrow \quad y = 32 - x \\ 2x + y = 40 \end{cases}$$

Substitute and solve:

$$2x + 32 - x = 40 \rightarrow x = 8 \rightarrow y = 32 - 8 = 24$$

The point of intersection is (8, 24).

The corner points are (0, 0), (0, 32), (20, 0), (8, 24).

Evaluate the objective function:

Vertex	Value of $P = 70x + 50y$
(0, 0)	$P = 70(0) + 50(0) = 0$
(0, 32)	$P = 70(0) + 50(32) = 1600$
(20, 0)	$P = 70(20) + 50(0) = 1400$
(8, 24)	$P = 70(8) + 50(24) = 1760$

The maximum profit is $1760, when 8 downhill skis and 24 cross-country skis are produced.

With the increase of the manufacturing time to 48 hours, we do the following:

The constraints are:

$x \geq 0, \ y \geq 0$	A positive number of skis must be produced.
$2x + y \leq 48$	Only 48 hours of manufacturing time is available.
$x + y \leq 32$	Only 32 hours of finishing time is available.

Graph the constraints.

To find the intersection of $x + y = 32$ and $2x + y = 48$, solve the system:

$$\begin{cases} x + y = 32 & \rightarrow \quad y = 32 - x \\ 2x + y = 48 \end{cases}$$

Substitute and solve: $2x + 32 - x = 48 \rightarrow x = 16 \rightarrow y = 32 - 16 = 16$

The point of intersection is (16, 16).

The corner points are (0, 0), (0, 32), (24, 0), (16, 16).

Evaluate the objective function:

Vertex	Value of $P = 70x + 50y$
(0, 0)	$P = 70(0) + 50(0) = 0$
(0, 32)	$P = 70(0) + 50(32) = 1600$
(24, 0)	$P = 70(24) + 50(0) = 1680$
(16, 16)	$P = 70(16) + 50(16) = 1920$

The maximum profit is $1920, when 16 downhill skis and 16 cross-country skis are produced.

53.　Let x = the number of acres of corn planted; y = the number of acres of soybeans planted. The total profit is: $P = 250x + 200y$. Profit is to be maximized; thus, this is the objective function.

The constraints are:

$x \geq 0, \ y \geq 0$　　　　A non-negative number of acres must be planted.

$x + y \leq 100$　　　　Acres available to plant.

$60x + 40y \leq 1800$　　　　Money available for cultivation costs.

$60x + 60y \leq 2400$　　　　Money available for labor costs.

Graph the constraints.

To find the intersection of $60x + 40y = 1800$ and $60x + 60y = 2400$, solve the system:

$$\begin{cases} 60x + 40y = 1800 & \rightarrow \quad 60x = 1800 - 40y \\ 60x + 60y = 2400 \end{cases}$$

Substitute and solve:

$$1800 - 40y + 60y = 2400 \rightarrow 20y = 600 \rightarrow y = 30$$

$$60x = 1800 - 40(30) \rightarrow 60x = 600 \rightarrow x = 10$$

The point of intersection is (10, 30).

The corner points are (0, 0), (0, 40), (30, 0), (10, 30).

Evaluate the objective function:

Vertex	Value of $P = 250x + 200y$
(0, 0)	$P = 250(0) + 200(0) = 0$
(0, 40)	$P = 250(0) + 200(40) = 8000$
(30, 0)	$P = 250(30) + 200(0) = 7500$
(10, 30)	$P = 250(10) + 200(30) = 8500$

The maximum profit is $8500, when 10 acres of corn and 30 acres of soybeans are planted.

55. Let x = the number of hours that machine 1 is operated.
Let y = the number of hours that machine 2 is operated.
The total cost is: $C = 50x + 30y$. Cost is to be minimized; thus, this is the objective function.
The constraints are:

$x \geq 0, \;\; y \geq 0$	A positive number of hours must be used.
$x \leq 10$	10 hours available on machine 1.
$y \leq 10$	10 hours available on machine 2.
$60x + 40y \geq 240$	At least 240 8-inch pliers must be produced.
$70x + 20y \geq 140$	At least 140 6-inch pliers must be produced.

Graph the constraints.

To find the intersection of $60x + 40y = 240$ and $70x + 20y = 140$, solve the system:
$$\begin{cases} 60x + 40y = 240 \\ 70x + 20y = 140 \quad \rightarrow \quad 20y = 140 - 70x \end{cases}$$
Substitute and solve:
$$60x + 2(140 - 70x) = 240 \rightarrow 60x + 280 - 140x = 240$$
$$-80x = -40 \rightarrow x = 0.5$$
$$20y = 140 - 70(0.5) \rightarrow 20y = 105 \rightarrow y = 5.25$$
The point of intersection is $(0.5, 5.25)$.

The corner points are (0, 7), (0, 10), (4, 0), (10, 0), (10, 10), $(0.5, 5.25)$.

Evaluate the objective function:

Vertex	Value of $C = 50x + 30y$
(0, 7)	$C = 50(0) + 30(7) = 210$
(0, 10)	$C = 50(0) + 30(10) = 300$
(4, 0)	$C = 50(4) + 30(0) = 200$
(10, 0)	$C = 50(10) + 30(0) = 500$
(10, 10)	$C = 50(10) + 30(10) = 800$
$(0.5, 5.25)$	$C = 50(0.5) + 30(5.25) = 182.50$

The minimum cost is \$182.50, when machine 1 is used for 0.5 hours and machine 2 is used for 5.25 hours.

57. Let x = the number of pounds of ground beef.
Let y = the number of pounds of ground pork.
The total cost is: $C = 0.75x + 0.45y$. Cost is to be minimized; thus, this is the objective function.

The constraints are:

$x \geq 0, \ y \geq 0$　　　　A positive number of pounds must be used.

$x \leq 200$　　　　Only 200 pounds of ground beef are available.

$y \geq 50$　　　　At least 50 pounds of ground pork must be used.

$0.75x + 0.60y \geq 0.70(x + y) \rightarrow 0.05x \geq 0.10y$　　Leanness condition to be met.

Graph the constraints.

The corner points are (100, 50), (200, 50), (200, 100).

Evaluate the objective function:

Vertex	Value of $C = 0.75x + 0.45y$
(100, 50)	$C = 0.75(100) + 0.45(50) = 97.50$
(200, 50)	$C = 0.75(200) + 0.45(50) = 172.50$
(200,100)	$C = 0.75(200) + 0.45(100) = 195.00$

The minimum cost is $97.50, when 100 pounds of ground beef and 50 pounds of ground pork are used.

59.　Let x = the number of racing skates manufactured.

Let y = the number of figure skates manufactured.

The total profit is: $P = 10x + 12y$. Profit is to be maximized; thus, this is the objective function.

The constraints are:

$x \geq 0, \ y \geq 0$　　　　A positive number of skates must be manufactured.

$6x + 4y \leq 120$　　　　Only 120 hours are available for fabrication.

$x + 2y \leq 40$　　　　Only 40 hours are available for finishing.

Graph the constraints.

To find the intersection of $6x + 4y = 120$ and $x + 2y = 40$, solve the system:

$$\begin{cases} 6x + 4y = 120 \\ x + 2y = \ 40 \end{cases} \rightarrow \ x = 40 - 2y$$

Substitute and solve:
$$6(40-2y)+4y=120 \rightarrow 240-12y+4y=120$$
$$-8y=-120 \rightarrow y=15 \rightarrow x=40-2(15)=10$$
The point of intersection is (10, 15).
The corner points are (0, 0), (0, 20), (20, 0), (10, 15).
Evaluate the objective function:

Vertex	Value of $P = 10x + 12y$
(0, 0)	P = 10(0) + 12(0) = 0
(0, 20)	P = 10(0) + 12(20) = 240
(20, 0)	P = 10(20) + 12(0) = 200
(10, 15)	P = 10(10) + 12(15) = 280

The maximum profit is $280, when 10 racing skates and 15 figure skates are produced.

61. Let x = the number of metal fasteners.
Let y = the number of plastic fasteners.
The total cost is: $C = 9x + 4y$. Cost is to be minimized; thus, this is the objective function.
The constraints are:

$x \ge 2, \ y \ge 2$ At least 2 of each fastener must be made.

$x + y \ge 6$ At least 6 fasteners are needed.

$4x + 2y \le 24$ Only 24 hours are available.

Graph the constraints.

The corner points are (2, 4), (2, 8), (4, 2), (5, 2).
Evaluate the objective function:

Vertex	Value of $C = 9x + 4y$
(2, 4)	C = 9(2) + 4(4) = 34
(2, 8)	C = 9(2) + 4(8) = 50
(4, 2)	C = 9(4) + 4(2) = 44
(5, 2)	C = 9(5) + 4(2) = 53

The minimum cost is $34, when 2 metal fasteners and 4 plastic fasteners are ordered.

63. Let x = the number of first-class seats.
Let y = the number of coach seats.
The constraints are:

$8 \le x \le 16$ Restriction on first-class seats.

$80 \le y \le 120$ Restriction on coach seats.

(a) $\dfrac{x}{y} \le \dfrac{1}{12}$ Ratio of seats.

If $y = 120$, then $\dfrac{x}{120} \le \dfrac{1}{12} \rightarrow 12x \le 120 \rightarrow x \le 10$

The maximum revenue will be obtained with 120 coach seats and 10 first-class seats. (Note that the first-class seats meet their constraint.)

(b) $\dfrac{x}{y} \le \dfrac{1}{8}$ Ratio of seats.

If $y = 120$, then $\dfrac{x}{120} \le \dfrac{1}{8} \rightarrow 8x \le 120 \rightarrow x \le 15$

The maximum revenue will be obtained with 120 coach seats and 15 first-class seats. (Note that the first-class seats meet their constraint.)

Systems of Equations and Inequalities

7.7 Partial Fraction Decomposition

1. The rational expression $\dfrac{x}{x^2-1}$ is proper, since the degree of the numerator is less than the degree of the denominator.

3. The rational expression $\dfrac{x^2+5}{x^2-4}$ is improper, so perform the division:

$$
\begin{array}{r}
1 \\
x^2-4\overline{\smash{\big)}\,x^2+5} \\
\underline{x^2-4} \\
9
\end{array}
$$

The proper rational expression is:

$$\frac{x^2+5}{x^2-4}=1+\frac{9}{x^2-4}$$

5. The rational expression $\dfrac{5x^3+2x-1}{x^2-4}$ is improper, so perform the division:

$$
\begin{array}{r}
5x \\
x^2-4\overline{\smash{\big)}\,5x^3+0x^2+\ 2x-1} \\
\underline{5x^3\qquad-20x} \\
22x-1
\end{array}
$$

The proper rational expression is:

$$\frac{5x^3+2x-1}{x^2-4}=5x+\frac{22x-1}{x^2-4}$$

7. The rational expression $\dfrac{x(x-1)}{(x+4)(x-3)}=\dfrac{x^2-x}{x^2+x-12}$ is improper, so perform the division:

$$
\begin{array}{r}
1 \\
x^2+x-12\overline{\smash{\big)}\,x^2-x+\ 0} \\
\underline{x^2+x-12} \\
-2x+12
\end{array}
$$

The proper rational expression is: $\qquad \dfrac{x(x-1)}{(x+4)(x-3)}=1+\dfrac{-2x+12}{x^2+x-12}$

9. Find the partial fraction decomposition:

$$\frac{4}{x(x-1)}=\frac{A}{x}+\frac{B}{x-1}$$

$\qquad\qquad 4 = A(x-1)+Bx \qquad$ (Multiply both sides by $x(x-1)$.)

Let $x=1$: then $4 = A(0)+B \rightarrow B=4$

Let $x=0$: then $4 = A(-1)+B(0) \rightarrow A=-4$

$$\frac{4}{x(x-1)}=\frac{-4}{x}+\frac{4}{x-1}$$

11.   Find the partial fraction decomposition:

$$\frac{1}{x(x^2+1)} = \frac{A}{x} + \frac{Bx+C}{x^2+1}$$

$$1 = A(x^2+1) + (Bx+C)x \quad \text{(Multiply both sides by } x(x^2+1).)$$

Let $x = 0$:   then $1 = A(1) + (B(0)+C)(0) \rightarrow A = 1$

Let $x = 1$:   then $1 = A(1+1) + (B(1)+C)(1) \rightarrow 1 = 2A + B + C$

         so $1 = 2(1) + B + C \rightarrow -1 = B + C$

Let $x = -1$: then $1 = A(1+1) + (B(-1)+C)(-1) \rightarrow 1 = 2A + B - C$

         so $1 = 2(1) + B - C \rightarrow -1 = B - C$

Solve the system of equations:

$$\begin{array}{ll} B + C = -1 & \\ \underline{B - C = -1} & \\ 2B \quad\quad = -2 & \quad -1 + C = -1 \\ B \quad\quad = -1 & \quad\quad C = 0 \end{array}$$

$$\frac{1}{x(x^2+1)} = \frac{1}{x} + \frac{-x}{x^2+1}$$

13.   Find the partial fraction decomposition:

$$\frac{x}{(x-1)(x-2)} = \frac{A}{x-1} + \frac{B}{x-2}$$

$$x = A(x-2) + B(x-1) \quad \text{(Multiply both sides by } (x-1)(x-2).)$$

Let $x = 1$:   then $1 = A(1-2) + B(1-1) \rightarrow 1 = -A \rightarrow A = -1$

Let $x = 2$:   then $2 = A(2-2) + B(2-1) \rightarrow 2 = B \rightarrow B = 2$

$$\frac{x}{(x-1)(x-2)} = \frac{-1}{x-1} + \frac{2}{x-2}$$

15.   Find the partial fraction decomposition:

$$\frac{x^2}{(x-1)^2(x+1)} = \frac{A}{x-1} + \frac{B}{(x-1)^2} + \frac{C}{x+1} \quad \text{(Multiply both sides by } (x-1)^2(x+1).)$$

$$x^2 = A(x-1)(x+1) + B(x+1) + C(x-1)^2$$

Let $x = 1$:   then $1^2 = A(1-1)(1+1) + B(1+1) + C(1-1)^2$

$$\rightarrow 1 = 2B \rightarrow B = \frac{1}{2}$$

Let $x = -1$:   then $(-1)^2 = A(-1-1)(-1+1) + B(-1+1) + C(-1-1)^2$

$$\rightarrow 1 = 4C \rightarrow C = \frac{1}{4}$$

Let $x = 0$:   then $0^2 = A(0-1)(0+1) + B(0+1) + C(0-1)^2$

$$\rightarrow 0 = -A + B + C \rightarrow A = \frac{1}{2} + \frac{1}{4} = \frac{3}{4}$$

$$\frac{x^2}{(x-1)^2(x+1)} = \frac{\left(\frac{3}{4}\right)}{x-1} + \frac{\left(\frac{1}{2}\right)}{(x-1)^2} + \frac{\left(\frac{1}{4}\right)}{x+1}$$

17. Find the partial fraction decomposition:
$$\frac{1}{x^3-8} = \frac{1}{(x-2)(x^2+2x+4)} = \frac{A}{x-2} + \frac{Bx+C}{x^2+2x+4}$$

(Multiply both sides by $(x-2)(x^2+2x+4)$.)

$$1 = A(x^2+2x+4) + (Bx+C)(x-2)$$

Let $x=2$:   then $1 = A\left(2^2+2(2)+4\right) + (B(2)+C)(2-2)$

$$\rightarrow 1 = 12A \;\rightarrow\; A = \frac{1}{12}$$

Let $x=0$:   then $1 = A\left(0^2+2(0)+4\right) + (B(0)+C)(0-2)$

$$\rightarrow 1 = 4A - 2C \rightarrow 1 = 4\left(\frac{1}{12}\right) - 2C$$

$$\rightarrow -2C = \frac{2}{3} \;\rightarrow\; C = -\frac{1}{3}$$

Let $x=1$:   then $1 = A\left(1^2+2(1)+4\right) + (B(1)+C)(1-2)$

$$\rightarrow 1 = 7A - B - C \;\rightarrow\; 1 = 7\left(\frac{1}{12}\right) - B + \frac{1}{3} \;\rightarrow\; B = -\frac{1}{12}$$

$$\frac{1}{x^3-8} = \frac{\left(\dfrac{1}{12}\right)}{x-2} + \frac{-\left(\dfrac{1}{12}\right)x - \dfrac{1}{3}}{x^2+2x+4}$$

19. Find the partial fraction decomposition:
$$\frac{x^2}{(x-1)^2(x+1)^2} = \frac{A}{x-1} + \frac{B}{(x-1)^2} + \frac{C}{x+1} + \frac{D}{(x+1)^2}$$

(Multiply both sides by $(x-1)^2(x+1)^2$.)

$$x^2 = A(x-1)(x+1)^2 + B(x+1)^2 + C(x-1)^2(x+1) + D(x-1)^2$$

Let $x=1$:   then $1^2 = A(1-1)(1+1)^2 + B(1+1)^2 + C(1-1)^2(1+1) + D(1-1)^2$

$$\rightarrow 1 = 4B \;\rightarrow\; B = \frac{1}{4}$$

Let $x=-1$:   then

$$(-1)^2 = A(-1-1)(-1+1)^2 + B(-1+1)^2 + C(-1-1)^2(-1+1) + D(-1-1)^2$$

$$\rightarrow 1 = 4D \;\rightarrow\; D = \frac{1}{4}$$

Let $x=0$:   then

$$0^2 = A(0-1)(0+1)^2 + B(0+1)^2 + C(0-1)^2(0+1) + D(0-1)^2$$

$$\rightarrow 0 = -A + B + C + D \;\rightarrow\; A - C = \frac{1}{4} + \frac{1}{4} = \frac{1}{2}$$

Let $x = 2$: then

$$2^2 = A(2-1)(2+1)^2 + B(2+1)^2 + C(2-1)^2(2+1) + D(2-1)^2$$

$$\rightarrow 4 = 9A + 9B + 3C + D \rightarrow 9A + 3C = 4 - \frac{9}{4} - \frac{1}{4} = \frac{3}{2}$$

$$\rightarrow 3A + C = \frac{1}{2}$$

Solve the system of equations:

$$A - C = \frac{1}{2}$$

$$\underline{ 3A + C = \frac{1}{2}}$$

$$4A \quad = 1$$

$$A \quad = \frac{1}{4} \rightarrow \frac{3}{4} + C = \frac{1}{2} \rightarrow C = -\frac{1}{4}$$

$$\frac{x^2}{(x-1)^2(x+1)^2} = \frac{\left(\frac{1}{4}\right)}{x-1} + \frac{\left(\frac{1}{4}\right)}{(x-1)^2} + \frac{\left(-\frac{1}{4}\right)}{x+1} + \frac{\left(\frac{1}{4}\right)}{(x+1)^2}$$

21. Find the partial fraction decomposition:

$$\frac{x-3}{(x+2)(x+1)^2} = \frac{A}{x+2} + \frac{B}{x+1} + \frac{C}{(x+1)^2}$$

(Multiply both sides by $(x+2)(x+1)^2$.)

$$x - 3 = A(x+1)^2 + B(x+2)(x+1) + C(x+2)$$

Let $x = -2$: then $-2 - 3 = A(-2+1)^2 + B(-2+2)(-2+1) + C(-2+2)$

$$\rightarrow -5 = A \rightarrow A = -5$$

Let $x = -1$: then $-1 - 3 = A(-1+1)^2 + B(-1+2)(-1+1) + C(-1+2)$

$$\rightarrow -4 = C \rightarrow C = -4$$

Let $x = 0$: then

$$0 - 3 = A(0+1)^2 + B(0+2)(0+1) + C(0+2) \rightarrow -3 = A + 2B + 2C$$

$$\rightarrow -3 = -5 + 2B + 2(-4) \rightarrow 2B = 10 \rightarrow B = 5$$

$$\frac{x-3}{(x+2)(x+1)^2} = \frac{-5}{x+2} + \frac{5}{x+1} + \frac{-4}{(x+1)^2}$$

23. Find the partial fraction decomposition:

$$\frac{x+4}{x^2(x^2+4)} = \frac{A}{x} + \frac{B}{x^2} + \frac{Cx+D}{x^2+4} \quad \text{(Multiply both sides by } x^2(x^2+4).)$$

$$x + 4 = Ax(x^2+4) + B(x^2+4) + (Cx+D)x^2$$

Let $x = 0$: then $0 + 4 = A(0)(0^2+4) + B(0^2+4) + (C0+D)(0)^2$

$$\rightarrow 4 = 4B \rightarrow B = 1$$

Let $x = 1$: then $1 + 4 = A(1)(1^2+4) + B(1^2+4) + (C(1)+D)(1)^2$

$$\rightarrow 5 = 5A + 5B + C + D \rightarrow 5 = 5A + 5 + C + D$$

$$\rightarrow 5A + C + D = 0$$

Let $x = -1$: then

$$-1 + 4 = A(-1)((-1)^2 + 4) + B((-1)^2 + 4) + (C(-1) + D)(-1)^2$$
$$\rightarrow \ 3 = -5A + 5B - C + D \ \rightarrow \ 3 = -5A + 5 - C + D$$
$$\rightarrow \ -5A - C + D = -2$$

Let $x = 2$:   then $2 + 4 = A(2)(2^2 + 4) + B(2^2 + 4) + (C(2) + D)(2)^2$
$$\rightarrow \ 6 = 16A + 8B + 8C + 4D \ \rightarrow \ 6 = 16A + 8 + 8C + 4D$$
$$\rightarrow \ 16A + 8C + 4D = -2$$

Solve the system of equations:

$$5A + C + D = \ \ \ 0$$
$$\underline{-5A - C + D = -2}$$
$$2D = -2 \qquad\qquad 5A + C - 1 = 0$$
$$D = -1 \qquad\qquad\quad C = 1 - 5A$$
$$16A + 8(1 - 5A) + 4(-1) = -2$$
$$16A + 8 - 40A - 4 = -2 \qquad C = 1 - 5\left(\frac{1}{4}\right)$$
$$-24A = -6$$
$$A = \frac{1}{4} \qquad\qquad C = 1 - \frac{5}{4} = -\frac{1}{4}$$

$$\frac{x + 4}{x^2(x^2 + 4)} = \frac{\left(\dfrac{1}{4}\right)}{x} + \frac{1}{x^2} + \frac{\left(-\dfrac{1}{4}x - 1\right)}{x^2 + 4}$$

25. Find the partial fraction decomposition:

$$\frac{x^2 + 2x + 3}{(x + 1)(x^2 + 2x + 4)} = \frac{A}{x + 1} + \frac{Bx + C}{x^2 + 2x + 4} \text{(Multiply both sides by } (x + 1)(x^2 + 2x + 4).)$$

$$x^2 + 2x + 3 = A(x^2 + 2x + 4) + (Bx + C)(x + 1)$$

Let $x = -1$: then

$$(-1)^2 + 2(-1) + 3 = A((-1)^2 + 2(-1) + 4) + (B(-1) + C)(-1 + 1)$$
$$\rightarrow \ 2 = 3A \ \rightarrow \ A = \frac{2}{3}$$

Let $x = 0$:   then $0^2 + 2(0) + 3 = A(0^2 + 2(0) + 4) + (B(0) + C)(0 + 1)$
$$\rightarrow \ 3 = 4A + C \ \rightarrow \ 3 = 4\left(\frac{2}{3}\right) + C \ \rightarrow \ C = \frac{1}{3}$$

Let $x = 1$: then

$$1^2 + 2(1) + 3 = A(1^2 + 2(1) + 4) + (B(1) + C)(1 + 1)$$
$$\rightarrow \ 6 = 7A + 2B + 2C \ \rightarrow \ 6 = 7\left(\frac{2}{3}\right) + 2B + 2\left(\frac{1}{3}\right)$$
$$\rightarrow \ 2B = 6 - \frac{14}{3} - \frac{2}{3} \ \rightarrow \ 2B = \frac{2}{3} \ \rightarrow \ B = \frac{1}{3}$$

$$\frac{x^2 + 2x + 3}{(x + 1)(x^2 + 2x + 4)} = \frac{\left(\dfrac{2}{3}\right)}{x + 1} + \frac{\left(\dfrac{1}{3}x + \dfrac{1}{3}\right)}{x^2 + 2x + 4}$$

27. Find the partial fraction decomposition:

$$\frac{x}{(3x-2)(2x+1)} = \frac{A}{3x-2} + \frac{B}{2x+1} \quad \text{(Multiply both sides by } (3x-2)(2x+1).)$$

$$x = A(2x+1) + B(3x-2)$$

Let $x = -\frac{1}{2}$: then $-\frac{1}{2} = A\left(2\left(-\frac{1}{2}\right)+1\right) + B\left(3\left(-\frac{1}{2}\right)-2\right) \rightarrow -\frac{1}{2} = -\frac{7}{2}B \rightarrow B = \frac{1}{7}$

Let $x = \frac{2}{3}$: then $\frac{2}{3} = A\left(2\left(\frac{2}{3}\right)+1\right) + B\left(3\left(\frac{2}{3}\right)-2\right) \rightarrow \frac{2}{3} = \frac{7}{3}A \rightarrow A = \frac{2}{7}$

$$\frac{x}{(3x-2)(2x+1)} = \frac{\left(\frac{2}{7}\right)}{3x-2} + \frac{\left(\frac{1}{7}\right)}{2x+1}$$

29. Find the partial fraction decomposition:

$$\frac{x}{x^2+2x-3} = \frac{x}{(x+3)(x-1)} = \frac{A}{x+3} + \frac{B}{x-1}$$

$$\text{(Multiply both sides by } (x+3)(x-1).)$$

$$x = A(x-1) + B(x+3)$$

Let $x = 1$: then $1 = A(1-1) + B(1+3) \rightarrow 1 = 4B \rightarrow B = \frac{1}{4}$

Let $x = -3$: then $-3 = A(-3-1) + B(-3+3) \rightarrow -3 = -4A \rightarrow A = \frac{3}{4}$

$$\frac{x}{x^2+2x-3} = \frac{\left(\frac{3}{4}\right)}{x+3} + \frac{\left(\frac{1}{4}\right)}{x-1}$$

31. Find the partial fraction decomposition:

$$\frac{x^2+2x+3}{(x^2+4)^2} = \frac{Ax+B}{x^2+4} + \frac{Cx+D}{(x^2+4)^2}$$

$$\text{(Multiply both sides by } (x^2+4)^2.)$$

$$x^2+2x+3 = (Ax+B)(x^2+4) + Cx+D$$

$$x^2+2x+3 = Ax^3 + Bx^2 + 4Ax + 4B + Cx + D$$

$$x^2+2x+3 = Ax^3 + Bx^2 + (4A+C)x + 4B+D$$

$$A = 0$$

$$B = 1$$

$$4A+C = 2 \rightarrow 4(0)+C = 2 \rightarrow C = 2$$

$$4B+D = 3 \rightarrow 4(1)+D = 3 \rightarrow D = -1$$

$$\frac{x^2+2x+3}{(x^2+4)^2} = \frac{1}{x^2+4} + \frac{2x-1}{(x^2+4)^2}$$

33. Find the partial fraction decomposition:
$$\frac{7x+3}{x^3-2x^2-3x} = \frac{7x+3}{x(x-3)(x+1)} = \frac{A}{x}+\frac{B}{x-3}+\frac{C}{x+1}$$
(Multiply both sides by $x(x-3)(x+1)$.)
$$7x+3 = A(x-3)(x+1)+Bx(x+1)+Cx(x-3)$$
Let $x=0$:   then $7(0)+3 = A(0-3)(0+1)+B(0)(0+1)+C(0)(0-3)$
$$\rightarrow 3 = -3A \rightarrow A = -1$$
Let $x=3$:   then $7(3)+3 = A(3-3)(3+1)+B(3)(3+1)+C(3)(3-3)$
$$\rightarrow 24 = 12B \rightarrow B = 2$$
Let $x=-1$:   then
$$7(-1)+3 = A(-1-3)(-1+1)+B(-1)(-1+1)+C(-1)(-1-3)$$
$$\rightarrow -4 = 4C \rightarrow C = -1$$
$$\frac{7x+3}{x^3-2x^2-3x} = \frac{-1}{x}+\frac{2}{x-3}+\frac{-1}{x+1}$$

35. Perform synthetic division to find a factor:
$$2)\overline{1 \quad -4 \quad 5 \quad -2}$$
$$\quad\quad 2 \quad -4 \quad 2$$
$$\overline{1 \quad -2 \quad 1 \quad 0}$$
$$x^3-4x^2+5x-2 = (x-2)(x^2-2x+1) = (x-2)(x-1)^2$$
Find the partial fraction decomposition:
$$\frac{x^2}{x^3-4x^2+5x-2} = \frac{x^2}{(x-2)(x-1)^2} = \frac{A}{x-2}+\frac{B}{x-1}+\frac{C}{(x-1)^2}$$
(Multiply both sides by $(x-2)(x-1)^2$.)
$$x^2 = A(x-1)^2+B(x-2)(x-1)+C(x-2)$$
Let $x=2$:   then $2^2 = A(2-1)^2+B(2-2)(2-1)+C(2-2)$
$$\rightarrow 4 = A \rightarrow A = 4$$
Let $x=1$:   then $1^2 = A(1-1)^2+B(1-2)(1-1)+C(1-2)$
$$\rightarrow 1 = -C \rightarrow C = -1$$
Let $x=0$:   then $0^2 = A(0-1)^2+B(0-2)(0-1)+C(0-2)$
$$\rightarrow 0 = A+2B-2C \rightarrow 0 = 4+2B-2(-1)$$
$$\rightarrow 2B = -6 \rightarrow B = -3$$
$$\frac{x^2}{x^3-4x^2+5x-2} = \frac{4}{x-2}+\frac{-3}{x-1}+\frac{-1}{(x-1)^2}$$

37. Find the partial fraction decomposition:
$$\frac{x^3}{(x^2+16)^3} = \frac{Ax+B}{x^2+16}+\frac{Cx+D}{(x^2+16)^2}+\frac{Ex+F}{(x^2+16)^3}$$ (Multiply both sides by $(x^2+16)^3$.)
$$x^3 = (Ax+B)(x^2+16)^2+(Cx+D)(x^2+16)+Ex+F$$
$$x^3 = (Ax+B)(x^4+32x^2+256)+Cx^3+Dx^2+16Cx+16D+Ex+F$$

$$x^3 = Ax^5 + Bx^4 + 32Ax^3 + 32Bx^2 + 256Ax + 256B + Cx^3 + Dx^2$$
$$+16Cx + 16D + Ex + F$$
$$x^3 = Ax^5 + Bx^4 + (32A + C)x^3 + (32B + D)x^2 + (256A + 16C + E)x$$
$$+(256B + 16D + F)$$
$$A = 0$$
$$B = 0$$
$$32A + C = 1 \rightarrow 32(0) + C = 1 \rightarrow C = 1$$
$$32B + D = 0 \rightarrow 32(0) + D = 0 \rightarrow D = 0$$
$$256A + 16C + E = 0 \rightarrow 256(0) + 16(1) + E = 0 \rightarrow E = -16$$
$$256B + 16D + F = 0 \rightarrow 256(0) + 16(0) + F = 0 \rightarrow F = 0$$
$$\frac{x^3}{(x^2 + 16)^3} = \frac{x}{(x^2 + 16)^2} + \frac{-16x}{(x^2 + 16)^3}$$

39. Find the partial fraction decomposition:

$$\frac{4}{2x^2 - 5x - 3} = \frac{4}{(x - 3)(2x + 1)} = \frac{A}{x - 3} + \frac{B}{2x + 1}$$

(Multiply both sides by $(x - 3)(2x + 1)$.)

$$4 = A(2x + 1) + B(x - 3)$$

Let $x = -\dfrac{1}{2}$:   then $4 = A\left(2\left(-\dfrac{1}{2}\right) + 1\right) + B\left(-\dfrac{1}{2} - 3\right)$

$$\rightarrow 4 = -\frac{7}{2}B \rightarrow B = -\frac{8}{7}$$

Let $x = 3$:   then $4 = A(2(3) + 1) + B(3 - 3) \rightarrow 4 = 7A \rightarrow A = \dfrac{4}{7}$

$$\frac{4}{2x^2 - 5x - 3} = \frac{4}{(x - 3)(2x + 1)} = \frac{\left(\dfrac{4}{7}\right)}{x - 3} + \frac{\left(-\dfrac{8}{7}\right)}{2x + 1}$$

41. Find the partial fraction decomposition:

$$\frac{2x + 3}{x^4 - 9x^2} = \frac{2x + 3}{x^2(x - 3)(x + 3)} = \frac{A}{x} + \frac{B}{x^2} + \frac{C}{x - 3} + \frac{D}{x + 3}$$

(Multiply both sides by $x^2(x - 3)(x + 3)$.)

$$2x + 3 = Ax(x - 3)(x + 3) + B(x - 3)(x + 3) + Cx^2(x + 3) + Dx^2(x - 3)$$

Let $x = 0$:   then

$$2 \cdot 0 + 3 = A \cdot 0(0 - 3)(0 + 3) + B(0 - 3)(0 + 3) + C \cdot 0^2(0 + 3) + D \cdot 0^2(0 - 3)$$

$$\rightarrow 3 = -9B \rightarrow B = -\frac{1}{3}$$

Let $x = 3$:   then

$$2 \cdot 3 + 3 = A \cdot 3(3 - 3)(3 + 3) + B(3 - 3)(3 + 3) + C \cdot 3^2(3 + 3) + D \cdot 3^2(3 - 3)$$

$$\rightarrow 9 = 54C \rightarrow C = \frac{1}{6}$$

Let $x = -3$: then

$$2(-3) + 3 = A(-3)(-3-3)(-3+3) + B(-3-3)(-3+3) + C(-3)^2(-3+3)$$
$$+ D(-3)^2(-3-3)$$

$$\rightarrow -3 = -54D \rightarrow D = \frac{1}{18}$$

Let $x = 1$: then

$$2 \cdot 1 + 3 = A \cdot 1(1-3)(1+3) + B(1-3)(1+3) + C \cdot 1^2(1+3) + D \cdot 1^2(1-3)$$

$$\rightarrow 5 = -8A - 8B + 4C - 2D$$

$$\rightarrow 5 = -8A - 8\left(-\frac{1}{3}\right) + 4\left(\frac{1}{6}\right) - 2\left(\frac{1}{18}\right)$$

$$\rightarrow 5 = -8A + \frac{8}{3} + \frac{2}{3} - \frac{1}{9} \rightarrow -8A = \frac{16}{9} \rightarrow A = -\frac{2}{9}$$

$$\frac{2x+3}{x^4 - 9x^2} = \frac{2x+3}{x^2(x-3)(x+3)} = \frac{\left(-\frac{2}{9}\right)}{x} + \frac{\left(-\frac{1}{3}\right)}{x^2} + \frac{\left(\frac{1}{6}\right)}{x-3} + \frac{\left(\frac{1}{18}\right)}{x+3}$$

Systems of Equations and Inequalities

7.R   Chapter Review

1. Solve the first equation for y, substitute into the second equation and solve:

$$\begin{cases} 2x - y = 5 & \to \quad y = 2x - 5 \\ 5x + 2y = 8 \end{cases}$$

$$5x + 2(2x - 5) = 8 \to 5x + 4x - 10 = 8$$

$$9x = 18 \to x = 2 \to y = 2(2) - 5 = 4 - 5 = -1$$

The solution is $x = 2, \ y = -1$.

3. Solve the second equation for x, substitute into the first equation and solve:

$$\begin{cases} 3x - 4y = 4 \\ \ \ x - 3y = \dfrac{1}{2} & \to \quad x = 3y + \dfrac{1}{2} \end{cases}$$

$$3\left(3y + \frac{1}{2}\right) - 4y = 4 \to 9y + \frac{3}{2} - 4y = 4 \to 5y = \frac{5}{2} \to y = \frac{1}{2} \to x = 3\left(\frac{1}{2}\right) + \frac{1}{2} = 2$$

The solution is $x = 2, \ y = \dfrac{1}{2}$.

5. Solve the first equation for x, substitute into the second equation and solve:

$$\begin{cases} \ x - 2y - 4 = 0 & \to \quad x = 2y + 4 \\ 3x + 2y - 4 = 0 \end{cases}$$

$$3(2y + 4) + 2y - 4 = 0 \to 6y + 12 + 2y - 4 = 0$$

$$8y = -8 \to y = -1 \to x = 2(-1) + 4 = 2$$

The solution is $x = 2, \ y = -1$.

7. Substitute the first equation into the second equation and solve:

$$\begin{cases} y = 2x - 5 \\ x = 3y + 4 \end{cases}$$

$$x = 3(2x - 5) + 4 \to x = 6x - 15 + 4$$

$$-5x = -11 \to x = \frac{11}{5} \to y = 2\left(\frac{11}{5}\right) - 5 = -\frac{3}{5}$$

The solution is $x = \dfrac{11}{5}, \ y = -\dfrac{3}{5}$.

9. Multiply each side of the first equation by 3 and each side of the second equation by −6 and add:

$$\begin{cases} x - 3y + 4 = 0 \\ \dfrac{1}{2}x - \dfrac{3}{2}y + \dfrac{4}{3} = 0 \end{cases} \quad \begin{array}{l} \xrightarrow{3} \quad 3x - 9y + 12 = 0 \\ \xrightarrow{-6} \quad \dfrac{-3x + 9y - 8 = 0}{4 \neq 0} \end{array}$$

There is no solution to the system. The system is inconsistent.

11. Multiply each side of the first equation by 2 and each side of the second equation by 3 and add to eliminate y:

$$\begin{cases} 2x + 3y - 13 = 0 \\ 3x - 2y \quad = 0 \end{cases} \quad \begin{array}{l} \xrightarrow{2} \quad 4x + 6y - 26 = 0 \\ \xrightarrow{3} \quad \dfrac{9x - 6y \quad = 0}{13x \quad - 26 = 0} \\ \qquad\qquad 13x = 26 \\ \qquad\qquad\quad x = 2 \end{array}$$

Substitute and solve for y:

$$3(2) - 2y = 0$$
$$-2y = -6$$
$$y = 3$$

The solution of the system is $x = 2$, $y = 3$.

13. Multiply each side of the second equation by −3 and add to eliminate x:

$$\begin{cases} 3x - 2y = 8 \\ x - \dfrac{2}{3}y = 12 \end{cases} \quad \begin{array}{l} \xrightarrow{\quad} \quad 3x - 2y = 8 \\ \xrightarrow{-3} \quad \dfrac{-3x + 2y = -36}{0 \neq -28} \end{array}$$

The system has no solution, so the system is inconsistent.

15. Multiply each side of the first equation by −2 and add to the second equation to eliminate x; and multiply each side of the first equation by −3 and add to the third equation to eliminate x:

$$\begin{cases} x + 2y - z = 6 \\ 2x - y + 3z = -13 \\ 3x - 2y + 3z = -16 \end{cases}$$

$$\begin{array}{l} \xrightarrow{-2} \quad -2x - 4y + 2z = -12 \\ \xrightarrow{\quad} \quad \dfrac{2x - y + 3z = -13}{-5y + 5z = -25} \xrightarrow{-1/5} y - z = 5 \\ \xrightarrow{-3} \quad -3x - 6y + 3z = -18 \\ \xrightarrow{\quad} \quad \dfrac{3x - 2y + 3z = -16}{-8y + 6z = -34} \end{array}$$

Multiply each side of the first result by 8 and add to the second result to eliminate y:

$$\begin{array}{l} y - z = 5 \quad \xrightarrow{8} \quad 8y - 8z = 40 \\ -8y + 6z = -34 \quad \xrightarrow{\quad} \quad \dfrac{-8y + 6z = -34}{-2z = 6} \\ \qquad\qquad\qquad\qquad\qquad\qquad z = -3 \end{array}$$

Substituting and solving for the other variables:

$$y - (-3) = 5 \qquad\qquad x + 2(2) - (-3) = 6$$
$$y = 2 \qquad\qquad\qquad x + 4 + 3 = 6$$
$$\qquad\qquad\qquad\qquad\qquad x = -1$$

The solution is $x = -1$, $y = 2$, $z = -3$.

17. Multiply the first equation by -1 and the second equation by 2 and then add to eliminate x; then multiply the second equation by -5 and add to the third equation to eliminate x:

$$\begin{cases} 2x - 4y + z = -15 & \xrightarrow{\;-1\;} -2x + 4y - z = 15 \\ x + 2y - 4z = 27 & \xrightarrow{\;2\;} \underline{\;\;2x + 4y - 8z = 54\;} \\ 5x - 6y - 2z = -3 & \qquad\qquad 8y - 9z \;\;= 69 \end{cases}$$

$$x + 2y - 4z = 27 \xrightarrow{\;-5\;} \quad -5x - 10y + 20z = -135$$
$$5x - 6y - 2z = -3 \longrightarrow \quad \underline{\;5x - 6y - 2z \qquad = -3\;}$$
$$\qquad\qquad\qquad\qquad\qquad -16y + 18z \;\;= -138$$

Now eliminate y in the resulting system:

$$8y - 9z = \quad 69 \xrightarrow{\;2\;} 16y - 18z = 138$$
$$-16y + 18z = -138 \longrightarrow \underline{-16y + 18z = -138}$$
$$\qquad\qquad\qquad\qquad\qquad 0 = 0$$

$$-16y + 18z = -138 \Rightarrow 18z + 138 = 16y \Rightarrow y = \frac{9}{8}z + \frac{69}{8}, \; z \text{ is any real number}$$

Substituting into the second equation and solving for the other x:

$$x + 2\left(\frac{9}{8}z + \frac{69}{8}\right) - 4z = 27$$

$$x + \frac{9}{4}z + \frac{69}{4} - 4z = 27 \Rightarrow x = \frac{7}{4}z + \frac{39}{4}, \; z \text{ is any real number}$$

The solution is $x = \frac{7}{4}z + \frac{39}{4}$, $y = \frac{9}{8}z + \frac{69}{8}$, z is any real number.

19. $\begin{cases} 3x + 2y = 8 \\ x + 4y = -1 \end{cases}$

21. $A + C = \begin{bmatrix} 1 & 0 \\ 2 & 4 \\ -1 & 2 \end{bmatrix} + \begin{bmatrix} 3 & -4 \\ 1 & 5 \\ 5 & -2 \end{bmatrix} = \begin{bmatrix} 4 & -4 \\ 3 & 9 \\ 4 & 0 \end{bmatrix}$

23. $6A = 6 \cdot \begin{bmatrix} 1 & 0 \\ 2 & 4 \\ -1 & 2 \end{bmatrix} = \begin{bmatrix} 6 & 0 \\ 12 & 24 \\ -6 & 12 \end{bmatrix}$

25. $AB = \begin{bmatrix} 1 & 0 \\ 2 & 4 \\ -1 & 2 \end{bmatrix} \cdot \begin{bmatrix} 4 & -3 & 0 \\ 1 & 1 & -2 \end{bmatrix} = \begin{bmatrix} 4 & -3 & 0 \\ 12 & -2 & -8 \\ -2 & 5 & -4 \end{bmatrix}$

27. $CB = \begin{bmatrix} 3 & -4 \\ 1 & 5 \\ 5 & -2 \end{bmatrix} \cdot \begin{bmatrix} 4 & -3 & 0 \\ 1 & 1 & -2 \end{bmatrix} = \begin{bmatrix} 8 & -13 & 8 \\ 9 & 2 & -10 \\ 18 & -17 & 4 \end{bmatrix}$

29. Augment the matrix with the identity and use row operations to find the inverse:

$$A = \begin{bmatrix} 4 & 6 \\ 1 & 3 \end{bmatrix} \;\rightarrow\; \left[\begin{array}{cc|cc} 4 & 6 & 1 & 0 \\ 1 & 3 & 0 & 1 \end{array}\right]$$

$$\rightarrow \begin{bmatrix} 1 & 3 & 0 & 1 \\ 4 & 6 & 1 & 0 \end{bmatrix} \rightarrow \begin{bmatrix} 1 & 3 & 0 & 1 \\ 0 & -6 & 1 & -4 \end{bmatrix} \rightarrow \begin{bmatrix} 1 & 3 & 0 & 1 \\ 0 & 1 & -\frac{1}{6} & \frac{2}{3} \end{bmatrix} \rightarrow \begin{bmatrix} 1 & 0 & \frac{1}{2} & -1 \\ 0 & 1 & -\frac{1}{6} & \frac{2}{3} \end{bmatrix}$$

Interchange $\quad R_2 = -4r_1 + r_2 \quad R_2 = -\frac{1}{6}r_2 \quad\quad R_1 = -3r_2 + r_1$

r_1 and r_2

$$A^{-1} = \begin{bmatrix} \frac{1}{2} & -1 \\ -\frac{1}{6} & \frac{2}{3} \end{bmatrix}$$

31. Augment the matrix with the identity and use row operations to find the inverse:

$$A = \begin{bmatrix} 1 & 3 & 3 \\ 1 & 2 & 1 \\ 1 & -1 & 2 \end{bmatrix} \rightarrow \begin{bmatrix} 1 & 3 & 3 & 1 & 0 & 0 \\ 1 & 2 & 1 & 0 & 1 & 0 \\ 1 & -1 & 2 & 0 & 0 & 1 \end{bmatrix}$$

$$\rightarrow \begin{bmatrix} 1 & 3 & 3 & 1 & 0 & 0 \\ 0 & -1 & -2 & -1 & 1 & 0 \\ 0 & -4 & -1 & -1 & 0 & 1 \end{bmatrix} \rightarrow \begin{bmatrix} 1 & 3 & 3 & 1 & 0 & 0 \\ 0 & 1 & 2 & 1 & -1 & 0 \\ 0 & -4 & -1 & -1 & 0 & 1 \end{bmatrix} \rightarrow \begin{bmatrix} 1 & 0 & -3 & -2 & 3 & 0 \\ 0 & 1 & 2 & 1 & -1 & 0 \\ 0 & 0 & 7 & 3 & -4 & 1 \end{bmatrix}$$

$R_2 = -r_1 + r_2 \quad\quad\quad R_2 = -r_2 \quad\quad\quad\quad R_1 = -3r_2 + r_1$

$R_3 = -r_1 + r_3 \quad\quad\quad\quad\quad\quad\quad\quad\quad\quad R_3 = 4r_2 + r_3$

$$\rightarrow \begin{bmatrix} 1 & 0 & -3 & -2 & 3 & 0 \\ 0 & 1 & 2 & 1 & -1 & 0 \\ 0 & 0 & 1 & \frac{3}{7} & -\frac{4}{7} & \frac{1}{7} \end{bmatrix} \rightarrow \begin{bmatrix} 1 & 0 & 0 & -\frac{5}{7} & \frac{9}{7} & \frac{3}{7} \\ 0 & 1 & 0 & \frac{1}{7} & \frac{1}{7} & -\frac{2}{7} \\ 0 & 0 & 1 & \frac{3}{7} & -\frac{4}{7} & \frac{1}{7} \end{bmatrix} \longrightarrow A^{-1} = \begin{bmatrix} -\frac{5}{7} & \frac{9}{7} & \frac{3}{7} \\ \frac{1}{7} & \frac{1}{7} & -\frac{2}{7} \\ \frac{3}{7} & -\frac{4}{7} & \frac{1}{7} \end{bmatrix}$$

$R_3 = \frac{1}{7}r_3 \quad\quad\quad\quad R_1 = 3r_3 + r_1$

$\quad\quad\quad\quad\quad\quad R_2 = -2r_3 + r_2$

33. Augment the matrix with the identity and use row operations to find the inverse:

$$A = \begin{bmatrix} 4 & -8 \\ -1 & 2 \end{bmatrix} \rightarrow \begin{bmatrix} 4 & -8 & 1 & 0 \\ -1 & 2 & 0 & 1 \end{bmatrix}$$

$$\rightarrow \begin{bmatrix} -1 & 2 & 0 & 1 \\ 4 & -8 & 1 & 0 \end{bmatrix} \rightarrow \begin{bmatrix} -1 & 2 & 0 & 1 \\ 0 & 0 & 1 & 4 \end{bmatrix} \rightarrow \begin{bmatrix} 1 & -2 & 0 & -1 \\ 0 & 0 & 1 & 4 \end{bmatrix}$$

Interchange $\quad\quad R_2 = 4r_1 + r_2 \quad R_1 = -r_1$

r_1 and r_2

There is no inverse because there is no way to obtain the identity on the left side. The matrix is singular.

35. $\begin{cases} 3x - 2y = 1 \\ 10x + 10y = 5 \end{cases}$ can be written as: $\begin{bmatrix} 3 & -2 & 1 \\ 10 & 10 & 5 \end{bmatrix}$

$$\rightarrow \begin{bmatrix} 3 & -2 & 1 \\ 1 & 16 & 2 \end{bmatrix} \rightarrow \begin{bmatrix} 1 & 16 & 2 \\ 3 & -2 & 1 \end{bmatrix} \rightarrow \begin{bmatrix} 1 & 16 & 2 \\ 0 & -50 & -5 \end{bmatrix} \rightarrow \begin{bmatrix} 1 & 16 & 2 \\ 0 & 1 & \frac{1}{10} \end{bmatrix} \rightarrow \begin{bmatrix} 1 & 0 & \frac{2}{5} \\ 0 & 1 & \frac{1}{10} \end{bmatrix}$$

$R_2 = -3r_1 + r_2 \quad$ Interchange $\quad R_2 = -3r_1 + r_2 \quad R_2 = -\frac{1}{50}r_2 \quad R_1 = -16r_2 + r_1$

$\quad\quad\quad\quad\quad\quad r_1$ and r_2

The solution is $x = \dfrac{2}{5}, y = \dfrac{1}{10}$.

37. $\begin{cases} 5x + 6y - 3z = 6 \\ 4x - 7y - 2z = -3 \\ 3x + y - 7z = 1 \end{cases}$ can be written as: $\begin{bmatrix} 5 & 6 & -3 & | & 6 \\ 4 & -7 & -2 & | & -3 \\ 3 & 1 & -7 & | & 1 \end{bmatrix}$

$$\rightarrow \begin{bmatrix} 1 & 13 & -1 & | & 9 \\ 4 & -7 & -2 & | & -3 \\ 3 & 1 & -7 & | & 1 \end{bmatrix} \rightarrow \begin{bmatrix} 1 & 13 & -1 & | & 9 \\ 0 & -59 & 2 & | & -39 \\ 0 & -38 & -4 & | & -26 \end{bmatrix} \rightarrow \begin{bmatrix} 1 & 13 & -1 & | & 9 \\ 0 & 1 & -\frac{2}{59} & | & \frac{39}{59} \\ 0 & -38 & -4 & | & -26 \end{bmatrix}$$

$R_1 = -r_2 + r_1$ $R_2 = -4r_1 + r_2$ $R_2 = -\frac{1}{59}r_2$
                          $R_3 = -3r_1 + r_3$

$$\rightarrow \begin{bmatrix} 1 & 0 & -\frac{33}{59} & | & \frac{24}{59} \\ 0 & 1 & -\frac{2}{59} & | & \frac{39}{59} \\ 0 & 0 & -\frac{312}{59} & | & -\frac{52}{59} \end{bmatrix} \rightarrow \begin{bmatrix} 1 & 0 & -\frac{33}{59} & | & \frac{24}{59} \\ 0 & 1 & -\frac{2}{59} & | & \frac{39}{59} \\ 0 & 0 & 1 & | & \frac{1}{6} \end{bmatrix} \rightarrow \begin{bmatrix} 1 & 0 & 0 & | & \frac{1}{2} \\ 0 & 1 & 0 & | & \frac{2}{3} \\ 0 & 0 & 1 & | & \frac{1}{6} \end{bmatrix}$$

$R_1 = -13r_2 + r_1$ $R_3 = -\frac{59}{312}r_3$ $R_1 = \frac{33}{59}r_3 + r_1$
$R_3 = 38r_2 + r_3$ $R_2 = \frac{2}{59}r_3 + r_2$

The solution is $x = \dfrac{1}{2}, y = \dfrac{2}{3}, z = \dfrac{1}{6}$.

39. $\begin{cases} x - 2z = 1 \\ 2x + 3y = -3 \\ 4x - 3y - 4z = 3 \end{cases}$ can be written as: $\begin{bmatrix} 1 & 0 & -2 & | & 1 \\ 2 & 3 & 0 & | & -3 \\ 4 & -3 & -4 & | & 3 \end{bmatrix}$

$$\rightarrow \begin{bmatrix} 1 & 0 & -2 & | & 1 \\ 0 & 3 & 4 & | & -5 \\ 0 & -3 & 4 & | & -1 \end{bmatrix} \rightarrow \begin{bmatrix} 1 & 0 & -2 & | & 1 \\ 0 & 1 & \frac{4}{3} & | & -\frac{5}{3} \\ 0 & -3 & 4 & | & -1 \end{bmatrix} \rightarrow \begin{bmatrix} 1 & 0 & -2 & | & 1 \\ 0 & 1 & \frac{4}{3} & | & -\frac{5}{3} \\ 0 & 0 & 8 & | & -6 \end{bmatrix}$$

$R_2 = -2r_1 + r_2$ $R_2 = \frac{1}{3}r_2$ $R_3 = 3r_2 + r_3$
$R_3 = -4r_1 + r_3$

$$\rightarrow \begin{bmatrix} 1 & 0 & -2 & | & 1 \\ 0 & 1 & \frac{4}{3} & | & -\frac{5}{3} \\ 0 & 0 & 1 & | & -\frac{3}{4} \end{bmatrix} \rightarrow \begin{bmatrix} 1 & 0 & 0 & | & -\frac{1}{2} \\ 0 & 1 & 0 & | & -\frac{2}{3} \\ 0 & 0 & 1 & | & -\frac{3}{4} \end{bmatrix}$$

$R_3 = \frac{1}{8}r_3$ $R_1 = 2r_3 + r_1$
              $R_2 = -\frac{4}{3}r_3 + r_2$

The solution is $x = -\dfrac{1}{2}, y = -\dfrac{2}{3}, z = -\dfrac{3}{4}$.

41. $\begin{cases} x - y + z = 0 \\ x - y - 5z = 6 \\ 2x - 2y + z = 1 \end{cases}$ can be written as: $\begin{bmatrix} 1 & -1 & 1 & | & 0 \\ 1 & -1 & -5 & | & 6 \\ 2 & -2 & 1 & | & 1 \end{bmatrix}$

$$\rightarrow \begin{bmatrix} 1 & -1 & 1 & | & 0 \\ 0 & 0 & -6 & | & 6 \\ 0 & 0 & -1 & | & 1 \end{bmatrix} \rightarrow \begin{bmatrix} 1 & -1 & 1 & | & 0 \\ 0 & 0 & 1 & | & -1 \\ 0 & 0 & -1 & | & 1 \end{bmatrix} \rightarrow \begin{bmatrix} 1 & -1 & 0 & | & 1 \\ 0 & 0 & 1 & | & -1 \\ 0 & 0 & 0 & | & 0 \end{bmatrix} \rightarrow \begin{cases} x = y + 1 \\ z = -1 \end{cases}$$

$R_2 = -r_1 + r_2$ $R_2 = -\frac{1}{6}r_2$ $R_1 = -r_2 + r_1$
$R_3 = -2r_1 + r_3$ $R_3 = r_2 + r_3$

The solution is $x = y + 1, z = -1, y$ is any real number..

43. $\begin{cases} x - y - z - t = 1 \\ 2x + y - z + 2t = 3 \\ x - 2y - 2z - 3t = 0 \\ 3x - 4y + z + 5t = -3 \end{cases}$ can be written as: $\begin{vmatrix} 1 & -1 & -1 & -1 & 1 \\ 2 & 1 & -1 & 2 & 3 \\ 1 & -2 & -2 & -3 & 0 \\ 3 & -4 & 1 & 5 & -3 \end{vmatrix}$

$\rightarrow \begin{vmatrix} 1 & -1 & -1 & -1 & 1 \\ 0 & 3 & 1 & 4 & 1 \\ 0 & -1 & -1 & -2 & -1 \\ 0 & -1 & 4 & 8 & -6 \end{vmatrix} \rightarrow \begin{vmatrix} 1 & -1 & -1 & -1 & 1 \\ 0 & -1 & -1 & -2 & -1 \\ 0 & 3 & 1 & 4 & 1 \\ 0 & -1 & 4 & 8 & -6 \end{vmatrix} \rightarrow \begin{vmatrix} 1 & -1 & -1 & -1 & 1 \\ 0 & 1 & 1 & 2 & 1 \\ 0 & 3 & 1 & 4 & 1 \\ 0 & -1 & 4 & 8 & -6 \end{vmatrix}$

$R_2 = -2r_1 + r_2$ Interchange r_2 and r_3 $R_2 = -r_2$
$R_3 = -r_1 + r_3$
$R_4 = -3r_1 + r_4$

$\rightarrow \begin{vmatrix} 1 & 0 & 0 & 1 & 2 \\ 0 & 1 & 1 & 2 & 1 \\ 0 & 0 & -2 & -2 & -2 \\ 0 & 0 & 5 & 10 & -5 \end{vmatrix} \rightarrow \begin{vmatrix} 1 & 0 & 0 & 1 & 2 \\ 0 & 1 & 1 & 2 & 1 \\ 0 & 0 & 1 & 1 & 1 \\ 0 & 0 & 1 & 2 & -1 \end{vmatrix} \rightarrow \begin{vmatrix} 1 & 0 & 0 & 1 & 2 \\ 0 & 1 & 1 & 2 & 1 \\ 0 & 0 & 1 & 1 & 1 \\ 0 & 0 & 0 & 1 & -2 \end{vmatrix}$

$R_1 = r_2 + r_1$ $R_3 = -\frac{1}{2}r_3$ $R_4 = r_4 - r_3$
$R_3 = -3r_2 + r_3$ $R_4 = \frac{1}{5}r_4$
$R_4 = r_2 + r_4$

$\rightarrow \begin{vmatrix} 1 & 0 & 0 & 0 & 4 \\ 0 & 1 & 0 & 0 & 2 \\ 0 & 0 & 1 & 0 & 3 \\ 0 & 0 & 0 & 1 & -2 \end{vmatrix}$

$R_1 = r_1 - r_4$
$R_2 = r_2 - r_3 - r_4$
$R_3 = r_3 - r_4$

The solution is $x = 4, y = 2, z = 3, t = -2$.

45. Evaluating the determinant:

$$\begin{vmatrix} 3 & 4 \\ 1 & 3 \end{vmatrix} = 3(3) - 4(1) = 9 - 4 = 5$$

47. Evaluating the determinant:

$$\begin{vmatrix} 1 & 4 & 0 \\ -1 & 2 & 6 \\ 4 & 1 & 3 \end{vmatrix} = 1\begin{vmatrix} 2 & 6 \\ 1 & 3 \end{vmatrix} - 4\begin{vmatrix} -1 & 6 \\ 4 & 3 \end{vmatrix} + 0\begin{vmatrix} -1 & 2 \\ 4 & 1 \end{vmatrix}$$

$$= 1[2(3) - 6(1)] - 4[-1(3) - 6(4)] + 0[-1(1) - 2(4)]$$

$$= 1(6 - 6) - 4(-3 - 24) + 0(-1 - 8)$$

$$= 1(0) - 4(-27) + 0(-9) = 0 + 108 + 0 = 108$$

49. Evaluating the determinant:

$$\begin{vmatrix} 2 & 1 & -3 \\ 5 & 0 & 1 \\ 2 & 6 & 0 \end{vmatrix} = 2\begin{vmatrix} 0 & 1 \\ 6 & 0 \end{vmatrix} - 1\begin{vmatrix} 5 & 1 \\ 2 & 0 \end{vmatrix} + (-3)\begin{vmatrix} 5 & 0 \\ 2 & 6 \end{vmatrix}$$

$$= 2(0-6) - 1(0-2) + (-3)(30-0) = -12 + 2 - 90 = -100$$

51. Set up and evaluate the determinants to use Cramer's Rule:

$$\begin{cases} x - 2y = 4 \\ 3x + 2y = 4 \end{cases}$$

$$D = \begin{vmatrix} 1 & -2 \\ 3 & 2 \end{vmatrix} = 1(2) - 3(-2) = 2 + 6 = 8$$

$$D_x = \begin{vmatrix} 4 & -2 \\ 4 & 2 \end{vmatrix} = 4(2) - 4(-2) = 8 + 8 = 16$$

$$D_y = \begin{vmatrix} 1 & 4 \\ 3 & 4 \end{vmatrix} = 1(4) - 4(3) = 4 - 12 = -8$$

Find the solutions by Cramer's Rule: $x = \dfrac{D_x}{D} = \dfrac{16}{8} = 2 \qquad y = \dfrac{D_y}{D} = \dfrac{-8}{8} = -1$

53. Set up and evaluate the determinants to use Cramer's Rule:

$$\begin{cases} 2x + 3y = 13 \\ 3x - 2y = 0 \end{cases}$$

$$D = \begin{vmatrix} 2 & 3 \\ 3 & -2 \end{vmatrix} = -4 - 9 = -13$$

$$D_x = \begin{vmatrix} 13 & 3 \\ 0 & -2 \end{vmatrix} = -26 - 0 = -26; \quad D_y = \begin{vmatrix} 2 & 13 \\ 3 & 0 \end{vmatrix} = 0 - 39 = -39$$

Find the solutions by Cramer's Rule: $x = \dfrac{D_x}{D} = \dfrac{-26}{-13} = 2 \qquad y = \dfrac{D_y}{D} = \dfrac{-39}{-13} = 3$

55. Set up and evaluate the determinants to use Cramer's Rule:

$$\begin{cases} x + 2y - z = 6 \\ 2x - y + 3z = -13 \\ 3x - 2y + 3z = -16 \end{cases}$$

$$D = \begin{vmatrix} 1 & 2 & -1 \\ 2 & -1 & 3 \\ 3 & -2 & 3 \end{vmatrix} = 1\begin{vmatrix} -1 & 3 \\ -2 & 3 \end{vmatrix} - 2\begin{vmatrix} 2 & 3 \\ 3 & 3 \end{vmatrix} + (-1)\begin{vmatrix} 2 & -1 \\ 3 & -2 \end{vmatrix}$$

$$= 1(-3+6) - 2(6-9) - 1(-4+3) = 3 + 6 + 1 = 10$$

$$D_x = \begin{vmatrix} 6 & 2 & -1 \\ -13 & -1 & 3 \\ -16 & -2 & 3 \end{vmatrix} = 6\begin{vmatrix} -1 & 3 \\ -2 & 3 \end{vmatrix} - 2\begin{vmatrix} -13 & 3 \\ -16 & 3 \end{vmatrix} + (-1)\begin{vmatrix} -13 & -1 \\ -16 & -2 \end{vmatrix}$$

$$= 6(-3+6) - 2(-39+48) - 1(26-16) = 18 - 18 - 10 = -10$$

$$D_y = \begin{vmatrix} 1 & 6 & -1 \\ 2 & -13 & 3 \\ 3 & -16 & 3 \end{vmatrix} = 1\begin{vmatrix} -13 & 3 \\ -16 & 3 \end{vmatrix} - 6\begin{vmatrix} 2 & 3 \\ 3 & 3 \end{vmatrix} + (-1)\begin{vmatrix} 2 & -13 \\ 3 & -16 \end{vmatrix}$$

$$= 1(-39 + 48) - 6(6 - 9) - 1(-32 + 39) = 9 + 18 - 7 = 20$$

$$D_z = \begin{vmatrix} 1 & 2 & 6 \\ 2 & -1 & -13 \\ 3 & -2 & -16 \end{vmatrix} = 1\begin{vmatrix} -1 & -13 \\ -2 & -16 \end{vmatrix} - 2\begin{vmatrix} 2 & -13 \\ 3 & -16 \end{vmatrix} + 6\begin{vmatrix} 2 & -1 \\ 3 & -2 \end{vmatrix}$$

$$= 1(16 - 26) - 2(-32 + 39) + 6(-4 + 3) = -10 - 14 - 6 = -30$$

Find the solutions by Cramer's Rule:

$$x = \frac{D_x}{D} = \frac{-10}{10} = -1 \qquad y = \frac{D_y}{D} = \frac{20}{10} = 2 \qquad z = \frac{D_z}{D} = \frac{-30}{10} = -3$$

57. Let $\begin{vmatrix} x & y \\ a & b \end{vmatrix} = 8$

Then $\begin{vmatrix} 2x & y \\ 2a & b \end{vmatrix} = 16$ by Theorem 14.

The value of the determinant is multiplied by k when the elements of a column are multiplied by k.

59. $3x + 4y \le 12$

(a) Graph the line $3x + 4y = 12$. Use a solid line since the inequality uses $\le$.
Choose a test point not on the line, such as (0, 0).
Since $3(0) + 4(0) \le 12$ is true, shade the side of the line containing (0, 0).

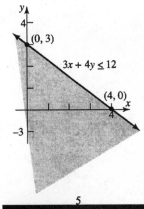

(b) Use the SHADE function in the calculator's DRAW menu: Shade$(-5, -(3/4)x + 3)$.

61. Graph the system of linear inequalities:
$$\begin{cases} -2x + y \le 2 \\ x + y \ge 2 \end{cases}$$

(a) Graph the line $-2x + y = 2$. Use a solid line since the inequality uses $\le$.
Choose a test point not on the line, such as $(0, 0)$. Since $-2(0) + 0 \le 2$ is true, shade the side of the line containing $(0, 0)$.

(b) Graph the line $x + y = 2$. Use a solid line since the inequality uses $\ge$.
Choose a test point not on the line, such as $(0, 0)$. Since $0 + 0 \ge 2$ is false, shade the opposite side of the line from $(0, 0)$.

(c) The overlapping region is the solution.

(d) The graph is unbounded.

(e) Find the vertices:
To find the intersection of $x + y = 2$ and $-2x + y = 2$, solve the system:
$$\begin{cases} x + y = 2 \quad \rightarrow \quad x = 2 - y \\ -2x + y = 2 \end{cases}$$
Substitute and solve:
$$-2(2 - y) + y = 2 \rightarrow -4 + 2y + y = 2 \rightarrow 3y = 6 \rightarrow y = 2$$
$$x = 2 - 2 = 0$$
The point of intersection is $(0, 2)$.
The corner point is $(0, 2)$.

63. Graph the system of linear inequalities:
$$\begin{cases} x \ge 0 \\ y \ge 0 \\ x + y \le 4 \\ 2x + 3y \le 6 \end{cases}$$

(a) Graph $x \ge 0$; $y \ge 0$. Shaded region is the first quadrant.

(b) Graph the line $x + y = 4$. Use a solid line since the inequality uses $\le$.
Choose a test point not on the line, such as $(0, 0)$. Since $0 + 0 \le 4$ is true, shade the side of the line containing $(0, 0)$.

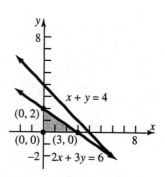

(c) Graph the line $2x + 3y = 6$. Use a solid line since the inequality uses $\le$.
Choose a test point not on the line, such as $(0, 0)$. Since $2(0) + 3(0) \le 6$ is true, shade the side of the line containing $(0, 0)$.

(d) The overlapping region is the solution.

(e) The graph is bounded.

(f)   Find the vertices:
The x-axis and y-axis intersect at $(0, 0)$.
The intersection of $2x + 3y = 6$ and the y-axis is $(0, 2)$.
The intersection of $2x + 3y = 6$ and the x-axis is $(3, 0)$.
The three corner points are $(0, 0)$, $(0, 2)$, and $(3, 0)$.

65.   Graph the system of linear inequalities:
$$\begin{cases} x \geq 0 \\ y \geq 0 \\ 2x + y \leq 8 \\ x + 2y \geq 2 \end{cases}$$

(a)   Graph $x \geq 0$; $y \geq 0$. Shaded region is the first quadrant.

(b)   Graph the line $2x + y = 8$. Use a solid line since the inequality uses $\leq$.
Choose a test point not on the line, such as $(0, 0)$. Since $2(0) + 0 \leq 8$ is true, shade the side of the line containing $(0, 0)$.

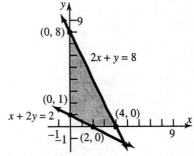

(c)   Graph the line $x + 2y = 2$. Use a solid line since the inequality uses $\geq$.
Choose a test point not on the line, such as $(0, 0)$. Since $0 + 2(0) \geq 2$ is false, shade the opposite side of the line from $(0, 0)$.

(d)   The overlapping region is the solution.

(e)   The graph is bounded

(f)   Find the vertices:
The intersection of $x + 2y = 2$ and the y-axis is $(0, 1)$.
The intersection of $x + 2y = 2$ and the x-axis is $(2, 0)$.
The intersection of $2x + y = 8$ and the y-axis is $(0, 8)$.
The intersection of $2x + y = 8$ and the x-axis is $(4, 0)$.
The four corner points are $(0, 1)$, $(0, 8)$, $(2, 0)$, and $(4, 0)$.

67.   Maximize $z = 3x + 4y$ Subject to $x \geq 0$, $y \geq 0$, $3x + 2y \geq 6$, $x + y \leq 8$
Graph the constraints.

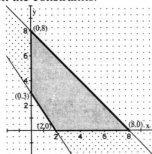

The corner points are $(0, 3)$, $(2, 0)$, $(0, 8)$, $(8, 0)$.

Evaluate the objective function:

Vertex	Value of $z = 3x + 4y$
(0, 3)	$z = 3(0) + 4(3) = 12$
(0, 8)	$z = 3(0) + 4(8) = 32$
(2, 0)	$z = 3(2) + 4(0) = 6$
(8, 0)	$z = 3(8) + 4(0) = 24$

The maximum value is 32 at (0, 8).

69. Minimize $z = 3x + 5y$

Subject to $x \geq 0$, $y \geq 0$, $x + y \geq 1$, $3x + 2y \leq 12$, $x + 3y \leq 12$

Graph the constraints.

To find the intersection of $3x + 2y = 12$ and $x + 3y = 12$, solve the system:

$$\begin{cases} 3x + 2y = 12 \\ x + 3y = 12 \quad \rightarrow \quad x = 12 - 3y \end{cases}$$

Substitute and solve:

$$3(12 - 3y) + 2y = 12 \rightarrow 36 - 9y + 2y = 12 \rightarrow -7y = -24 \rightarrow y = \frac{24}{7}$$

$$x = 12 - 3\left(\frac{24}{7}\right) = 12 - \frac{72}{7} = \frac{12}{7}$$

The point of intersection is $\left(\dfrac{12}{7}, \dfrac{24}{7}\right)$.

The corner points are (0, 1), (1, 0), (0, 4), (4, 0), $\left(\dfrac{12}{7}, \dfrac{24}{7}\right)$.

Evaluate the objective function:

Vertex	Value of $z = 3x + 5y$
(0, 1)	$z = 3(0) + 5(1) = 5$
(0, 4)	$z = 3(0) + 5(4) = 20$
(1, 0)	$z = 3(1) + 5(0) = 3$
(4, 0)	$z = 3(4) + 5(0) = 12$
$\left(\dfrac{12}{7}, \dfrac{24}{7}\right)$	$z = 3\left(\dfrac{12}{7}\right) + 5\left(\dfrac{24}{7}\right) = \dfrac{36}{7} + \dfrac{120}{7} = \dfrac{156}{7} \approx 22.3$

The minimum value is 3 at (1, 0).

71. Find the partial fraction decomposition:

$$\frac{6}{x(x-4)} = \frac{A}{x} + \frac{B}{x-4} \quad \text{(Multiply both sides by } x(x-4).)$$

$$6 = A(x-4) + Bx$$

Let $x = 4$: then $6 = A(4-4) + B(4) \rightarrow 4B = 6 \rightarrow B = \frac{3}{2}$

Let $x = 0$: then $6 = A(0-4) + B(0) \rightarrow -4A = 6 \rightarrow A = -\frac{3}{2}$

$$\frac{6}{x(x-4)} = \frac{\left(-\dfrac{3}{2}\right)}{x} + \frac{\left(\dfrac{3}{2}\right)}{x-4}$$

73. Find the partial fraction decomposition:

$$\frac{x-4}{x^2(x-1)} = \frac{A}{x} + \frac{B}{x^2} + \frac{C}{x-1} \text{(Multiply both sides by } x^2(x-1).)$$

$$x - 4 = Ax(x-1) + B(x-1) + Cx^2$$

Let $x = 1$: then $1 - 4 = A(1)(1-1) + B(1-1) + C(1)^2 \rightarrow -3 = C \rightarrow C = -3$

Let $x = 0$: then $0 - 4 = A(0)(0-1) + B(0-1) + C(0)^2 \rightarrow -4 = -B \rightarrow B = 4$

Let $x = 2$: then $2 - 4 = A(2)(2-1) + B(2-1) + C(2)^2 \rightarrow -2 = 2A + B + 4C$

$$\rightarrow 2A = -2 - 4 - 4(-3) \rightarrow 2A = 6 \rightarrow A = 3$$

$$\frac{x-4}{x^2(x-1)} = \frac{3}{x} + \frac{4}{x^2} + \frac{-3}{x-1}$$

75. Find the partial fraction decomposition:

$$\frac{x}{(x^2+9)(x+1)} = \frac{A}{x+1} + \frac{Bx+C}{x^2+9} \quad \text{(Multiply both sides by } (x+1)(x^2+9).)$$

$$x = A(x^2+9) + (Bx+C)(x+1)$$

Let $x = -1$: then $-1 = A((-1)^2+9) + (B(-1)+C)(-1+1)$

$$\rightarrow -1 = A(10) + (-B+C)(0) \rightarrow -1 = 10A \rightarrow A = -\frac{1}{10}$$

Let $x = 1$: then $1 = A(1^2+9) + (B(1)+C)(1+1) \rightarrow 1 = 10A + 2B + 2C$

$$\rightarrow 1 = 10\left(-\frac{1}{10}\right) + 2B + 2C \rightarrow 2 = 2B + 2C \rightarrow B + C = 1$$

Let $x = 0$: then $0 = A(0^2+9) + (B(0)+C)(0+1) \rightarrow 0 = 9A + C$

$$\rightarrow 0 = 9\left(-\frac{1}{10}\right) + C \rightarrow C = \frac{9}{10} \quad B = 1 - C \rightarrow B = 1 - \frac{9}{10} \rightarrow B = \frac{1}{10}$$

$$\frac{x}{(x^2+9)(x+1)} = \frac{-\left(\dfrac{1}{10}\right)}{x+1} + \frac{\left(\dfrac{1}{10}x + \dfrac{9}{10}\right)}{x^2+9}$$

77. Find the partial fraction decomposition:

$$\frac{x^3}{(x^2+4)^2} = \frac{Ax+B}{x^2+4} + \frac{Cx+D}{(x^2+4)^2} \quad \text{(Multiply both sides by } (x^2+4)^2.)$$

$$x^3 = (Ax+B)(x^2+4) + Cx+D$$

$$x^3 = Ax^3 + Bx^2 + 4Ax + 4B + Cx + D$$

$$x^3 = Ax^3 + Bx^2 + (4A+C)x + 4B + D$$

$$A=1$$

$$B=0$$

$$4A+C=0 \;\rightarrow\; 4(1)+C=0 \;\rightarrow\; C=-4$$

$$4B+D=0 \;\rightarrow\; 4(0)+D=0 \;\rightarrow\; D=0$$

$$\frac{x^3}{(x^2+4)^2} = \frac{x}{x^2+4} + \frac{-4x}{(x^2+4)^2}$$

79. Find the partial fraction decomposition:

$$\frac{x^2}{(x^2+1)(x^2-1)} = \frac{x^2}{(x^2+1)(x-1)(x+1)} = \frac{A}{x-1} + \frac{B}{x+1} + \frac{Cx+D}{x^2+1}$$

$$\text{(Multiply both sides by } (x-1)(x+1)(x^2+1).)$$

$$x^2 = A(x+1)(x^2+1) + B(x-1)(x^2+1) + (Cx+D)(x-1)(x+1)$$

Let $x=1$: then $1^2 = A(1+1)(1^2+1) + B(1-1)(1^2+1) + (C(1)+D)(1-1)(1+1)$

$$\rightarrow 1 = 4A \;\rightarrow\; A = \frac{1}{4}$$

Let $x=-1$: then

$$(-1)^2 = A(-1+1)((-1)^2+1) + B(-1-1)((-1)^2+1) + (C(-1)$$
$$+ D)(-1-1)(-1+1)$$

$$\rightarrow 1 = -4B \;\rightarrow\; B = -\frac{1}{4}$$

Let $x=0$: then

$$0^2 = A(0+1)(0^2+1) + B(0-1)(0^2+1) + (C(0)+D)(0-1)(0+1)$$

$$\rightarrow 0 = A - B - D \;\rightarrow\; 0 = \frac{1}{4} - \left(-\frac{1}{4}\right) - D \;\rightarrow\; D = \frac{1}{2}$$

Let $x=2$: then

$$2^2 = A(2+1)(2^2+1) + B(2-1)(2^2+1) + (C(2)+D)(2-1)(2+1)$$

$$\rightarrow 4 = 15A + 5B + 6C + 3D \;\rightarrow\; 4 = 15\left(\frac{1}{4}\right) + 5\left(-\frac{1}{4}\right) + 6C + 3\left(\frac{1}{2}\right)$$

$$\rightarrow 6C = 4 - \frac{15}{4} + \frac{5}{4} - \frac{3}{2} \;\rightarrow\; 6C = 0 \;\rightarrow\; C = 0$$

$$\frac{x^2}{(x^2+1)(x^2-1)} = \frac{x^2}{(x^2+1)(x-1)(x+1)} = \frac{\left(\frac{1}{4}\right)}{x-1} + \frac{-\left(\frac{1}{4}\right)}{x+1} + \frac{\left(\frac{1}{2}\right)}{x^2+1}$$

81. Multiply each side of the first equation by –2 and eliminate x:

$$\begin{cases} 2x + 5y = 5 \\ 4x + 10y = A \end{cases} \xrightarrow{\;-2\;} \quad \begin{aligned} -4x - 10y &= -10 \\ \underline{4x + 10y = \quad A} \\ 0 = A - 10 \end{aligned}$$

If there are to be infinitely many solutions, the sum in elimination should be $0 = 0$.
Therefore, $A - 10 = 0$ or $A = 10$.

83. $y = ax^2 + bx + c$

At (0, 1) the equation becomes:

$$1 = a(0)^2 + b(0) + c$$
$$c = 1$$

At (1, 0) the equation becomes:

$$0 = a(1)^2 + b(1) + c$$
$$0 = a + b + c$$
$$a + b + c = 0$$

At (–2, 1) the equation becomes:

$$1 = a(-2)^2 + b(-2) + c = 4a - 2b + c \rightarrow 4a - 2b + c = 1$$

The system of equations is:

$$\begin{cases} a + b + c = 0 \\ 4a - 2b + c = 1 \\ c = 1 \end{cases}$$

Substitute $c = 1$ into the first and second equations and simplify:

$$\begin{cases} a + b + 1 = 0 \;\rightarrow\; a + b = -1 \;\rightarrow\; a = -b - 1 \\ 4a - 2b + 1 = 1 \;\rightarrow\; 4a - 2b = 0 \end{cases}$$

Solve the first equation for a, substitute into the second equation and solve:

$$4(-b - 1) - 2b = 0 \rightarrow -4b - 4 - 2b = 0$$

$$-6b = 4 \rightarrow b = -\frac{2}{3} \rightarrow a = \frac{2}{3} - 1 = -\frac{1}{3}$$

The quadratic function is $y = -\frac{1}{3}x^2 - \frac{2}{3}x + 1$.

85. Let x = the number of pounds of coffee that costs \$3.00 per pound.
Let y = the number of pounds of coffee that costs \$6.00 per pound.
Then $x + y = 100$ represents the total amount of coffee in the blend.
The value of the blend will be represented by the equation: $3x + 6y = 3.90(100)$.
Solve the system of equations:

$$\begin{cases} x + y = 100 \;\rightarrow\; y = 100 - x \\ 3x + 6y = 390 \end{cases}$$

Solve by substitution:

$$3x + 6(100 - x) = 390 \rightarrow 3x + 600 - 6x = 390$$

$$-3x = -210 \rightarrow x = 70$$

$$y = 100 - 70 = 30$$

The blend is made up of 70 pounds of the \$3 per pound coffee and 30 pounds of the \$6 per pound coffee.

87.   Let x = the number of small boxes.
Let y = the number of medium boxes.
Let z = the number of large boxes.
Oatmeal raisin equation: $x + 2y + 2z = 15$
Chocolate chip equation: $x + y + 2z = 10$
Shortbread equation: $y + 3z = 11$
Multiply each side of the second equation by –1 and add to the first equation to eliminate x:

$$\begin{cases} x + 2y + 2z = 15 \\ x + y + 2z = 10 \\ y + 3z = 11 \end{cases} \quad \begin{array}{l} \xrightarrow{} \\ \xrightarrow{-1} \end{array} \quad \begin{array}{r} x + 2y + 2z = 15 \\ -x - y - 2z = -10 \\ \hline y = 5 \end{array}$$

Substituting and solving for the other variables:

$$5 + 3z = 11 \qquad\qquad x + 5 + 2(2) = 10$$
$$3z = 6 \qquad\qquad\qquad x + 9 = 10$$
$$z = 2 \qquad\qquad\qquad\quad x = 1$$

1 small box, 5 medium boxes, and 2 large boxes of cookies should be purchased.

89.   Let x = the speed of the boat in still water.
Let y = the speed of the river current.
Let d = the distance from Chiritza to the Flotel Orellana (100 kilometers)

	Rate	Time	Distance
trip downstream	$x + y$	$\frac{5}{2}$	100
trip downstream	$x - y$	3	100

The system of equations is:

$$\begin{cases} (x + y)\left(\dfrac{5}{2}\right) = 100 & \rightarrow \quad 5x + 5y = 200 \\ (x - y)(3) = d & \rightarrow \quad 3x - 3y = 100 \end{cases}$$

$$5x + 5y = 200 \xrightarrow{3} \quad 15x + 15y = 600$$
$$3x - 3y = 100 \xrightarrow{5} \underline{+ \; 15x - 15y = 500} \qquad \therefore x = \frac{1100}{30} = \frac{110}{3}$$
$$\qquad\qquad\qquad\qquad\quad 30x = 1100$$

$$\rightarrow 3\left(\frac{110}{3}\right) - 3y = 100 \rightarrow 110 - 3y = 100 \rightarrow 10 = 3y \rightarrow y = \frac{10}{3}$$

The speed of the boat $= \dfrac{110}{3} \approx 36.67$ km/hr; the speed of the current $= \dfrac{10}{3} \approx 3.33$ km/hr.

91.   Let x = the number of hours for Bruce to do the job alone.
Let y = the number of hours for Bryce to do the job alone.
Let z = the number of hours for Marty to do the job alone.

Then $\dfrac{1}{x}$ represents the fraction of the job that Bruce does in one hour.

$\dfrac{1}{y}$ represents the fraction of the job that Bryce does in one hour.

$\dfrac{1}{z}$ represents the fraction of the job that Marty does in one hour.

The equation representing Bruce and Bryce working together is:

$$\frac{1}{x}+\frac{1}{y}=\frac{1}{\left(\dfrac{4}{3}\right)}=\frac{3}{4}=0.75$$

The equation representing Bryce and Marty working together is:

$$\frac{1}{y}+\frac{1}{z}=\frac{1}{\left(\dfrac{8}{5}\right)}=\frac{5}{8}=0.675$$

The equation representing Bruce and Marty working together is:

$$\frac{1}{x}+\frac{1}{z}=\frac{1}{\left(\dfrac{8}{3}\right)}=0.375$$

Solve the system of equations:

$$\begin{cases} x^{-1}+y^{-1}=0.75 \\ y^{-1}+z^{-1}=0.675 \\ x^{-1}+z^{-1}=0.375 \end{cases}$$

Let
$$u=x^{-1},\ v=y^{-1},\ w=z^{-1}$$
$$\begin{cases} u+v=0.75 \ \rightarrow \ u=0.75-v \\ v+w=0.675 \ \rightarrow \ w=0.675-v \\ u+w=0.375 \end{cases}$$

Substitute into the third equation and solve:
$$0.75-v+0.675-v=0.375 \rightarrow -2v=-1 \rightarrow v=0.5$$
$$u=0.75-0.5=0.25$$
$$w=0.675-0.5=0.125$$

Solve for x, y, and z: $x=4$, $y=2$, $z=8$ (reciprocals)

Bruce can do the job in 4 hours, Bryce in 2 hours, and Marty in 8 hours.

93. Let x = the number of gasoline engines produced each week.
Let y = the number of diesel engines produced each week.
The total cost is: $C=450x+550y$. Cost is to be minimized; thus, this is the objective function.
The constraints are:

$20 \le x \le 60$ number of gasoline engines needed and capacity each week.
$15 \le y \le 40$ number of diesel engines needed and capacity each week.
$x+y \ge 50$ number of engines produced to prevent layoffs.

Graph the constraints.

The corner points are (20, 30), (20, 40), (35, 15), (60, 15), (60, 40).

Evaluate the objective function:

Vertex	Value of $C = 450x + 550y$
(20, 30)	$C = 450(20) + 550(30) = 25{,}500$
(20, 40)	$C = 450(20) + 550(40) = 31{,}000$
(35, 15)	$C = 450(35) + 550(15) = 24{,}000$
(60, 15)	$C = 450(60) + 550(15) = 35{,}250$
(60, 40)	$C = 450(60) + 550(40) = 49{,}000$

The minimum cost is $24,000, when 35 gasoline engines and 15 diesel engines are produced.

The excess capacity is 15 gasoline engines, since only 20 gasoline engines had to be delivered.

Systems of Equations and Inequalities

7.CR Cumulative Review

1. $2x^2 - x = -3$

$2x^2 - x + 3 = 0$

$x = \dfrac{-(-1) \pm \sqrt{(-1)^2 - 4 \cdot 2 \cdot 3}}{2 \cdot 2} = \dfrac{1 \pm \sqrt{1 - 24}}{4}$

$= \dfrac{1 \pm \sqrt{-23}}{4} = \dfrac{1 \pm \sqrt{23}i}{4}$

The solution set is $\left\{ \dfrac{1 - \sqrt{23}i}{4}, \dfrac{1 + \sqrt{23}i}{4} \right\}$.

3. $2x^3 - 3x^2 - 8x - 3 = 0$

The graph of $y_1 = 2x^3 - 3x^2 - 8x - 3$ appears to have an x-intercept at $x = 3$.

Using synthetic division:

$$
\begin{array}{r|rrrr}
3 & 2 & -3 & -8 & -3 \\
  &   & 6 & 9 & 3 \\
\hline
  & 2 & 3 & 1 & 0
\end{array}
$$

Therefore,

$2x^3 - 3x^2 - 8x - 3 = 0$

$(x - 3)(2x^2 + 3x + 1) = 0$

$(x - 3)(2x + 1)(x + 1) = 0$

$x = 3 \text{ or } x = -\dfrac{1}{2} \text{ or } x = -1$

The solution set is $\left\{ -1, -\dfrac{1}{2}, 3 \right\}$.

5. $\log_3(x - 1) + \log_3(2x + 1) = 2$

$\log_3((x - 1)(2x + 1)) = 2$

$(x - 1)(2x + 1) = 3^2$

$2x^2 - x - 1 = 9$

$2x^2 - x - 10 = 0$

$(2x - 5)(x + 2) = 0$

$x = \dfrac{5}{2} \text{ or } x = -2$

Since $x = -2$ makes the original logarithms undefined, the solution set is $\left\{ \dfrac{5}{2} \right\}$.

7. $f(x) = \dfrac{2x^3}{x^4+1}$

$$f(-x) = \dfrac{2(-x)^3}{(-x)^4+1} = \dfrac{-2x^3}{x^4+1} = -f(x),$$

therefore f is an odd function and its graph is symmetric with respect to the origin.

9. $f(x) = 3^{x-2} + 1$

Using the graph of $y = 3^x$, shift the graph horizontally 2 units to the right, then shift the graph vertically 1 unit upward.

Domain: $(-\infty, \infty)$

Range: $(1, \infty)$

Horizontal Asymptote: $y = 1$

11. (a) This relation is not a function since the points $(2, 15900)$ and $(2, 16980)$ cause the graph to fail the Vertical Line Test.

    (b)

    (c) Using LINearREGression yields $P = -2054.646a + 20976.213$

    (d) For each 1 year increase in the age of the car, the price decreases by $2054.65.

    (e) $P(a) = -2054.646a + 20976.213$

    (f) $P(7) = -2054.646(7) + 20976.213 \approx \$6593.69$

Chapter 8

Sequences; Induction; The Binomial Theorem

8.1 Sequences

1. $a_1 = 1, \ a_2 = 2, \ a_3 = 3, \ a_4 = 4, \ a_5 = 5$

3. $a_1 = \dfrac{1}{1+2} = \dfrac{1}{3}, \ a_2 = \dfrac{2}{2+2} = \dfrac{2}{4} = \dfrac{1}{2}, \ a_3 = \dfrac{3}{3+2} = \dfrac{3}{5}, \ a_4 = \dfrac{4}{4+2} = \dfrac{4}{6} = \dfrac{2}{3},$
$$a_5 = \dfrac{5}{5+2} = \dfrac{5}{7}$$

5. $a_1 = (-1)^{1+1}(1^2) = 1, \ a_2 = (-1)^{2+1}(2^2) = -4, \ a_3 = (-1)^{3+1}(3^2) = 9,$
$$a_4 = (-1)^{4+1}(4^2) = -16, \ a_5 = (-1)^{5+1}(5^2) = 25$$

7. $a_1 = \dfrac{2^1}{3^1+1} = \dfrac{2}{4} = \dfrac{1}{2}, \ a_2 = \dfrac{2^2}{3^2+1} = \dfrac{4}{10} = \dfrac{2}{5}, \ a_3 = \dfrac{2^3}{3^3+1} = \dfrac{8}{28} = \dfrac{2}{7},$
$$a_4 = \dfrac{2^4}{3^4+1} = \dfrac{16}{82} = \dfrac{8}{41}, \ a_5 = \dfrac{2^5}{3^5+1} = \dfrac{32}{244} = \dfrac{8}{61}$$

9. $a_1 = \dfrac{(-1)^1}{(1+1)(1+2)} = \dfrac{-1}{2 \cdot 3} = -\dfrac{1}{6}, \ a_2 = \dfrac{(-1)^2}{(2+1)(2+2)} = \dfrac{1}{3 \cdot 4} = \dfrac{1}{12},$
$$a_3 = \dfrac{(-1)^3}{(3+1)(3+2)} = \dfrac{-1}{4 \cdot 5} = -\dfrac{1}{20}, \ a_4 = \dfrac{(-1)^4}{(4+1)(4+2)} = \dfrac{1}{5 \cdot 6} = \dfrac{1}{30},$$
$$a_5 = \dfrac{(-1)^5}{(5+1)(5+2)} = \dfrac{-1}{6 \cdot 7} = -\dfrac{1}{42}$$

11. $a_1 = \dfrac{1}{e^1} = \dfrac{1}{e}, \ a_2 = \dfrac{2}{e^2}, \ a_3 = \dfrac{3}{e^3}, \ a_4 = \dfrac{4}{e^4}, \ a_5 = \dfrac{5}{e^5}$

13. $\dfrac{n}{n+1}$ 15. $\dfrac{1}{2^{n-1}}$ 17. $(-1)^{n+1}$ 19. $(-1)^{n+1}n$

21. $a_1 = 2, \ a_2 = 3+2 = 5, \ a_3 = 3+5 = 8, \ a_4 = 3+8 = 11, \ a_5 = 3+11 = 14$

23. $a_1 = -2, \ a_2 = 2+(-2) = 0, \ a_3 = 3+0 = 3, \ a_4 = 4+3 = 7, \ a_5 = 5+7 = 12$

25. $a_1 = 5, \ a_2 = 2 \cdot 5 = 10, \ a_3 = 2 \cdot 10 = 20, \ a_4 = 2 \cdot 20 = 40, \ a_5 = 2 \cdot 40 = 80$

27. $a_1 = 3$, $a_2 = \dfrac{3}{2}$, $a_3 = \dfrac{\left(\dfrac{3}{2}\right)}{3} = \dfrac{1}{2}$, $a_4 = \dfrac{\left(\dfrac{1}{2}\right)}{4} = \dfrac{1}{8}$, $a_5 = \dfrac{\left(\dfrac{1}{8}\right)}{5} = \dfrac{1}{40}$

29. $a_1 = 1$, $a_2 = 2$, $a_3 = 2 \cdot 1 = 2$, $a_4 = 2 \cdot 2 = 4$, $a_5 = 4 \cdot 2 = 8$

31. $a_1 = A$, $a_2 = A + d$, $a_3 = (A + d) + d = A + 2d$, $a_4 = (A + 2d) + d = A + 3d$,
$a_5 = (A + 3d) + d = A + 4d$

33. $a_1 = \sqrt{2}$, $a_2 = \sqrt{2 + \sqrt{2}}$, $a_3 = \sqrt{2 + \sqrt{2 + \sqrt{2}}}$, $a_4 = \sqrt{2 + \sqrt{2 + \sqrt{2 + \sqrt{2}}}}$,
$a_5 = \sqrt{2 + \sqrt{2 + \sqrt{2 + \sqrt{2 + \sqrt{2}}}}}$

35. $\displaystyle\sum_{k=1}^{5} (k + 2) = 3 + 4 + 5 + 6 + 7$

37. $\displaystyle\sum_{k=1}^{8} \dfrac{k^2}{2} = \dfrac{1}{2} + 2 + \dfrac{9}{2} + 8 + \dfrac{25}{2} + 18 + \dfrac{49}{2} + 32$

39. $\displaystyle\sum_{k=0}^{n} \dfrac{1}{3^k} = 1 + \dfrac{1}{3} + \dfrac{1}{9} + \dfrac{1}{27} + \cdots + \dfrac{1}{3^n}$

41. $\displaystyle\sum_{k=0}^{n-1} \dfrac{1}{3^{k+1}} = \dfrac{1}{3} + \dfrac{1}{9} + \dfrac{1}{27} + \cdots + \dfrac{1}{3^n}$

43. $\displaystyle\sum_{k=2}^{n} (-1)^k \ln k = \ln 2 - \ln 3 + \ln 4 - \ln 5 + \cdots + (-1)^n \ln n$

45. $1 + 2 + 3 + \cdots + 20 = \displaystyle\sum_{k=1}^{20} k$ 47. $\dfrac{1}{2} + \dfrac{2}{3} + \dfrac{3}{4} + \cdots + \dfrac{13}{13 + 1} = \displaystyle\sum_{k=1}^{13} \dfrac{k}{k+1}$

49. $1 - \dfrac{1}{3} + \dfrac{1}{9} - \dfrac{1}{27} + \cdots + (-1)^6 \left(\dfrac{1}{3^6}\right) = \displaystyle\sum_{k=0}^{6} (-1)^k \left(\dfrac{1}{3^k}\right)$

51. $3 + \dfrac{3^2}{2} + \dfrac{3^3}{3} + \cdots + \dfrac{3^n}{n} = \displaystyle\sum_{k=1}^{n} \dfrac{3^k}{k}$

53. $a + (a + d) + (a + 2d) + \cdots + (a + nd) = \displaystyle\sum_{k=0}^{n} (a + kd)$

55.   (a) $\sum\limits_{k=1}^{10} 5 = \underbrace{5+5+5+...+5}_{10 \text{ times}} = 50$

(b) use the sum(seq) feature:

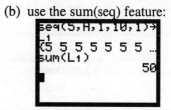

57.   (a) $\sum\limits_{k=1}^{6} k = 1+2+3+4+5+6 = 21$

(b) use the sum(seq) feature

59.   (a) $\sum\limits_{k=1}^{5} (5k+3) = 8+13+18+23+28 = 90$

(b) use the sum(seq) feature

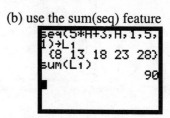

61.   (a) $\sum\limits_{k=1}^{3} (k^2 + 4) = 5+8+13 = 26$

(b) use the sum(seq) feature

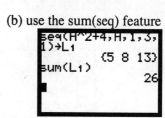

63.   (a) $\sum\limits_{k=1}^{6} (-1)^k 2^k = (-1)^1 \cdot 2^1 + (-1)^2 \cdot 2^2 + (-1)^3 \cdot 2^3 + (-1)^4 \cdot 2^4 + (-1)^5 \cdot 2^5 + (-1)^6 \cdot 2^6$

$= -2+4-8+16-32+64 = 42$

(b) use the sum(seq) feature

65.   (a) $\sum\limits_{k=1}^{4} (k^3 - 1) = 0+7+26+63 = 96$

(b) use the sum(seq) feature

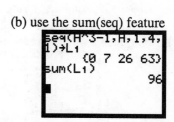

67.   (a) $B_2 = 1.01(3000) - 100 = \$2930$

(b)   Put the graphing utility in SEQuence mode. Enter Y= as follows, then examine the TABLE:

From the table we see that the balance is below \$2000 after 14 payments have been made. The balance then is \$1953.70.

(c)   Scrolling down the table, we find that balance is paid off in the 36th month. The last payment is \$83.78. There are 35 payments of \$100 and the last payment of \$83.78. The total amount paid is: $35(100) + 83.78(1.01) = \$3584.62$. (We have to add the interest for the last month).

(d)   The interest expense is: $3584.62 - 3000.00 = \$584.62$

69.   (a) $p_1 = 1.03(2000) + 20 = 2080;$ $p_2 = 1.03(2080) + 20 = 2162.4$

(b)   Scrolling down the table, we find the trout population exceeds 5000 at the beginning of the 26th month when the population is 5084.

71.   (a)   Since the fund returns 8% compound annually, this is equivalent to a return of 2% each quarter. Defining a recursive sequence, we have: $a_1 = 500,$ $a_n = 1.02a_{n-1} + 500$

(b)   Insert the formulas in your graphing utility and use the table feature to find when the value of the account will exceed \$100,000:

In the 83rd quarter (during the 21st year) the value of the account will exceed \$100,000 with a value of \$101,810.

(c)   Find the value of the account in 25 years or 100 quarters:

The value of the account will be \$156,116.

73. (a) Since the interest rate is 6% per annum compounded monthly, this is equivalent to a rate of 0.5% each month. Defining a recursive sequence, we have:
$$a_1 = 150,000, \quad a_n = 1.005a_{n-1} - 899.33$$

(b) $1.005(150,000) - 899.33 = \$149,850.67$

(c) Enter the recursive formula in Y= and create the table:

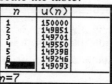

(d) Scroll through the table:

n	$u(n)$
54	140963
55	140769
56	140573
57	140377
58	140180
59	139981
60	139782

$n=60$

At the beginning of the 59th month, or after 58 payments have been made, the balance is below \$140,000. The balance is \$139,981.

(e) Scroll through the table:

n	$u(n)$
355	5298.7
356	4425.9
357	3548.7
358	2667.1
359	1781.1
360	890.65
361	-4.231

$n=355$

The loan will be paid off at the end of 360 months or 30 years.
Total amount paid = $(359)(\$899.33) + \$890.65(1.005) = \$323,754.57$.

(f) The total interest expense is the difference of the total of the payments and the original loan: $323,754.57 - 150,000 = \$173,754.57$

(g) (a) Since the interest rate is 6% per annum compounded monthly, this is equivalent to a rate of 0.5% each month. Defining a recursive sequence, we have:
$$a_1 = 150,000, \quad a_n = 1.005a_{n-1} - 999.33$$

(b) $1.005(150,000) - 999.33 = \$149,750.67$

(c) Enter the recursive formula in Y= and create the table:

(d) Scroll through the table:

n	$u(n)$
34	141079
35	140785
36	140489
37	140192
38	139894
39	139594
40	139293

$n=40$

At the beginning of the 38th month, or after 37 payments have been made, the balance is below \$140,000. The balance is \$139,894.

(e) Scroll through the table:

n	$u(n)$	
275	4294.6	
276	3316.7	
277	2333.9	
278	1346.3	
279	353.69	
280	‾643.9	
281	‾1646	

$n=281$

The loan will be paid off at the end of 279 months or 23 years and 3 months.
Total amount paid = (279)($999.33) + 353.69(1.005) = $279,168.50

(f) The total interest expense is the difference of the total of the payments and the original loan: $279,168.50 - 150,000 = \$129,168.50$

75. $a_1 = 1,\ a_2 = 1,\ a_3 = 2,\ a_4 = 3,\ a_5 = 5,\ a_6 = 8,\ a_7 = 13,\ a_8 = 21,\ a_n = a_{n-1} + a_{n-2}$
$a_8 = a_7 + a_6 = 13 + 8 = 21$
After 7 months there are 21 mature pairs of rabbits.

77. 1, 1, 2, 3, 5, 8, 13   This is the Fibonacci sequence.

79.   To show that $1 + 2 + 3 + ... + (n-1) + n = \dfrac{n(n+1)}{2}$

Let

$S = 1 + 2 + 3 + ...+ (n-1) + n,$ we can reverse the order to get

$+S = n + (n-1) + (n-2) + ... + 2 + 1,$ now add these two lines to get

$2S = [1+n] + [2+(n-1)] + [3+(n-2)] + ... + [(n-1)+2] + [n+1]$

$\underbrace{\qquad\qquad\qquad\qquad\qquad\qquad\qquad\qquad\qquad}_{\text{n terms}}$

So we have

$2S = [1+n] + [1+n] + [1+n] + ... + [n+1] + [n+1] = n \cdot [n+1]$

$\underbrace{\qquad\qquad\qquad\qquad\qquad\qquad}_{\text{n terms}}$

$\therefore\ S = \dfrac{n \cdot (n+1)}{2}$

Chapter 8

Sequences; Induction; The Binomial Theorem

8.2 Arithmetic Sequences

1. $d = a_{n+1} - a_n = (n+1+4) - (n+4) = n+5-n-4 = 1$
   $a_1 = 1+4 = 5,\ a_2 = 2+4 = 6,\ a_3 = 3+4 = 7,\ a_4 = 4+4 = 8$

3. $d = a_{n+1} - a_n = (2(n+1)-5) - (2n-5) = 2n+2-5-2n+5 = 2$
   $a_1 = 2\cdot1-5 = -3,\ a_2 = 2\cdot2-5 = -1,\ a_3 = 2\cdot3-5 = 1,\ a_4 = 2\cdot4-5 = 3$

5. $d = a_{n+1} - a_n = (6-2(n+1)) - (6-2n) = 6-2n-2-6+2n = -2$
   $a_1 = 6-2\cdot1 = 4,\ a_2 = 6-2\cdot2 = 2,\ a_3 = 6-2\cdot3 = 0,\ a_4 = 6-2\cdot4 = -2$

7. $d = a_{n+1} - a_n = \left(\frac{1}{2} - \frac{1}{3}(n+1)\right) - \left(\frac{1}{2} - \frac{1}{3}n\right) = \frac{1}{2} - \frac{1}{3}n - \frac{1}{3} - \frac{1}{2} + \frac{1}{3}n = -\frac{1}{3}$
   $a_1 = \frac{1}{2} - \frac{1}{3}\cdot1 = \frac{1}{6},\ a_2 = \frac{1}{2} - \frac{1}{3}\cdot2 = -\frac{1}{6},\ a_3 = \frac{1}{2} - \frac{1}{3}\cdot3 = -\frac{1}{2},\ a_4 = \frac{1}{2} - \frac{1}{3}\cdot4 = -\frac{5}{6}$

9. $d = a_{n+1} - a_n = \ln(3^{n+1}) - \ln(3^n) = (n+1)\ln(3) - n\ln(3) = \ln 3(n+1-n) = \ln(3)$
   $a_1 = \ln(3^1) = \ln(3),\ a_2 = \ln(3^2) = 2\ln(3),\ a_3 = \ln(3^3) = 3\ln(3),\ a_4 = \ln(3^4) = 4\ln(3)$

11. $a_n = a + (n-1)d = 2 + (n-1)3 = 2+3n-3 = 3n-1$
    $a_5 = 3\cdot5-1 = 14$

13. $a_n = a + (n-1)d = 5 + (n-1)(-3) = 5-3n+3 = 8-3n$
    $a_5 = 8-3\cdot5 = -7$

15. $a_n = a + (n-1)d = 0 + (n-1)\frac{1}{2} = \frac{1}{2}n - \frac{1}{2} = \frac{1}{2}(n-1)$
    $a_5 = \frac{1}{2}\cdot5 - \frac{1}{2} = 2$

17. $a_n = a + (n-1)d = \sqrt{2} + (n-1)\sqrt{2} = \sqrt{2} + \sqrt{2}n - \sqrt{2} = \sqrt{2}n$
    $a_5 = 5\sqrt{2}$

19. $a_1 = 2,\ d = 2,\ a_n = a + (n-1)d$
    $a_{12} = 2 + (12-1)2 = 2 + 11(2) = 2+22 = 24$

21. $a_1 = 1, \ d = -2 - 1 = -3, \ a_n = a + (n-1)d$
     $a_{10} = 1 + (10 - 1)(-3) = 1 + 9(-3) = 1 - 27 = -26$

23. $a_1 = a, \ d = (a + b) - a = b, \ a_n = a + (n-1)d$
     $a_8 = a + (8 - 1)b = a + 7b$

25. $a_8 = a + 7d = 8 \qquad a_{20} = a + 19d = 44$
     Solve the system of equations:
     $$8 - 7d + 19d = 44$$
     $$12d = 36 \rightarrow d = 3 \rightarrow a = 8 - 7(3) = 8 - 21 = -13$$
     Recursive formula: $a_1 = -13 \qquad a_n = a_{n-1} + 3$

27. $a_9 = a + 8d = -5 \qquad a_{15} = a + 14d = 31$
     Solve the system of equations:
     $$-5 - 8d + 14d = 31 \rightarrow 6d = 36 \rightarrow d = 6$$
     $$a = -5 - 8(6) = -5 - 48 = -53$$
     Recursive formula: $a_1 = -53 \qquad a_n = a_{n-1} + 6$

29. $a_{15} = a + 14d = 0 \qquad a_{40} = a + 39d = -50$
     Solve the system of equations:
     $$-14d + 39d = -50 \rightarrow 25d = -50 \rightarrow d = -2$$
     $$a = -14(-2) = 28$$
     Recursive formula: $a_1 = 28 \qquad a_n = a_{n-1} - 2$

31. $a_{14} = a + 13d = -1 \qquad a_{18} = a + 17d = -9$
     Solve the system of equations:
     $$-1 - 13d + 17d = -9$$
     $$4d = -8 \rightarrow d = -2 \rightarrow a = -1 - 13(-2) = -1 + 26 = 25$$
     Recursive formula: $a_1 = 25 \qquad a_n = a_{n-1} - 2$

33. $S_n = \dfrac{n}{2}(a + a_n) = \dfrac{n}{2}(1 + (2n - 1)) = \dfrac{n}{2}(2n) = n^2$

35. $S_n = \dfrac{n}{2}(a + a_n) = \dfrac{n}{2}(7 + (2 + 5n)) = \dfrac{n}{2}(9 + 5n)$

37. $a_1 = 2, \ d = 4 - 2 = 2, \ a_n = a + (n-1)d$

     $$70 = 2 + (n-1)2 \rightarrow 70 = 2 + 2n - 2 \rightarrow 70 = 2n \rightarrow n = 35$$
     $$S_n = \frac{n}{2}(a + a_n) = \frac{35}{2}(2 + 70) = \frac{35}{2}(72) = 35(36) = 1260$$

39. $a_1 = 5, \ d = 9 - 5 = 4, \ a_n = a + (n-1)d$
     $$49 = 5 + (n-1)4 \rightarrow 49 = 5 + 4n - 4 \rightarrow 48 = 4n \rightarrow n = 12$$
     $$S_n = \frac{n}{2}(a + a_n) = \frac{12}{2}(5 + 49) = 6(54) = 324$$

41.   Using the sum of the sequence feature:

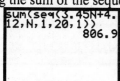

43. $d = 5.2 - 2.8 = 2.4$

$a = 2.8$

$36.4 = 2.8 + (n-1)2.4$

$36.4 = 2.8 + 2.4n - 2.4$

$36 = 2.4n$

$n = 15$

$a_n = 2.8 + (n-1)2.4 = 2.8 + 2.4n - 2.4 = 2.4n + 0.4$

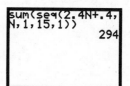

45. $d = 7.48 - 4.9 = 2.58$

$a = 4.9$

$66.82 = 4.9 + (n-1)2.58$

$66.82 = 4.9 + 2.58n - 2.58$

$64.5 = 2.58n$

$n = 25$

$a_n = 4.9 + (n-1)2.58 = 4.9 + 2.58n - 2.58$

$a_n = 2.58n + 2.32$

47.   Find the common difference of the terms and solve the system of equations:

$(2x+1) - (x+3) = d \;\rightarrow\; x - 2 = d$

$(5x+2) - (2x+1) = d \;\rightarrow\; 3x + 1 = d$

$3x + 1 = x - 2 \rightarrow 2x = -3 \rightarrow x = -1.5$

49.   The total number of seats is: $S = 25 + 26 + 27 + \cdots$

This is the sum of an arithmetic sequence with $d = 1$, $a = 25$, and $n = 30$.

Find the sum of the sequence: $S_{30} = \dfrac{30}{2}[2(25) + (30-1)(1)] = 15(50 + 29) = 15(79) = 1185$

There are 1185 seats in the theater.

51.   The lighter colored tiles have 20 tiles in the bottom row and 1 tile in the top row. The number decreases by 1 as we move up the triangle. This is an arithmetic sequence with $a_1 = 20$, $d = -1$, and $n = 20$. Find the sum:

$S = \dfrac{20}{2}[2(20) + (20-1)(-1)] = 10(40 - 19) = 10(21) = 210$ lighter tiles.

The darker colored tiles have 19 tiles in the bottom row and 1 tile in the top row. The number decreases by 1 as we move up the triangle. This is an arithmetic sequence with $a_1 = 19$, $d = -1$, and $n = 19$. Find the sum:

$S = \dfrac{19}{2}[2(19) + (19-1)(-1)] = \dfrac{19}{2}(38 - 18) = \dfrac{19}{2}(20) = 190$ darker tiles.

53.   Find n in an arithmetic sequence with $a_1 = 10$, $d = 4$, $s_n = 2040$.

$$s_n = \frac{n}{2}[2a_1 + (n-1)d] \rightarrow 2040 = \frac{n}{2}[2(10) + (n-1)4]$$

$$4080 = n[20 + 4n - 4] \rightarrow 4080 = n(4n + 16)$$

$$4080 = 4n^2 + 16n \rightarrow 1020 = n^2 + 4n$$

$$n^2 + 4n - 1020 = 0 \rightarrow (n + 34)(n - 30) = 0 \rightarrow n = -34 \text{ or } n = 30$$

There are 30 rows in the corner section of the stadium.

55.   Answers will vary.

Sequences; Induction; The Binomial Theorem

8.3 Geometric Sequences; Geometric Series

1. $r = \dfrac{3^{n+1}}{3^n} = 3^{n+1-n} = 3$

 $a_1 = 3^1 = 3, \quad a_2 = 3^2 = 9, \quad a_3 = 3^3 = 27, \quad a_4 = 3^4 = 81$

3. $r = \dfrac{-3\left(\dfrac{1}{2}\right)^{n+1}}{-3\left(\dfrac{1}{2}\right)^n} = \left(\dfrac{1}{2}\right)^{n+1-n} = \dfrac{1}{2}$

 $a_1 = -3\left(\dfrac{1}{2}\right)^1 = -\dfrac{3}{2}, \quad a_2 = -3\left(\dfrac{1}{2}\right)^2 = -\dfrac{3}{4}, \quad a_3 = -3\left(\dfrac{1}{2}\right)^3 = -\dfrac{3}{8}, \quad a_4 = -3\left(\dfrac{1}{2}\right)^4 = -\dfrac{3}{16}$

5. $r = \dfrac{\left(\dfrac{2^{n+1-1}}{4}\right)}{\left(\dfrac{2^{n-1}}{4}\right)} = \dfrac{2^n}{2^{n-1}} = 2^{n-(n-1)} = 2$

 $a_1 = \dfrac{2^{1-1}}{4} = \dfrac{2^0}{2^2} = 2^{-2} = \dfrac{1}{4}, \quad a_2 = \dfrac{2^{2-1}}{4} = \dfrac{2^1}{2^2} = 2^{-1} = \dfrac{1}{2}, \quad a_3 = \dfrac{2^{3-1}}{4} = \dfrac{2^2}{2^2} = 1,$

 $a_4 = \dfrac{2^{4-1}}{4} = \dfrac{2^3}{2^2} = 2$

7. $r = \dfrac{2^{\left(\frac{n+1}{3}\right)}}{2^{\left(\frac{n}{3}\right)}} = 2^{\left(\frac{n+1}{3} - \frac{n}{3}\right)} = 2^{1/3}; \quad a_1 = 2^{1/3}, \quad a_2 = 2^{2/3}, \quad a_3 = 2^{3/3} = 2, \quad a_4 = 2^{4/3}$

9. $r = \dfrac{\left(\dfrac{3^{n+1-1}}{2^{n+1}}\right)}{\left(\dfrac{3^{n-1}}{2^n}\right)} = \dfrac{3^n}{3^{n-1}} \cdot \dfrac{2^n}{2^{n+1}} = 3^{n-(n-1)} \cdot 2^{n-(n+1)} = 3 \cdot 2^{-1} = \dfrac{3}{2}$

 $a_1 = \dfrac{3^{1-1}}{2^1} = \dfrac{3^0}{2} = \dfrac{1}{2}, \quad a_2 = \dfrac{3^{2-1}}{2^2} = \dfrac{3^1}{2^2} = \dfrac{3}{4}, \quad a_3 = \dfrac{3^{3-1}}{2^3} = \dfrac{3^2}{2^3} = \dfrac{9}{8},$

 $a_4 = \dfrac{3^{4-1}}{2^4} = \dfrac{3^3}{2^4} = \dfrac{27}{16}$

11. $\{n+2\}$ Arithmetic

$d = (n+1+2)-(n+2) = n+3-n-2 = 1$

13. $\{4n^2\}$ Examine the terms of the sequence: 4, 16, 36, 64, 100, ...

There is no common difference; there is no common ratio; neither.

15. $\left\{3-\dfrac{2}{3}n\right\}$ Arithmetic

$d = \left(3-\dfrac{2}{3}(n+1)\right)-\left(3-\dfrac{2}{3}n\right) = 3-\dfrac{2}{3}n-\dfrac{2}{3}-3+\dfrac{2}{3}n = -\dfrac{2}{3}$

17. 1, 3, 6, 10, ...   Neither

There is no common difference or common ratio.

19. $\left\{\left(\dfrac{2}{3}\right)^n\right\}$ Geometric $r = \dfrac{\left(\dfrac{2}{3}\right)^{n+1}}{\left(\dfrac{2}{3}\right)^n} = \left(\dfrac{2}{3}\right)^{n+1-n} = \dfrac{2}{3}$

21. $-1, -2, -4, -8, ...$ Geometric $r = \dfrac{-2}{-1} = \dfrac{-4}{-2} = \dfrac{-8}{-4} = 2$

23. $\{3^{n/2}\}$ Geometric $r = \dfrac{3^{\left(\frac{n+1}{2}\right)}}{3^{\left(\frac{n}{2}\right)}} = 3^{\left(\frac{n+1}{2}-\frac{n}{2}\right)} = 3^{1/2}$

25. $a_5 = 2\cdot 3^{5-1} = 2\cdot 3^4 = 2\cdot 81 = 162$ $a_n = 2\cdot 3^{n-1}$

27. $a_5 = 5(-1)^{5-1} = 5(-1)^4 = 5\cdot 1 = 5$ $a_n = 5\cdot(-1)^{n-1}$

29. $a_5 = 0\cdot\left(\dfrac{1}{2}\right)^{5-1} = 0\cdot\left(\dfrac{1}{2}\right)^4 = 0$ $a_n = 0\cdot\left(\dfrac{1}{2}\right)^{n-1} = 0$

31. $a_5 = \sqrt{2}\cdot\left(\sqrt{2}\right)^{5-1} = \sqrt{2}\cdot\left(\sqrt{2}\right)^4 = \sqrt{2}\cdot 4 = 4\sqrt{2}$ $a_n = \sqrt{2}\cdot\left(\sqrt{2}\right)^{n-1} = \left(\sqrt{2}\right)^n$

33. $a = 1,\ r = \dfrac{1}{2},\ n = 7$ $a_7 = 1\cdot\left(\dfrac{1}{2}\right)^{7-1} = \left(\dfrac{1}{2}\right)^6 = \dfrac{1}{64}$

35. $a = 1,\ r = -1,\ n = 9$ $a_9 = 1\cdot(-1)^{9-1} = (-1)^8 = 1$

37. $a = 0.4,\ r = 0.1,\ n = 8$ $a_8 = 0.4\cdot(0.1)^{8-1} = 0.4(0.1)^7 = 0.00000004$

39. $a = \frac{1}{4}, \; r = 2 \qquad S_n = a\left(\frac{1-r^n}{1-r}\right) = \frac{1}{4}\left(\frac{1-2^n}{1-2}\right) = -\frac{1}{4}\left(1-2^n\right)$

41. $a = \frac{2}{3}, \; r = \frac{2}{3} \qquad S_n = a\left(\frac{1-r^n}{1-r}\right) = \frac{2}{3}\left(\dfrac{1-\left(\frac{2}{3}\right)^n}{1-\frac{2}{3}}\right) = \frac{2}{3}\left(\dfrac{1-\left(\frac{2}{3}\right)^n}{\frac{1}{3}}\right) = 2\left(1-\left(\frac{2}{3}\right)^n\right)$

43. $a = -1, \; r = 2 \qquad S_n = a\left(\frac{1-r^n}{1-r}\right) = -1\left(\frac{1-2^n}{1-2}\right) = 1-2^n$

45. Using the sum of the sequence feature:

```
sum(seq(2^N/4,N,
0,14,1))
        8191.75
```

47. Using the sum of the sequence feature:

```
sum(seq((2/3)^N,
N,1,15,1))
      1.995432683
```

49. Using the sum of the sequence feature:

```
sum(seq(-1*2^N,N
,0,14,1))
          -32767
```

51. $a = 1, \; r = \frac{1}{3} \qquad$ Since $|r| < 1, \; S_n = \dfrac{a}{1-r} = \dfrac{1}{\left(1-\frac{1}{3}\right)} = \dfrac{1}{\left(\frac{2}{3}\right)} = \dfrac{3}{2}$

53. $a = 8, \; r = \frac{1}{2} \qquad$ Since $|r| < 1, \; S_n = \dfrac{a}{1-r} = \dfrac{8}{\left(1-\frac{1}{2}\right)} = \dfrac{8}{\left(\frac{1}{2}\right)} = 16$

55. $a = 2, \; r = -\frac{1}{4} \qquad$ Since $|r| < 1, \; S_n = \dfrac{a}{1-r} = \dfrac{2}{\left(1-\left(-\frac{1}{4}\right)\right)} = \dfrac{2}{\left(\frac{5}{4}\right)} = \dfrac{8}{5}$

57. $a = 5, \; r = \frac{1}{4} \qquad$ Since $|r| < 1, \; S_n = \dfrac{a}{1-r} = \dfrac{5}{\left(1-\frac{1}{4}\right)} = \dfrac{5}{\left(\frac{3}{4}\right)} = \dfrac{20}{3}$

59. $a = 6, \; r = -\frac{2}{3} \qquad$ Since $|r| < 1, \; S_n = \dfrac{a}{1-r} = \dfrac{6}{\left(1-\left(-\frac{2}{3}\right)\right)} = \dfrac{6}{\left(\frac{5}{3}\right)} = \dfrac{18}{5}$

61. Find the common ratio of the terms and solve the system of equations:

$$\frac{x+2}{x} = r; \quad \frac{x+3}{x+2} = r$$

$$\frac{x+2}{x} = \frac{x+3}{x+2} \rightarrow x^2 + 4x + 4 = x^2 + 3x \rightarrow x = -4$$

63. This is a geometric series with $a = \$18,000, \quad r = 1.05, \quad n = 5$. Find the 5th term:

$$a_5 = 18000(1.05)^{5-1} = 18000(1.05)^4 = \$21,879.11$$

65. (a) Find the 10th term of the geometric sequence:

$$a = 2, \quad r = 0.9, \quad n = 10 \qquad a_{10} = 2(0.9)^{10-1} = 2(0.9)^9 = 0.775 \text{ feet}$$

   (b) Find n when $a_n < 1$:

$$2(0.9)^{n-1} < 1 \Rightarrow (0.9)^{n-1} < 0.5$$

$$(n-1)\log(0.9) < \log(0.5) \Rightarrow n-1 > \frac{\log(0.5)}{\log(0.9)} \Rightarrow n > \frac{\log(0.5)}{\log(0.9)} + 1 \approx 7.58$$

   On the 8th swing the arc is less than 1 foot.

   (c) Find the sum of the first 15 swings:

$$S_{15} = 2\left(\frac{1-(0.9)^{15}}{1-0.9}\right) = 2\left(\frac{1-(0.9)^{15}}{0.1}\right) = 20\left(1-(0.9)^{15}\right) = 15.88 \text{ feet}$$

   (d) Find the infinite sum of the geometric series:

$$S = \frac{2}{1-0.9} = \frac{2}{0.1} = 20 \text{ feet}$$

67. Both options are geometric sequences:

   Option A: $a = \$20,000; \quad r = 1.06; \quad n = 5$

$$a_5 = 20,000(1.06)^{5-1} = 20,000(1.06)^4 = \$25,250$$

$$S_5 = 20000\left(\frac{1-(1.06)^5}{1-1.06}\right) = \$112,742$$

   Option B: $a = \$22,000; \quad r = 1.03; \quad n = 5$

$$a_5 = 22,000(1.03)^{5-1} = 22,000(1.03)^4 = \$24,761$$

$$S_5 = 22000\left(\frac{1-(1.03)^5}{1-1.03}\right) = \$116,801$$

   Option A provides more money in the 5th year, while Option B provides the greatest total amount of money over the 5 year period.

69. Option 1: Total Salary $= \$2,000,000(7) + \$100,000(7) = \$14,700,000$

   Option 2: Geometric series with: $a = \$2,000,000, \quad r = 1.045, \quad n = 7$

   Find the sum of the geometric series:

$$S = 2,000,000\left(\frac{1-(1.045)^7}{1-1.045}\right) \approx \$16,038,304$$

Option 3:   Arithmetic series with: $a = \$2,000,000,$ $d = \$95,000,$ $n = 7$
Find the sum of the arithmetic series:
$$S_7 = \frac{7}{2}(2(2,000,000) + (7-1)(95,000)) = \$15,995,000$$
Option 2 provides the most money; Option 1 provides the least money.

71. This is a geometric sequence with $a = 1,$ $r = 2,$ $n = 64.$
Find the sum of the geometric series:
$$S_{64} = 1\left(\frac{1-2^{64}}{1-2}\right) = \frac{1-2^{64}}{-1} = 2^{64} - 1 = 1.845 \times 10^{19} \text{ grains}$$

73. The common ratio, $r = 0.90 < 1.$ The sum is: $S = \dfrac{1}{1-0.9} = \dfrac{1}{0.10} = 10.$
The multiplier is 10.

75. This is an infinite geometric series with $a = 4,$ and $r = \dfrac{1.03}{1.09}.$

Find the sum: Price $= \dfrac{4}{\left(1 - \dfrac{1.03}{1.09}\right)} \approx \$72.67.$

77. Yes, a sequence can be both arithmetic and geometric. For example, the constant sequence
3,3,3,3,..... can be viewed as an arithmetic sequence with $a = 3$ and $d = 0.$ Alternatively,
the same sequence can be viewed as a geometric sequence with $a = 3$ and $r = 1.$

79. Answers will vary.

Chapter 8

Sequences; Induction; The Binomial Theorem

8.4 Mathematical Induction

1. I: $n = 1$: $2 \cdot 1 = 2$ and $1(1+1) = 2$
    II: If $2 + 4 + 6 + \cdots + 2k = k(k+1)$
         then $2 + 4 + 6 + \cdots + 2k + 2(k+1)$
$$= [2 + 4 + 6 + \cdots + 2k] + 2(k+1) = k(k+1) + 2(k+1)$$
$$= (k+1)(k+2)$$
Conditions I and II are satisfied; the statement is true.

3. I: $n = 1$: $1 + 2 = 3$ and $\dfrac{1}{2} \cdot 1(1+5) = 3$

    II: If $3 + 4 + 5 + \cdots + (k+2) = \dfrac{1}{2} \cdot k(k+5)$
         then $3 + 4 + 5 + \cdots + (k+2) + [(k+1)+2]$
$$= [3 + 4 + 5 + \cdots + (k+2)] + (k+3) = \frac{1}{2} \cdot k(k+5) + (k+3)$$
$$= \frac{1}{2}k^2 + \frac{5}{2}k + k + 3 = \frac{1}{2}k^2 + \frac{7}{2}k + 3 = \frac{1}{2} \cdot \left(k^2 + 7k + 6\right)$$
$$= \frac{1}{2} \cdot (k+1)(k+6)$$
Conditions I and II are satisfied; the statement is true.

5. I: $n = 1$: $3 \cdot 1 - 1 = 2$ and $\dfrac{1}{2} \cdot 1(3 \cdot 1 + 1) = 2$

    II: If $2 + 5 + 8 + \cdots + (3k - 1) = \dfrac{1}{2} \cdot k(3k+1)$
         then $2 + 5 + 8 + \cdots + (3k - 1) + [3(k+1) - 1]$
$$= [2 + 5 + 8 + \cdots + (3k - 1)] + (3k + 2) = \frac{1}{2} \cdot k(3k+1) + (3k+2)$$
$$= \frac{3}{2}k^2 + \frac{1}{2}k + 3k + 2 = \frac{3}{2}k^2 + \frac{7}{2}k + 2 = \frac{1}{2} \cdot \left(3k^2 + 7k + 4\right)$$
$$= \frac{1}{2} \cdot (k+1)(3k+4)$$
Conditions I and II are satisfied; the statement is true.

7. I: $n = 1$: $2^{1-1} = 1$ and $2^1 - 1 = 1$

    II: If $1 + 2 + 2^2 + \cdots + 2^{k-1} = 2^k - 1$

        then $1 + 2 + 2^2 + \cdots + 2^{k-1} + 2^{k+1-1} = \left[1 + 2 + 2^2 + \cdots + 2^{k-1}\right] + 2^k = 2^k - 1 + 2^k$

$$= 2 \cdot 2^k - 1 = 2^{k+1} - 1$$

Conditions I and II are satisfied; the statement is true.

9. I: $n = 1$: $4^{1-1} = 1$ and $\dfrac{1}{3} \cdot \left(4^1 - 1\right) = 1$

    II: If $1 + 4 + 4^2 + \cdots + 4^{k-1} = \dfrac{1}{3} \cdot \left(4^k - 1\right)$

        then $1 + 4 + 4^2 + \cdots + 4^{k-1} + 4^{k+1-1}$

$$= \left[1 + 4 + 4^2 + \cdots + 4^{k-1}\right] + 4^k = \dfrac{1}{3} \cdot \left(4^k - 1\right) + 4^k$$

$$= \dfrac{1}{3} \cdot 4^k - \dfrac{1}{3} + 4^k = \dfrac{4}{3} \cdot 4^k - \dfrac{1}{3} = \dfrac{1}{3}\left(4 \cdot 4^k - 1\right) = \dfrac{1}{3} \cdot \left(4^{k+1} - 1\right)$$

Conditions I and II are satisfied; the statement is true.

11. I: $n = 1$: $\dfrac{1}{1(1+1)} = \dfrac{1}{2}$ and $\dfrac{1}{1+1} = \dfrac{1}{2}$

    II: If $\dfrac{1}{1 \cdot 2} + \dfrac{1}{2 \cdot 3} + \dfrac{1}{3 \cdot 4} + \cdots + \dfrac{1}{k(k+1)} = \dfrac{k}{k+1}$

        then $\dfrac{1}{1 \cdot 2} + \dfrac{1}{2 \cdot 3} + \dfrac{1}{3 \cdot 4} + \cdots + \dfrac{1}{k(k+1)} + \dfrac{1}{(k+1)(k+1+1)}$

$$= \left[\dfrac{1}{1 \cdot 2} + \dfrac{1}{2 \cdot 3} + \dfrac{1}{3 \cdot 4} + \cdots + \dfrac{1}{k(k+1)}\right] + \dfrac{1}{(k+1)(k+2)}$$

$$= \dfrac{k}{k+1} + \dfrac{1}{(k+1)(k+2)} = \dfrac{k}{k+1} \cdot \dfrac{k+2}{k+2} + \dfrac{1}{(k+1)(k+2)}$$

$$= \dfrac{k^2 + 2k + 1}{(k+1)(k+2)} = \dfrac{(k+1)(k+1)}{(k+1)(k+2)} = \dfrac{k+1}{k+2}$$

Conditions I and II are satisfied; the statement is true.

13. I: $n = 1$: $1^2 = 1$ and $\dfrac{1}{6} \cdot 1(1+1)(2 \cdot 1 + 1) = 1$

    II: If $1^2 + 2^2 + 3^2 + \cdots + k^2 = \dfrac{1}{6} \cdot k(k+1)(2k+1)$

    then $1^2 + 2^2 + 3^2 + \cdots + k^2 + (k+1)^2$

$$= \left[1^2 + 2^2 + 3^2 + \cdots + k^2\right] + (k+1)^2 = \dfrac{1}{6} k(k+1)(2k+1) + (k+1)^2$$

$$= (k+1)\left[\dfrac{1}{6} k(2k+1) + k + 1\right] = (k+1)\left[\dfrac{1}{3} k^2 + \dfrac{1}{6} k + k + 1\right]$$

$$= (k+1)\left[\dfrac{1}{3} k^2 + \dfrac{7}{6} k + 1\right] = \dfrac{1}{6}(k+1)\left[2k^2 + 7k + 6\right] = \dfrac{1}{6} \cdot (k+1)(k+2)(2k+3)$$

Conditions I and II are satisfied; the statement is true.

15. I: $n = 1$: $5 - 1 = 4$ and $\dfrac{1}{2} \cdot 1(9 - 1) = 4$

    II: If $4 + 3 + 2 + \cdots + (5 - k) = \dfrac{1}{2} \cdot k(9 - k)$

    then $4 + 3 + 2 + \cdots + (5 - k) + (5 - (k + 1))$

    $$= \left[4 + 3 + 2 + \cdots + (5 - k)\right] + (4 - k) = \dfrac{1}{2}k(9 - k) + (4 - k)$$

    $$= \dfrac{9}{2}k - \dfrac{1}{2}k^2 + 4 - k = -\dfrac{1}{2}k^2 + \dfrac{7}{2}k + 4 = -\dfrac{1}{2} \cdot \left[k^2 - 7k - 8\right]$$

    $$= -\dfrac{1}{2} \cdot (k + 1)(k - 8) = \dfrac{1}{2} \cdot (k + 1)(8 - k) = \dfrac{1}{2} \cdot (k + 1)\left[9 - (k + 1)\right]$$

    Conditions I and II are satisfied; the statement is true.

17. I: $n = 1$: $1(1 + 1) = 2$ and $\dfrac{1}{3} \cdot 1(1 + 1)(1 + 2) = 2$

    II: If $1 \cdot 2 + 2 \cdot 3 + 3 \cdot 4 + \cdots + k(k + 1) = \dfrac{1}{3} \cdot k(k + 1)(k + 2)$

    then $1 \cdot 2 + 2 \cdot 3 + 3 \cdot 4 + \cdots + k(k + 1) + (k + 1)(k + 1 + 1)$

    $$= \left[1 \cdot 2 + 2 \cdot 3 + 3 \cdot 4 + \cdots + k(k + 1)\right] + (k + 1)(k + 2)$$

    $$= \dfrac{1}{3} \cdot k(k + 1)(k + 2) + (k + 1)(k + 2) = (k + 1)(k + 2)\left[\dfrac{1}{3}k + 1\right]$$

    $$= \dfrac{1}{3} \cdot (k + 1)(k + 2)(k + 3) \quad \text{Conditions I and II are satisfied; the statement is true.}$$

19. I: $n = 1$: $1^2 + 1 = 2$ is divisible by 2
    II: If $k^2 + k$ is divisible by 2
           then $(k + 1)^2 + (k + 1) = k^2 + 2k + 1 + k + 1 = (k^2 + k) + (2k + 2)$
           Since $k^2 + k$ is divisible by 2 and $2k + 2$ is divisible by 2, then $(k + 1)^2 + (k + 1)$
           is divisible by 2. Conditions I and II are satisfied; the statement is true.

21. I: $n = 1$: $1^2 - 1 + 2 = 2$ is divisible by 2
    II: If $k^2 - k + 2$ is divisible by 2
           then $(k + 1)^2 - (k + 1) + 2 = k^2 + 2k + 1 - k - 1 + 2 = (k^2 - k + 2) + (2k)$
           Since $k^2 - k + 2$ is divisible by 2 and $2k$ is divisible by 2, then
           $(k + 1)^2 - (k + 1) + 2$ is divisible by 2. Conditions I and II are satisfied; the statement is true.

23. I: $n = 1$: If $x > 1$ then $x^1 = x > 1$.
    II: Assume, for some natural number k, that if $x > 1$, then $x^k > 1$.
           Show that if $x^k > 1$, then $x^{k+1} > 1$:   Conditions I and II are satisfied; the
                                                                 statement is true.
           $$x^{k+1} = x^k \cdot x > 1 \cdot x = x > 1$$
                      $\uparrow$

           $(x^k > 1)$

25. I: $n = 1$: $a - b$ is a factor of $a^1 - b^1 = a - b$.

    II: If $a - b$ is a factor of $a^k - b^k$

    Show that $a - b$ is a factor of $a^{k+1} - b^{k+1} = a \cdot a^k - b \cdot b^k$

    $$= a \cdot a^k - a \cdot b^k + a \cdot b^k - b \cdot b^k = a(a^k - b^k) + b^k(a - b)$$

    Since $a - b$ is a factor of $a^k - b^k$ and $a - b$ is a factor of $a - b$, then

    $a - b$ is a factor of $a^{k+1} - b^{k+1}$. Conditions I and II are satisfied; the statement is true.

27. $n = 1$: $1^2 - 1 + 41 = 41$ is a prime number.
     $n = 41$: $41^2 - 41 + 41 = 41^2$ is not a prime number.

29. I: $n = 1$: $ar^{1-1} = a$ and $a\left(\dfrac{1 - r^1}{1 - r}\right) = a$

    II: If $a + ar + ar^2 + \cdots + ar^{k-1} = a\left(\dfrac{1 - r^k}{1 - r}\right)$

    then $a + ar + ar^2 + \cdots + ar^{k-1} + ar^{k+1-1}$

    $$= \left[a + ar + ar^2 + \cdots + ar^{k-1}\right] + ar^k = a\left(\dfrac{1 - r^k}{1 - r}\right) + ar^k$$

    $$= \frac{a(1 - r^k) + ar^k(1 - r)}{1 - r} = \frac{a - ar^k + ar^k - ar^{k+1}}{1 - r} = a\left(\frac{1 - r^{k+1}}{1 - r}\right)$$

    Conditions I and II are satisfied; the statement is true.

31. I: $n = 4$: The number of diagonals of a quadrilateral is $\dfrac{1}{2} \cdot 4(4 - 3) = 2$

    II: Assume that for any integer k the number of diagonals of a convex polygon with k sides (k vertices) is $\dfrac{1}{2} \cdot k(k - 3)$. A convex polygon with $k + 1$ sides ($k + 1$ vertices) consists of a convex polygon with k sides (k vertices) plus a triangle for a total of $k + 1$ vertices. The number of diagonals of this convex polygon consists of the original ones plus $k - 1$ additional ones,

    namely, $\dfrac{1}{2} \cdot k(k - 3) + (k - 1) = \dfrac{1}{2}k^2 - \dfrac{3}{2}k + k - 1 = \dfrac{1}{2}k^2 - \dfrac{1}{2}k - 1$

    $$= \frac{1}{2} \cdot (k^2 - k - 2) = \frac{1}{2} \cdot (k + 1)(k - 2)$$

    Conditions I and II are satisfied; the statement is true.

33. Answers will vary.

Chapter 8

Sequences; Induction; The Binomial Theorem

8.5 The Binomial Theorem

1. $\dbinom{5}{3} = \dfrac{5!}{3!\,2!} = \dfrac{5\cdot4\cdot3\cdot2\cdot1}{3\cdot2\cdot1\cdot2\cdot1} = \dfrac{5\cdot4}{2\cdot1} = 10$

3. $\dbinom{7}{5} = \dfrac{7!}{5!\,2!} = \dfrac{7\cdot6\cdot5\cdot4\cdot3\cdot2\cdot1}{5\cdot4\cdot3\cdot2\cdot1\cdot2\cdot1} = \dfrac{7\cdot6}{2\cdot1} = 21$

5. $\dbinom{50}{49} = \dfrac{50!}{49!\,1!} = \dfrac{50\cdot49!}{49!\cdot1} = \dfrac{50}{1} = 50$

7. $\dbinom{1000}{1000} = \dfrac{1000!}{1000!\,0!} = \dfrac{1}{1} = 1$

9. $\dbinom{55}{23} = \dfrac{55!}{23!\,32!} = 1.866442159 \times 10^{15}$

11. $\dbinom{47}{25} = \dfrac{47!}{25!\,22!} = 1.483389769 \times 10^{13}$

13. $(x+1)^5 = \dbinom{5}{0}x^5 + \dbinom{5}{1}x^4 + \dbinom{5}{2}x^3 + \dbinom{5}{3}x^2 + \dbinom{5}{4}x^1 + \dbinom{5}{5}x^0$
$= x^5 + 5x^4 + 10x^3 + 10x^2 + 5x + 1$

15. $(x-2)^6 = \dbinom{6}{0}x^6 + \dbinom{6}{1}x^5(-2) + \dbinom{6}{2}x^4(-2)^2 + \dbinom{6}{3}x^3(-2)^3 + \dbinom{6}{4}x^2(-2)^4$
$+ \dbinom{6}{5}x(-2)^5 + \dbinom{6}{6}x^0(-2)^6$
$= x^6 + 6x^5(-2) + 15x^4\cdot4 + 20x^3(-8) + 15x^2\cdot16 + 6x\cdot(-32) + 64$
$= x^6 - 12x^5 + 60x^4 - 160x^3 + 240x^2 - 192x + 64$

17. $(3x+1)^4 = \dbinom{4}{0}(3x)^4 + \dbinom{4}{1}(3x)^3 + \dbinom{4}{2}(3x)^2 + \dbinom{4}{3}(3x) + \dbinom{4}{4}$
$= 81x^4 + 4\cdot27x^3 + 6\cdot9x^2 + 4\cdot3x + 1 = 81x^4 + 108x^3 + 54x^2 + 12x + 1$

19. $(x^2+y^2)^5 = \binom{5}{0}(x^2)^5(y^2)^0 + \binom{5}{1}(x^2)^4(y^2) + \binom{5}{2}(x^2)^3(y^2)^2 + \binom{5}{3}(x^2)^2(y^2)^3$

$$+ \binom{5}{4}x^2(y^2)^4 + \binom{5}{5}(y^2)^5$$

$$= x^{10} + 5x^8y^2 + 10x^6y^4 + 10x^4y^6 + 5x^2y^8 + y^{10}$$

21. $(\sqrt{x}+\sqrt{2})^6 = \binom{6}{0}(\sqrt{x})^6(\sqrt{2})^0 + \binom{6}{1}(\sqrt{x})^5(\sqrt{2})^1 + \binom{6}{2}(\sqrt{x})^4(\sqrt{2})^2 + \binom{6}{3}(\sqrt{x})^3(\sqrt{2})^3$

$$\binom{6}{4}(\sqrt{x})^2(\sqrt{2})^4 + \binom{6}{5}(\sqrt{x})(\sqrt{2})^5 + \binom{6}{6}(\sqrt{x})^0(\sqrt{2})^6$$

$$= x^3 + 6\sqrt{2}x^{5/2} + 15 \cdot 2x^2 + 20 \cdot 2\sqrt{2}x^{3/2} + 15 \cdot 4x + 6 \cdot 4\sqrt{2}x^{1/2} + 8$$

$$= x^3 + 6\sqrt{2}x^{5/2} + 30x^2 + 40\sqrt{2}x^{3/2} + 60x + 24\sqrt{2}x^{1/2} + 8$$

23. $(ax+by)^5 = \binom{5}{0}(ax)^5 + \binom{5}{1}(ax)^4 \cdot by + \binom{5}{2}(ax)^3(by)^2 + \binom{5}{3}(ax)^2(by)^3$

$$+ \binom{5}{4}ax(by)^4 + \binom{5}{5}(by)^5$$

$$= a^5x^5 + 5a^4x^4by + 10a^3x^3b^2y^2 + 10a^2x^2b^3y^3 + 5axb^4y^4 + b^5y^5$$

25. $n=10,\ j=4,\ x=x,\ a=3$

$$\binom{10}{4}x^6 \cdot 3^4 = \frac{10!}{4!\,6!} \cdot 81x^6 = \frac{10 \cdot 9 \cdot 8 \cdot 7}{4 \cdot 3 \cdot 2 \cdot 1} \cdot 81x^6 = 17{,}010x^6$$

The coefficient of x^6 is 17,010.

27. $n=12,\ j=5,\ x=2x,\ a=-1$

$$\binom{12}{5}(2x)^7 \cdot (-1)^5 = \frac{12!}{5!\,7!} \cdot 128x^7(-1) = \frac{12 \cdot 11 \cdot 10 \cdot 9 \cdot 8}{5 \cdot 4 \cdot 3 \cdot 2 \cdot 1} \cdot (-128)x^7 = -101{,}376x^7$$

The coefficient of x^7 is $-101{,}376$.

29. $n=9,\ j=2,\ x=2x,\ a=3$

$$\binom{9}{2}(2x)^7 \cdot 3^2 = \frac{9!}{2!\,7!} \cdot 128x^7(9) = \frac{9 \cdot 8}{2 \cdot 1} \cdot 128x^7 \cdot 9 = 41{,}472x^7$$

The coefficient of x^7 is 41,472.

31. $n=7,\ j=4,\ x=x,\ a=3$

$$\binom{7}{4}x^3 \cdot 3^4 = \frac{7!}{4!\,3!} \cdot 81x^3 = \frac{7 \cdot 6 \cdot 5}{3 \cdot 2 \cdot 1} \cdot 81x^3 = 2835x^3$$

33. $n=9,\ j=2,\ x=3x,\ a=-2$

$$\binom{9}{2}(3x)^7 \cdot (-2)^2 = \frac{9!}{2!\,7!} \cdot 2187x^7 \cdot 4 = \frac{9 \cdot 8}{2 \cdot 1} \cdot 8748x^7 = 314{,}928x^7$$

35.   The constant term in $\dbinom{12}{j}\left(x^2\right)^{12-j}\left(\dfrac{1}{x}\right)^j$ occurs when:

$$2(12-j)=j \ \rightarrow \ 24-2j=j \ \rightarrow \ 3j=24 \ \rightarrow \ j=8.$$

Evaluate the 9th term:

$$\dbinom{12}{8}\left(x^2\right)^4\cdot\left(\dfrac{1}{x}\right)^8 = \dfrac{12!}{8!\,4!}x^8\cdot\dfrac{1}{x^8} = \dfrac{12\cdot11\cdot10\cdot9}{4\cdot3\cdot2\cdot1}x^0 = 495$$

37.   The x^4 term in $\dbinom{10}{j}(x)^{10-j}\left(\dfrac{-2}{\sqrt{x}}\right)^j$ occurs when:

$$10-j-\dfrac{1}{2}j=4 \ \rightarrow \ -\dfrac{3}{2}j=-6 \ \rightarrow \ j=4.$$

Evaluate the 5th term:

$$\dbinom{10}{4}(x)^6\cdot\left(\dfrac{-2}{\sqrt{x}}\right)^4 = \dfrac{10!}{6!\,4!}x^6\cdot\dfrac{16}{x^2} = \dfrac{10\cdot9\cdot8\cdot7}{4\cdot3\cdot2\cdot1}\cdot16x^4 = 3360x^4$$

The coefficient is 3360.

39. $(1.001)^5 = \left(1+10^{-3}\right)^5 = \dbinom{5}{0}\cdot1^5 + \dbinom{5}{1}\cdot1^4\cdot10^{-3} + \dbinom{5}{2}\cdot1^3\cdot\left(10^{-3}\right)^2 + \dbinom{5}{3}\cdot1^2\cdot\left(10^{-3}\right)^3 + \ldots$

$$= 1 + 5(0.001) + 10(0.000001) + 10(0.000000001) + \ldots$$
$$= 1 + 0.005 + 0.000010 + 0.000000010 + \ldots$$
$$= 1.00501 \quad \text{(correct to 5 decimal places)}$$

41. $\dbinom{n}{n-1} = \dfrac{n!}{(n-1)!(n-(n-1))!} = \dfrac{n!}{(n-1)!(1)!} = n$

$$\dbinom{n}{n} = \dfrac{n!}{n!(n-n)!} = \dfrac{n!}{n!\,0!} = \dfrac{n!}{n!\cdot1} = \dfrac{n!}{n!} = 1$$

43.   Show that $\dbinom{n}{0} + \dbinom{n}{1} + \ldots + \dbinom{n}{n} = 2^n$

$$2^n = (1+1)^n$$

$$= \dbinom{n}{0}\cdot1^n + \dbinom{n}{1}\cdot1^{n-1}\cdot1 + \dbinom{n}{2}\cdot1^{n-2}\cdot1^2 + \ldots + \dbinom{n}{n}\cdot1^{n-n}\cdot1^n$$

$$= \dbinom{n}{0} + \dbinom{n}{1} + \ldots + \dbinom{n}{n}$$

45. $\dbinom{5}{0}\left(\dfrac{1}{4}\right)^5 + \dbinom{5}{1}\left(\dfrac{1}{4}\right)^4\left(\dfrac{3}{4}\right) + \dbinom{5}{2}\left(\dfrac{1}{4}\right)^3\left(\dfrac{3}{4}\right)^2 + \dbinom{5}{3}\left(\dfrac{1}{4}\right)^2\left(\dfrac{3}{4}\right)^3$

$$+ \dbinom{5}{4}\left(\dfrac{1}{4}\right)\left(\dfrac{3}{4}\right)^4 + \dbinom{5}{5}\left(\dfrac{3}{4}\right)^5 = \left(\dfrac{1}{4}+\dfrac{3}{4}\right)^5 = (1)^5 = 1$$

47. We can use Mathematical Induction to prove the Binomial Theorem.

I: $n = 1$: $(x + a)^1 = x + a = \binom{1}{0} x^1 + \binom{1}{1} a^1$. Therefore, the Theorem holds for $n = 1$.

II: Now assume the Theorem holds for some natural number k.
That is, assume

$$(x + a)^k = \binom{k}{0} x^k + \binom{k}{1} a x^{k-1} + \ldots + \binom{k}{j-1} a^{j-1} x^{k-j+1} + \binom{k}{j} a^j x^{k-j} + \ldots + \binom{k}{k} a^k$$

We now calculate $(x + a)^{k+1}$:

$$(x + a)^{k+1} = (x + a)(x + a)^k$$

$$= (x + a)\left(\binom{k}{0} x^k + \binom{k}{1} a x^{k-1} + \ldots + \binom{k}{j-1} a^{j-1} x^{k-j+1} + \binom{k}{j} a^j x^{k-j} + \ldots + \binom{k}{k} a^k \right)$$

$$= x\left(\binom{k}{0} x^k + \binom{k}{1} a x^{k-1} + \ldots + \binom{k}{j-1} a^{j-1} x^{k-j+1} + \binom{k}{j} a^j x^{k-j} + \ldots + \binom{k}{k} a^k \right)$$

$$+ a\left(\binom{k}{0} x^k + \binom{k}{1} a x^{k-1} + \ldots + \binom{k}{j-1} a^{j-1} x^{k-j+1} + \binom{k}{j} a^j x^{k-j} + \ldots + \binom{k}{k} a^k \right)$$

$$= \left(\binom{k}{0} x^{k+1} + \binom{k}{1} a x^k + \ldots + \binom{k}{j-1} a^{j-1} x^{k-j+2} + \binom{k}{j} a^j x^{k-j+1} + \ldots + \binom{k}{k} a^k x \right)$$

$$+ \left(\binom{k}{0} a x^k + \binom{k}{1} a^2 x^{k-1} + \ldots + \binom{k}{j-1} a^j x^{k-j+1} + \binom{k}{j} a^{j+1} x^{k-j} + \ldots + \binom{k}{k} a^{k+1} \right)$$

$$= \binom{k}{0} x^{k+1} + \left(\binom{k}{1} + \binom{k}{0} \right) a x^k + \ldots + \left(\binom{k}{j} + \binom{k}{j-1} \right) a^j x^{k-j+1} + \ldots + \left(\binom{k}{k} + \binom{k}{k-1} \right) a^k x + \binom{k}{k} a^{k+1}$$

Note that

$$\binom{k}{1} = 1 = \binom{k+1}{0}; \quad \binom{k}{1} + \binom{k}{0} = \binom{k+1}{1}; \quad \binom{k}{2} + \binom{k}{1} = \binom{k+1}{2}; \ldots; \binom{k}{j} + \binom{k}{j-1} = \binom{k+1}{j}$$

and $\binom{k}{k} = 1 = \binom{k+1}{k+1}$.

So we have $(x + a)^{k+1} = \binom{k+1}{0} x^{k+1} + \binom{k+1}{1} a x^k + \ldots + \binom{k+1}{j} a^j x^{k-j+1} + \ldots + \binom{k+1}{k+1} a^{k+1}$

Conditions I and II are satisfied; the Theorem is true.

Chapter 8

Sequences; Induction; The Binomial Theorem

8.R   Chapter Review

1. $a_1 = (-1)^1 \dfrac{1+3}{1+2} = -\dfrac{4}{3}$, $a_2 = (-1)^2 \dfrac{2+3}{2+2} = \dfrac{5}{4}$, $a_3 = (-1)^3 \dfrac{3+3}{3+2} = -\dfrac{6}{5}$,

$a_4 = (-1)^4 \dfrac{4+3}{4+2} = \dfrac{7}{6}$, $a_5 = (-1)^5 \dfrac{5+3}{5+2} = -\dfrac{8}{7}$

3. $a_1 = \dfrac{2^1}{1^2} = \dfrac{2}{1} = 2$, $a_2 = \dfrac{2^2}{2^2} = \dfrac{4}{4} = 1$, $a_3 = \dfrac{2^3}{3^2} = \dfrac{8}{9}$, $a_4 = \dfrac{2^4}{4^2} = \dfrac{16}{16} = 1$, $a_5 = \dfrac{2^5}{5^2} = \dfrac{32}{25}$

5. $a_1 = 3$, $a_2 = \dfrac{2}{3} \cdot 3 = 2$, $a_3 = \dfrac{2}{3} \cdot 2 = \dfrac{4}{3}$, $a_4 = \dfrac{2}{3} \cdot \dfrac{4}{3} = \dfrac{8}{9}$, $a_5 = \dfrac{2}{3} \cdot \dfrac{8}{9} = \dfrac{16}{27}$

7. $a_1 = 2$, $a_2 = 2 - 2 = 0$, $a_3 = 2 - 0 = 2$, $a_4 = 2 - 2 = 0$, $a_5 = 2 - 0 = 2$

9. $\displaystyle\sum_{k=1}^{4}(4k+2) = (4\cdot1+2)+(4\cdot2+2)+(4\cdot3+2)+(4\cdot4+2) = (6)+(10)+(14)+(18) = 48$

11. $1 - \dfrac{1}{2} + \dfrac{1}{3} - \dfrac{1}{4} + \cdots + \dfrac{1}{13} = \displaystyle\sum_{k=1}^{13}(-1)^{k+1}\left(\dfrac{1}{k}\right)$

13. $\{n+5\}$ Arithmetic

$d = (n+1+5) - (n+5) = n+6-n-5 = 1$

$S_n = \dfrac{n}{2}[6+n+5] = \dfrac{n}{2}(n+11)$

15. $\{2n^3\}$ Examine the terms of the sequence: 2, 16, 54, 128, 250, ...

There is no common difference; there is no common ratio; neither.

17. $\{2^{3n}\}$ Geometric $\quad r = \dfrac{2^{3(n+1)}}{2^{3n}} = \dfrac{2^{3n+3}}{2^{3n}} = 2^{3n+3-3n} = 2^3 = 8$

$S_n = 8\left(\dfrac{1-8^n}{1-8}\right) = 8\left(\dfrac{1-8^n}{-7}\right) = \dfrac{8}{7}(8^n - 1)$

19. 0, 4, 8, 12, ...   Arithmetic $d = 4 - 0 = 4$

$S_n = \dfrac{n}{2}(2(0) + (n-1)4) = \dfrac{n}{2}(4(n-1)) = 2n(n-1)$

488

21. $3, \dfrac{3}{2}, \dfrac{3}{4}, \dfrac{3}{5}, \dfrac{3}{16}, \ldots$ Geometric $r = \dfrac{\left(\dfrac{3}{2}\right)}{3} = \dfrac{3}{2} \cdot \dfrac{1}{3} = \dfrac{1}{2}$

$$S_n = 3\left(\frac{1-\left(\dfrac{1}{2}\right)^n}{1-\dfrac{1}{2}}\right) = 3\left(\frac{1-\left(\dfrac{1}{2}\right)^n}{\left(\dfrac{1}{2}\right)}\right) = 6\left(1-\left(\dfrac{1}{2}\right)^n\right)$$

23. Neither.   There is no common difference or common ratio.

25. (a) $\displaystyle\sum_{k=1}^{5}(k^2 + 12) = 13 + 16 + 21 + 28 + 37 = 115$ (b) use the sum(seq) feature:

27. (a) $\displaystyle\sum_{k=1}^{10}(3k - 9) = \sum_{k=1}^{10}3k - \sum_{k=1}^{10}9 = 3\sum_{k=1}^{10}k - \sum_{k=1}^{10}9 = 3\left(\frac{10(10+1)}{2}\right) - 10(9) = 165 - 90 = 75$

(b) use the sum(seq) feature:

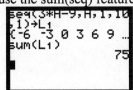

29. (a) $\displaystyle\sum_{k=1}^{7}\left(\frac{1}{3}\right)^k = \frac{1}{3}\left(\frac{1-\left(\dfrac{1}{3}\right)^7}{1-\dfrac{1}{3}}\right) = \frac{1}{3}\left(\frac{1-\left(\dfrac{1}{3}\right)^7}{\left(\dfrac{2}{3}\right)}\right) = \frac{1}{2}\left(1-\frac{1}{2187}\right) = \frac{1}{2}\cdot\frac{2186}{2187} = \frac{1093}{2187} \approx 0.49977$

(b) use the sum(seq) feature:

31.   (a) Arithmetic $a = 3, \ d = 4, \ a_n = a + (n-1)d$
$$a_9 = 3 + (9-1)4 = 3 + 8(4) = 3 + 32 = 35$$
   (b) scroll to the end of the list:

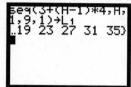

33.   (a) Geometric $a = 1, \ r = \dfrac{1}{10}, \ n = 11; a_n = ar^{n-1}$
$$a_{11} = 1 \cdot \left(\frac{1}{10}\right)^{11-1} = \left(\frac{1}{10}\right)^{10} = \frac{1}{10{,}000{,}000{,}000}$$
   (b) scroll to the end of the list:

35.   (a) Arithmetic $a = \sqrt{2}, \ d = \sqrt{2}, \ n = 9, \ a_n = a + (n-1)d$
$$a_9 = \sqrt{2} + (9-1)\sqrt{2} = \sqrt{2} + 8\sqrt{2} = 9\sqrt{2} \approx 12.7279$$
   (b) scroll to the end of the list:

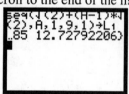

37. $a_7 = a + 6d = 31 \qquad a_{20} = a + 19d = 96;$ $a_n = a + (n-1)d$
   Solve the system of equations:
$$31 - 6d + 19d = 96$$
$$13d = 65$$
$$d = 5$$ General formula: $\{5n - 4\}$
$$a = 31 - 6(5) = 31 - 30 = 1$$

39. $a_{10} = a + 9d = 0 \qquad a_{18} = a + 17d = 8;$ $a_n = a + (n-1)d$
   Solve the system of equations:
$$-9d + 17d = 8$$
$$8d = 8$$
$$d = 1$$ General formula: $\{n - 10\}$
$$a = -9(1) = -9$$

41. $a = 3$, $r = \dfrac{1}{3}$ Since $|r| < 1$, $S_n = \dfrac{a}{1-r} = \dfrac{3}{\left(1 - \dfrac{1}{3}\right)} = \dfrac{3}{\left(\dfrac{2}{3}\right)} = \dfrac{9}{2}$

43. $a = 2$, $r = -\dfrac{1}{2}$ Since $|r| < 1$, $S_n = \dfrac{a}{1-r} = \dfrac{2}{\left(1 - \left(-\dfrac{1}{2}\right)\right)} = \dfrac{2}{\left(\dfrac{3}{2}\right)} = \dfrac{4}{3}$

45. $a = 4$, $r = \dfrac{1}{2}$ Since $|r| < 1$, $S_n = \dfrac{a}{1-r} = \dfrac{4}{\left(1 - \dfrac{1}{2}\right)} = \dfrac{4}{\left(\dfrac{1}{2}\right)} = 8$

47.   I: $n = 1$: $3 \cdot 1 = 3$ and $\dfrac{3 \cdot 1}{2}(1 + 1) = 3$

    II: If $3 + 6 + 9 + \cdots + 3k = \dfrac{3k}{2}(k + 1)$

    then $3 + 6 + 9 + \cdots + 3k + 3(k + 1)$

$$= [3 + 6 + 9 + \cdots + 3k] + 3(k + 1) = \dfrac{3k}{2}(k + 1) + 3(k + 1)$$

$$= (k + 1)\left(\dfrac{3k}{2} + 3\right) = \dfrac{3}{2}(k + 1)(k + 2) \quad \text{Conditions I and II are satisfied; the statement is true.}$$

49.   I: $n = 1$: $2 \cdot 3^{1-1} = 2$ and $3^1 - 1 = 2$

    II: If $2 + 6 + 18 + \cdots + 2 \cdot 3^{k-1} = 3^k - 1$

        then $2 + 6 + 18 + \cdots + 2 \cdot 3^{k-1} + 2 \cdot 3^{k+1-1}$

$$= [2 + 6 + 18 + \cdots + 2 \cdot 3^{k-1}] + 2 \cdot 3^k = 3^k - 1 + 2 \cdot 3^k = 3 \cdot 3^k - 1 = 3^{k+1} - 1$$

Conditions I and II are satisfied; the statement is true.

51.   I: $n = 1$: $(3 \cdot 1 - 2)^2 = 1$ and $\dfrac{1}{2} \cdot 1(6 \cdot 1^2 - 3 \cdot 1 - 1) = 1$

    II: If $1^2 + 4^2 + 7^2 + \cdots + (3k - 2)^2 = \dfrac{1}{2} \cdot k\left(6k^2 - 3k - 1\right)$

        then $1^2 + 4^2 + 7^2 + \cdots + (3k - 2)^2 + \left(3(k + 1) - 2\right)^2$

$$= \left[1^2 + 4^2 + 7^2 + \cdots + (3k - 2)^2\right] + (3k + 1)^2$$

$$= \dfrac{1}{2} \cdot k\left(6k^2 - 3k - 1\right) + (3k + 1)^2$$

$$= \dfrac{1}{2} \cdot \left[6k^3 - 3k^2 - k + 18k^2 + 12k + 2\right] = \dfrac{1}{2} \cdot \left[6k^3 + 15k^2 + 11k + 2\right]$$

$$= \dfrac{1}{2} \cdot (k + 1)\left[6k^2 + 9k + 2\right] = \dfrac{1}{2} \cdot (k + 1)\left[6k^2 + 12k + 6 - 3k - 3 - 1\right]$$

$$= \dfrac{1}{2} \cdot (k + 1)\left[6(k^2 + 2k + 1) - 3(k + 1) - 1\right]$$

$$= \frac{1}{2} \cdot (k+1)\left[6(k+1)^2 - 3(k+1) - 1\right]$$

Conditions I and II are satisfied; the statement is true.

53. $\dbinom{5}{2} = \dfrac{5!}{2!\,3!} = \dfrac{5 \cdot 4 \cdot 3 \cdot 2 \cdot 1}{2 \cdot 1 \cdot 3 \cdot 2 \cdot 1} = \dfrac{5 \cdot 4}{2 \cdot 1} = 10$

55. $(x+2)^5 = \dbinom{5}{0}x^5 + \dbinom{5}{1}x^4 \cdot 2 + \dbinom{5}{2}x^3 \cdot 2^2 + \dbinom{5}{3}x^2 \cdot 2^3 + \dbinom{5}{4}x^1 \cdot 2^4 + \dbinom{5}{5} \cdot 2^5$

$= x^5 + 5 \cdot 2x^4 + 10 \cdot 4x^3 + 10 \cdot 8x^2 + 5 \cdot 16x + 1 \cdot 32$

$= x^5 + 10x^4 + 40x^3 + 80x^2 + 80x + 32$

57. $(2x+3)^5 = \dbinom{5}{0}(2x)^5 + \dbinom{5}{1}(2x)^4 \cdot 3 + \dbinom{5}{2}(2x)^3 \cdot 3^2 + \dbinom{5}{3}(2x)^2 \cdot 3^3$

$+ \dbinom{5}{4}(2x)^1 \cdot 3^4 + \dbinom{5}{5} \cdot 3^5$

$= 32x^5 + 5 \cdot 16x^4 \cdot 3 + 10 \cdot 8x^3 \cdot 9 + 10 \cdot 4x^2 \cdot 27 + 5 \cdot 2x \cdot 81 + 1 \cdot 243$

$= 32x^5 + 240x^4 + 720x^3 + 1080x^2 + 810x + 243$

59. $n = 9, \ j = 2, \ x = x, \ a = 2$

$\dbinom{9}{2}x^7 \cdot 2^2 = \dfrac{9!}{2!\,7!} \cdot 4x^7 = \dfrac{9 \cdot 8}{2 \cdot 1} \cdot 4x^7 = 144x^7$

The coefficient of x^7 is 144.

61. $n = 7, \ j = 5, \ x = 2x, \ a = 1$

$\dbinom{7}{5}(2x)^2 \cdot 1^5 = \dfrac{7!}{5!\,2!} \cdot 4x^2(1) = \dfrac{7 \cdot 6}{2 \cdot 1} \cdot 4x^2 = 84x^2$

The coefficient of x^2 is 84.

63. This is an arithmetic sequence with $a = 80, \ d = -3, \ n = 25$

(a) $a_{25} = 80 + (25-1)(-3) = 80 - 72 = 8$ bricks

(b) $S_{25} = \dfrac{25}{2}(80 + 8) = 25(44) = 1100$ bricks. 1100 bricks are needed to build the steps.

65. This is a geometric sequence with $a = 20, \ r = \dfrac{3}{4}$.

(a)   After striking the ground the third time, the height is $20\left(\dfrac{3}{4}\right)^3 = \dfrac{135}{16} \approx 8.44$ feet.

(b)   After striking the ground the nth time, the height is $20\left(\dfrac{3}{4}\right)^n$ feet.

(c)   If the height is less than 6 inches or 0.5 feet, then:

$$0.5 = 20\left(\frac{3}{4}\right)^n \Rightarrow 0.025 = \left(\frac{3}{4}\right)^n \Rightarrow \log(0.025) = n\log\left(\frac{3}{4}\right) \Rightarrow n = \frac{\log(0.025)}{\log\left(\dfrac{3}{4}\right)} \approx 12.82$$

The height is less than 6 inches after the 13th strike.

(d)   Since this is a geometric sequence with $|r| < 1$, the distance is the sum of the two infinite geometric series - the distances going down plus the distances going up.

Distance going down: $S_{down} = \dfrac{20}{\left(1-\dfrac{3}{4}\right)} = \dfrac{20}{\left(\dfrac{1}{4}\right)} = 80$ feet.

Distance going up: $S_{up} = \dfrac{15}{\left(1-\dfrac{3}{4}\right)} = \dfrac{15}{\left(\dfrac{1}{4}\right)} = 60$ feet.

The total distance traveled is 140 feet.

67.   (a) $b_1 = 5,000, \quad b_n = 1.015b_{n-1} - 100$
$b_2 = 1.015b_{(2-1)} - 100 = 1.015b_1 - 100 = 1.015(5000) - 100 = \$4975$

(b)   Enter the recursive formula in Y= and draw the graph:

(c)   Scroll through the table:

n	$u(n)$
30	4100
31	4061.5
32	4022.5
33	3982.8
34	3942.5
35	3901.7
36	3860.2

$n=33$

At the beginning of the 33rd month, or after 32 payments have been made, the balance is below \$4,000. The balance is \$3982.8.

(d)   Scroll through the table:

n	$u(n)$
90	395.82
91	301.75
92	206.28
93	109.37
94	11.014
95	-88.82
96	-190.2

$n=94$

The balance will be paid off at the end of 94 months or 7years and 10 months.
Total payments $= 100(93) + 11.01 = \$9,311.01$

(e)   The total interest expense is the difference of the total of the payments and the original balance: $100(93) + 11.01 - 5,000 = \$4,311.01$

Sequences; Induction; The Binomial Theorem

8.CR   Cumulative Review

1. $\left|x^2\right| = 9$

   $x^2 = 9$ or $x^2 = -9$

   $x = \pm 3$ or $x = \pm 3i$

3. $2e^x = 5$

   $e^x = \dfrac{5}{2} = 2.5$

   $\ln\left(e^x\right) = \ln(2.5)$

   $x = \ln(2.5) \approx 0.916$

5. $f(x) = \dfrac{1}{x+3} - 2$

   (a) Shift the graph of $y = \dfrac{1}{x}$ horizontally to the left 3 units, then shift vertically downward 2 units.

(b) $f(x) = \dfrac{1}{x+3} - 2$ will be defined provided $x + 3 \neq 0$. Therefore, the domain of f is $\{x | x \neq -3\}$.

(c) From the graph, we can see that the range of f is $\{y | y \neq -2\}$.

(d) vertical asymptote: $x = -3$
   horizontal asymptote: $y = -2$

7. $f(x) = 4x^5 + 23x^4 + 42x^3 + 60x^2 + 90x - 27$
   graphing utility:

2 turning points: local maximum: $(-3, 0)$; local minimum: $(-1.32, -84.06)$.
f is increasing on the intervals $(-\infty, -3) \cup (-1.32, \infty)$

The graph appears to indicate x-intercepts at -3 and 0.25.
Using synthetic division with -3:

$$-3)\overline{\begin{array}{cccccc} 4 & 23 & 42 & 60 & 90 & -27 \end{array}}$$

$$\begin{array}{cccccc} & -12 & -33 & -27 & -99 & 27 \end{array}$$

$$\begin{array}{cccccc} 4 & 11 & 9 & 33 & -9 & 0 \end{array}$$

So -3 is a zero, therefore $x-(-3)=x+3$ is a factor of f. The other factor is
the quotient $4x^4+11x^3+9x^2+33x-9$.

Using synthetic division on this quotient with 0.25:

$$0.25)\overline{\begin{array}{cccc} 4 & 11 & 9 & 33 & -9 \end{array}}$$

$$\begin{array}{cccc} & 1 & 3 & 3 & 9 \end{array}$$

$$\begin{array}{cccc} 4 & 12 & 12 & 36 & 0 \end{array}$$

So 0.25 is a zero, therefore $x-0.25$ is a factor of f. The other factor is
the quotient $4x^3+12x^2+12x+36=4x^2(x+3)+12(x+3)=4(x+3)(x^2+3)$.
Therefore, $f(x)=4x^5+23x^4+42x^3+60x^2+90x-27=4(x+3)^2(x-0.25)(x^2+3)$.
x-intercepts: $-3, 0.25$; y-intercept: -27
Graphing by hand:

	-3		0.25

Interval	$(-\infty, -3)$	$(-3, 0.25)$	$(0.25, \infty)$
Number Chosen	-4	0	1
Value of f	$f(-4)=-323$	$f(0)=-27$	$f(1)=192$
Location of Graph	Below x-axis	Below x-axis	Above x-axis
Point on Graph	$(-4, -323)$	$(0, -27)$	$(1, 192)$

Chapter 9

Counting and Probability

9.1 Sets and Counting

1. $A \cup B = \{1, 3, 5, 7, 9\} \cup \{1, 5, 6, 7\} = \{1, 3, 5, 6, 7, 9\}$

3. $A \cap B = \{1, 3, 5, 7, 9\} \cap \{1, 5, 6, 7\} = \{1, 5, 7\}$

5. $(A \cup B) \cap C = (\{1, 3, 5, 7, 9\} \cup \{1, 5, 6, 7\}) \cap \{1, 2, 4, 6, 8, 9\}$
$$= \{1, 3, 5, 6, 7, 9\} \cap \{1, 2, 4, 6, 8, 9\}$$
$$= \{1, 6, 9\}$$

7. $(A \cap B) \cup C = (\{1, 3, 5, 7, 9\} \cap \{1, 5, 6, 7\}) \cup \{1, 2, 4, 6, 8, 9\}$
$$= \{1, 5, 7\} \cup \{1, 2, 4, 6, 8, 9\}$$
$$= \{1, 2, 4, 5, 6, 7, 8, 9\}$$

9. $(A \cup C) \cap (B \cup C)$
$$= (\{1, 3, 5, 7, 9\} \cup \{1, 2, 4, 6, 8, 9\}) \cap (\{1, 5, 6, 7\} \cup \{1, 2, 4, 6, 8, 9\})$$
$$= \{1, 2, 3, 4, 5, 6, 7, 8, 9\} \cap \{1, 2, 4, 5, 6, 7, 8, 9\}$$
$$= \{1, 2, 4, 5, 6, 7, 8, 9\}$$

11. $\overline{A} = \{0, 2, 6, 7, 8\}$

13. $\overline{A \cap B} = \overline{\{1, 3, 4, 5, 9\} \cap \{2, 4, 6, 7, 8\}} = \overline{\{4\}} = \{0, 1, 2, 3, 5, 6, 7, 8, 9\}$

15. $\overline{A} \cup \overline{B} = \{0, 2, 6, 7, 8\} \cup \{0, 1, 3, 5, 9\} = \{0, 1, 2, 3, 5, 6, 7, 8, 9\}$

17. $\overline{A \cap \overline{C}} = \overline{\{1, 3, 4, 5, 9\} \cap \{0, 2, 5, 7, 8, 9\}} = \overline{\{5, 9\}} = \{0, 1, 2, 3, 4, 6, 7, 8\}$

19. $\overline{A \cup B \cup C} = \overline{\{1, 3, 4, 5, 9\} \cup \{2, 4, 6, 7, 8\} \cup \{1, 3, 4, 6\}}$
$$= \overline{\{1, 2, 3, 4, 5, 6, 7, 8, 9\}} = \{0\}$$

21. $\{a\}, \{b\}, \{c\}, \{d\}, \{a, b\}, \{a, c\}, \{a, d\}, \{b, c\}, \{b, d\}, \{c, d\}, \{a, b, c\}, \{a, b, d\},$
$\{a, c, d\}, \{b, c, d\}, \{a, b, c, d\}, \varnothing$

23. $n(A) = 15, n(B) = 20, n(A \cap B) = 10$
$$n(A \cup B) = n(A) + n(B) - n(A \cap B) = 15 + 20 - 10 = 25$$

25. $n(A \cup B) = 50, n(A \cap B) = 10, n(B) = 20$
$$n(A \cup B) = n(A) + n(B) - n(A \cap B)$$
$$50 = n(A) + 20 - 10$$
$$40 = n(A)$$

27.   From the figure:
$$n(A) = 15 + 3 + 5 + 2 = 25$$

29.   From the figure:
$$n(A \text{ or } B) = n(A \cup B) = n(A) + n(B) - n(A \cap B) = 25 + 20 - 8 = 37$$

31.   From the figure:
$$n(A \text{ but not } C) = n(A) - n(A \cap C) = 25 - 7 = 18$$

33.   From the figure:
$$n(A \text{ and } B \text{ and } C) = n(A \cap B \cap C) = 5$$

35.   Let $A = \{$those who will purchase a major appliance$\}$
$B = \{$those who will buy a car$\}$
$n(U) = 500, \ n(A) = 200, \ n(B) = 150, \ n(A \cap B) = 25$
$n(A \cup B) = n(A) + n(B) - n(A \cap B) = 200 + 150 - 25 = 325$
$n(\text{purchase neither}) = 500 - 325 = 175$
$n(\text{purchase only a car}) = 150 - 25 = 125$

37.   Construct a Venn diagram:

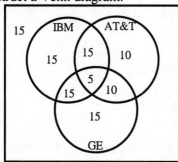

(a)   15
(b)   15
(c)   15
(d)   25
(e)   40

39.   (a) $n(\text{married or widowed}) = n(\text{married}) + n(\text{widowed})$
$$= 58,986 + 2,542 = 61,528 \text{ thousand}$$
(b) $n(\text{widowed or divorced}) = n(\text{widowed}) + n(\text{divorced})$
$$= 2,542 + 8,543 = 11,085 \text{ thousand}$$
(c) $n(\text{married, widowed or divorced})$
$$= n(\text{married}) + n(\text{widowed}) + n(\text{divorced})$$
$$= 58,986 + 2,542 + 8,543 = 70,071 \text{ thousand}$$

41.   Answers will vary.

Counting and Probability

9.2 Permutations and Combinations

1. $P(6, 2) = \dfrac{6!}{(6-2)!} = \dfrac{6!}{4!} = \dfrac{6 \cdot 5 \cdot 4!}{4!} = 30$

3. $P(4, 4) = \dfrac{4!}{(4-4)!} = \dfrac{4!}{0!} = \dfrac{4 \cdot 3 \cdot 2 \cdot 1}{1} = 24$

5. $P(7, 0) = \dfrac{7!}{(7-0)!} = \dfrac{7!}{7!} = 1$

7. $P(8, 4) = \dfrac{8!}{(8-4)!} = \dfrac{8!}{4!} = \dfrac{8 \cdot 7 \cdot 6 \cdot 5 \cdot 4!}{4!} = 1680$

9. $C(8, 2) = \dfrac{8!}{(8-2)!\,2!} = \dfrac{8!}{6!\,2!} = \dfrac{8 \cdot 7 \cdot 6!}{6! \cdot 2 \cdot 1} = 28$

11. $C(7, 4) = \dfrac{7!}{(7-4)!\,4!} = \dfrac{7!}{3!\,4!} = \dfrac{7 \cdot 6 \cdot 5 \cdot 4!}{4! \cdot 3 \cdot 2 \cdot 1} = 35$

13. $C(15, 15) = \dfrac{15!}{(15-15)!\,15!} = \dfrac{15!}{0!\,15!} = \dfrac{15!}{15! \cdot 1} = 1$

15. $C(26, 13) = \dfrac{26!}{(26-13)!\,13!} = \dfrac{26!}{13!\,13!} = 10,400,600$

17. {*abc, abd, abe, acb, acd, ace, adb, adc, ade, aeb, aec, aed, bac, bad, bae, bca, bcd, bce, bda, bdc, bde, bea, bec, bed, cab, cad, cae, cba, cbd, cbe, cda, cdb, cde, cea, ceb, ced, dab, dac, dae, dba, dbc, dbe, dca, dcb, dce, dea, deb, dec, eab, eac, ead, eba, ebc, ebd, eca, ecb, ecd, eda, edb, edc*}

$P(5,3) = \dfrac{5!}{(5-3)!} = \dfrac{5!}{2!} = \dfrac{5 \cdot 4 \cdot 3 \cdot 2!}{2!} = 60$

19. {123, 124, 132, 134, 142, 143, 213, 214, 231, 234, 241, 243, 312, 314, 321, 324, 341, 342, 412, 413, 421, 423, 431, 432}

$P(4,3) = \dfrac{4!}{(4-3)!} = \dfrac{4!}{1!} = \dfrac{4 \cdot 3 \cdot 2 \cdot 1}{1} = 24$

21. {*abc, abd, abe, acd, ace, ade, bcd, bce, bde, cde*}

$C(5,3) = \dfrac{5!}{(5-3)!\,3!} = \dfrac{5 \cdot 4 \cdot 3!}{2 \cdot 1 \cdot 3!} = 10$

23. $\{123, 124, 134, 234\}$ $C(4,3) = \dfrac{4!}{(4-3)!\,3!} = \dfrac{4 \cdot 3!}{1!\,3!} = 4$

25.   There are 5 choices of shirts and 3 choices of ties; there are $(5)(3) = 15$ combinations.

27.   There are 4 choices for the first letter in the code and 4 choices for the second letter in the code; there are $(4)(4) = 16$ possible two-letter codes.

29.   There are two choices for each of three positions; there are $(2)(2)(2) = 8$ possible three-digit numbers.

31.   To line up the four people, there are 4 choices for the first position, 3 choices for the second position, 2 choices for the third position, and 1 choice for the fourth position. Thus there are $(4)(3)(2)(1) = 24$ possible ways four people can be lined up.

33.   Since no letter can be repeated, there are 5 choices for the first letter, 4 choices for the second letter, and 3 choices for the third letter. Thus, there are $(5)(4)(3) = 60$ possible three-letter codes.

35.   There are 26 possible one-letter names. There are $(26)(26) = 676$ possible two-letter names. There are $(26)(26)(26) = 17576$ possible three-letter names. Thus, there are $26 + 676 + 17576 = 18{,}278$ possible companies that can be listed on the New York Stock Exchange.

37.   A committee of 4 from a total of 7 students is given by:
$$C(7,4) = \dfrac{7!}{(7-4)!\,4!} = \dfrac{7!}{3!\,4!} = \dfrac{7 \cdot 6 \cdot 5 \cdot 4!}{3 \cdot 2 \cdot 1 \cdot 4!} = 35$$
35 committees are possible.

39.   There are 2 possible answers for each question. Therefore, there are $2^{10} = 1024$ different possible arrangements of the answers.

41.   There are 9 choices for the first digit, and 10 choices for each of the other three digits. Thus, there are $(9)(10)(10)(10) = 9000$ possible four-digit numbers.

43.   There are 5 choices for the first position, 4 choices for the second position, 3 choices for the third position, 2 choices for the fourth position, and 1 choice for the fifth position. Thus, there are $(5)(4)(3)(2)(1) = 120$ possible arrangements of the books.

45.   There are 8 choices for the DOW stocks, 15 choices for the NASDAQ stocks, and 4 choices for the global stocks. Thus, there are $(8)(15)(4) = 480$ different portfolios.

47.   The first person can have any of 365 days, the second person can have any of the remaining 364 days. Thus, there are $(365)(364) = 132{,}860$ possible ways two people can have different birthdays.

49.   Choosing 2 boys from the 4 boys can be done C(4,2) ways, and choosing 3 girls from the 8 girls can be done in C(8,3) ways. Thus, there are a total of:

$$C(4,2) \cdot C(8,3) = \frac{4!}{(4-2)!\,2!} \cdot \frac{8!}{(8-3)!\,3!} = \frac{4!}{2!\,2!} \cdot \frac{8!}{5!\,3!}$$

$$= \frac{4 \cdot 3!}{2 \cdot 1 \cdot 2 \cdot 1} \cdot \frac{8 \cdot 7 \cdot 6 \cdot 5!}{5!\,3!} = 336$$

51.   This is a permutation with repetition. There are $\frac{9!}{2!\,2!} = 90,720$ different words.

53.   (a) $C(7,2) \cdot C(3,1) = 21 \cdot 3 = 63$
       (b) $C(7,3) = 35$
       (c) $C(3,3) = 1$

55.   There are C(100, 22) ways to form the first committee. There are 78 senators left, so there are C(78, 13) ways to form the second committee. There are C(65, 10) ways to form the third committee. There are C(55, 5) ways to form the fourth committee. There are C(50, 16) ways to form the fifth committee. There are C(34, 17) ways to form the sixth committee. There are C(17, 17) ways to form the seventh committee.
The total number of committees =

$$= C(100,22) \cdot C(78,13) \cdot C(65,10) \cdot C(55,5) \cdot C(50,16) \cdot C(34,17) \cdot C(17,17)$$

$$= 1.1568 \times 10^{76}$$

57.   There are 9 choices for the first position, 8 choices for the second position, 7 for the third position, etc. There are $9 \cdot 8 \cdot 7 \cdot 6 \cdot 5 \cdot 4 \cdot 3 \cdot 2 \cdot 1 = 9! = 362,880$ possible batting orders.

59.   The team must have 1 pitcher and 8 position players (non-pitchers). For pitcher, choose 1 player from a group of 4 players, i.e. C(4, 1). For position players, choose 8 players from a group of 11 players, i.e. C(11, 8). Therefore, the number different teams possible is

$$C(4,1) \cdot C(11,8) = \frac{4!}{(4-1)!\cdot 1!} \cdot \frac{11!}{(11-8)!\cdot 8!} = \frac{4!}{3!} \cdot \frac{11!}{3!\cdot 8!} = \frac{4 \cdot 3!}{3!} \cdot \frac{11 \cdot 10 \cdot 9 \cdot 8!}{3!\cdot 8!}$$

$$= 4 \cdot \left(\frac{11 \cdot 10 \cdot 9}{3!} \right) = 4 \cdot \left(\frac{990}{6} \right) = 4 \cdot 165 = 660$$

61.   Choose 2 players from a group of 6 players. Therefore, there are $C(6,2) = 15$ different teams possible.

63. – 65.   Answers will vary.

Chapter 9

Counting and Probability

9.3 Probability

1. Probabilities must be between 0 and 1, inclusive. Thus, 0, 0.01, 0.35, and 1 are probabilities.

3. All the probabilities are between 0 and 1.
   The sum of the probabilities is $0.2 + 0.3 + 0.1 + 0.4 = 1$.
   This is a probability model.

5. All the probabilities are between 0 and 1.
   The sum of the probabilities is $0.3 + 0.2 + 0.1 + 0.3 = 0.9$.
   This is not a probability model.

7. The sample space is: $S = \{HH, HT, TH, TT\}$.
   Each outcome is equally likely to occur; so $P(E) = \dfrac{n(E)}{n(S)}$.
   The probabilities are: $P(HH) = \dfrac{1}{4}$, $P(HT) = \dfrac{1}{4}$, $P(TH) = \dfrac{1}{4}$, $P(TT) = \dfrac{1}{4}$.

9. The sample space of tossing two fair coins and a fair die is:
   $$S = \{HH1, HH2, HH3, HH4, HH5, HH6, HT1, HT2, HT3, HT4, HT5,$$
   $$HT6, TH1, TH2, TH3, TH4, TH5, TH6, TT1, TT2, TT3, TT4, TT5, TT6\}$$
   There are 24 equally likely outcomes and the probability of each is $\dfrac{1}{24}$.

11. The sample space for tossing three fair coins is:
    $$S = \{HHH, HHT, HTH, THH, HTT, THT, TTH, TTT\}$$
    There are 8 equally likely outcomes and the probability of each is $\dfrac{1}{8}$.

13. The sample space is:
    $$S = \{1 \text{ Yellow}, 1 \text{ Red}, 1 \text{ Green}, 2 \text{ Yellow}, 2 \text{ Red}, 2 \text{ Green}, 3 \text{ Yellow}, 3 \text{ Red},$$
    $$3 \text{ Green}, 4 \text{ Yellow}, 4 \text{ Red}, 4 \text{ Green}\}$$
    There are 12 equally likely events and the probability of each is $\dfrac{1}{12}$. The probability of getting a 2 or 4 followed by a Red is $P(2 \text{ Red}) + P(4 \text{ Red}) = \dfrac{1}{12} + \dfrac{1}{12} = \dfrac{1}{6}$.

15. The sample space is:
    S = {1 Yellow Forward, 1 Yellow Backward, 1 Red Forward, 1 Red Backward, 1 Green Forward, 1 Green Backward, 2 Yellow Forward, 2 Yellow Backward, 2 Red Forward, 2 Red Backward, 2 Green Forward, 2 Green Backward, 3 Yellow Forward, 3 Yellow Backward, 3 Red Forward, 3 Red Backward, 3 Green Forward, 3 Green Backward, 4 Yellow Forward, 4 Yellow Backward, 4 Red Forward, 4 Red Backward, 4 Green Forward, 4 Green Backward}

    There are 24 equally likely events and the probability of each is $\frac{1}{24}$.

    The probability of getting a 1, followed by a Red or Green, followed by a Backward is

    $P(1 \text{ Red Backward}) + P(1 \text{ Green Backward}) = \frac{1}{24} + \frac{1}{24} = \frac{1}{12}$.

17. The sample space is:
    S = {1 1 Yellow, 1 1 Red, 1 1 Green, 1 2 Yellow, 1 2 Red, 1 2 Green, 1 3 Yellow, 1 3 Red, 1 3 Green, 1 4 Yellow, 1 4 Red, 1 4 Green, 2 1 Yellow, 2 1 Red, 2 1 Green, 2 2 Yellow, 2 2 Red, 2 2 Green, 2 3 Yellow, 2 3 Red, 2 3 Green, 2 4 Yellow, 2 4 Red, 2 4 Green, 3 1 Yellow, 3 1 Red, 3 1 Green, 3 2 Yellow, 3 2 Red, 3 2 Green, 3 3 Yellow, 3 3 Red, 3 3 Green, 3 4 Yellow, 3 4 Red, 3 4 Green, 4 1 Yellow, 4 1 Red, 4 1 Green, 4 2 Yellow, 4 2 Red, 4 2 Green, 4 3 Yellow, 4 3 Red, 4 3 Green, 4 4 Yellow, 4 4 Red, 4 4 Green}

    There are 48 equally likely events and the probability of each is $\frac{1}{48}$.

    The probability of getting a 2, followed by a 2 or 4, followed by a Red or Green is

    $P(2 \text{ 2 Red}) + P(2 \text{ 4 Red}) + P(2 \text{ 2 Green}) + P(2 \text{ 4 Green}) = \frac{1}{48} + \frac{1}{48} + \frac{1}{48} + \frac{1}{48} = \frac{1}{12}$

19. A, B, C, F   21. B

23. Let $P(\text{tails}) = x$, then $P(\text{heads}) = 4x$

    $x + 4x = 1 \rightarrow 5x = 1 \rightarrow x = \frac{1}{5}$ $P(\text{tails}) = \frac{1}{5}$, $P(\text{heads}) = \frac{4}{5}$

25. $P(2) = P(4) = P(6) = x$ $P(1) = P(3) = P(5) = 2x$
    $P(1) + P(2) + P(3) + P(4) + P(5) + P(6) = 1$

    $2x + x + 2x + x + 2x + x = 1 \rightarrow 9x = 1 \rightarrow x = \frac{1}{9}$

    $P(2) = P(4) = P(6) = \frac{1}{9}$ $P(1) = P(3) = P(5) = \frac{2}{9}$

27. $P(E) = \frac{n(E)}{n(S)} = \frac{n\{1,2,3\}}{10} = \frac{3}{10}$

29. $P(E) = \frac{n(E)}{n(S)} = \frac{n\{2,4,6,8,10\}}{10} = \frac{5}{10} = \frac{1}{2}$

31. $P(\text{white}) = \frac{n(\text{white})}{n(S)} = \frac{5}{5+10+8+7} = \frac{5}{30} = \frac{1}{6}$

33. The sample space is: S = {BBB, BBG, BGB, GBB, BGG, GBG, GGB, GGG}

$P(3 \text{ boys}) = \dfrac{n(3 \text{ boys})}{n(S)} = \dfrac{1}{8}$

35. The sample space is:

S = {BBBB, BBBG, BBGB, BGBB, GBBB, BBGG, BGBG, GBBG, BGGB, GBGB, GGBB, BGGG, GBGG, GGBG, GGGB, GGGG}

$P(1 \text{ girl, } 3 \text{ boys}) = \dfrac{n(1 \text{ girl, } 3 \text{ boys})}{n(S)} = \dfrac{4}{16} = \dfrac{1}{4}$

37. $P(\text{sum of two die is } 7) = \dfrac{n(\text{sum of two die is } 7)}{n(S)}$

$= \dfrac{n\{1,6 \text{ or } 2,5 \text{ or } 3,4 \text{ or } 4,3 \text{ or } 5,2 \text{ or } 6,1\}}{n(S)} = \dfrac{6}{36} = \dfrac{1}{6}$

39. $P(\text{sum of two die is } 3) = \dfrac{n(\text{sum of two die is } 3)}{n(S)} = \dfrac{n\{1,2 \text{ or } 2,1\}}{n(S)} = \dfrac{2}{36} = \dfrac{1}{18}$

41. $P(A \cup B) = P(A) + P(B) - P(A \cap B) = 0.25 + 0.45 - 0.15 = 0.55$

43. $P(A \cup B) = P(A) + P(B) = 0.25 + 0.45 = 0.70$

45. $P(A \cup B) = P(A) + P(B) - P(A \cap B)$
     $0.85 = 0.60 + P(B) - 0.05$
     $P(B) = 0.85 - 0.60 + 0.05 = 0.30$

47. $P(\text{not victim}) = 1 - P(\text{victim}) = 1 - 0.253 = 0.747$

49. $P(\text{not in 70's}) = 1 - P(\text{in 70's}) = 1 - 0.3 = 0.7$

51. $P(\text{white or green}) = P(\text{white}) + P(\text{green}) = \dfrac{n(\text{white}) + n(\text{green})}{n(S)} = \dfrac{9+8}{9+8+3} = \dfrac{17}{20}$

53. $P(\text{not white}) = 1 - P(\text{white}) = 1 - \dfrac{n(\text{white})}{n(S)} = 1 - \dfrac{9}{20} = \dfrac{11}{20}$

55. $P(\text{strike or one}) = P(\text{strike}) + P(\text{one}) = \dfrac{n(\text{strike}) + n(\text{one})}{n(S)} = \dfrac{3+1}{8} = \dfrac{4}{8} = \dfrac{1}{2}$

57. There are 30 households out of 100 with an income of $30,000 or more.

$P(E) = \dfrac{n(E)}{n(S)} = \dfrac{n(30,000 \text{ or more})}{n(\text{total households})} = \dfrac{30}{100} = \dfrac{3}{10}$

59. There are 40 households out of 100 with an income of less than $20,000.

$P(E) = \dfrac{n(E)}{n(S)} = \dfrac{n(\text{less than } \$20,000)}{n(\text{total households})} = \dfrac{40}{100} = \dfrac{2}{5}$

61. (a) $P(1 \text{ or } 2) = P(1) + P(2) = 0.24 + 0.33 = 0.57$

(b) $P(1 \text{ or more}) = P(1) + P(2) + P(3) + P(4 \text{ or more})$
$$= 0.24 + 0.33 + 0.21 + 0.17 = 0.95$$

(c) $P(3 \text{ or fewer}) = P(0) + P(1) + P(2) + P(3) = 0.05 + 0.24 + 0.33 + 0.21 = 0.83$

(d) $P(3 \text{ or more}) = P(3) + P(4 \text{ or more}) = 0.21 + 0.17 = 0.38$

(e) $P(\text{less than } 2) = P(0) + P(1) = 0.05 + 0.24 = 0.29$

(f) $P(\text{less than } 1) = P(0) = 0.05$

(g) $P(1, 2, \text{ or } 3) = P(1) + P(2) + P(3) = 0.24 + 0.33 + 0.21 = 0.78$

(h) $P(2 \text{ or more}) = P(2) + P(3) + P(4 \text{ or more}) = 0.33 + 0.21 + 0.17 = 0.71$

63. (a) $P(\text{freshman or female}) = P(\text{freshman}) + P(\text{female}) - P(\text{freshman and female})$
$$= \frac{n(\text{freshman}) + n(\text{female}) - n(\text{freshman and female})}{n(S)}$$
$$= \frac{18 + 15 - 8}{33} = \frac{25}{33}$$

(b) $P(\text{sophomore or male}) = P(\text{sophomore}) + P(\text{male}) - P(\text{sophomore and male})$
$$= \frac{n(\text{sophomore}) + n(\text{male}) - n(\text{sophomore and male})}{n(S)}$$
$$= \frac{15 + 18 - 8}{33} = \frac{25}{33}$$

65. $P(\text{at least 2 with same birthday}) = 1 - P(\text{none with same birthday})$
$$= 1 - \frac{n(\text{different birthdays})}{n(S)}$$
$$= 1 - \frac{365 \cdot 364 \cdot 363 \cdot 362 \cdot 361 \cdot 360 \cdot \ldots \cdot 354}{365^{12}}$$
$$\approx 1 - 0.833 = 0.167$$

67.   The sample space for picking 5 out of 10 numbers in a particular order contains
$$P(10,5) = \frac{10!}{(10-5)!} = \frac{10!}{5!} = 30,240 \text{ possible outcomes.}$$
One of these is the desired outcome. Thus, the probability of winning is:
$$P(E) = \frac{n(E)}{n(S)} = \frac{n(\text{winning})}{n(\text{total possible outcomes})} = \frac{1}{30240} \approx 0.000033069$$

69. (a) $P(3 \text{ heads}) = \dfrac{C(5,3)}{2^5} = \dfrac{10}{32} = \dfrac{5}{16}$ (b) $P(0 \text{ heads}) = \dfrac{C(5,0)}{2^5} = \dfrac{1}{32}$

71. (a) $P(\text{sum } = 7 \text{ three times}) = P(\text{sum } = 7) \cdot P(\text{sum } = 7) \cdot P(\text{sum } = 7)$
$$= \frac{1}{6} \cdot \frac{1}{6} \cdot \frac{1}{6} = \frac{1}{216} \approx 0.00463$$

(b) $P(\text{sum } = 7 \text{ or } 11 \text{ at least twice})$
$$= P(\text{sum } = 7 \text{ or } 11) \cdot P(\text{sum } = 7 \text{ or } 11) \cdot P(\text{sum } \neq 7 \text{ or } 11) +$$
$$P(\text{sum } = 7 \text{ or } 11) \cdot P(\text{sum } = 7 \text{ or } 11) \cdot P(\text{sum } = 7 \text{ or } 11)$$
$$= 3\left(\frac{8}{36} \cdot \frac{8}{36} \cdot \frac{28}{36}\right) + \frac{8}{36} \cdot \frac{8}{36} \cdot \frac{8}{36} = 0.049$$

73. $P(\text{all 5 defective}) = \dfrac{n(5 \text{ defective})}{n(S)} = \dfrac{1}{C(30,5)} = 7.02 \times 10^{-6}$

$P(\text{at least 2 defective}) = 1 - (P(\text{none defective}) + P(\text{one defective}))$

$$= 1 - \left(\frac{C(5,0) \cdot C(25,5)}{C(30,5)} + \frac{C(5,1) \cdot C(25,4)}{C(30,5)} \right) = 1 - 0.817 = 0.183$$

75. $P(\text{one of 5 coins is valued at more than } \$10,000) = \dfrac{C(49,4) \cdot C(1,1)}{C(50,5)} = 0.1$

Chapter 9

Counting and Probability

9.4   Obtaining Probabilities From Data

1.   (a)

Cause of Death	Probability
Accidents and adverse effects	0.436
Homicide and legal intervention	0.180
Suicide	0.135
Malignant neoplasms	0.055
Diseases of heart	0.035
Human immunodeficiency virus infection	0.006
Congenital anomalies	0.015
Chronic obstructive pulmonary diseases	0.008
Pneumonia and influenza	0.007
Cerebrovascular diseases	0.006
All other causes	0.118

(b) $P(\text{suicide}) = 0.1350 = 13.50\%$

(c) $P(\text{suicide or malignant neoplasms}) = P(\text{suicide}) + P(\text{malignant neoplasms})$
$$= 0.1350 + 0.0555 = 0.1905 = 19.05\%$$

(d) $P(\text{not suicide nor malignant neoplasms}) = 1 - P(\text{suicide or malignant neoplasms})$
$$= 1 - 0.1905 = 0.8095 = 80.95\%$$

3.   (a)

Seatbelt Worn	Probability
Never	0.0262
Rarely	0.0678
Sometimes	0.1156
Most of the Time	0.2632
Always	0.5272

(b) $P(\text{Never}) = 0.0262 = 2.62\%$

(c) $P(\text{Never or Rarely}) = P(\text{Never}) + P(\text{Rarely})$
$$= 0.0262 + 0.0678 = 0.0940 = 9.40\%$$

5.   (a)

Weight (in grams)	Probability
Less than 500	0.0015
500 – 999	0.0057
1000 – 1499	0.0073
1500 – 1999	0.0150
2000 – 2499	0.0463
2500 – 2999	0.1650
3000 – 3499	0.3702
3500 – 3999	0.2884
4000 – 4499	0.0851
4500 – 4999	0.0139
5000 or more	0.0016

(b) $P(3500-3999) = 0.2884 = 28.84\%$

(c) $P(3500-4499) = P(3500-3999 \text{ or } 4000-4499) = P(3500-3999) + P(4000-4499)$
$$= 0.2884 + 0.0851 = 0.3735 = 37.35\%$$

(d) $P(\text{not 5000 or more}) = 1 - P(5000 \text{ or more}) = 1 - 0.0016 = 0.9984 = 99.84\%$

7. $P(\text{Titleist}) = \dfrac{n(\text{Titleist})}{n(S)} = \dfrac{4}{10} = \dfrac{2}{5} = 0.40$

9. $P(2\text{boys, 1 girl}) = \dfrac{n(2\text{boys, 1 girl})}{n(S)} = \dfrac{20}{50} = \dfrac{2}{5} = 0.40$

11. $P(\text{tornado, 5-6PM}) = \dfrac{n(\text{tornado, 5-6PM})}{n(S)} = \dfrac{3262}{28538} = 0.1143 = 11.43\%$

$P(\text{tornado, not 5-6PM}) = 1 - P(\text{tornado, 5-6PM})$
$$= 1 - \dfrac{3262}{28538} = 1 - 0.1143 = 0.8857 = 88.57\%$$

13. $P(\text{cloudy}) = \dfrac{n(\text{cloudy})}{n(S)} = \dfrac{11.2}{30} = 0.3733 = 37.33\%$

$P(\text{clear}) = \dfrac{n(\text{clear})}{n(S)} = \dfrac{7.3}{30} = 0.2433 = 24.33\%$

$P(\text{not clear}) = 1 - P(\text{clear}) = 1 - 0.2433 = 0.7567 = 75.67\%$

15. $P(\text{thunderstorm day}) = \dfrac{n(\text{thunderstorm day})}{n(S)} = \dfrac{6.4}{30} = 0.2133 = 21.33\%$

$P(\text{not thunderstorm day}) = 1 - P(\text{thunderstorm day})$
$$= 1 - 0.2133 = 0.7867 = 78.67\%$$

17. (a)

Field of Home Run	Probability
Left	0.4194
Left center	0.3387
Center	0.1935
Right center	0.0484
Right	0

(b) $P(\text{left field}) = 0.4194 = 41.94\%$

(c) $P(\text{center field}) = 0.1935 = 19.35\%$

(d) $P(\text{right field}) = 0 = 0\%$

(e) Answers will vary.

19. Use the randInt function on the calculator as follows (answers will vary):

(a) randInt(1,6,100)

The plot shows the probability of rolling a "1" to be $\dfrac{13}{100} = 0.13$.

(b) randInt(1,6,100)

The plot shows the probability of rolling a "1" to be $\dfrac{17}{100} = 0.17$.

(c) randInt(1,6,500)

The plot shows the probability of rolling a "1" to be $\dfrac{84}{500} = 0.168$.

(d) The simulation in part (c) yields the closest estimate to the probability obtained using equally likely outcomes, $\dfrac{1}{6} \approx 0.16\overline{6}$.

Chapter 9

Counting and Probability

9.R   Chapter Review

1.   {Melody}, {Dave}, {Joanne}, {Erica},
     {Melody, Dave}, {Melody, Joanne}, {Melody, Erica},
     {Dave, Joanne}, {Dave, Erica}, {Joanne, Erica},
     {Melody, Dave, Joanne}, {Melody, Dave, Erica}, {Melody, Joanne, Erica}, {Dave, Joanne, Erica}
     {Melody, Dave, Joanne, Erica}, $\varnothing$

3. $A \cup B = \{1, 3, 5, 7\} \cup \{3, 5, 6, 7, 8\} = \{1, 3, 5, 6, 7, 8\}$

5. $A \cap C = \{1, 3, 5, 7\} \cap \{2, 3, 7, 8, 9\} = \{3, 7\}$

7. $\overline{A} \cup \overline{B} = \overline{\{1, 3, 5, 7\}} \cup \overline{\{3, 5, 6, 7, 8\}} = \{2, 4, 6, 8, 9\} \cup \{1, 2, 4, 9\} = \{1, 2, 4, 6, 8, 9\}$

9. $\overline{B \cap C} = \overline{\{3, 5, 6, 7, 8\} \cap \{2, 3, 7, 8, 9\}} = \overline{\{3, 7, 8\}} = \{1, 2, 4, 5, 6, 9\}$

11. $n(A) = 8, n(B) = 12, n(A \cap B) = 3$
     $n(A \cup B) = n(A) + n(B) - n(A \cap B) = 8 + 12 - 3 = 17$

13. From the figure:
     $n(A) = 20 + 2 + 6 + 1 = 29$

15. From the figure:
     $n(A \text{ and } C) = n(A \cap C) = 1 + 6 = 7$

17. From the figure:
     $n(\text{neither in } A \text{ nor in } C) = n(\overline{A \cup C}) = 20 + 5 = 25$

19. $5! = 5 \cdot 4 \cdot 3 \cdot 2 \cdot 1 = 120$ 21. $P(8,3) = \dfrac{8!}{(8-3)!} = \dfrac{8!}{5!} = \dfrac{8 \cdot 7 \cdot 6 \cdot 5!}{5!} = 336$

23. $C(8,3) = \dfrac{8!}{(8-3)! \, 3!} = \dfrac{8!}{5! \, 3!} = \dfrac{8 \cdot 7 \cdot 6 \cdot 5!}{5! \cdot 3 \cdot 2 \cdot 1} = 56$

25. There are 2 choices of material, 3 choices of color, and 10 choices of size. The complete
     assortment would have: $2 \cdot 3 \cdot 10 = 60$ suits.

27.   There are two possible outcomes for each game or
$2 \cdot 2 \cdot 2 \cdot 2 \cdot 2 \cdot 2 \cdot 2 = 2^7 = 128$ outcomes for 7 games.

29.   Since order is significant, this is a permutation.
$$P(9,4) = \frac{9!}{(9-4)!} = \frac{9!}{5!} = \frac{9 \cdot 8 \cdot 7 \cdot 6 \cdot 5!}{5!} = 3024 \text{ ways to seat 4 people in 9 seats.}$$

31.   Choose 4 runners - order is not significant:
$$C(8,4) = \frac{8!}{(8-4)!\,4!} = \frac{8!}{4!\,4!} = \frac{8 \cdot 7 \cdot 6 \cdot 5 \cdot 4!}{4 \cdot 3 \cdot 2 \cdot 1 \cdot 4!} = 70 \text{ ways a squad can be chosen.}$$

33.   Choose 14 teams 2 at a time:
$$C(14,2) = \frac{14!}{(14-2)!\,2!} = \frac{14!}{12!\,2!} = \frac{14 \cdot 13 \cdot 12!}{12! \cdot 2 \cdot 1} = 91 \text{ ways to pair 14 teams.}$$

35.   There are $8 \cdot 10 \cdot 10 \cdot 10 \cdot 10 \cdot 10 \cdot 2 = 1{,}600{,}000$ possible phone numbers.

37.   There are $24 \cdot 9 \cdot 10 \cdot 10 \cdot 10 = 216{,}000$ possible license plates.

39.   Since there are repeated letters:
$$\frac{7!}{2! \cdot 2!} = \frac{7 \cdot 6 \cdot 5 \cdot 4 \cdot 3 \cdot 2 \cdot 1}{2 \cdot 1 \cdot 2 \cdot 1} = 1260 \text{ different words can be formed.}$$

41.   (a)

Age	Probability
20 – 24	0.1709
25 – 29	0.1410
30 – 34	0.1344
35 – 39	0.1227
40 – 44	0.0990
45 – 49	0.0816
50 – 54	0.0602
55 – 59	0.0460
60 – 64	0.0389
65 – 69	0.0321
70 – 74	0.0293
75 – 79	0.0248
80 – 84	0.0190

(b) $P(25-29) = 0.1410 = 14.10\%$

(c) $P(20-29) = P(20-24 \text{ or } 25-29) = P(20-24) + P(25-29)$
$$= 0.1709 + 0.1410 = 0.3119 = 31.19\%$$

(d) $P(\text{not } 20-24) = 1 - P(20-24) = 1 - 0.1709 = 0.8291 = 82.91\%$

43.   (a) $365 \cdot 364 \cdot 363 \cdot 362 \cdot \ldots \cdot 348 = 8.634628387 \times 10^{45}$

(b) $P(\text{no one has same birthday}) = \dfrac{365 \cdot 364 \cdot 363 \cdot 362 \cdot \ldots \cdot 348}{365^{18}} = 0.6531 = 65.31\%$

(c) P(at least 2 have same birthday) $= 1 - P$(no one has same birthday)

$$= 1 - 0.6531 = 0.3469 = 34.69\%$$

45.   (a) P(unemployed) $= 0.054 = 5.4\%$

(b) P(not unemployed) $= 1 - P$(unemployed) $= 1 - 0.054 = 0.946 = 94.6\%$

47. $P(\$1 \text{ bill}) = \dfrac{n(\$1 \text{ bill})}{n(S)} = \dfrac{4}{9}$

49.   Let S be all possible selections, let D be a card that is divisible by 5, and let PN be a 1 or a prime number.

$n(S) = 100$

$n(D) = 20$ (There are 20 numbers divisible by 5 between 1 and 100.)

$n(PN) = 26$ (There are 25 prime numbers less than or equal to 100.)

$$P(D) = \frac{n(D)}{n(S)} = \frac{20}{100} = \frac{1}{5} = 0.2$$

$$P(PN) = \frac{n(PN)}{n(S)} = \frac{26}{100} = \frac{13}{50} = 0.26$$

51.   (a) $P(5 \text{ heads}) = \dfrac{n(5 \text{ heads})}{n(S)} = \dfrac{C(10,5)}{2^{10}} = \dfrac{\left(\dfrac{10!}{5!\,5!}\right)}{1024} = \dfrac{252}{1024} \approx 0.2461$

(b) $P(\text{all heads}) = \dfrac{n(\text{all heads})}{n(S)} = \dfrac{1}{2^{10}} = \dfrac{1}{1024} = 0.00098$

53.   (a) $P(\text{all students}) = \dfrac{C(8,5)}{C(18,5)} = \dfrac{56}{8568} \approx 0.0065$

(b) $P(\text{all faculty}) = \dfrac{C(10,5)}{C(18,5)} = \dfrac{252}{8568} \approx 0.0294$

(c) $P(2 \text{ students and 3 faculty}) = \dfrac{C(8,2) \cdot C(10,3)}{C(18,5)} = \dfrac{28 \cdot 120}{8568} \approx 0.3922$

55.   Use the randInt function on the calculator as follows (answers will vary):

(a)   randInt(1,6,100)

The plot shows the probability of rolling a "1" to be $\dfrac{23}{100} = 0.23$.

(b)   randInt(1,6,100)

The plot shows the probability of rolling a "1" to be $\dfrac{11}{100} = 0.11$.

(c)   randInt(1,6,500)

The plot shows the probability of rolling a "1" to be $\dfrac{69}{500} = 0.138$.

(d)   The simulation in part (c) yields the closest estimate to the probability obtained using equally likely outcomes, $\dfrac{1}{6} = 0.16\overline{6}$.

Chapter 9

Counting and Probability

9.CR   Cumulative Review

1. $3x^2 - 2x = -1 \Rightarrow 3x^2 - 2x + 1 = 0$

$$x = \frac{-b \pm \sqrt{b^2 - 4ac}}{2a} = \frac{-(-2) \pm \sqrt{(-2)^2 - 4(3)(1)}}{2(3)}$$

$$= \frac{4 \pm \sqrt{4 - 12}}{6} = \frac{4 \pm \sqrt{-8}}{6} = \frac{4 \pm 2\sqrt{2}i}{6} = \frac{2 \pm \sqrt{2}i}{3}$$

The solution set is $\left\{ \dfrac{2 - \sqrt{2}i}{3}, \dfrac{2 + \sqrt{2}i}{3} \right\}$.

3. $y = 2(x + 1)^2 - 4$

Using the graph of $y = x^2$, horizontally shift to the left 1 unit, vertically stretch by a factor of 2, and vertically shift down 4 units.

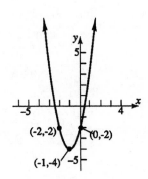

5. $f(x) = 5x^4 - 9x^3 - 7x^2 - 31x - 6$

Step 1: $f(x)$ has at most 4 real zeros.

Step 2:   Possible rational zeros:
$$p = \pm 1, \pm 2, \pm 3, \pm 6; \quad q = \pm 1, \pm 5;$$

$$\frac{p}{q} = \pm 1, \pm \frac{1}{5}, \pm 2, \pm \frac{2}{5}, \pm 3, \pm \frac{4}{5}, \pm 6, \pm \frac{6}{5}$$

Step 3:   Using the Bounds on Zeros Theorem:
$$f(x) = 5\left(x^4 - 1.8x^3 - 1.4x^2 - 6.2x - 1.2\right)$$

$$a_3 = -1.8, \quad a_2 = -1.4, \quad a_1 = -6.2, \quad a_0 = -1.2$$

$$\text{Max}\left\{1, |-1.2| + |-6.2| + |-1.4| + |-1.8|\right\} = \text{Max}\left\{1, 6.2\right\} = 6.2$$

$$1 + \text{Max}\left\{|-1.2|, |-6.2|, |-1.4|, |-1.8|\right\} = 1 + 6.2 = 7.2$$

The smaller of the two numbers is 6.2. Thus, every zero of f lies between -6.2 and 6.2.

Graphing using the bounds and ZOOM-FIT: (Second graph has a better window.)

Step 4: From the graph it appears that there are x-intercepts at −0.2 and 3.
Using synthetic division with 3:

$$3\overline{)5 \quad -9 \quad -7 \quad -31 \quad -6}$$

$$ \quad 15 \quad 18 \quad 33 \quad 6$$

$$ 5 \quad 6 \quad 11 \quad 2 \quad 0$$

Since the remainder is 0, $x-3$ is a factor. The other factor is the
quotient: $5x^3 + 6x^2 + 11x + 2$.

Using synthetic division with 2 on the quotient:

$$-0.2\overline{)5 \quad 6 \quad 11 \quad 2}$$

$$ -1 \quad -1 \quad -2$$

$$ 5 \quad 5 \quad 10 \quad 0$$

Since the remainder is 0, $x - (-0.2) = x + 0.2$ is a factor. The other factor is
the quotient: $5x^2 + 5x + 10 = 5(x^2 + x + 2)$.

Factoring,

$$f(x) = 5(x^2 + x + 2)(x - 3)(x + 0.2)$$

The real zeros are 3 and $-.02$.
The complex zeros come from solving $x^2 + x + 2 = 0$.

$$x = \frac{-b \pm \sqrt{b^2 - 4ac}}{2a} = \frac{-1 \pm \sqrt{1^2 - 4(1)(2)}}{2(1)}$$

$$= \frac{-1 \pm \sqrt{1-8}}{2} = \frac{-1 \pm \sqrt{-7}}{2} = \frac{-1 \pm \sqrt{7}i}{2}$$

Therefore, the over the set of complex numbers, $f(x) = 5x^4 - 9x^3 - 7x^2 - 31x - 6$ has

zeros $-0.2, 3, \dfrac{-1 - \sqrt{7}i}{2}, \dfrac{-1 + \sqrt{7}i}{2}$.

7. $\log_3(9^x) = \log_3\left((3^2)^x\right) = \log_3(3^{2x}) = 2x$

9. $f(x) = \log(x^2 - 4)$

f will be defined provided $x^2 - 4 > 0$.
Solving the inequality $x^2 - 4 > 0$:

$$(x + 2)(x - 2) > 0 \qquad g(x) = (x + 2)(x - 2)$$

$x = -2$, $x = 2$ are the zeros of g.

Interval	Test Number	$g(x)$	Positive/Negative
$-\infty < x < -2$	-3	5	Positive
$-2 < x < 2$	0	-4	Negative
$2 < x < \infty$	3	5	Positive

The domain of $f(x) = \log(x^2 - 4)$ is $\{x \mid -\infty < x < -2 \ \text{ or } \ 2 < x < \infty\}$.

11.   Multiply each side of the first equation by -3 and add to the second equation to eliminate x; and multiply each side of the first equation by 2 and add to the third equation to eliminate x:

$$\begin{cases} x - 2y + z = 15 \\ 3x + y - 3z = -8 \\ -2x + 4y - z = -27 \end{cases}$$

$$x - 2y + z = 15 \xrightarrow{\ -3\ } -3x + 6y - 3z = -45$$
$$3x + y - 3z = -8 \longrightarrow \underline{\ 3x + y - 3z = -8\ }$$
$$7y - 6z = -53$$

$$x - 2y + z = 15 \xrightarrow{\ 2\ } 2x - 4y + 2z = 30$$
$$-2x + 4y - z = -27 \longrightarrow \underline{\ -2x + 4y - z = -27\ }$$
$$z = 3$$

Substituting and solving for the other variables:
$$z = 3 \Rightarrow 7y - 6(3) = -53$$

$$7y = -35 \qquad\qquad\qquad z = 3, y = -5 \Rightarrow x - 2(-5) + 3 = 15$$
$$y = -5 \qquad\qquad\qquad\qquad\qquad x + 10 + 3 = 15 \Rightarrow x = 2$$

The solution is $x = 2$, $y = -5$, $z = 3$.

Conics

10.2 The Parabola

1. B   3. E   5. H   7. C

9. E   11. D   13. C

15. The focus is (4, 0) and the vertex is (0, 0). Both lie on the horizontal line $y = 0$. $a = 4$ and since (4, 0) is to the right of (0, 0), the parabola opens to the right. The equation of the parabola is:
$$y^2 = 4ax$$
$$y^2 = 4 \cdot 4 \cdot x$$
$$y^2 = 16x$$
Letting $x = 4$, we find $y^2 = 64$ or $y = \pm 8$.
The points (4, 8) and (4, –8) define the latus rectum.

17. The focus is (0, –3) and the vertex is (0, 0). Both lie on the vertical line $x = 0$. $a = 3$ and since (0, –3) is below (0, 0), the parabola opens down. The equation of the parabola is:
$$x^2 = -4ay$$
$$x^2 = -4 \cdot 3 \cdot y$$
$$x^2 = -12y$$
Letting $y = -3$, we find $x^2 = 36$ or $x = \pm 6$.
The points (6, 3) and (6, –3) define the latus rectum.

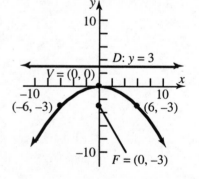

19. The focus is (–2, 0) and the directrix is $x = 2$. The vertex is (0, 0). $a = 2$ and since (–2, 0) is to the left of (0, 0), the parabola opens to the left. The equation of the parabola is:
$$y^2 = -4ax$$
$$y^2 = -4 \cdot 2 \cdot x$$
$$y^2 = -8x$$
Letting $x = -2$, we find $y^2 = 16$ or $y = \pm 4$. The points (–2, 4) and (–2, –4) define the latus rectum.

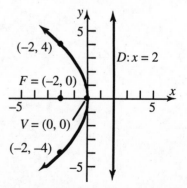

21. The directrix is $y = -\dfrac{1}{2}$ and the vertex is $(0, 0)$. The

focus is $\left(0, \dfrac{1}{2}\right)$. $a = \dfrac{1}{2}$ and since $\left(0, \dfrac{1}{2}\right)$ is above

$(0, 0)$, the parabola opens up. The equation of the parabola is:

$$x^2 = 4ay$$

$$x^2 = 4 \cdot \frac{1}{2} \cdot y \rightarrow x^2 = 2y$$

Letting $y = \dfrac{1}{2}$, we find $x^2 = 1$ or $x = \pm 1$.

The points $\left(1, \dfrac{1}{2}\right)$ and $\left(-1, \dfrac{1}{2}\right)$ define the latus

rectum.

23. The focus is $(2, -5)$ and the vertex is $(2, -3)$. Both
lie on the vertical line $x = 2$. $a = 2$ and since
$(2, -5)$ is below $(2, -3)$, the parabola opens down.
The equation of the parabola is:

$$(x - h)^2 = -4a(y - k)$$

$$(x - 2)^2 = -4 \cdot 2 \cdot (y - (-3))$$

$$(x - 2)^2 = -8(y + 3)$$

Letting $y = -5$, we find $(x - 2)^2 = 16$ or $x - 2 = \pm 4$.
So, $x = 6$ or $x = -2$. The points $(6, -5)$ and
$(-2, -5)$ define the latus rectum.

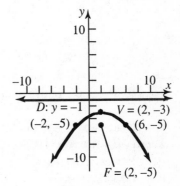

25. Vertex: $(0,0)$. Since the axis of symmetry is
vertical, the parabola opens up or down. Since
$(2, 3)$ is above $(0, 0)$, the parabola opens up. The
equation has the form $x^2 = 4ay$. Substitute the
coordinates of $(2, 3)$ into the equation to find a:

$$2^2 = 4a \cdot 3 \Rightarrow 4 = 12a \Rightarrow a = \frac{1}{3}$$

The equation of the parabola is: $x^2 = \dfrac{4}{3}y$. The

focus is $\left(0, \dfrac{1}{3}\right)$. Letting $y = \dfrac{1}{3}$,

we find $x^2 = \dfrac{4}{9}$ or $x = \pm\dfrac{2}{3}$. The points $\left(\dfrac{2}{3}, \dfrac{1}{3}\right)$ and

$\left(-\dfrac{2}{3}, \dfrac{1}{3}\right)$ define the latus rectum.

27. The directrix is $y = 2$ and the focus is $(-3, 4)$.
This is a vertical case, so the vertex is $(-3, 3)$.
$a = 1$ and since $(-3, 4)$ is above $y = 2$, the
parabola opens up. The equation of the parabola
is: $(x - h)^2 = 4a(y - k)$

$$(x - (-3))^2 = 4 \cdot 1 \cdot (y - 3)$$

$$(x + 3)^2 = 4(y - 3)$$

Letting $y = 4$, we find $(x + 3)^2 = 4$ or $x + 3 = \pm 2$.
So, $x = -1$ or $x = -5$. The points $(-1, 4)$ and
$(-5, 4)$ define the latus rectum.

29. The directrix is $x = 1$ and the focus is $(-3, -2)$. This
is a horizontal case, so the vertex is $(-1, -2)$. $a = 2$
and since $(-3, -2)$ is to the left of $x = 1$, the
parabola opens to the left. The equation of the
parabola is: $(y - k)^2 = -4a(x - h)$

$$(y - (-2))^2 = -4 \cdot 2 \cdot (x - (-1))$$

$$(y + 2)^2 = -8(x + 1)$$

Letting $x = -3$, we find $(y + 2)^2 = 16$ or $y + 2 = \pm 4$.
So, $y = 2$ or $y = -6$. The points $(-3, 2)$ and
$(-3, -6)$ define the latus rectum.

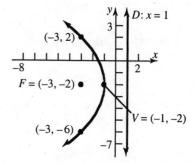

31. The equation $x^2 = 4y$ is in the form $x^2 = 4ay$
where $4a = 4$ or $a = 1$. Thus, we have:
    Vertex: $(0, 0)$
    Focus: $(0, 1)$
    Directrix: $y = -1$
To graph, enter: $y_1 = x^2 / 4$

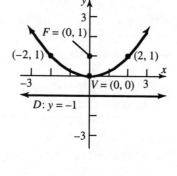

33. The equation $y^2 = -16x$ is in the form $y^2 = -4ax$
where $-4a = -16$ or $a = 4$. Thus, we have:
    Vertex: $(0, 0)$
    Focus: $(-4, 0)$
    Directrix: $x = 4$
To graph, enter: $y_1 = \sqrt{-16x}$; $y_2 = -\sqrt{-16x}$

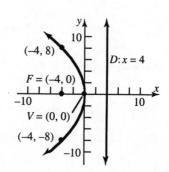

35. The equation $(y-2)^2 = 8(x+1)$ is in the form
$(y-k)^2 = 4a(x-h)$ where $4a = 8$ or $a = 2$,
$h = -1$, and $k = 2$. Thus, we have:

  Vertex: $(-1, 2)$
  Focus: $(1, 2)$
  Directrix: $x = -3$

To graph, enter: $y_1 = 2 + \sqrt{8(x+1)}$;
  $y_2 = 2 - \sqrt{8(x+1)}$

37. The equation $(x-3)^2 = -(y+1)$ is in the form
$(x-h)^2 = -4a(y-k)$ where $-4a = -1$ or $a = \dfrac{1}{4}$,
$h = 3$, and $k = -1$. Thus, we have:

  Vertex: $(3, -1)$
  Focus: $\left(3, -\dfrac{5}{4}\right)$

  Directrix: $y = -\dfrac{3}{4}$

To graph, enter: $y_1 = -1 - (x-3)^2$

39. The equation $(y+3)^2 = 8(x-2)$ is in the form
$(y-k)^2 = 4a(x-h)$ where $4a = 8$ or $a = 2$,
$h = 2$, and $k = -3$. Thus, we have:

  Vertex: $(2, -3)$
  Focus: $(4, -3)$
  Directrix: $x = 0$

To graph, enter:
  $y_1 = -3 + \sqrt{8(x-2)}$; $y_2 = -3 - \sqrt{8(x-2)}$

41. Complete the square to put in standard form:

$$y^2 - 4y + 4x + 4 = 0$$

$$y^2 - 4y + 4 = -4x$$

$$(y - 2)^2 = -4x$$

The equation is in the form $(y - k)^2 = -4a(x - h)$
where $-4a = -4$ or $a = 1$, $h = 0$, and $k = 2$.
Thus, we have:

    Vertex: $(0, 2)$
    Focus: $(-1, 2)$
    Directrix: $x = 1$

To graph, enter: $y_1 = 2 + \sqrt{-4x}$; $y_2 = 2 - \sqrt{-4x}$

43. Complete the square to put in standard form:

$$x^2 + 8x = 4y - 8$$

$$x^2 + 8x + 16 = 4y - 8 + 16$$

$$(x + 4)^2 = 4(y + 2)$$

The equation is in the form $(x - h)^2 = 4a(y - k)$
where $4a = 4$ or $a = 1$, $h = -4$, and $k = -2$.
Thus, we have:

    Vertex: $(-4, -2)$
    Focus: $(-4, -1)$
    Directrix: $y = -3$

To graph, enter: $y_1 = -2 + (x + 4)^2 / 4$

45. Complete the square to put in standard form:

$$y^2 + 2y - x = 0$$
$$y^2 + 2y + 1 = x + 1$$
$$(y + 1)^2 = x + 1$$

The equation is in the form

$(y - k)^2 = 4a(x - h)$ where $4a = 1$ or $a = \dfrac{1}{4}$,

$h = -1$, and $k = -1$.

Thus, we have:

Vertex: $(-1, -1)$

Focus: $\left(-\dfrac{3}{4}, -1\right)$

Directrix: $x = -\dfrac{5}{4}$

To graph, enter:

$$y_1 = -1 + \sqrt{x+1}; \ \ y_2 = -1 - \sqrt{x+1}$$

47. Complete the square to put in standard form:

$$x^2 - 4x = y + 4$$
$$x^2 - 4x + 4 = y + 4 + 4$$
$$(x - 2)^2 = y + 8$$

The equation is in the form $(x - h)^2 = 4a(y - k)$

where $4a = 1$ or $a = \dfrac{1}{4}$, $h = 2$, and $k = -8$. Thus,

we have:

Vertex: $(2, -8)$

Focus: $\left(2, -\dfrac{31}{4}\right)$

Directrix: $y = -\dfrac{33}{4}$

To graph, enter: $y_1 = -8 + (x - 2)^2$

49. $(y-1)^2 = c(x-0)$
     $(y-1)^2 = cx$
     $(2-1)^2 = c(1) \rightarrow 1 = c$
     $(y-1)^2 = x$

51. $(y-1)^2 = c(x-2)$
     $(0-1)^2 = c(1-2)$
     $1 = -c \rightarrow c = -1$
     $(y-1)^2 = -(x-2)$

53. $(x-0)^2 = c(y-1)$
     $(2-0)^2 = c(2-1) \rightarrow 4 = c$
     $x^2 = 4(y-1)$

55. $(y-0)^2 = c(x-(-2))$
     $y^2 = c(x+2)$
     $1^2 = c(0+2) \rightarrow 1 = 2c \rightarrow c = \dfrac{1}{2}$
     $y^2 = \dfrac{1}{2}(x+2)$

57. Set up the problem so that the vertex of the parabola is at (0, 0) and it opens up. Then the equation of the parabola has the form: $x^2 = 4ay$. Since the parabola is 10 feet across and 4 feet deep, the points (5, 4) and (–5, 4) are on the parabola.

Substitute and solve for a: $5^2 = 4a(4) \rightarrow 25 = 16a \rightarrow a = \dfrac{25}{16}$

a is the distance from the vertex to the focus. Thus, the receiver (located at the focus) is $\dfrac{25}{16} = 1.5625$ feet, or 18.75 inches from the base of the dish, along the axis of the parabola.

59. Set up the problem so that the vertex of the parabola is at (0, 0) and it opens up. Then the equation of the parabola has the form: $x^2 = 4ay$. Since the parabola is 4 inches across and 1 inch deep, the points (2, 1) and (–2, 1) are on the parabola.
Substitute and solve for a: $2^2 = 4a(1) \rightarrow 4 = 4a \rightarrow a = 1$, a is the distance from the vertex to the focus. Thus, the bulb (located at the focus) should be 1 inch, from the vertex.

61. Set up the problem so that the vertex of the parabola is at (0, 0) and it opens up. Then the equation of the parabola has the form: $x^2 = cy$.
The point (300, 80) is a point on the parabola.
Solve for c and find the equation:

$300^2 = c(80) \rightarrow c = 1125$

$x^2 = 1125y$

Since the height of the cable, 150 feet from the center, is to be found, the point   (150, h) is a point on the parabola. Solve for h: $150^2 = 1125h \rightarrow 22500 = 1125h \rightarrow h = 20$
The height of the cable, 150 feet from the center, is 20 feet.

63. Set up the problem so that the vertex of the parabola is at (0, 0) and it opens up. Then the equation of the parabola has the form: $x^2 = 4ay$. a is the distance from the vertex to the focus (where the source is located), so $a = 2$. Since the opening is 5 feet across, there is a point (2.5, y) on the parabola.
Solve for y: $x^2 = 8y \rightarrow 2.5^2 = 8y \rightarrow 6.25 = 8y \rightarrow y = 0.78125$ feet
The depth of the searchlight should be 0.78125 feet.

65. Set up the problem so that the vertex of the parabola is at (0, 0) and it opens up. Then the equation of the parabola has the form: $x^2 = 4ay$. Since the parabola is 20 feet across and 6 feet deep, the points (10, 6) and (–10, 6) are on the parabola.
Substitute and solve for a: $10^2 = 4a(6) \rightarrow 100 = 24a \rightarrow a \approx 4.17$ feet
The heat source will be concentrated 4.17 feet from the base, along the axis of symmetry.

67. Set up the problem so that the vertex of the parabola is at (0, 0) and it opens down. Then the equation of the parabola has the form: $x^2 = cy$.
The point (60, –25) is a point on the parabola.
Solve for c and find the equation:
$$60^2 = c(-25) \rightarrow c = -144$$

$$x^2 = -144y$$
To find the height of the bridge, 10 feet from the center, the point (10, y) is a point on the parabola. Solve for y: $10^2 = -144y \rightarrow 100 = -144y \rightarrow y = -0.69$
The height of the bridge, 10 feet from the center, is 25 – 0.69 = 24.31 feet.
To find the height of the bridge, 30 feet from the center, the point (30, y) is a point on the parabola. Solve for y: $30^2 = -144y \rightarrow 900 = -144y \rightarrow y = -6.25$
The height of the bridge, 30 feet from the center, is 25 – 6.25 = 18.75 feet.
To find the height of the bridge, 50 feet from the center, the point (50, y) is a point on the parabola. Solve for y: $50^2 = -144y \rightarrow 2500 = -144y \rightarrow y = -17.36$
The height of the bridge, 50 feet from the center, is 25 – 17.36 = 7.64 feet.

69. $Ax^2 + Ey = 0 \quad A \neq 0, \ E \neq 0$
$$Ax^2 = -Ey \rightarrow x^2 = \frac{-E}{A}y$$
This is the equation of a parabola with vertex at (0, 0) and axis of symmetry being the y-axis. The focus is $\left(0, \dfrac{-E}{4A}\right)$. The directrix is $y = \dfrac{E}{4A}$.

71. $Ax^2 + Dx + Ey + F = 0 \quad A \neq 0$
(a)   If $E \neq 0$, then:
$$Ax^2 + Dx = -Ey - F \rightarrow A\left(x^2 + \frac{D}{A}x + \frac{D^2}{4A^2}\right) = -Ey - F + \frac{D^2}{4A}$$
$$\left(x + \frac{D}{2A}\right)^2 = \frac{1}{A}\left(-Ey - F + \frac{D^2}{4A}\right) \rightarrow \left(x + \frac{D}{2A}\right)^2 = \frac{-E}{A}\left(y + \frac{F}{E} - \frac{D^2}{4AE}\right)$$
$$\left(x + \frac{D}{2A}\right)^2 = \frac{-E}{A}\left(y - \frac{D^2 - 4AF}{4AE}\right)$$
This is the equation of a parabola whose vertex is $\left(\dfrac{-D}{2A}, \dfrac{D^2 - 4AF}{4AE}\right)$.

(b)   If $E = 0$, then

$$Ax^2 + Dx + F = 0 \rightarrow x = \frac{-D \pm \sqrt{D^2 - 4AF}}{2A}$$

If $D^2 - 4AF = 0$, then $x = \dfrac{-D}{2A}$ is a vertical line.

(c)   If $E = 0$, then

$$Ax^2 + Dx + F = 0 \rightarrow x = \frac{-D \pm \sqrt{D^2 - 4AF}}{2A}$$

If $D^2 - 4AF > 0$,

then $x = \dfrac{-D + \sqrt{D^2 - 4AF}}{2A}$ or $x = \dfrac{-D - \sqrt{D^2 - 4AF}}{2A}$ are two vertical lines.

(d)   If $E = 0$, then

$$Ax^2 + Dx + F = 0 \rightarrow x = \frac{-D \pm \sqrt{D^2 - 4AF}}{2A}$$

If $D^2 - 4AF < 0$, there is no real solution. The graph contains no points.

Conics

10.3 The Ellipse

1. C   3. B   5. C   7. D

9. $\dfrac{x^2}{25} + \dfrac{y^2}{4} = 1$

The center of the ellipse is at the origin.
$a = 5,\ b = 2$. The vertices are $(5, 0)$ and $(-5, 0)$. Find the value of c:
$$c^2 = a^2 - b^2 = 25 - 4 = 21 \rightarrow c = \sqrt{21}$$
The foci are $\left(\sqrt{21}, 0\right)$ and $\left(-\sqrt{21}, 0\right)$.

To graph, enter:
$$y_1 = 2\sqrt{(1 - x^2/25)};\quad y_1 = -2\sqrt{(1 - x^2/25)}$$

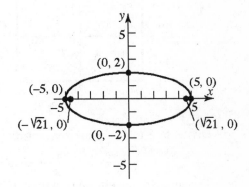

11. $\dfrac{x^2}{9} + \dfrac{y^2}{25} = 1$

The center of the ellipse is at the origin.
$a = 5,\ b = 3$. The vertices are $(0, 5)$ and $(0, -5)$.
Find the value of c:
$$c^2 = a^2 - b^2 = 25 - 9 = 16$$
$$c = 4$$
The foci are $(0, 4)$ and $(0, -4)$.

To graph, enter:
$$y_1 = 5\sqrt{(1 - x^2/9)};\quad y_1 = -5\sqrt{(1 - x^2/9)}$$

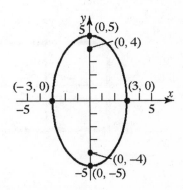

13. $4x^2 + y^2 = 16$

Divide by 16 to put in standard form:

$$\frac{4x^2}{16} + \frac{y^2}{16} = \frac{16}{16} \quad \rightarrow \quad \frac{x^2}{4} + \frac{y^2}{16} = 1$$

The center of the ellipse is at the origin. $a = 4, \ b = 2$.
The vertices are $(0, 4)$ and $(0, -4)$. Find the value of c:

$$c^2 = a^2 - b^2 = 16 - 4 = 12$$

$$c = \sqrt{12} = 2\sqrt{3}$$

The foci are $\left(0, 2\sqrt{3}\right)$ and $\left(0, -2\sqrt{3}\right)$.

To graph, enter:

$$y_1 = \sqrt{(16 - 4x^2)}; \ \ y_1 = -\sqrt{(16 - 4x^2)}$$

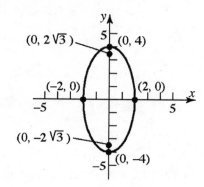

15. $4y^2 + x^2 = 8$

Divide by 8 to put in standard form:

$$\frac{4y^2}{8} + \frac{x^2}{8} = \frac{8}{8} \quad \rightarrow \quad \frac{x^2}{8} + \frac{y^2}{2} = 1$$

The center of the ellipse is at the origin. $a = \sqrt{8} = 2\sqrt{2}, \ b = \sqrt{2}$.
The vertices are $\left(2\sqrt{2}, 0\right)$ and $\left(-2\sqrt{2}, 0\right)$. Find the value of c:

$$c^2 = a^2 - b^2 = 8 - 2 = 6$$

$$c = \sqrt{6}$$

The foci are $\left(\sqrt{6}, 0\right)$ and $\left(-\sqrt{6}, 0\right)$.

To graph, enter:

$$y_1 = \sqrt{(2 - x^2 / 4)}; \ \ y_1 = -\sqrt{(2 - x^2 / 4)}$$

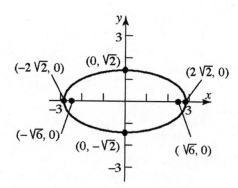

17. $x^2 + y^2 = 16$

This is the equation of a circle whose center is at
(0, 0) and radius = 4.

To graph, enter: $y_1 = \sqrt{(16 - x^2)}$; $y_1 = -\sqrt{(16 - x^2)}$

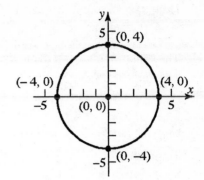

19. Center: (0, 0); Focus: (3, 0); Vertex: (5, 0);
Major axis is the x-axis; $a = 5$; $c = 3$. Find b:

$$b^2 = a^2 - c^2 = 25 - 9 = 16$$
$$b = 4$$

Write the equation: $\dfrac{x^2}{25} + \dfrac{y^2}{16} = 1$

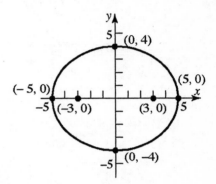

21. Center: (0, 0); Focus: (0, –4); Vertex: (0, 5);
Major axis is the y-axis; $a = 5$; $c = 4$. Find b:

$$b^2 = a^2 - c^2 = 25 - 16 = 9$$
$$b = 3$$

Write the equation: $\dfrac{x^2}{9} + \dfrac{y^2}{25} = 1$

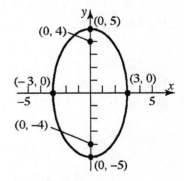

23. Foci: (±2, 0); Length of major axis is 6.
Center: (0, 0); Major axis is the x-axis;
$a = 3$; $c = 2$. Find b:

$$b^2 = a^2 - c^2 = 9 - 4 = 5$$
$$b = \sqrt{5}$$

Write the equation: $\dfrac{x^2}{9} + \dfrac{y^2}{5} = 1$

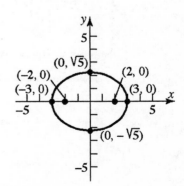

25. Foci: $(0, \pm3)$; x-intercepts are ±2. Center: $(0, 0)$;
    Major axis is the y-axis; $c = 3$; $b = 2$. Find a:
    $$a^2 = b^2 + c^2 = 4 + 9 = 13$$
    $$a = \sqrt{13}$$
    Write the equation: $\dfrac{x^2}{4} + \dfrac{y^2}{13} = 1$

27. Center: $(0, 0)$; Vertex: $(0, 4)$; $b = 1$; Major axis is
    the y-axis; $a = 4$; $b = 1$.

    Write the equation: $\dfrac{x^2}{1} + \dfrac{y^2}{16} = 1$

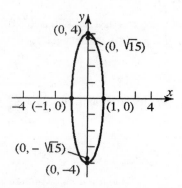

29. $\dfrac{(x+1)^2}{4} + \dfrac{(y-1)^2}{1} = 1$ 31. $\dfrac{(x-1)^2}{1} + \dfrac{y^2}{4} = 1$

33. The equation $\dfrac{(x-3)^2}{4} + \dfrac{(y+1)^2}{9} = 1$ is in the form $\dfrac{(x-h)^2}{b^2} + \dfrac{(y-k)^2}{a^2} = 1$
    (major axis parallel to the y-axis) where $a = 3$, $b = 2$, $h = 3$, and $k = -1$.
    Solving for c:
    $$c^2 = a^2 - b^2 = 9 - 4 = 5 \rightarrow c = \sqrt{5}$$
    Thus, we have:
    Center: $(3, -1)$
    Foci: $\left(3, -1+\sqrt{5}\right),\ \left(3, -1-\sqrt{5}\right)$
    Vertices: $(3, 2), (3, -4)$
    To graph, enter: $y_1 = -1 + 3\sqrt{1 - (x-3)^2 / 4}$;
    $$y_2 = -1 - 3\sqrt{1 - (x-3)^2 / 4}$$

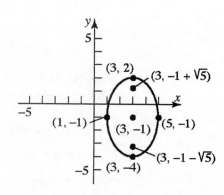

35. Divide by 16 to put the equation in standard form:
$$(x+5)^2 + 4(y-4)^2 = 16$$
$$\frac{(x+5)^2}{16} + \frac{4(y-4)^2}{16} = \frac{16}{16}$$
$$\frac{(x+5)^2}{16} + \frac{(y-4)^2}{4} = 1$$

The equation is in the form $\dfrac{(x-h)^2}{a^2} + \dfrac{(y-k)^2}{b^2} = 1$ (major axis parallel to the x-axis) where $a = 4$, $b = 2$, $h = -5$, and $k = 4$.

Solving for c:
$$c^2 = a^2 - b^2 = 16 - 4 = 12 \rightarrow c = \sqrt{12} = 2\sqrt{3}$$

Thus, we have:

Center: $(-5, 4)$

Foci: $\left(-5 - 2\sqrt{3}, 4\right)$, $\left(-5 + 2\sqrt{3}, 4\right)$

Vertices: $(-9, 4)$, $(-1, 4)$

To graph, enter:
$$y_1 = 4 + 2\sqrt{1 - (x+5)^2/16};$$
$$y_2 = 4 - 2\sqrt{1 - (x+5)^2/16}$$

37. Complete the square to put the equation in standard form:
$$x^2 + 4x + 4y^2 - 8y + 4 = 0$$
$$(x^2 + 4x + 4) + 4(y^2 - 2y + 1) = -4 + 4 + 4$$
$$(x+2)^2 + 4(y-1)^2 = 4$$
$$\frac{(x+2)^2}{4} + \frac{4(y-1)^2}{4} = \frac{4}{4}$$
$$\frac{(x+2)^2}{4} + \frac{(y-1)^2}{1} = 1$$

The equation is in the form $\dfrac{(x-h)^2}{a^2} + \dfrac{(y-k)^2}{b^2} = 1$ (major axis parallel to the x-axis) where $a = 2$, $b = 1$, $h = -2$, and $k = 1$.

Solving for c: $c^2 = a^2 - b^2 = 4 - 1 = 3 \rightarrow c = \sqrt{3}$

Thus, we have:

  Center: (−2, 1)

  Foci: $\left(-2-\sqrt{3},1\right),\ \left(-2+\sqrt{3},1\right)$

  Vertices: (−4, 1), (0, 1)

To graph, enter: $y_1 = 1 + \sqrt{1-(x+2)^2/4}$;

  $y_2 = 1 - \sqrt{1-(x+2)^2/4}$

39. Complete the square to put the equation in standard form:

$$2x^2 + 3y^2 - 8x + 6y + 5 = 0$$

$$2(x^2 - 4x) + 3(y^2 + 2y) = -5$$

$$2(x^2 - 4x + 4) + 3(y^2 + 2y + 1) = -5 + 8 + 3$$

$$2(x-2)^2 + 3(y+1)^2 = 6$$

$$\frac{2(x-2)^2}{6} + \frac{3(y+1)^2}{6} = \frac{6}{6}$$

$$\frac{(x-2)^2}{3} + \frac{(y+1)^2}{2} = 1$$

The equation is in the form $\dfrac{(x-h)^2}{a^2} + \dfrac{(y-k)^2}{b^2} = 1$ (major axis parallel to the x-axis) where

$a = \sqrt{3}$, $b = \sqrt{2}$, $h = 2$, and $k = -1$.

Solving for c: $c^2 = a^2 - b^2 = 3 - 2 = 1\ \rightarrow\ c = 1$

Thus, we have:

  Center: (2, −1)

  Foci: (1, −1), (3, −1)

  Vertices: $\left(2-\sqrt{3},-1\right),\ \left(2+\sqrt{3},-1\right)$

To graph, enter: $y_1 = -1 + \sqrt{2 - 2(x-2)^2/3}$;

  $y_2 = -1 - \sqrt{2 - 2(x-2)^2/3}$

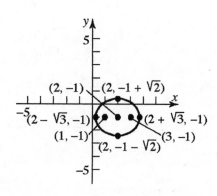

41. Complete the square to put the equation in standard form:

$$9x^2 + 4y^2 - 18x + 16y - 11 = 0$$

$$9(x^2 - 2x) + 4(y^2 + 4y) = 11$$

$$9(x^2 - 2x + 1) + 4(y^2 + 4y + 4) = 11 + 9 + 16$$

$$9(x-1)^2 + 4(y+2)^2 = 36$$

$$\frac{9(x-1)^2}{36} + \frac{4(y+2)^2}{36} = \frac{36}{36}$$

$$\frac{(x-1)^2}{4} + \frac{(y+2)^2}{9} = 1$$

The equation is in the form $\dfrac{(x-h)^2}{b^2} + \dfrac{(y-k)^2}{a^2} = 1$ (major axis parallel to the y-axis) where

$a = 3$, $b = 2$, $h = 1$, and $k = -2$.

Solving for c:

$$c^2 = a^2 - b^2 = 9 - 4 = 5 \rightarrow c = \sqrt{5}$$

Thus, we have:

   Center: $(1,-2)$

   Foci: $\left(1, -2 + \sqrt{5}\right)$, $\left(1, -2 - \sqrt{5}\right)$

   Vertices: $(1, 1)$, $(1, -5)$

To graph, enter: $y_1 = -2 + 3\sqrt{1 - (x-1)^2 / 4}$;

$$y_2 = -2 - 3\sqrt{1 - (x-1)^2 / 4}$$

43. Complete the square to put the equation in standard form:

$$4x^2 + y^2 + 4y = 0$$

$$4x^2 + y^2 + 4y + 4 = 4$$

$$4x^2 + (y+2)^2 = 4$$

$$\frac{4x^2}{4} + \frac{(y+2)^2}{4} = \frac{4}{4}$$

$$\frac{x^2}{1} + \frac{(y+2)^2}{4} = 1$$

The equation is in the form $\dfrac{(x-h)^2}{b^2} + \dfrac{(y-k)^2}{a^2} = 1$ (major axis parallel to the y-axis) where

$a = 2$, $b = 1$, $h = 0$, and $k = -2$.

Solving for c:

$$c^2 = a^2 - b^2 = 4 - 1 = 3 \quad \rightarrow \quad c = \sqrt{3}$$

Thus, we have:

Center: $(0, -2)$

Foci: $\left(0, -2 + \sqrt{3}\right),\ \left(0, -2 - \sqrt{3}\right)$

Vertices: $(0, 0),\ (0, -4)$

To graph, enter: $y_1 = -2 + 2\sqrt{1 - x^2}$;

$y_2 = -2 - 2\sqrt{1 - x^2}$

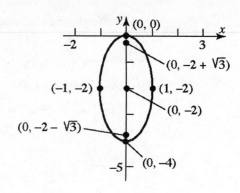

45.   Center: $(2, -2)$; Vertex: $(7, -2)$;
Focus: $(4, -2)$; Major axis parallel
to the x-axis; $a = 5$; $c = 2$.
Find b:

$b^2 = a^2 - c^2 = 25 - 4 = 21$

$b = \sqrt{21}$

Write the equation:

$\dfrac{(x - 2)^2}{25} + \dfrac{(y + 2)^2}{21} = 1$

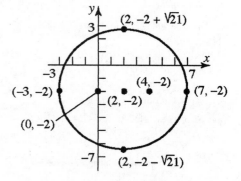

47.   Vertices: $(4, 3),\ (4, 9)$; Focus: $(4, 8)$;
Center: $(4, 6)$; Major axis parallel to the
y-axis; $a = 3$; $c = 2$.
Find b:

$b^2 = a^2 - c^2 = 9 - 4 = 5$

$b = \sqrt{5}$

Write the equation: $\dfrac{(x - 4)^2}{5} + \dfrac{(y - 6)^2}{9} = 1$

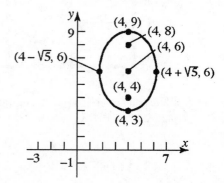

49.   Foci: $(5, 1),\ (-1, 1)$; length of the major axis = 8;
Center: $(2, 1)$; Major axis parallel to the x-axis;
$a = 4$; $c = 3$.   Find b:

$b^2 = a^2 - c^2 = 16 - 9 = 7$

$b = \sqrt{7}$

Write the equation: $\dfrac{(x - 2)^2}{16} + \dfrac{(y - 1)^2}{7} = 1$

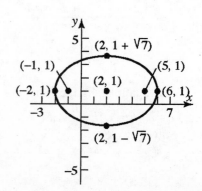

51. Center: $(1, 2)$; Focus: $(4, 2)$; contains the point $(1, 3)$; Major axis parallel to the x-axis; $c = 3$.

The equation has the form:
$$\frac{(x-1)^2}{a^2} + \frac{(y-2)^2}{b^2} = 1$$

Since the point $(1, 3)$ is on the curve:
$$\frac{0}{a^2} + \frac{1}{b^2} = 1$$

$$\frac{1}{b^2} = 1 \rightarrow b^2 = 1 \rightarrow b = 1$$

Find a:
$$a^2 = b^2 + c^2 = 1 + 9 = 10 \rightarrow a = \sqrt{10}$$

Write the equation: $\dfrac{(x-1)^2}{10} + \dfrac{(y-2)^2}{1} = 1$

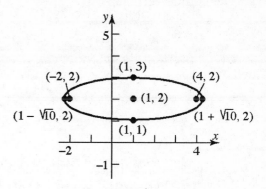

53. Center: $(1, 2)$; Vertex: $(4, 2)$; contains the point $(1, 3)$; Major axis parallel to the x-axis; $a = 3$.

The equation has the form:
$$\frac{(x-1)^2}{a^2} + \frac{(y-2)^2}{b^2} = 1$$

Since the point $(1, 3)$ is on the curve:
$$\frac{0}{9} + \frac{1}{b^2} = 1$$

$$\frac{1}{b^2} = 1 \rightarrow b^2 = 1 \rightarrow b = 1$$

Write the equation: $\dfrac{(x-1)^2}{9} + \dfrac{(y-2)^2}{1} = 1$

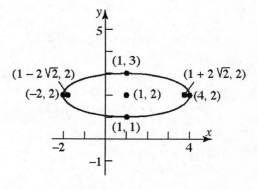

55. Rewrite the equation:
$$y = \sqrt{16 - 4x^2}$$
$$y^2 = 16 - 4x^2, \quad y \geq 0$$
$$4x^2 + y^2 = 16, \quad\quad y \geq 0$$
$$\frac{x^2}{4} + \frac{y^2}{16} = 1, \quad\quad y \geq 0$$

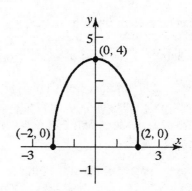

57. Rewrite the equation:

$$y = -\sqrt{64 - 16x^2}$$
$$y^2 = 64 - 16x^2, \quad y \le 0$$
$$16x^2 + y^2 = 64, \quad\quad y \le 0$$
$$\frac{x^2}{4} + \frac{y^2}{64} = 1, \quad\quad y \le 0$$

59. The center of the ellipse is $(0, 0)$. The length of the major axis is 20, so $a = 10$. The length of half the minor axis is 6, so $b = 6$. The ellipse is situated with its major axis on the x-axis. The equation is: $\dfrac{x^2}{100} + \dfrac{y^2}{36} = 1$.

61. Assume that the half ellipse formed by the gallery is centered at $(0, 0)$. Since the hall is 100 feet long, $2a = 100$ or $a = 50$. The distance from the center to the foci is 25 feet, so $c = 25$. Find the height of the gallery which is b:
$$b^2 = a^2 - c^2 = 2500 - 625 = 1875 \;\rightarrow\; b = \sqrt{1875} \approx 43.3$$
The ceiling will be 43.3 feet high in the center.

63. Place the semielliptical arch so that the x-axis coincides with the water and the y-axis passes through the center of the arch. Since the bridge has a span of 120 feet, the length of the major axis is 120, or $2a = 120$ or $a = 60$. The maximum height of the bridge is 25 feet, so $b = 25$. The equation is: $\dfrac{x^2}{3600} + \dfrac{y^2}{625} = 1$.
The height 10 feet from the center:
$$\frac{10^2}{3600} + \frac{y^2}{625} = 1 \rightarrow \frac{y^2}{625} = 1 - \frac{100}{3600} \rightarrow y^2 = 625 \cdot \frac{3500}{3600} \rightarrow y \approx 24.65 \text{ feet}$$
The height 30 feet from the center:
$$\frac{30^2}{3600} + \frac{y^2}{625} = 1 \rightarrow \frac{y^2}{625} = 1 - \frac{900}{3600} \rightarrow y^2 = 625 \cdot \frac{2700}{3600} \rightarrow y \approx 21.65 \text{ feet}$$
The height 50 feet from the center:
$$\frac{50^2}{3600} + \frac{y^2}{625} = 1 \rightarrow \frac{y^2}{625} = 1 - \frac{2500}{3600} \rightarrow y^2 = 625 \cdot \frac{1100}{3600} \rightarrow y \approx 13.82 \text{ feet}$$

65. Place the semielliptical arch so that the x-axis coincides with the major axis and the y-axis passes through the center of the arch. Since the ellipse is 40 feet wide, the length of the major axis is 40, or $2a = 40$ or $a = 20$. The height is 15 feet at the center, so $b = 15$. The equation is: $\dfrac{x^2}{400} + \dfrac{y^2}{225} = 1$.
The height 10 feet either side of the center:
$$\frac{10^2}{400} + \frac{y^2}{225} = 1 \rightarrow \frac{y^2}{225} = 1 - \frac{100}{400} \rightarrow y^2 = 225 \cdot \frac{3}{4} \rightarrow y \approx 12.99 \text{ feet}$$

The height 20 feet either side of the center:
$$\frac{20^2}{400} + \frac{y^2}{225} = 1 \rightarrow \frac{y^2}{225} = 1 - \frac{400}{400} \rightarrow y^2 = 225 \cdot 0 \rightarrow y \approx 0 \text{ feet}$$

67. Since the mean distance is 93 million miles, $a = 93$ million. The length of the major axis is 186 million. The perihelion is 186 million $- 94.5$ million $= 91.5$ million miles. The distance from the center of the ellipse to the sun (focus) is 93 million $- 91.5$ million $= 1.5$ million miles; therefore, $c = 1.5$ million. Find b:

$$b^2 = a^2 - c^2 = \left(93 \times 10^6\right)^2 - \left(1.5 \times 10^6\right)^2 = 8.64675 \times 10^{15} \;\rightarrow\; b = 92.99 \times 10^6$$

The equation of the orbit is: $\dfrac{x^2}{\left(93 \times 10^6\right)^2} + \dfrac{y^2}{\left(92.99 \times 10^6\right)^2} = 1.$

69. The mean distance is 507 million $- 23.2$ million $= 483.8$ million miles.
The perihelion is 483.8 million $- 23.2$ million $= 460.6$ million miles.
Since $a = 483.8 \times 10^6$ and $c = 23.2 \times 10^6$, we can find b:

$$b^2 = a^2 - c^2 = \left(483.8 \times 10^6\right)^2 - \left(23.2 \times 10^6\right)^2 = 2.335242 \times 10^{17} \;\rightarrow\; b = 483.2 \times 10^6$$

The equation of the orbit of Jupiter is: $\dfrac{x^2}{\left(483.8 \times 10^6\right)^2} + \dfrac{y^2}{\left(483.2 \times 10^6\right)^2} = 1.$

71. If the x-axis is placed along the 100 foot length and the y-axis is placed along the 50 foot length, the equation for the ellipse is: $\dfrac{x^2}{50^2} + \dfrac{y^2}{25^2} = 1.$

Find y when x = 40:

$$\frac{40^2}{50^2} + \frac{y^2}{25^2} = 1 \rightarrow \frac{y^2}{625} = 1 - \frac{1600}{2500} \rightarrow y^2 = 625 \cdot \frac{9}{25} \rightarrow y \approx 15 \text{ feet}$$

The width 10 feet from the side is 30 feet.

73. (a)   Put the equation in standard ellipse form:
$$Ax^2 + Cy^2 + F = 0 \qquad A \neq 0, C \neq 0, F \neq 0$$
$$Ax^2 + Cy^2 = -F$$
$$\frac{Ax^2}{-F} + \frac{Cy^2}{-F} = 1$$
$$\frac{x^2}{(-F/A)} + \frac{y^2}{(-F/C)} = 1 \qquad \text{where } -F/A \text{ and } -F/C \text{ are positive}$$

This is the equation of an ellipse with center at $(0, 0)$.

  (b)   If $A = C$, the equation becomes:
$$Ax^2 + Ay^2 = -F \;\rightarrow\; x^2 + y^2 = \frac{-F}{A}$$

This is the equation of a circle with center at $(0, 0)$ and radius of $\sqrt{\dfrac{-F}{A}}$.

75. Answers will vary.

Conics

10.4 The Hyperbola

1.   B   3.   A   5.   B   7.   C

9.   Center: $(0, 0)$; Focus: $(3, 0)$; Vertex: $(1, 0)$;
Transverse axis is the x-axis; $a = 1$; $c = 3$.
Find b:
$$b^2 = c^2 - a^2 = 9 - 1 = 8$$
$$b = \sqrt{8} = 2\sqrt{2}$$
Write the equation: $\dfrac{x^2}{1} - \dfrac{y^2}{8} = 1$

To graph, enter:
$$y_1 = \sqrt{8(x^2 - 1)}\ ;\ y_2 = -\sqrt{8(x^2 - 1)}$$

11.   Center: $(0, 0)$; Focus: $(0, -6)$; Vertex: $(0, 4)$
Transverse axis is the y-axis; $a = 4$; $c = 6$.
Find b:
$$b^2 = c^2 - a^2 = 36 - 16 = 20$$
$$b = \sqrt{20} = 2\sqrt{5}$$
Write the equation: $\dfrac{y^2}{16} - \dfrac{x^2}{20} = 1$

To graph, enter:
$$y_1 = 4\sqrt{1 + x^2 / 20}\ ;\ y_2 = -4\sqrt{1 + x^2 / 20}$$

13. Foci: $(-5, 0), (5, 0)$; Vertex: $(3, 0)$
Center: $(0, 0)$; Transverse axis is the
x-axis; $a = 3$; $c = 5$. Find b:
$$b^2 = c^2 - a^2 = 25 - 9 = 16 \rightarrow b = 4$$

Write the equation: $\dfrac{x^2}{9} - \dfrac{y^2}{16} = 1$

To graph, enter:
$$y_1 = 4\sqrt{x^2/9 - 1}\,;\; y_2 = -4\sqrt{x^2/9 - 1}$$

15. Vertices: $(0, -6), (0, 6)$; Asymptote: $y = 2x$;
Center: $(0, 0)$; Transverse axis is the y-axis;
$a = 6$. Find b using the slope of the
asymptote: $\dfrac{a}{b} = \dfrac{6}{b} = 2 \rightarrow 2b = 6 \rightarrow b = 3$

Write the equation: $\dfrac{y^2}{36} - \dfrac{x^2}{9} = 1$

To graph, enter:
$$y_1 = 6\sqrt{1 + x^2/9}\,;\; y_2 = -6\sqrt{1 + x^2/9}$$

17. Foci: $(-4, 0), (4, 0)$; Asymptote: $y = -x$; Center: $(0, 0)$;
Transverse axis is the x-axis; $c = 4$. Using the slope of the
asymptote: $-\dfrac{b}{a} = -1 \rightarrow -b = -a \rightarrow b = a$

Find b:
$$b^2 = c^2 - a^2 \rightarrow a^2 + b^2 = c^2 \quad (c = 4)$$
$$b^2 + b^2 = 16 \rightarrow 2b^2 = 16 \rightarrow b^2 = 8$$
$$b = \sqrt{8} = 2\sqrt{2}$$
$$a = \sqrt{8} = 2\sqrt{2} \quad (a = b)$$

Write the equation: $\dfrac{x^2}{8} - \dfrac{y^2}{8} = 1$

To graph, enter: $y_1 = \sqrt{x^2 - 8}$; $y_2 = -\sqrt{x^2 - 8}$

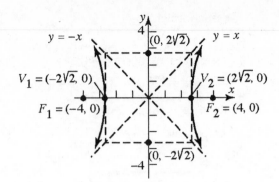

19. $\dfrac{x^2}{25} - \dfrac{y^2}{9} = 1$

The center of the hyperbola is at $(0, 0)$.
$a = 5$, $b = 3$. The vertices are $(5, 0)$ and
$(-5, 0)$. Find the value of c:
$c^2 = a^2 + b^2 = 25 + 9 = 34 \rightarrow c = \sqrt{34}$
The foci are $\left(\sqrt{34}, 0\right)$ and $\left(-\sqrt{34}, 0\right)$.

The transverse axis is $y = 0$.

The asymptotes are $y = \dfrac{3}{5}x$; $y = -\dfrac{3}{5}x$.

To graph, enter:
$y_1 = 3\sqrt{(x^2/25 - 1)}$; $y_2 = -3\sqrt{(x^2/25 - 1)}$

21. $4x^2 - y^2 = 16$

Divide both sides by 16 to put in standard form: $\dfrac{4x^2}{16} - \dfrac{y^2}{16} = \dfrac{16}{16} \rightarrow \dfrac{x^2}{4} - \dfrac{y^2}{16} = 1$

The center of the hyperbola is at $(0, 0)$. $a = 2$, $b = 4$. The vertices are $(2, 0)$ and $(-2, 0)$.
Find the value of c:

$c^2 = a^2 + b^2 = 4 + 16 = 20$

$c = \sqrt{20} = 2\sqrt{5}$

The foci are $\left(2\sqrt{5}, 0\right)$ and $\left(-2\sqrt{5}, 0\right)$.

The transverse axis is $y = 0$.
The asymptotes are $y = 2x$; $y = -2x$.

To graph, enter:

$$y_1 = 4\sqrt{(x^2/4 - 1)}; \quad y_2 = -4\sqrt{(x^2/4 - 1)}$$

23. $y^2 - 9x^2 = 9$

Divide both sides by 9 to put in standard form: $\dfrac{y^2}{9} - \dfrac{9x^2}{9} = \dfrac{9}{9} \rightarrow \dfrac{y^2}{9} - \dfrac{x^2}{1} = 1$

The center of the hyperbola is at $(0, 0)$.
$a = 3, \ b = 1$. The vertices are $(0, 3)$ and
$(0, -3)$. Find the value of c:

$$c^2 = a^2 + b^2 = 9 + 1 = 10$$

$$c = \sqrt{10}$$

The foci are $\left(0, \sqrt{10}\right)$ and $\left(0, -\sqrt{10}\right)$.

The transverse axis is $x = 0$.
The asymptotes are $y = 3x; \ y = -3x$.
To graph, enter:

$$y_1 = \sqrt{(9x^2 + 9)}; \quad y_2 = -\sqrt{(9x^2 + 9)}$$

25. $y^2 - x^2 = 25$

Divide both sides by 25 to put in standard form: $\dfrac{y^2}{25} - \dfrac{x^2}{25} = 1$

The center of the hyperbola is at $(0, 0)$. $a = 5, \ b = 5$. The vertices are $(0, 5)$ and $(0, -5)$.
Find the value of c:

$$c^2 = a^2 + b^2 = 25 + 25 = 50$$

$$c = \sqrt{50} = 5\sqrt{2}$$

The foci are $\left(0, 5\sqrt{2}\right)$ and $\left(0, -5\sqrt{2}\right)$.

The transverse axis is $x = 0$.
The asymptotes are $y = x; \ y = -x$.

To graph, enter:

$$y_1 = \sqrt{(x^2 + 25)}; \quad y_2 = -\sqrt{(x^2 + 25)}$$

27. $x^2 - y^2 = 1$

29. $\dfrac{y^2}{36} - \dfrac{x^2}{9} = 1$

31. Center: $(4, -1)$; Focus: $(7, -1)$;
Vertex: $(6, -1)$; Transverse axis is
parallel to the x-axis; $a = 2$; $c = 3$.
Find b:
$$b^2 = c^2 - a^2 = 9 - 4 = 5 \rightarrow b = \sqrt{5}$$
Write the equation:
$$\frac{(x-4)^2}{4} - \frac{(y+1)^2}{5} = 1$$

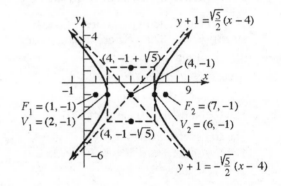

33. Center: $(-3, -4)$;
Focus: $(-3, -8)$;
Vertex: $(-3, -2)$;
Transverse axis is parallel to the
y-axis; $a = 2$; $c = 4$.
Find b:
$$b^2 = c^2 - a^2 = 16 - 4 = 12$$
$$b = \sqrt{12} = 2\sqrt{3}$$
Write the equation:
$$\frac{(y+4)^2}{4} - \frac{(x+3)^2}{12} = 1$$

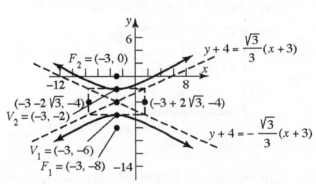

35. Foci: $(3, 7)$, $(7, 7)$; Vertex: $(6, 7)$;
Center: $(5, 7)$; Transverse axis is parallel to
the x-axis; $a = 1$; $c = 2$.
Find b:
$$b^2 = c^2 - a^2 = 4 - 1 = 3$$
$$b = \sqrt{3}$$

Write the equation: $\dfrac{(x-5)^2}{1} - \dfrac{(y-7)^2}{3} = 1$

37. Vertices: $(-1, -1)$, $(3, -1)$;
Center: $(1, -1)$; Transverse
axis is parallel to the x-axis;
$a = 2$.

Asymptote: $\dfrac{x-1}{2} = \dfrac{y+1}{3}$

Using the slope of the
asymptote:
$$\frac{b}{a} = \frac{b}{2} = \frac{3}{2} \rightarrow b = 3$$
Write the equation:
$$\frac{(x-1)^2}{4} - \frac{(y+1)^2}{9} = 1$$

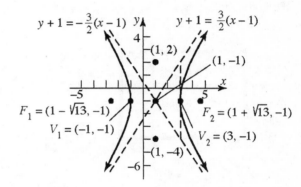

39. $\dfrac{(x-2)^2}{4} - \dfrac{(y+3)^2}{9} = 1$

The center of the hyperbola is at $(2, -3)$. $a = 2$, $b = 3$.
The vertices are $(0, -3)$ and $(4, -3)$. Find the value of c:
$$c^2 = a^2 + b^2 = 4 + 9 = 13 \rightarrow c = \sqrt{13}$$
Foci: $\left(2 - \sqrt{13}, -3\right)$ and $\left(2 + \sqrt{13}, -3\right)$.

Transverse axis: $y = -3$.

Asymptotes : $y + 3 = \dfrac{3}{2}(x - 2)$;

$$y + 3 = -\frac{3}{2}(x - 2)$$

To graph, enter:
$$y_1 = -3 + 3\sqrt{((x-2)^2 / 4 - 1)};$$
$$y_2 = -3 - 3\sqrt{((x-2)^2 / 4 - 1)}$$

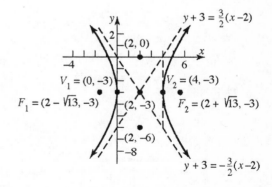

41. $(y-2)^2 - 4(x+2)^2 = 4$

Divide both sides by 4 to put in standard form: $\dfrac{(y-2)^2}{4} - \dfrac{(x+2)^2}{1} = 1$

The center of the hyperbola is at $(-2, 2)$. $a = 2,\ b = 1$.

The vertices are $(-2, 4)$ and $(-2, 0)$. Find the value of c:

$$c^2 = a^2 + b^2 = 4 + 1 = 5 \to c = \sqrt{5}$$

Foci: $\left(-2, 2 - \sqrt{5}\right)$ and $\left(-2, 2 + \sqrt{5}\right)$.

Transverse axis: $x = -2$.

Asymptotes:

$y - 2 = 2(x + 2);\ y - 2 = -2(x + 2)$.

To graph, enter: $y_1 = 2 + 2\sqrt{((x+2)^2 + 1)}$;

$$y_2 = 2 - 2\sqrt{((x+2)^2 + 1)}$$

43. $(x+1)^2 - (y+2)^2 = 4$

Divide both sides by 4 to put in standard form: $\dfrac{(x+1)^2}{4} - \dfrac{(y+2)^2}{4} = 1$

The center of the hyperbola is at $(-1, -2)$. $a = 2,\ b = 2$.

The vertices are $(-3, -2)$ and $(1, -2)$.

Find the value of c:

$$c^2 = a^2 + b^2 = 4 + 4 = 8$$

$$c = \sqrt{8} = 2\sqrt{2}$$

Foci : $\left(-1 - 2\sqrt{2}, -2\right)$

and $\left(-1 + 2\sqrt{2}, -2\right)$.

Transverse axis: $y = -2$.

Asymptotes : $y + 2 = x + 1$;

$$y + 2 = -(x + 1).$$

To graph, enter:

$y_1 = -2 + 2\sqrt{((x+1)^2 / 4 - 1)}$;

$y_2 = -2 - 2\sqrt{((x+1)^2 / 4 - 1)}$

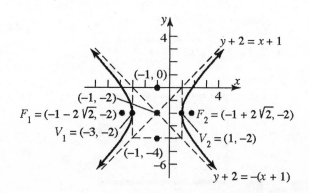

45.   Complete the square to put in standard form:

$$x^2 - y^2 - 2x - 2y - 1 = 0$$

$$(x^2 - 2x + 1) - (y^2 + 2y + 1) = 1 + 1 - 1$$

$$(x - 1)^2 - (y + 1)^2 = 1$$

The center of the hyperbola is at
$(1, -1)$. $a = 1$, $b = 1$.
The vertices are $(0, -1)$ and $(2, -1)$.
Find the value of c:

$$c^2 = a^2 + b^2 = 1 + 1 = 2 \Rightarrow c = \sqrt{2}$$

Foci: $\left(1 - \sqrt{2}, -1\right)$ and $\left(1 + \sqrt{2}, -1\right)$.

Transverse axis: $y = -1$.

Asymptotes:

$$y + 1 = x - 1; \ y + 1 = -(x - 1).$$

To graph, enter:

$$y_1 = -1 + \sqrt{((x - 1)^2 - 1)};$$

$$y_2 = -1 - \sqrt{((x - 1)^2 - 1)}$$

47.   Complete the square to put in standard form:

$$y^2 - 4x^2 - 4y - 8x - 4 = 0$$

$$(y^2 - 4y + 4) - 4(x^2 + 2x + 1) = 4 + 4 - 4$$

$$(y - 2)^2 - 4(x + 1)^2 = 4$$

$$\frac{(y - 2)^2}{4} - \frac{(x + 1)^2}{1} = 1$$

The center of the hyperbola is at $(-1, 2)$. $a = 2$, $b = 1$.
The vertices are $(-1, 4)$ and $(-1, 0)$.
Find the value of c:

$$c^2 = a^2 + b^2 = 4 + 1 = 5 \Rightarrow c = \sqrt{5}$$

Foci: $\left(-1, 2 - \sqrt{5}\right)$ and $\left(-1, 2 + \sqrt{5}\right)$.

Transverse axis: $x = -1$.

Asymptotes: $y - 2 = 2(x + 1); \ y - 2 = -2(x + 1)$

To graph, enter: $y_1 = 2 + 2\sqrt{((x+1)^2 + 1)}$;

$y_2 = 2 - 2\sqrt{((x+1)^2 + 1)}$

49.   Complete the square to put in standard form:

$$4x^2 - y^2 - 24x - 4y + 16 = 0$$

$$4(x^2 - 6x + 9) - (y^2 + 4y + 4) = -16 + 36 - 4$$

$$4(x-3)^2 - (y+2)^2 = 16$$

$$\frac{(x-3)^2}{4} - \frac{(y+2)^2}{16} = 1$$

The center of the hyperbola is at
$(3, -2)$. $a = 2$, $b = 4$.
The vertices are $(1, -2)$
and $(5, -2)$. Find the value of c:

$$c^2 = a^2 + b^2 = 4 + 16 = 20$$

$$c = \sqrt{20} = 2\sqrt{5}$$

Foci:

$\left(3 - 2\sqrt{5}, -2\right)$ and $\left(3 + 2\sqrt{5}, -2\right)$.

Transverse axis: $y = -2$.
Asymptotes: $y + 2 = 2(x - 3)$;

$$y + 2 = -2(x - 3)$$

To graph, enter: $y_1 = -2 + 4\sqrt{((x-3)^2 / 4 - 1)}$;

$$y_2 = -2 - 4\sqrt{((x-3)^2 / 4 - 1)}$$

51.   Complete the square to put in standard form:

$$y^2 - 4x^2 - 16x - 2y - 19 = 0$$

$$(y^2 - 2y + 1) - 4(x^2 + 4x + 4) = 19 + 1 - 16$$

$$(y-1)^2 - 4(x+2)^2 = 4$$

$$\frac{(y-1)^2}{4} - \frac{(x+2)^2}{1} = 1$$

The center of the hyperbola is at $(-2, 1)$. $a = 2$, $b = 1$.

The vertices are $(-2, 3)$ and $(-2, -1)$. Find the value of c:

$$c^2 = a^2 + b^2 = 4 + 1 = 5$$

$$c = \sqrt{5}$$

Foci: $\left(-2, 1 - \sqrt{5}\right)$ and $\left(-2, 1 + \sqrt{5}\right)$.

Transverse axis: $x = -2$.

Asymptotes: $y - 1 = 2(x + 2); y - 1 = -2(x + 2)$.

To graph, enter:

$$y_1 = 1 + 2\sqrt{((x + 2)^2 + 1)};$$

$$y_2 = 1 - 2\sqrt{((x + 2)^2 + 1)}$$

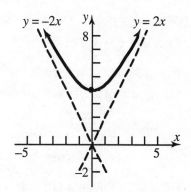

53.   Rewrite the equation:

$$y = \sqrt{16 + 4x^2}$$

$$y^2 = 16 + 4x^2, \quad y \geq 0$$

$$y^2 - 4x^2 = 16, \quad y \geq 0$$

$$\frac{y^2}{16} - \frac{x^2}{4} = 1, \quad y \geq 0$$

55.   Rewrite the equation:

$$y = -\sqrt{-25 + x^2}$$

$$y^2 = -25 + x^2, \quad y \leq 0$$

$$x^2 - y^2 = 25, \quad y \leq 0$$

$$\frac{x^2}{25} - \frac{y^2}{25} = 1, \quad y \leq 0$$

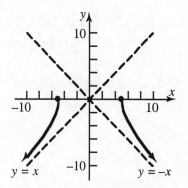

57. (a) Set up a coordinate system so that the
two stations lie on the x-axis and the
origin is midway between them. The
ship lies on a hyperbola whose foci are
the locations of the two stations. Since
the time difference is 0.00038 seconds
and the speed of the signal is 186,000
miles per second, the difference in the
distances of the ships from each station
is: (186,000)(0.00038) $\approx$ 70.68 miles

The difference of the distances from the ship to each station, 70.68, equals $2a$, so
$a = 35.34$ and the vertex of the corresponding hyperbola is at (35.34, 0). Since the
focus is at (100, 0), following this hyperbola, the ship would reach shore 64.66 miles
from the master station.

(b) The ship should follow a hyperbola with a vertex at (80, 0). For this hyperbola,
$a = 80$, so the constant difference of the distances from the ship to each station is
160. The time difference the ship should look for is:

$$\text{time} = \frac{160}{186,000} \approx 0.00086 \text{ seconds}$$

(c) Find the equation of the hyperbola with vertex at (80, 0) and a focus at (100, 0). The

form of the equation of the hyperbola is: $\dfrac{x^2}{a^2} - \dfrac{y^2}{b^2} = 1$ where $a = 80$.

Since $c = 100$ and $b^2 = c^2 - a^2 \rightarrow b^2 = 100^2 - 80^2 = 3600$.

The equation of the hyperbola is: $\dfrac{x^2}{6400} - \dfrac{y^2}{3600} = 1$.

Since the ship is 50 miles off shore, we have $y = 50$. Solve the equation for x:

$$\frac{x^2}{6400} - \frac{50^2}{3600} = 1 \rightarrow \frac{x^2}{6400} = 1 + \frac{2500}{3600} = \frac{61}{36}$$

$$x^2 = 6400 \cdot \frac{61}{36} \Rightarrow x \approx 104 \text{ miles}$$

The ship's location is (104, 50).

59. (a) Set up a rectangular coordinate system so that the two devices lie on the x-axis and the
origin is midway between them. The devices serve as foci to the hyperbola so

$c = \dfrac{2000}{2} = 1000$. Since the explosion occurs 200 feet from point B, the vertex of the

hyperbola is (800, 0); therefore, $a = 800$. Finding b:
$$b^2 = c^2 - a^2 \rightarrow b^2 = 1000^2 - 800^2 = 360000 \rightarrow b = 600$$

The equation of the hyperbola is: $\dfrac{x^2}{800^2} - \dfrac{y^2}{600^2} = 1$

If $x = 1000$, find y:

$$\frac{1000^2}{800^2} - \frac{y^2}{600^2} = 1 \rightarrow \frac{y^2}{600^2} = \frac{1000^2}{800^2} - 1 = \frac{600^2}{800^2}$$

$$y^2 = 600^2 \cdot \frac{600^2}{800^2} \Rightarrow y = 450 \text{ feet}$$

The second detonation should take place 450 feet north of point B.

61.   If the eccentricity is close to 1, then $c \approx a$ and $b \approx 0$. When b is close to 0, the hyperbola is very narrow, because the slopes of the asymptotes are close to 0.
       If the eccentricity is very large, then c is much larger than a and b is very large. The result is a hyperbola that is very wide.

63. $\dfrac{x^2}{4} - y^2 = 1$ $(a = 2, \ b = 1)$

       is a hyperbola with horizontal transverse axis, centered at $(0, 0)$ and

       has asymptotes: $y = \pm\dfrac{1}{2}x$

       $y^2 - \dfrac{x^2}{4} = 1$ $(a = 1, \ b = 2)$

       is a hyperbola with vertical transverse axis, centered at $(0, 0)$ and has

       asymptotes: $y = \pm\dfrac{1}{2}x$

       Since the two hyperbolas have the same asymptotes, they are conjugate.

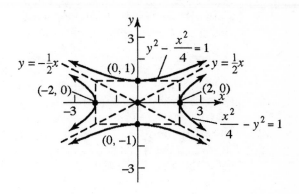

65.   Put the equation in standard hyperbola form:
       $$Ax^2 + Cy^2 + F = 0 \qquad A \neq 0, \ C \neq 0, \ F \neq 0$$

       $$Ax^2 + Cy^2 = -F \rightarrow \dfrac{Ax^2}{-F} + \dfrac{Cy^2}{-F} = 1$$

       $$\dfrac{x^2}{-F/A} + \dfrac{y^2}{-F/C} = 1$$

       Since $-F/A$ and $-F/C$ have opposite signs, this is a hyperbola with center at $(0, 0)$.

Conics

10.5 Systems of Nonlinear Equations

1. $\begin{cases} y = x^2 + 1 \\ y = x + 1 \end{cases}$

   Graph: $y_1 = x^2 + 1; \quad y_2 = x + 1$

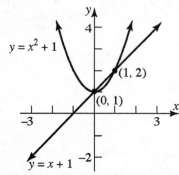

(0, 1) and (1, 2) are the intersection points.

Solve by substitution:
$$x^2 + 1 = x + 1$$
$$x^2 - x = 0$$
$$x(x - 1) = 0$$
$$x = 0 \ \text{ or } \ x = 1$$
$$y = 1 \qquad y = 2$$
Solutions: (0, 1) and (1, 2)

3. $\begin{cases} y = \sqrt{36 - x^2} \\ y = 8 - x \end{cases}$

   Graph: $y_1 = \sqrt{36 - x^2}; \quad y_2 = 8 - x$

(2.59, 5.41) and (5.41, 2.59) are the intersection points.

Solve by substitution:
$$\sqrt{36 - x^2} = 8 - x$$
$$36 - x^2 = 64 - 16x + x^2$$
$$2x^2 - 16x + 28 = 0$$
$$x^2 - 8x + 14 = 0$$
$$x = \frac{8 \pm \sqrt{64 - 56}}{2}$$
$$x = \frac{8 \pm 2\sqrt{2}}{2}$$
$$x = 4 \pm \sqrt{2}$$
If $x = 4 + \sqrt{2}, \ y = 8 - \left(4 + \sqrt{2}\right) = 4 - \sqrt{2}$

If $x = 4 - \sqrt{2}, \ y = 8 - \left(4 - \sqrt{2}\right) = 4 + \sqrt{2}$

Solutions:
$$\left(4 + \sqrt{2}, 4 - \sqrt{2}\right) \text{ and } \left(4 - \sqrt{2}, 4 + \sqrt{2}\right)$$

5. $\begin{cases} y = \sqrt{x} \\ y = 2 - x \end{cases}$

Graph: $y_1 = \sqrt{x}$; $y_2 = 2 - x$

(1, 1) is the intersection point.

Solve by substitution:
$$\sqrt{x} = 2 - x$$
$$x = 4 - 4x + x^2$$
$$x^2 - 5x + 4 = 0$$
$$(x - 4)(x - 1) = 0$$
$$x = 4 \quad \text{or} \quad x = 1$$
$$y = -2 \quad \text{or} \quad y = 1$$
Eliminate (4, –2); it does not check.
Solution: (1, 1)

7. $\begin{cases} x = 2y \\ x = y^2 - 2y \end{cases}$

Solve each equation for y in order to enter it into the graphing utility:
$$y^2 - 2y + 1 = x + 1 \rightarrow (y - 1)^2 = x + 1 \rightarrow y - 1 = \pm\sqrt{x + 1} \rightarrow y = 1 \pm \sqrt{x + 1}$$

Graph: $y_1 = \dfrac{x}{2}$; $y_2 = 1 + \sqrt{x + 1}$; $y_3 = 1 - \sqrt{x + 1}$

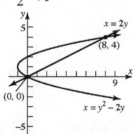

Solve by substitution:
$$2y = y^2 - 2y$$
$$y^2 - 4y = 0$$
$$y(y - 4) = 0$$
$$y = 0 \quad \text{or} \quad y = 4$$
$$x = 0 \quad \text{or} \quad x = 8$$
Solutions: (0, 0) and (8, 4)

(0, 0) and (8, 4) are the intersection points.

9. $\begin{cases} x^2 + y^2 = 4 \\ x^2 + 2x + y^2 = 0 \end{cases}$

Graph: $y_1 = \sqrt{4 - x^2}$; $y_2 = -\sqrt{4 - x^2}$; $y_3 = \sqrt{-x^2 - 2x}$; $y_4 = -\sqrt{-x^2 - 2x}$

Substitute 4 for $x^2 + y^2$ in the second equation:
$$2x + 4 = 0$$
$$2x = -4$$
$$x = -2$$
$$y = \sqrt{4 - (-2)^2} = 0$$
Solution: (–2, 0)

(–2, 0) is the intersection point.   Note: This intersection point is impossible to find on your graphing utility unless you have just the right window and make an excellent guess.

11. $\begin{cases} y = 3x - 5 \\ x^2 + y^2 = 5 \end{cases}$

Graph: $y_1 = 3x - 5$; $y_2 = \sqrt{5 - x^2}$;
$y_3 = -\sqrt{5 - x^2}$

$(1, -2)$ and $(2, 1)$ are the intersection points.

Solve by substitution:
$$x^2 + (3x - 5)^2 = 5$$
$$x^2 + 9x^2 - 30x + 25 = 5$$
$$10x^2 - 30x + 20 = 0$$
$$x^2 - 3x + 2 = 0$$
$$(x - 1)(x - 2) = 0$$
$$x = 1 \qquad \text{or } x = 2$$
$$y = 3(1) - 5 \qquad y = 3(2) - 5$$
$$y = -2 \qquad\quad y = 1$$
Solutions: $(1, -2)$ and $(2, 1)$

13. $\begin{cases} x^2 + y^2 = 4 \\ y^2 - x = 4 \end{cases}$

Graph: $y_1 = \sqrt{4 - x^2}$; $y_2 = -\sqrt{4 - x^2}$; $y_3 = \sqrt{x + 4}$; $y_4 = -\sqrt{x + 4}$

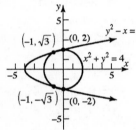

$(-1, 1.73)$, $(-1, -1.73)$, $(0, 2)$, and $(0, -2)$ are the intersection points.

Substitute $x + 4$ for y^2 in the first equation:
$$x^2 + x + 4 = 4$$
$$x^2 + x = 0$$
$$x(x + 1) = 0$$
$$x = 0 \qquad \text{or } x = -1$$
$$y^2 = 4 \qquad\quad y^2 = 3$$
$$y = \pm 2 \qquad\quad y^2 = \pm\sqrt{3}$$
Solutions:
$$(0, -2), (0, 2), \left(-1, \sqrt{3}\right), \left(-1, -\sqrt{3}\right)$$

15. $\begin{cases} xy = 4 \\ x^2 + y^2 = 8 \end{cases}$

Graph: $y_1 = \dfrac{4}{x}$; $y_2 = \sqrt{8 - x^2}$;
$y_3 = -\sqrt{8 - x^2}$

$(-2, -2)$ and $(2, 2)$ are the intersection points.

Solve by substitution:
$$x^2 + \left(\frac{4}{x}\right)^2 = 8$$
$$x^2 + \frac{16}{x^2} = 8$$
$$x^4 + 16 = 8x^2$$
$$x^4 - 8x^2 + 16 = 0$$
$$\left(x^2 - 4\right)^2 = 0$$
$$x^2 - 4 = 0$$
$$x^2 = 4$$
$$x = 2 \text{ or } x = -2$$
$$y = 2 \qquad y = -2$$
Solutions: $(-2, -2)$ and $(2, 2)$

17. $\begin{cases} x^2 + y^2 = 4 \\ \quad y = x^2 - 9 \end{cases}$

Graph: $y_1 = x^2 - 9$; $y_2 = \sqrt{4 - x^2}$;
$$y_3 = -\sqrt{4 - x^2}$$

No solution; Inconsistent.

Solve by substitution:
$$x^2 + (x^2 - 9)^2 = 4$$
$$x^2 + x^4 - 18x^2 + 81 = 4$$
$$x^4 - 17x^2 + 77 = 0$$
$$x^2 = \frac{17 \pm \sqrt{289 - 4(77)}}{2}$$
$$x^2 = \frac{17 \pm \sqrt{-19}}{2}$$

There are no real solutions to this expression; Inconsistent.

19. $\begin{cases} y = x^2 - 4 \\ y = 6x - 13 \end{cases}$

Graph: $y_1 = x^2 - 4$; $y_2 = 6x - 13$

(3,5) is the intersection point.

Solve by substitution:
$$x^2 - 4 = 6x - 13$$
$$x^2 - 6x + 9 = 0$$
$$(x - 3)^2 = 0$$
$$x - 3 = 0$$
$$x = 3$$
$$y = 6(3) - 13 = 5$$

Solutions: $(3,5)$

21. Solve the second equation for y, substitute into the first equation and solve:
$$\begin{cases} 2x^2 + y^2 = 18 \\ \quad xy = 4 \;\rightarrow\; y = \dfrac{4}{x} \end{cases}$$

$$2x^2 + \left(\frac{4}{x}\right)^2 = 18 \rightarrow 2x^2 + \frac{16}{x^2} = 18$$

$$2x^4 + 16 = 18x^2 \rightarrow 2x^4 - 18x^2 + 16 = 0 \rightarrow x^4 - 9x^2 + 8 = 0 \rightarrow \left(x^2 - 8\right)\left(x^2 - 1\right) = 0$$

$$x^2 = 8 \;\rightarrow\; x = \pm\sqrt{8} = \pm 2\sqrt{2}$$
$$\text{or } x^2 = 1 \rightarrow x = \pm 1$$

If $x = 2\sqrt{2}$: $y = \dfrac{4}{2\sqrt{2}} = \sqrt{2}$ If $x = 1$: $y = \dfrac{4}{1} = 4$

If $x = -2\sqrt{2}$: $y = \dfrac{4}{-2\sqrt{2}} = -\sqrt{2}$ If $x = -1$: $y = \dfrac{4}{-1} = -4$

Solutions: $\left(2\sqrt{2},\ \sqrt{2}\right), \left(-2\sqrt{2},\ -\sqrt{2}\right), (1, 4), (-1, -4)$

23. Substitute the first equation into the second equation and solve:

$$\begin{cases} y = 2x+1 \\ 2x^2 + y^2 = 1 \end{cases}$$

$$2x^2 + (2x+1)^2 = 1 \rightarrow 2x^2 + 4x^2 + 4x + 1 = 1 \rightarrow 6x^2 + 4x = 0 \rightarrow 2x(3x+2) = 0$$

$$2x = 0 \rightarrow x = 0$$

$$\text{or} \quad 3x + 2 = 0 \rightarrow x = -\frac{2}{3}$$

If $x = 0$: $\quad y = 2(0) + 1 = 1$

If $x = -\frac{2}{3}$: $\quad y = 2\left(-\frac{2}{3}\right) + 1 = -\frac{4}{3} + 1 = -\frac{1}{3}$

Solutions: $(0,1), \left(-\frac{2}{3}, -\frac{1}{3}\right)$

25. Solve the first equation for y, substitute into the second equation and solve:

$$\begin{cases} x + y + 1 = 0 \rightarrow y = -x - 1 \\ x^2 + y^2 + 6y - x = -5 \end{cases}$$

$$x^2 + (-x-1)^2 + 6(-x-1) - x = -5 \rightarrow x^2 + x^2 + 2x + 1 - 6x - 6 - x = -5$$

$$2x^2 - 5x = 0 \rightarrow x(2x-5) = 0 \rightarrow x = 0 \quad \text{or} \quad x = \frac{5}{2}$$

If $x = 0$: $\quad y = -(0) - 1 = -1$

If $x = \frac{5}{2}$: $\quad y = -\frac{5}{2} - 1 = -\frac{7}{2}$

Solutions: $(0, -1), \left(\frac{5}{2}, -\frac{7}{2}\right)$

27. Solve the second equation for y, substitute into the first equation and solve:

$$\begin{cases} 4x^2 - 3xy + 9y^2 = 15 \\ 2x + 3y = 5 \rightarrow y = -\frac{2}{3}x + \frac{5}{3} \end{cases}$$

$$4x^2 - 3x\left(-\frac{2}{3}x + \frac{5}{3}\right) + 9\left(-\frac{2}{3}x + \frac{5}{3}\right)^2 = 15 \rightarrow 4x^2 + 2x^2 - 5x + 4x^2 - 20x + 25 = 15$$

$$10x^2 - 25x + 10 = 0 \rightarrow 2x^2 - 5x + 2 = 0$$

$$(2x - 1)(x - 2) = 0 \rightarrow x = \frac{1}{2} \quad \text{or} \quad x = 2$$

If $x = \frac{1}{2}$: $\quad y = -\frac{2}{3}\left(\frac{1}{2}\right) + \frac{5}{3} = \frac{4}{3}$

If $x = 2$: $\quad y = -\frac{2}{3}(2) + \frac{5}{3} = \frac{1}{3}$

Solutions: $\left(\frac{1}{2}, \frac{4}{3}\right), \left(2, \frac{1}{3}\right)$

29. Multiply each side of the second equation by 4 and add the equations to eliminate y:

$$\begin{cases} x^2 - 4y^2 = -7 \longrightarrow \quad x^2 - 4y^2 = -7 \\ 3x^2 + y^2 = 31 \xrightarrow{\ 4\ } 12x^2 + 4y^2 = 124 \end{cases}$$

$$13x^2 \qquad = 117 \to x^2 = 9 \to x = \pm 3$$

If $x = 3$: $\quad 3(3)^2 + y^2 = 31 \ \to \ y^2 = 4 \ \to \ y = \pm 2$

If $x = -3$: $\quad 3(-3)^2 + y^2 = 31 \ \to \ y^2 = 4 \ \to \ y = \pm 2$

Solutions: $(3, 2), (3, -2), (-3, 2), (-3, -2)$

31. Multiply each side of the first equation by 5 and each side of the second equation by 3 to eliminate y:

$$\begin{cases} 7x^2 - 3y^2 + 5 = 0 \to 7x^2 - 3y^2 = -5 \xrightarrow{\ 5\ } 35x^2 - 15y^2 = -25 \\ 3x^2 + 5y^2 = 12 \to \quad 3x^2 + 5y^2 = 12 \xrightarrow{\ 3\ } \quad 9x^2 + 15y^2 = \ \ 36 \end{cases}$$

$$44x^2 \qquad = \ 11 \to x^2 = \frac{1}{4} \to x = \pm\frac{1}{2}$$

If $x = \frac{1}{2}$: $\quad 3\left(\frac{1}{2}\right)^2 + 5y^2 = 12 \ \to \ 5y^2 = \frac{45}{4} \ \to \ y^2 = \frac{9}{4} \ \to \ y = \pm\frac{3}{2}$

If $x = -\frac{1}{2}$: $\quad 3\left(-\frac{1}{2}\right)^2 + 5y^2 = 12 \ \to \ 5y^2 = \frac{45}{4} \ \to \ y^2 = \frac{9}{4} \ \to \ y = \pm\frac{3}{2}$

Solutions: $\left(\frac{1}{2}, \frac{3}{2}\right)\left(\frac{1}{2}, -\frac{3}{2}\right)\left(-\frac{1}{2}, \frac{3}{2}\right)\left(-\frac{1}{2}, -\frac{3}{2}\right)$

33. Multiply each side of the second equation by 2 and add to eliminate xy:

$$\begin{cases} x^2 + 2xy = 10 \longrightarrow \quad x^2 + 2xy = 10 \\ 3x^2 - xy = \ 2 \xrightarrow{\ 2\ } 6x^2 - 2xy = 4 \end{cases}$$

$$7x^2 \qquad = 14 \to x^2 = 2 \to x = \pm\sqrt{2}$$

If $x = \sqrt{2}$: $\quad 3\left(\sqrt{2}\right)^2 - \sqrt{2} \cdot y = 2 \ \to \ -\sqrt{2} \cdot y = -4 \ \to \ y = \frac{4}{\sqrt{2}} \ \to \ y = 2\sqrt{2}$

If $x = -\sqrt{2}$: $\quad 3\left(-\sqrt{2}\right)^2 - \left(-\sqrt{2}\right)y = 2 \ \to \ \sqrt{2} \cdot y = -4 \ \to \ y = \frac{-4}{\sqrt{2}} \ \to \ y = -2\sqrt{2}$

Solutions: $\left(\sqrt{2}, 2\sqrt{2}\right), \left(-\sqrt{2}, -2\sqrt{2}\right)$

35. Multiply each side of the first equation by 2 and add the equations to eliminate y:

$$\begin{cases} 2x^2 + y^2 = \ 2 \to 2x^2 + y^2 = \ 2 \xrightarrow{\ 2\ } 4x^2 + 2y^2 = \ 4 \\ x^2 - 2y^2 + 8 = 0 \to x^2 - 2y^2 = -8 \longrightarrow \quad x^2 - 2y^2 = -8 \end{cases}$$

$$5x^2 \qquad = -4 \to x^2 = -\frac{4}{5}$$

No solution. The system is inconsistent.

37. Multiply each side of the second equation by 2 and add the equations to eliminate y:

$$\begin{cases} x^2 + 2y^2 = 16 \longrightarrow x^2 + 2y^2 = 16 \\ 4x^2 - y^2 = 24 \xrightarrow{\ 2\ } 8x^2 - 2y^2 = 48 \end{cases}$$

$$9x^2 \qquad = 64 \to x^2 = \frac{64}{9} \ \to \ x = \pm\frac{8}{3}$$

If $x = \frac{8}{3}$: $\quad \left(\frac{8}{3}\right)^2 + 2y^2 = 16 \ \to \ 2y^2 = \frac{80}{9} \ \to \ y^2 = \frac{40}{9} \ \to \ y = \pm\frac{2\sqrt{10}}{3}$

If $x = -\frac{8}{3}$: $\quad \left(-\frac{8}{3}\right)^2 + 2y^2 = 16 \ \to \ 2y^2 = \frac{80}{9} \ \to \ y^2 = \frac{40}{9} \ \to \ y = \pm\frac{2\sqrt{10}}{3}$

Solutions: $\left(\frac{8}{3}, \frac{2\sqrt{10}}{3}\right), \left(\frac{8}{3}, \frac{-2\sqrt{10}}{3}\right), \left(-\frac{8}{3}, \frac{2\sqrt{10}}{3}\right), \left(-\frac{8}{3}, \frac{-2\sqrt{10}}{3}\right)$

39. Multiply each side of the second equation by 2 and add the equations to eliminate y:

$$\begin{cases} \dfrac{5}{x^2} - \dfrac{2}{y^2} + 3 = 0 \to \dfrac{5}{x^2} - \dfrac{2}{y^2} = -3 \longrightarrow \dfrac{5}{x^2} - \dfrac{2}{y^2} = -3 \\ \dfrac{3}{x^2} + \dfrac{1}{y^2} = 7 \ \to \dfrac{3}{x^2} + \dfrac{1}{y^2} = 7 \xrightarrow{\ 2\ } \dfrac{6}{x^2} + \dfrac{2}{y^2} = 14 \end{cases}$$

$$\frac{11}{x^2} \qquad = 11 \to 11 = 11x^2 \to x^2 = 1 \to x = \pm 1$$

If $x = 1$: $\qquad \dfrac{3}{(1)^2} + \dfrac{1}{y^2} = 7 \ \to \ \dfrac{1}{y^2} = 4 \ \to \ y^2 = \dfrac{1}{4} \ \to \ y = \pm\dfrac{1}{2}$

If $x = -1$: $\qquad \dfrac{3}{(-1)^2} + \dfrac{1}{y^2} = 7 \ \to \ \dfrac{1}{y^2} = 4 \ \to \ y^2 = \dfrac{1}{4} \ \to \ y = \pm\dfrac{1}{2}$

Solutions: $\left(1, \dfrac{1}{2}\right), \left(1, -\dfrac{1}{2}\right), \left(-1, \dfrac{1}{2}\right), \left(-1, -\dfrac{1}{2}\right)$

41. Multiply each side of the first equation by –2 and add the equations to eliminate x:

$$\begin{cases} \dfrac{1}{x^4} + \dfrac{6}{y^4} = 6 \xrightarrow{\ -2\ } \dfrac{-2}{x^4} - \dfrac{12}{y^4} = -12 \\ \dfrac{2}{x^4} - \dfrac{2}{y^4} = 19 \longrightarrow \dfrac{2}{x^4} - \dfrac{2}{y^4} = 19 \end{cases}$$

$$\frac{-14}{y^4} \qquad = 7 \to -14 = 7y^4 \to y^4 = -2$$

There are no real solutions. The system is inconsistent.

43. Factor the first equation, solve for x, substitute into the second equation and solve:

$$\begin{cases} x^2 - 3xy + 2y^2 = 0 \ \to \ (x - 2y)(x - y) = 0 \ \to \ x = 2y \ \text{or} \ x = y \\ x^2 + xy = 6 \end{cases}$$

Substitute $x = 2y$ and solve:

$$x^2 + xy = 6$$
$$(2y)^2 + (2y)y = 6$$
$$4y^2 + 2y^2 = 6 \rightarrow 6y^2 = 6$$
$$y^2 = 1 \rightarrow y = \pm 1$$

If $y = 1$: $\quad x = 2 \cdot 1 = 2$
If $y = -1$: $\quad x = 2(-1) = -2$

Solutions: $(2, 1), (-2, -1), \left(\sqrt{3}, \sqrt{3}\right), \left(-\sqrt{3}, -\sqrt{3}\right)$

Substitute $x = y$ and solve:

$$x^2 + xy = 6$$
$$y^2 + y \cdot y = 6$$
$$y^2 + y^2 = 6 \rightarrow 2y^2 = 6$$
$$y^2 = 3 \rightarrow y = \pm\sqrt{3}$$

If $y = \sqrt{3}$: $\quad x = \sqrt{3}$
If $y = -\sqrt{3}$: $\quad x = -\sqrt{3}$

45. Multiply each side of the second equation by $-y$ and add the equations to eliminate y:

$$\begin{cases} y^2 + y + x^2 - x - 2 = 0 \longrightarrow \quad y^2 + y + x^2 - x - 2 = 0 \\ y + 1 + \dfrac{x-2}{y} = 0 \xrightarrow{-y} \quad \underline{-y^2 - y \qquad - x + 2 = 0} \end{cases}$$

$$x^2 - 2x \quad = 0 \rightarrow x(x - 2) = 0$$
$$x = 0 \text{ or } x = 2$$

If $x = 0$: $\quad y^2 + y + 0^2 - 0 - 2 = 0 \rightarrow y^2 + y - 2 = 0 \rightarrow (y + 2)(y - 1) = 0$
$$\rightarrow y = -2 \text{ or } y = 1$$

If $x = 2$: $\quad y^2 + y + 2^2 - 2 - 2 = 0 \rightarrow y^2 + y = 0 \rightarrow y(y + 1) = 0$
$$\rightarrow y = 0 \text{ or } y = -1 \quad \text{Note}: y \neq 0 \text{ because of division by zero.}$$

Solutions: $(0, -2), (0, 1), (2, -1)$

47. Rewrite each equation in exponential form:

$$\begin{cases} \log_x y = 3 \rightarrow y = x^3 \\ \log_x(4y) = 5 \rightarrow 4y = x^5 \end{cases}$$

Substitute the first equation into the second and solve:

$$4x^3 = x^5$$

$$x^5 - 4x^3 = 0 \rightarrow x^3(x^2 - 4) = 0 \rightarrow x^3 = 0 \text{ or } x^2 = 4 \rightarrow x = 0 \text{ or } x = \pm 2$$

The base of a logarithm must be positive, thus $x \neq 0$ and $x \neq -2$.

If $x = 2$: $\quad y = 2^3 = 8$

Solution: $(2, 8)$

49. Rewrite each equation in exponential form:

$$\begin{cases} \ln x = 4\ln y \rightarrow x = e^{4\ln y} = e^{\ln y^4} = y^4 \\ \log_3 x = 2 + 2\log_3 y \rightarrow x = 3^{2 + 2\log_3 y} = 3^2 \cdot 3^{2\log_3 y} = 3^2 \cdot 3^{\log_3 y^2} = 9y^2 \end{cases}$$

So we have the system

$$\begin{cases} x = y^4 \\ x = 9y^2 \end{cases}$$

Therefore we have

$$9y^2 = y^4 \Rightarrow 9y^2 - y^4 = 0 \Rightarrow y^2(9 - y^2) = 0$$

$$y^2(3+y)(3-y)=0 \Rightarrow y=0 \text{ or } y=-3 \text{ or } y=3$$

Since $\ln y$ is undefined when $y \le 0$, the only solution is $y=3$.

If $y=3$:　　$x=y^4 \Rightarrow x=3^4=81$

Solution: $(81,3)$

51.　Solve the first equation for x, substitute into the second equation and solve:

$$\begin{cases} x+2y=0 \to x=-2y \\ (x-1)^2+(y-1)^2=5 \end{cases}$$

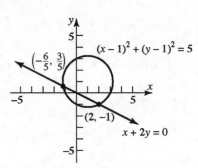

$$(-2y-1)^2+(y-1)^2=5$$

$$4y^2+4y+1+y^2-2y+1=5 \to 5y^2+2y-3=0$$

$$(5y-3)(y+1)=0$$

$$y=\frac{3}{5}=0.6 \text{ or } y=-1$$

$$x=-\frac{6}{5}=-1.2 \text{ or } x=2$$

The points of intersection are $(-1.2, 0.6), (2,-1)$.

53.　Complete the square on the second equation, substitute into the first equation and solve:

$$\begin{cases} (x-1)^2+(y+2)^2=4 \\ y^2+4y-x+1=0 \to y^2+4y+4=x-1+4 \to (y+2)^2=x+3 \end{cases}$$

$$(x-1)^2+x+3=4$$

$$x^2-2x+1+x+3=4$$

$$x^2-x=0$$

$$x(x-1)=0$$

$$x=0 \text{ or } x=1$$

If $x=0$: $(y+2)^2=0+3$

$$y+2=\pm\sqrt{3} \to y=-2\pm\sqrt{3}$$

If $x=1$: $(y+2)^2=1+3$

$$y+2=\pm2 \to y=-2\pm2$$

The points of intersection are:

$$\left(0,-2-\sqrt{3}\right), \left(0,-2+\sqrt{3}\right), (1,-4), (1,0).$$

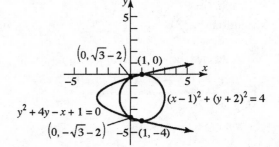

55. Solve the first equation for x, substitute into the second equation and solve:

$$\begin{cases} y = \dfrac{4}{x-3} \;\rightarrow\; x-3 = \dfrac{4}{y} \;\rightarrow\; x = \dfrac{4}{y}+3 \\ x^2 - 6x + y^2 + 1 = 0 \end{cases}$$

$$\left(\frac{4}{y}+3\right)^2 - 6\left(\frac{4}{y}+3\right) + y^2 + 1 = 0$$

$$\frac{16}{y^2} + \frac{24}{y} + 9 - \frac{24}{y} - 18 + y^2 + 1 = 0$$

$$\frac{16}{y^2} + y^2 - 8 = 0 \Rightarrow 16 + y^4 - 8y^2 = 0$$

$$y^4 - 8y^2 + 16 = 0 \Rightarrow (y^2 - 4)^2 = 0$$

$$y^2 - 4 = 0 \Rightarrow y^2 = 4 \Rightarrow y = \pm 2$$

If $y = 2$: $x = \dfrac{4}{2} + 3 = 5$

If $y = -2$: $x = \dfrac{4}{-2} + 3 = 1$

The points of intersection are: (1, –2), (5, 2).

57. Graph: $y_1 = x \wedge (2/3); \quad y_2 = e \wedge (-x)$
Use INTERSECT to solve:

Solution: (0.48, 0.62)

59. Graph: $y_1 = \sqrt[3]{(2 - x^2)}; \quad y_2 = 4/x^3$
Use INTERSECT to solve:

Solution: (–1.65, –0.89)

61. Graph:

$$y_1 = \sqrt[4]{(12 - x^4)}; \quad y_2 = -\sqrt[4]{(12 - x^4)};$$

$$y_3 = \sqrt{2/x}; \quad y_4 = -\sqrt{2/x}$$

Use INTERSECT to solve:

Solutions: (0.58, 1.86), (1.81, 1.05),
(1.81, –1.05), (0.58, –1.86)

63. Graph: $y_1 = 2/x; \quad y_2 = \ln x$
Use INTERSECT to solve:

Solution: (2.35, 0.85)

65. Let x and y be the two numbers. The system of equations is:
$$\begin{cases} x - y = 2 \\ x^2 + y^2 = 10 \end{cases}$$
Solve the first equation for x, substitute into the second equation and solve:
$$(y + 2)^2 + y^2 = 10 \rightarrow y^2 + 4y + 4 + y^2 = 10$$
$$2y^2 + 4y - 6 = 0 \rightarrow y^2 + 2y - 3 = 0 \rightarrow (y + 3)(y - 1) = 0 \rightarrow y = -3 \text{ or } y = 1$$
If $y = -3$: $x = -3 + 2 = -1$
If $y = 1$: $x = 1 + 2 = 3$
The two numbers are 1 and 3 or –1 and –3.

67. Let x and y be the two numbers. The system of equations is:
$$\begin{cases} xy = 4 \\ x^2 + y^2 = 8 \end{cases}$$
Solve the first equation for x, substitute into the second equation and solve:
$$\left(\frac{4}{y}\right)^2 + y^2 = 8 \rightarrow \frac{16}{y^2} + y^2 = 8 \rightarrow 16 + y^4 = 8y^2$$
$$y^4 - 8y^2 + 16 = 0 \rightarrow (y^2 - 4)^2 = 0 \rightarrow y^2 - 4 = 0 \rightarrow y^2 = 4 \rightarrow y = \pm 2$$
If $y = 2$: $x = \frac{4}{2} = 2$
If $y = -2$: $x = \frac{4}{-2} = -2$
The two numbers are 2 and 2 or –2 and –2.

69. Let x and y be the two numbers. The system of equations is:
$$\begin{cases} x - y = xy \\ \dfrac{1}{x} + \dfrac{1}{y} = 5 \end{cases}$$
Solve the first equation for x, substitute into the second equation and solve:
$$x - xy = y \rightarrow x(1 - y) = y \rightarrow x = \frac{y}{1 - y}$$
$$\frac{1}{\left(\dfrac{y}{1-y}\right)} + \frac{1}{y} = 5 \rightarrow \frac{1 - y}{y} + \frac{1}{y} = 5 \rightarrow \frac{2 - y}{y} = 5 \rightarrow 2 - y = 5y \rightarrow 6y = 2 \rightarrow y = \frac{1}{3}$$
If $y = \dfrac{1}{3}$: $x = \dfrac{\left(\dfrac{1}{3}\right)}{\left(1 - \dfrac{1}{3}\right)} = \dfrac{\left(\dfrac{1}{3}\right)}{\left(\dfrac{2}{3}\right)} = \dfrac{1}{2}$ $\therefore$ The two numbers are $\dfrac{1}{2}$ and $\dfrac{1}{3}$.

71. $$\begin{cases} \dfrac{a}{b} = \dfrac{2}{3} \\ a + b = 10 \end{cases}$$
Solve the second equation for a, substitute into the first equation and solve:
$$\frac{10 - b}{b} = \frac{2}{3} \Rightarrow 3(10 - b) = 2b$$

$$\Rightarrow 30 - 3b = 2b \Rightarrow 30 = 5b \Rightarrow b = 6 \Rightarrow a = 4$$

$a + b = 10; \quad b - a = 2 \quad \therefore$ The ratio of $a + b$ to $b - a$ is $\dfrac{10}{2} = 5.$

73. Let $x =$ the width of the rectangle.
     Let $y =$ the length of the rectangle.
$$\begin{cases} 2x + 2y = 16 \\ \quad xy = 15 \end{cases}$$
     Solve the first equation for y, substitute into the second equation and solve:
$$2x + 2y = 16 \rightarrow 2y = 16 - 2x \rightarrow y = 8 - x$$
$$x(8 - x) = 15 \rightarrow 8x - x^2 = 15 \rightarrow x^2 - 8x + 15 = 0 \rightarrow (x - 5)(x - 3) = 0$$
$$x = 5 \text{ or } x = 3$$
$$y = 3 \qquad y = 5$$
     The dimensions of the rectangle are 3 inches by 5 inches.

75. Let $x =$ the radius of the first circle.
     Let $y =$ the radius of the second circle.
$$\begin{cases} 2\pi x + 2\pi y = 12\pi \\ \pi x^2 + \pi y^2 = 20\pi \end{cases}$$
     Solve the first equation for y, substitute into the second equation and solve:

$$2\pi x + 2\pi y = 12\pi$$
$$x + y = 6$$
$$y = 6 - x$$

$$\pi x^2 + \pi y^2 = 20\pi$$
$$x^2 + y^2 = 20$$
$$x^2 + (6 - x)^2 = 20$$
$$x^2 + 36 - 12x + x^2 = 20$$
$$2x^2 - 12x + 16 = 0$$
$$x^2 - 6x + 8 = 0$$
$$(x - 4)(x - 2) = 0$$
$$x = 4 \text{ or } x = 2$$
$$y = 2 \qquad y = 4$$

     The radii of the circles are 2 centimeters and 4 centimeters.

77. The tortoise takes $9 + 3 = 12$ minutes or 0.2 hour longer to complete the race than the hare.
     Let $r =$ the rate of the hare.
     Let $t =$ the time for the hare to complete the race.
     Then $t + 0.2 =$ the time for the tortoise and $r - 0.5 =$ the rate for the tortoise.
     Since the length of the race is 21 meters, the distance equations are:
$$\begin{cases} rt = 21 \\ (r - 0.5)(t + 0.2) = 21 \end{cases}$$
     Solve the first equation for r, substitute into the second equation and solve:
$$\left(\frac{21}{t} - 0.5 \right)(t + 0.2) = 21 \rightarrow 21 + \frac{4.2}{t} - 0.5t - 0.1 = 21$$

$$10t \cdot \left(21 + \frac{4.2}{t} - 0.5t - 0.1 \right) = 10t \cdot (21)$$

$$210t + 42 - 5t^2 - t = 210t \rightarrow 5t^2 + t - 42 = 0 \rightarrow (5t - 14)(t + 3) = 0$$

$$t = \frac{14}{5} = 2.8 \text{ or } t = -3$$

$t = -3$ makes no sense, since time cannot be negative.

Solve for r: $r = \frac{21}{2.8} = 7.5$. The average speed of the hare is 7.5 meters per hour, and the average speed for the tortoise is 7 meters per hour.

79. Let x = the width of the cardboard. Let y = the length of the cardboard.
    The width of the box will be $x - 4$, the length of the box will be $y - 4$, and the height is 2.
    The volume is $V = (x - 4)(y - 4)(2)$.
    Solve the system of equations:
    $$\begin{cases} xy = 216 \\ 2(x - 4)(y - 4) = 224 \end{cases}$$
    Solve the first equation for y, substitute into the second equation and solve:
    $$(2x - 8)\left(\frac{216}{x} - 4\right) = 224 \rightarrow 432 - 8x - \frac{1728}{x} + 32 = 224$$

    $$432x - 8x^2 - 1728 + 32x = 224x \rightarrow -8x^2 + 240x - 1728 = 0$$

    $$x^2 - 30x + 216 = 0 \rightarrow (x - 12)(x - 18) = 0$$

    $$x = 12 \text{ or } x = 18$$

    $$y = 18 \qquad y = 12$$

    The cardboard should be 12 centimeters by 18 centimeters.

81. Find equations relating area and perimeter:
    $$\begin{cases} x^2 + y^2 = 4500 \\ 3x + 3y + (x - y) = 300 \end{cases}$$
    Solve the second equation for y, substitute into the first equation and solve:

$4x + 2y = 300$	$x^2 + (150 - 2x)^2 = 4500$
$2y = 300 - 4x$	$x^2 + 22500 - 600x + 4x^2 = 4500$
$y = 150 - 2x$	$5x^2 - 600x + 18000 = 0$
	$x^2 - 120x + 3600 = 0$
	$(x - 60)^2 = 0$
	$x - 60 = 0$
	$x = 60$
	$y = 150 - 2(60) = 30$

    The sides of the squares are 30 feet and 60 feet.

83. Solve the system for l and w:
    $$\begin{cases} 2l + 2w = P \\ lw = A \end{cases}$$
    Solve the first equation for l, substitute into the second equation and solve:
    $$2l = P - 2w \rightarrow l = \frac{P}{2} - w$$

$$\left(\frac{P}{2} - w\right)w = A \Rightarrow \frac{P}{2}w - w^2 = A \Rightarrow w^2 - \frac{P}{2}w + A = 0$$

$$w = \frac{\left(\frac{P}{2} \pm \sqrt{\frac{P^2}{4} - 4A}\right)}{2} = \frac{\left(\frac{P}{2} \pm \sqrt{\frac{P^2 - 16A}{4}}\right)}{2} = \frac{\left(\frac{P}{2} \pm \frac{\sqrt{P^2 - 16A}}{2}\right)}{2}$$

$$w = \frac{P \pm \sqrt{P^2 - 16A}}{4}$$

If $w = \dfrac{P + \sqrt{P^2 - 16A}}{4}$ then $l = \dfrac{P}{2} - \dfrac{P + \sqrt{P^2 - 16A}}{4} = \dfrac{P - \sqrt{P^2 - 16A}}{4}$

If $w = \dfrac{P - \sqrt{P^2 - 16A}}{4}$ then $l = \dfrac{P}{2} - \dfrac{P - \sqrt{P^2 - 16A}}{4} = \dfrac{P + \sqrt{P^2 - 16A}}{4}$

If it is required that length be greater than width, then the solution is:

$$w = \frac{P - \sqrt{P^2 - 16A}}{4} \text{ and } l = \frac{P + \sqrt{P^2 - 16A}}{4}$$

85. Solve the equation:
$$m^2 - 4(2m - 4) = 0 \rightarrow m^2 - 8m + 16 = 0 \rightarrow (m - 4)^2 = 0 \rightarrow m - 4 = 0 \rightarrow m = 4$$
Use the point-slope equation with slope 4 and the point $(2, 4)$ to obtain the equation of the tangent line: $y - 4 = 4(x - 2) \rightarrow y - 4 = 4x - 8 \rightarrow y = 4x - 4$

87. Solve the system:
$$\begin{cases} y = x^2 + 2 \\ y = mx + b \end{cases}$$
Solve the system by substitution:
$$x^2 + 2 = mx + b \rightarrow x^2 - mx + 2 - b = 0$$
Note that the tangent line passes through $(1, 3)$.
Find the relation between m and b: $3 = m(1) + b \rightarrow b = 3 - m$
Substitute into the quadratic to eliminate b: $x^2 - mx + 2 - (3 - m) = 0 \rightarrow x^2 - mx + (m - 1) = 0$
Find when the discriminant is 0:
$$(-m)^2 - 4(1)(m - 1) = 0 \rightarrow m^2 - 4m + 4 = 0 \rightarrow (m - 2)^2 = 0$$
$$m - 2 = 0 \rightarrow m = 2 \quad \rightarrow \quad b = 3 - 2 = 1$$
The equation of the tangent line is $y = 2x + 1$.

89. Solve the system:
$$\begin{cases} 2x^2 + 3y^2 = 14 \\ \qquad y = mx + b \end{cases}$$
Solve the system by substitution:
$$2x^2 + 3(mx + b)^2 = 14 \Rightarrow 2x^2 + 3m^2x^2 + 6mbx + 3b^2 = 14$$
$$(3m^2 + 2)x^2 + 6mbx + 3b^2 - 14 = 0$$
Note that the tangent line passes through $(1, 2)$. Find the relation between m and b:
$$2 = m(1) + b \Rightarrow b = 2 - m$$

Substitute into the quadratic to eliminate b:
$$(3m^2 + 2)x^2 + 6m(2 - m)x + 3(2 - m)^2 - 14 = 0$$
$$(3m^2 + 2)x^2 + (12m - 6m^2)x + 12 - 12m + 3m^2 - 14 = 0$$
$$(3m^2 + 2)x^2 + (12m - 6m^2)x + (3m^2 - 12m - 2) = 0$$
Find when the discriminant is 0:
$$(12m - 6m^2)^2 - 4(3m^2 + 2)(3m^2 - 12m - 2) = 0$$
$$144m^2 - 144m^3 + 36m^4 - 4(9m^4 - 36m^3 - 24m - 4) = 0$$
$$144m^2 - 144m^3 + 36m^4 - 36m^4 + 144m^3 + 96m + 16 = 0$$
$$144m^2 + 96m + 16 = 0$$
$$9m^2 + 6m + 1 = 0$$
$$(3m + 1)^2 = 0$$
$$3m + 1 = 0$$
$$m = -\frac{1}{3} \qquad b = 2 - \left(-\frac{1}{3}\right) = \frac{7}{3}$$

The equation of the tangent line is $y = -\frac{1}{3}x + \frac{7}{3}$.

91. Solve the system:
$$\begin{cases} x^2 - y^2 = 3 \\ \quad y = mx + b \end{cases}$$
Solve the system by substitution:
$$x^2 - (mx + b)^2 = 3$$
$$x^2 - m^2x^2 - 2mbx - b^2 = 3$$
$$(1 - m^2)x^2 - 2mbx - b^2 - 3 = 0$$
Note that the tangent line passes through (2, 1). Find the relation between m and b:
$$1 = m(2) + b \Rightarrow b = 1 - 2m$$
Substitute into the quadratic to eliminate b:
$$(1 - m^2)x^2 - 2m(1 - 2m)x - (1 - 2m)^2 - 3 = 0$$
$$(1 - m^2)x^2 + (-2m + 4m^2)x - 1 + 4m - 4m^2 - 3 = 0$$
$$(1 - m^2)x^2 + (-2m + 4m^2)x + (-4m^2 + 4m - 4) = 0$$
Find when the discriminant is 0:
$$(-2m + 4m^2)^2 - 4(1 - m^2)(-4m^2 + 4m - 4) = 0$$
$$4m^2 - 16m^3 + 16m^4 - 4(4m^4 - 4m^3 + 4m - 4) = 0$$
$$4m^2 - 16m^3 + 16m^4 - 16m^4 + 16m^3 - 16m + 16 = 0$$
$$4m^2 - 16m + 16 = 0$$
$$m^2 - 4m + 4 = 0$$
$$(m - 2)^2 = 0$$
$$m - 2 = 0$$
$$m = 2$$
$$b = 1 - 2(2) = -3$$
The equation of the tangent line is $y = 2x - 3$.

93. Solve for r_1 and r_2:

$$\begin{cases} r_1 + r_2 = -\dfrac{b}{a} \\ r_1 r_2 = \dfrac{c}{a} \end{cases}$$

Substitute and solve:

$$r_1 = -r_2 - \frac{b}{a} \rightarrow \left(-r_2 - \frac{b}{a}\right)r_2 = \frac{c}{a} \rightarrow -r_2^2 - \frac{b}{a}\, r_2 - \frac{c}{a} = 0 \rightarrow a\,r_2^2 + b\,r_2 + c = 0$$

$$r_2 = \frac{-b \pm \sqrt{b^2 - 4ac}}{2a}$$

$$r_1 = -r_2 - \frac{b}{a} = -\left(\frac{-b \pm \sqrt{b^2 - 4ac}}{2a}\right) - \frac{2b}{2a} = \frac{-b \mp \sqrt{b^2 - 4ac}}{2a}$$

The solutions are: $\dfrac{-b + \sqrt{b^2 - 4ac}}{2a}$ and $\dfrac{-b - \sqrt{b^2 - 4ac}}{2a}$.

95. Since the area of the square piece of sheet metal is 100 square feet, the sheet's dimensions are 10 feet by 10 feet. Let x = the length of the cut.

The dimensions of the box are length $= 10 - 2x$; width $= 10 - 2x$; height $= x$
Note that each of these expressions must be positive. So we must have
    $x > 0$ and $10 - 2x > 0 \Rightarrow x < 5$, that is, $0 < x < 5$.
So the volume of the box is given by

$$V = (\text{length}) \cdot (\text{width}) \cdot (\text{height}) = (10 - 2x)(10 - 2x)(x) = (10 - 2x)^2 (x)$$

(a) In order to get a volume equal to 9 cubic feet, we solve $(10 - 2x)^2(x) = 9$.

$$(10 - 2x)^2(x) = 9 \Rightarrow \left(100 - 40x + 4x^2\right)x = 9 \Rightarrow 100x - 40x^2 + 4x^3 = 9$$

So we need to solve the equation $4x^3 - 40x^2 + 100x - 9 = 0$.
Graphing the function $y_1 = 4x^3 - 40x^2 + 100x - 9$ on a calculator yields the graph

The graph indicates that there three real zeros on the interval $[0,6]$.
Using the ZERO feature of a graphing calculator, we find that the three roots shown occur at $x \approx 0.09$, $x \approx 4.27$ and $x \approx 5.63$.
But we've already noted that we must have $0 < x < 5$, so the only practical values for the cut are $x \approx 0.09$ feet and $x \approx 4.27$ feet.

(b) If the sheet metal has dimensions k feet by k feet, then the volume equation becomes

$$V = (k - 2x)(k - 2x)(x) = (k - 2x)^2(x) = 9$$

Solving for k we get the quadratic equation in the variable k.

$$xk^2 - 4x^2k + 4x^3 - 9 = 0$$

Using the quadratic formula we get:

$$k = \frac{-(-4x^2) \pm \sqrt{(-4x^2)^2 - 4(x)(4x^3 - 9)}}{2x} = \frac{4x^2 \pm \sqrt{16x^4 - 16x^4 + 36x}}{2x}$$

$$= \frac{4x^2 \pm \sqrt{36x}}{2x} = \frac{4x^2 \pm 6\sqrt{x}}{2x}$$

Therefore, we get a real solution for k provided $x > 0$ and $4x^2 \pm 6\sqrt{x} \geq 0$.

$$4x^2 \pm 6\sqrt{x} \geq 0 \Rightarrow 4x^2 \geq 6\sqrt{x} \Rightarrow 16x^4 \geq 36x$$

$$16x^4 - 36x \geq 0 \Rightarrow 4x(4x^3 - 9) \geq 0$$

This last inequality holds provided $x \geq \sqrt[3]{\dfrac{9}{4}}$.

Chapter 10

Conics

10.R Chapter Review

1. $y^2 = -16x$
   This is a parabola.
   $a = 4$
   Vertex: $(0, 0)$
   Focus: $(-4, 0)$
   Directrix: $x = 4$

3. $\dfrac{x^2}{25} - y^2 = 1$
   This is a hyperbola.
   $a = 5, \ b = 1$.

   Find the value of c:
   $$c^2 = a^2 + b^2 = 25 + 1 = 26$$
   $$c = \sqrt{26}$$
   Center: $(0, 0)$
   Vertices: $(5, 0), (-5, 0)$
   Foci: $\left(\sqrt{26}, 0\right), \left(-\sqrt{26}, 0\right)$
   Asymptotes: $y = \dfrac{1}{5}x; \ \ y = -\dfrac{1}{5}x$

5. $\dfrac{y^2}{25} + \dfrac{x^2}{16} = 1$
   This is an ellipse.
   $a = 5, \ b = 4$.

   Find the value of c:
   $$c^2 = a^2 - b^2 = 25 - 16 = 9$$
   $$c = 3$$
   Center: $(0, 0)$
   Vertices: $(0, 5), (0, -5)$
   Foci: $(0, 3), (0, -3)$

7. $x^2 + 4y = 4$
   This is a parabola.
   Write in standard form:
   $$x^2 = -4y + 4$$
   $$x^2 = -4(y - 1)$$

   $a = 1$
   Vertex: $(0, 1)$
   Focus: $(0, 0)$
   Directrix: $y = 2$

9. $4x^2 - y^2 = 8$
This is a hyperbola.
Write in standard form:
$$\frac{x^2}{2} - \frac{y^2}{8} = 1$$
$a = \sqrt{2}, \ b = \sqrt{8} = 2\sqrt{2}.$

Find the value of c:
$$c^2 = a^2 + b^2 = 2 + 8 = 10$$
$$c = \sqrt{10}$$
Center: $(0, 0)$
Vertices: $\left(-\sqrt{2}, 0\right), \left(\sqrt{2}, 0\right)$
Foci: $\left(-\sqrt{10}, 0\right), \left(\sqrt{10}, 0\right)$
Asymptotes: $y = 2x; \ \ y = -2x$

11. $x^2 - 4x = 2y$
This is a parabola.
Write in standard form:
$$x^2 - 4x + 4 = 2y + 4$$
$$(x - 2)^2 = 2(y + 2)$$

$$a = \frac{1}{2}$$
Vertex: $(2, -2)$
Focus: $\left(2, -\frac{3}{2}\right)$
Directrix: $y = -\frac{5}{2}$

13. $y^2 - 4y - 4x^2 + 8x = 4$
This is a hyperbola.
Write in standard form:
$$(y^2 - 4y + 4) - 4(x^2 - 2x + 1) = 4 + 4 - 4$$
$$(y - 2)^2 - 4(x - 1)^2 = 4$$
$$\frac{(y - 2)^2}{4} - \frac{(x - 1)^2}{1} = 1$$
$a = 2, \ b = 1.$

Find the value of c :
$$c^2 = a^2 + b^2 = 4 + 1 = 5$$
$$c = \sqrt{5}$$
Center: $(1, 2)$
Vertices: $(1, 0), (1, 4)$
Foci: $\left(1, 2 - \sqrt{5}\right), \left(1, 2 + \sqrt{5}\right)$
Asymptotes:
$y - 2 = 2(x - 1); \ \ y - 2 = -2(x - 1)$

15. $4x^2 + 9y^2 - 16x - 18y = 11$
This is an ellipse.
Write in standard form:
$$4x^2 + 9y^2 - 16x - 18y = 11$$
$$4(x^2 - 4x + 4) + 9(y^2 - 2y + 1) = 11 + 16 + 9$$
$$4(x - 2)^2 + 9(y - 1)^2 = 36$$
$$\frac{(x - 2)^2}{9} + \frac{(y - 1)^2}{4} = 1$$
$a = 3, \ b = 2.$

Find the value of c:
$$c^2 = a^2 - b^2 = 9 - 4 = 5$$
$$c = \sqrt{5}$$
Center: $(2, 1)$
Vertices: $(-1, 1), (5, 1)$
Foci: $\left(2 - \sqrt{5}, 1\right), \left(2 + \sqrt{5}, 1\right)$

17. $4x^2 - 16x + 16y + 32 = 0$
This is a parabola.
Write in standard form:
$$4(x^2 - 4x + 4) = -16y - 32 + 16$$
$$4(x - 2)^2 = -16(y + 1)$$
$$(x - 2)^2 = -4(y + 1)$$

$a = -1$
Vertex: $(2, -1)$
Focus: $(2, -2)$
Directrix: $y = 0$

19. $9x^2 + 4y^2 - 18x + 8y = 23$
This is an ellipse.
Write in standard form:
$9(x^2 - 2x + 1) + 4(y^2 + 2y + 1) = 23 + 9 + 4$
$$9(x-1)^2 + 4(y+1)^2 = 36$$
$$\frac{(x-1)^2}{4} + \frac{(y+1)^2}{9} = 1$$
$a = 3, \ b = 2$.

Find the value of c:
$$c^2 = a^2 - b^2 = 9 - 4 = 5$$
$$c = \sqrt{5}$$
Center: $(1, -1)$
Vertices: $(1, -4), (1, 2)$
Foci: $\left(1, -1 - \sqrt{5}\right), \left(1, -1 + \sqrt{5}\right)$

21.   Parabola: The focus is $(-2, 0)$ and the directrix is
$x = 2$. The vertex is $(0, 0)$. $a = 2$ and since $(-2, 0)$
is to the left of $(0, 0)$, the parabola opens to the left.
The equation of the parabola is:
$$y^2 = -4ax$$
$$y^2 = -4 \cdot 2 \cdot x$$
$$y^2 = -8x$$

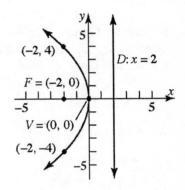

23.   Hyperbola: Center: $(0, 0)$;
Focus: $(0, 4)$;   Vertex: $(0, -2)$;
Transverse axis is the y-axis;
$a = 2; \ c = 4$.
Find b:
$$b^2 = c^2 - a^2 = 16 - 4 = 12$$
$$b = \sqrt{12} = 2\sqrt{3}$$
Write the equation: $\dfrac{y^2}{4} - \dfrac{x^2}{12} = 1$

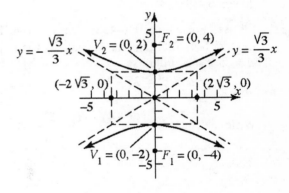

25.   Ellipse: Foci: $(-3, 0), (3, 0)$; Vertex: $(4, 0)$;
Center: $(0, 0)$; Major axis is the x-axis;
$a = 4; \ c = 3$. Find b:
$$b^2 = a^2 - c^2 = 16 - 9 = 7$$
$$b = \sqrt{7}$$
Write the equation: $\dfrac{x^2}{16} + \dfrac{y^2}{7} = 1$

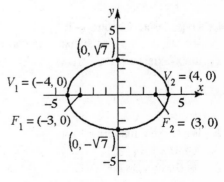

27. Parabola: The focus is $(2, -4)$ and the vertex is $(2, -3)$. Both lie on the vertical line $x = 2$. $a = 1$ and since $(2, -4)$ is below $(2, -3)$, the parabola opens down. The equation of the parabola is:
$$(x - h)^2 = -4a(y - k)$$
$$(x - 2)^2 = -4 \cdot 1 \cdot (y - (-3))$$
$$(x - 2)^2 = -4(y + 3)$$

29. Hyperbola: Center: $(-2, -3)$; Focus: $(-4, -3)$; Vertex: $(-3, -3)$; Transverse axis is parallel to the x-axis; $a = 1$; $c = 2$. Find b:
$$b^2 = c^2 - a^2 = 4 - 1 = 3$$
$$b = \sqrt{3}$$

Write the equation: $\dfrac{(x + 2)^2}{1} - \dfrac{(y + 3)^2}{3} = 1$

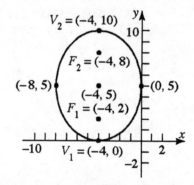

31. Ellipse: Foci: $(-4, 2)$, $(-4, 8)$; Vertex: $(-4, 10)$; Center: $(-4, 5)$; Major axis is parallel to the y-axis; $a = 5$; $c = 3$. Find b:
$$b^2 = a^2 - c^2 = 25 - 9 = 16$$
$$b = 4$$

Write the equation: $\dfrac{(x + 4)^2}{16} + \dfrac{(y - 5)^2}{25} = 1$

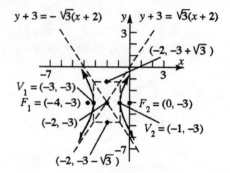

33. Hyperbola: Center: $(-1, 2)$; $a = 3$; $c = 4$; Transverse axis parallel to the x-axis;
Find b:
$$b^2 = c^2 - a^2 = 16 - 9 = 7$$
$$b = \sqrt{7}$$
Write the equation:
$$\dfrac{(x + 1)^2}{9} - \dfrac{(y - 2)^2}{7} = 1$$

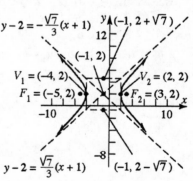

35. Hyperbola: Vertices: $(0, 1), (6, 1)$; Asymptote: $3y + 2x - 9 = 0$; Center: $(3, 1)$;

Transverse axis is parallel to the x-axis; $a = 3$; The slope of the asymptote is $-\dfrac{2}{3}$;

Find b:

$$\dfrac{-b}{a} = \dfrac{-b}{3} = \dfrac{-2}{3} \rightarrow -3b = -6 \rightarrow b = 2$$

Write the equation: $\dfrac{(x-3)^2}{9} - \dfrac{(y-1)^2}{4} = 1$

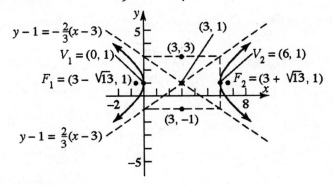

37. Solve the first equation for y, substitute into the second equation and solve:

$$\begin{cases} 2x + y + 3 = 0 \rightarrow y = -2x - 3 \\ x^2 + y^2 = 5 \end{cases}$$

$$x^2 + (-2x - 3)^2 = 5 \rightarrow x^2 + 4x^2 + 12x + 9 = 5$$

$$5x^2 + 12x + 4 = 0 \rightarrow (5x + 2)(x + 2) = 0 \Rightarrow x = -\dfrac{2}{5} \quad \text{or} \quad x = -2$$

$$y = -\dfrac{11}{5} \qquad y = 1$$

Solutions: $\left(-\dfrac{2}{5}, -\dfrac{11}{5}\right), (-2, 1)$.

39. Multiply each side of the second equation by 2 and add the equations to eliminate xy:

$$\begin{cases} 2xy + y^2 = 10 \quad \longrightarrow \quad 2xy + y^2 = 10 \\ -xy + 3y^2 = 2 \quad \xrightarrow{\ 2\ } \quad -2xy + 6y^2 = 4 \end{cases}$$

$$\overline{\qquad\qquad\qquad\quad 7y^2 = 14 \rightarrow y^2 = 2 \rightarrow y = \pm\sqrt{2}}$$

If $y = \sqrt{2}$: $2x(\sqrt{2}) + (\sqrt{2})^2 = 10 \rightarrow 2\sqrt{2}x = 8 \rightarrow x = \dfrac{8}{2\sqrt{2}} = 2\sqrt{2}$

If $y = -\sqrt{2}$: $2x(-\sqrt{2}) + (-\sqrt{2})^2 = 10 \rightarrow -2\sqrt{2}x = 8 \rightarrow x = \dfrac{8}{-2\sqrt{2}} = -2\sqrt{2}$

Solutions: $\left(2\sqrt{2}, \sqrt{2}\right), \left(-2\sqrt{2}, -\sqrt{2}\right)$

41. Substitute into the second equation into the first equation and solve:

$$\begin{cases} x^2 + y^2 = 6y \\ \quad x^2 = 3y \end{cases}$$

$3y + y^2 = 6y \rightarrow y^2 - 3y = 0 \rightarrow y(y-3) = 0 \rightarrow y = 0 \text{ or } y = 3$

If $y = 0$: $x^2 = 3(0) \rightarrow x^2 = 0 \rightarrow x = 0$

If $y = 3$: $x^2 = 3(3) \rightarrow x^2 = 9 \rightarrow x = \pm 3$

Solutions: $(0, 0)$, $(-3, 3)$, $(3, 3)$.

43. Factor the second equation, solve for x, substitute into the first equation and solve:

$$\begin{cases} 3x^2 + 4xy + 5y^2 = 8 \\ x^2 + 3xy + 2y^2 = 0 \end{cases} \rightarrow (x + 2y)(x + y) = 0 \rightarrow x = -2y \text{ or } x = -y$$

Substitute $x = -2y$ and solve:

$3x^2 + 4xy + 5y^2 = 8$

$3(-2y)^2 + 4(-2y)y + 5y^2 = 8$

$12y^2 - 8y^2 + 5y^2 = 8$

$9y^2 = 8$

$y^2 = \dfrac{8}{9} \Rightarrow y = \pm\dfrac{2\sqrt{2}}{3}$

If $y = \dfrac{2\sqrt{2}}{3}$: $x = -2\left(\dfrac{2\sqrt{2}}{3}\right) = \dfrac{-4\sqrt{2}}{3}$

If $y = \dfrac{-2\sqrt{2}}{3}$: $x = -2\left(\dfrac{-2\sqrt{2}}{3}\right) = \dfrac{4\sqrt{2}}{3}$

Substitute $x = -y$ and solve:

$3x^2 + 4xy + 5y^2 = 8$

$3(-y)^2 + 4(-y)y + 5y^2 = 8$

$3y^2 - 4y^2 + 5y^2 = 8$

$4y^2 = 8$

$y^2 = 2 \Rightarrow y = \pm\sqrt{2}$

If $y = \sqrt{2}$: $x = -\sqrt{2}$

If $y = -\sqrt{2}$: $x = \sqrt{2}$

Solutions: $\left(\dfrac{-4\sqrt{2}}{3}, \dfrac{2\sqrt{2}}{3}\right), \left(\dfrac{4\sqrt{2}}{3}, \dfrac{-2\sqrt{2}}{3}\right), \left(-\sqrt{2}, \sqrt{2}\right), \left(\sqrt{2}, -\sqrt{2}\right)$

45. Multiply each side of the second equation by $-y$ and add the equations to eliminate y:

$$\begin{cases} x^2 - 3x + y^2 + y = -2 \quad \longrightarrow \quad x^2 - 3x + y^2 + y = -2 \\ \dfrac{x^2 - x}{y} + y + 1 = 0 \quad \xrightarrow{-y} \quad -x^2 + x - y^2 - y = 0 \end{cases}$$

$$-2x \qquad = -2 \Rightarrow x = 1$$

If $x = 1$: $1^2 - 3(1) + y^2 + y = -2 \rightarrow y^2 + y = 0 \rightarrow y(y + 1) = 0$

$\rightarrow y = 0$ or $y = -1$

Note that $y \neq 0$ because that would cause division by zero in the original system.

Solution: $(1, -1)$

47. Write the equation in standard form:

$$4x^2 + 9y^2 = 36 \rightarrow \dfrac{x^2}{9} + \dfrac{y^2}{4} = 1$$

The center of the ellipse is $(0, 0)$. The major axis is the x-axis.

$a = 3$; $b = 2$; $c^2 = a^2 - b^2 = 9 - 4 = 5 \rightarrow c = \sqrt{5}$.

For the ellipse:

Vertices: $(-3, 0)$, $(3, 0)$;   Foci: $\left(-\sqrt{5}, 0\right), \left(\sqrt{5}, 0\right)$

For the hyperbola:

Foci: $(-3, 0)$, $(3, 0)$;   Vertices: $\left(-\sqrt{5}, 0\right), \left(\sqrt{5}, 0\right)$;   Center: $(0, 0)$

$a = \sqrt{5}$; $c = 3$; $b^2 = c^2 - a^2 = 9 - 5 = 4 \;\rightarrow\; b = 2$

The equation of the hyperbola is: $\dfrac{x^2}{5} - \dfrac{y^2}{4} = 1$

49. Let (x, y) be any point in the collection of points.

The distance from (x, y) to $(3, 0) = \sqrt{(x-3)^2 + y^2}$.

The distance from (x, y) to the line $x = \dfrac{16}{3}$ is $\left| x - \dfrac{16}{3} \right|$.

Relating the distances, we have:

$$\sqrt{(x-3)^2 + y^2} = \dfrac{3}{4} \left| x - \dfrac{16}{3} \right| \rightarrow (x-3)^2 + y^2 = \dfrac{9}{16}\left(x - \dfrac{16}{3} \right)^2$$

$$x^2 - 6x + 9 + y^2 = \dfrac{9}{16}\left(x^2 - \dfrac{32}{3}x + \dfrac{256}{9} \right)$$

$$16x^2 - 96x + 144 + 16y^2 = 9x^2 - 96x + 256$$

$$7x^2 + 16y^2 = 112 \rightarrow \dfrac{7x^2}{112} + \dfrac{16y^2}{112} = 1 \rightarrow \dfrac{x^2}{16} + \dfrac{y^2}{7} = 1$$

The set of points is an ellipse.

51. Locate the parabola so that the vertex is at $(0, 0)$ and opens up. It then has the equation: $x^2 = 4ay$. Since the light source is located at the focus and is 1 foot from the base, $a = 1$. The diameter is 2, so the point $(1, y)$ is located on the parabola. Solve for y:

$$1^2 = 4(1)y \rightarrow 1 = 4y \rightarrow y = 0.25 \text{ feet}$$

The mirror should be 0.25 feet deep or 3 inches deep.

53. Place the semielliptical arch so that the x-axis coincides with the water and the y-axis passes through the center of the arch. Since the bridge has a span of 60 feet, the length of the major axis is 60, or $2a = 60$ or $a = 30$. The maximum height of the bridge is 20 feet,

so $b = 20$. The equation is: $\dfrac{x^2}{900} + \dfrac{y^2}{400} = 1$.

The height 5 feet from the center:

$$\dfrac{5^2}{900} + \dfrac{y^2}{400} = 1 \rightarrow \dfrac{y^2}{400} = 1 - \dfrac{25}{900} \rightarrow y^2 = 400 \cdot \dfrac{875}{900} \rightarrow y \approx 19.72 \text{ feet}$$

The height 10 feet from the center:

$$\dfrac{10^2}{900} + \dfrac{y^2}{400} = 1 \rightarrow \dfrac{y^2}{400} = 1 - \dfrac{100}{900} \rightarrow y^2 = 400 \cdot \dfrac{800}{900} \rightarrow y \approx 18.86 \text{ feet}$$

The height 20 feet from the center:

$$\dfrac{20^2}{900} + \dfrac{y^2}{400} = 1 \rightarrow \dfrac{y^2}{400} = 1 - \dfrac{400}{900} \rightarrow y^2 = 400 \cdot \dfrac{500}{900} \rightarrow y \approx 14.91 \text{ feet}$$

55. (a) Set up a coordinate system so that the
two stations lie on the x-axis and the
origin is midway between them. The
ship lies on a hyperbola whose foci are
the locations of the two stations. Since
the time difference is 0.00032 seconds
and the speed of the signal is 186,000
miles per second, the difference in the
distances of the ships from each station
is: (186,000)(0.00032) = 59.52 miles

The difference of the distances from the ship to each station, 59.52, equals
$a = 29.76$ and the vertex of the corresponding hyperbola is at $(29.76, 0)$. Since the
focus is at $(75, 0)$, following this hyperbola, the ship would reach shore 45.24 miles
from the master station.

(b) The ship should follow a hyperbola with a vertex at $(60, 0)$. For this hyperbola,
$a = 60$, so the constant difference of the distances from the ship to each station is
120. The time difference the ship should look for is:

$$\text{time} = \frac{120}{186,000} = 0.000645 \text{ seconds}$$

(c) Find the equation of the hyperbola with vertex at $(60, 0)$ and a focus at $(75, 0)$. The

form of the equation of the hyperbola is: $\dfrac{x^2}{a^2} - \dfrac{y^2}{b^2} = 1$ where $a = 60$.

Since $c = 75$ and $b^2 = c^2 - a^2 \rightarrow b^2 = 75^2 - 60^2 = 2025$.

The equation of the hyperbola is: $\dfrac{x^2}{3600} - \dfrac{y^2}{2025} = 1$.

Since the ship is 20 miles off shore, we have $y = 20$.

Solve the equation for x:

$$\frac{x^2}{3600} - \frac{20^2}{2025} = 1 \rightarrow \frac{x^2}{3600} = 1 + \frac{400}{2025} = \frac{97}{81} \rightarrow x^2 = 3600 \cdot \frac{97}{81}$$

$$x \approx 66 \text{ miles}$$

The ship's location is $(66, 20)$.

Conics

10.CR   **Cumulative Review**

1. $2x^4 - 5x^3 + 7x^2 - 25x - 15 = 0$
     $f(x) = 2x^4 - 5x^3 + 7x^2 - 25x - 15$
     Step 1: $f(x)$ has 4 complex zeros.
     Step 2:   Possible rational zeros:
     $$p = \pm 1, \pm 3, \pm 5, \pm 15; \quad q = \pm 1, \pm 2;$$
     $$\frac{p}{q} = \pm 1, \pm 3, \pm 5, \pm 15, \pm \frac{1}{2}, \pm \frac{3}{2}, \pm \frac{5}{2}, \pm \frac{15}{2}$$
     Step 3:   Using synthetic division:

$$3\overline{)\begin{array}{ccccc} 2 & -5 & 7 & -25 & -15 \\ & 6 & 3 & 30 & 15 \\ \hline 2 & 1 & 10 & 5 & 0 \end{array}}$$

Since the remainder is 0, $x - 3$ is a factor. The other factor is
the quotient: $2x^3 + x^2 + 10x + 5$
$$= x^2(2x + 1) + 5(2x + 1) = (2x + 1)(x^2 + 5)$$
$$= (2x + 1)(x + \sqrt{5}i)(x - \sqrt{5}i)$$
Therefore, $f(x) = 2x^4 - 5x^3 + 7x^2 - 25x - 15$
$$= (x - 3)(2x + 1)(x + \sqrt{5}i)(x - \sqrt{5}i)$$
The complex zeros are $-\dfrac{1}{2}$, 3, $-\sqrt{5}i$, $\sqrt{5}i$.

3. $f(x) = \dfrac{3}{2x^2 + 5x + 2}$
     f will be defined provided $2x^2 + 5x + 2 \neq 0$.
     $$2x^2 + 5x + 2 = 0 \Rightarrow (2x + 1)(x + 2) = 0 \Rightarrow x = -\frac{1}{2}, x = -2$$
     The domain of $f(x) = \dfrac{3}{2x^2 + 5x + 2}$ is $\left\{ x \middle| x \neq -2, x \neq -\dfrac{1}{2} \right\}$.

5.   Subtract the equations:

$$\begin{cases} x+y=6 \\ y=x^2 \end{cases} \xrightarrow{\quad} \begin{aligned} x+y=6 \\ \underline{-x^2+y=0} \end{aligned}$$

$$x+x^2=6 \Rightarrow x^2+x-6=0$$

Solving $x^2+x-6=0$: $(x+3)(x-2)=0 \Rightarrow x=-3$ or $x=2$

Substitute and solve for y:

$$x=-3 \Rightarrow y=(-3)^2=9$$

$$x=2 \Rightarrow y=(2)^2=4$$

The solutions of the system are the ordered pairs $(-3,9)$ and $(2,4)$.

7. $6-x \ge x^2 \Rightarrow 0 \ge x^2+x-6 \Rightarrow x^2+x-6 \le 0 \Rightarrow x^2+x-6 \le 0 \Rightarrow (x+3)(x-2) \le 0$

$x=-3$, $x=2$ are the zeros. $g(x)=x^2+x-6$

Interval	Test Number	$g(x)$	Positive/Negative
$-\infty < x < -3$	-4	6	Positive
$-3 < x < 2$	0	-6	Negative
$2 < x < \infty$	3	6	Positive

The solution set is $\left\{ x \mid -3 \le x \le 2 \right\}$.

9.   (a) Line containing points $(0,-2)$ and $(1,0)$:

$$\text{slope} = \frac{\Delta y}{\Delta x} = \frac{0-(-2)}{1-0} = \frac{2}{1} = 2$$

using $y-y_1 = m(x-x_1)$:

$$y-0 = 2(x-1)$$

$$y=2x-2 \text{ or } 2x-y-2=0$$

(b) Circle with center point $(0,4)$; radius $= 4$

$$(x-h)^2 + (y-k)^2 = r^2$$

$$(x-2)^2 + (y-0)^2 = 2^2$$

$$x^2 - 4x + 4 + y^2 = 4$$

$$x^2 + y^2 - 4x = 0$$

(c) ellipse with center point $(0,0)$; vertices $(\pm 3,0)$ and $(0,\pm 2)$:

$$\frac{(x-h)^2}{a^2} + \frac{(y-k)^2}{b^2} = 1$$

$$\frac{(x-0)^2}{3^2} + \frac{(y-0)^2}{2^2} = 1$$

$$\frac{x^2}{9} + \frac{y^2}{4} = 1$$

(d) Parabola with vertex $(1,0)$ and y-intercept $(0,2)$:

$$(y-k) = 4a(x-h)^2$$

$$(2-0) = 4a(0-1)^2$$

$$2 = 4a(-1)^2$$

$$2 = 4a \Rightarrow a = \frac{1}{2}$$

$$(y-0) = 4\left(\frac{1}{2}\right)(x-1)^2$$

$$y = 2(x-1)^2$$

(e) hyperbola with center $(0,0)$ and vertices $(0,\pm1)$; containing the point $(3,2)$:

$$\frac{(y-k)^2}{b^2} - \frac{(x-h)^2}{a^2} = 1$$

$$\frac{y^2}{1} - \frac{x^2}{a^2} = 1$$

$$\frac{(2)^2}{1} - \frac{(3)^2}{a^2} = 1$$

$$\frac{4}{1} - \frac{9}{a^2} = 1 \Rightarrow 4 - \frac{9}{a^2} = 1$$

$$3 = \frac{9}{a^2} \Rightarrow 3a^2 = 9 \Rightarrow a^2 = 3 \Rightarrow a = \sqrt{3}$$

$$\frac{y^2}{1} - \frac{x^2}{\left(\sqrt{3}\right)^2} = 1 \Rightarrow \frac{y^2}{1} - \frac{x^2}{3} = 1$$

(f) Exponential with y-intercept $(0,1)$; containing the point $(1,4)$:

$$y = A \cdot b^x$$

y-intercept $(0,1)$

$$\Rightarrow 1 = A \cdot b^0 = A \cdot 1 \Rightarrow A = 1$$

point $(1,4) \Rightarrow 4 = b^1 = b$

Therefore, $y = 4^x$.